Selected Papers on the

THEORY OF THERMAL CONVECTION

with special application to
the earth's planetary atmosphere

Edited by

BARRY SALTZMAN

Senior Research Scientist
The Travelers Research Center, Inc.
Hartford, Connecticut

DOVER PUBLICATIONS, INC.
NEW YORK

Published simultaneously in Canada by McClelland and Stewart, Ltd.

Published in the United Kingdom by Constable and Company Limited, 10 Orange Street, London W.C.2.

This new Dover edition, first published in 1962, is a selection of papers published for the first time in collected form. The editor and publisher are indebted to the authors and original publishers of the articles for assistance and permission to reproduce these articles, and to the Physics Library of Columbia University for making certain papers available for reproduction purposes.

Manufactured in the United States of America

Dover Publications, Inc.
180 Varick Street
New York 14, N.Y.

P. Cannon 345

CONTENTS

PREFACE

THE MOTIONS of the earth's atmosphere are almost entirely of convective origin. On the largest scale the convective motions take the form of the global wind currents which constitute the general circulation, and on smaller scales they take the form of local updrafts, sea breezes, monsoons, and more violent circulations such as tornadoes and hurricanes. In all these cases the motions are a response to the temperature inequalities continuously being created by differential heating.

In this collection we have endeavored to bring together some of the basic theoretical papers on convection, with special emphasis on the general circulation of the atmosphere. The form of the convection in this latter case is greatly influenced by the earth's rotation. For this reason we have included two fundamental papers by G. I. Taylor (1917, 1921) which deal only with this effect. It was shown in these two papers that fluids under rotation tend to behave in a more two-dimensional way; i.e., vertical motions, such as would normally arise from buoyancy forces, are inhibited.

The first paper on convection proper included in this volume is Lord Rayleigh's pioneering work of 1916 dealing with cellular motions in a fluid uniformly heated from below (i.e., Bénard convection). In this paper the method of treating convection as a stability problem was set forth for the first time and the criterion for the onset of the Bénard motions established. Further contributions to the Bénard problem, mainly in the nature of refinements of the boundary conditions and methods of solution, were made by H. Jeffreys (1926, 1928, 1930), A. R. Low (1929), and A. Pellew and R. V. Southwell (1940). The effects of rotation were treated by S. Chandrasekhar (1953), who found that rotation indeed inhibits the onset of the cellular convection and that when the convection does set in, it is on a smaller horizontal scale than in the non-rotating case.

While the Bénard problem is characterized by an unstable temperature stratification in the vertical, the problem of the general circulation is characterized by a predominantly stable vertical stratification and an unstable temperature contrast in the horizontal caused by differential solar radiative heating between polar and equatorial regions. It is natural to expect that the convective motion generated by the solar heat input is in the form of an axially symmetric toroidal cell with rising motion at the equator and sinking motion at the poles (the so-called Hadley circulation). Accordingly, the first contributions toward the theory of the general circulation were aimed at deducing this type of flow (W. Ferrel, 1859; A. Oberbeck, 1888; and, later, F. Kropatscheck, 1935).* Modern observations have revealed, however, that symmetric toroidal motions form only a very small component of the complete flow and that only in low latitudes and very high latitudes are they of the direct Hadley type. In middle latitudes the toroidal component is in the form of a thermally indirect reverse cell as was first suggested by Ferrel. The main motions of the atmosphere are non-symmetric meandering westerly and easterly zonal currents extending through great depths of the atmosphere. The meanders constitute the great atmospheric cyclones and anticyclones, and may be considered as large amplitude wave-like disturbances in a uniform (symmetric) zonal flow. In spite of the realization that a purely symmetric theory cannot be taken as an explanation of the general circulation, there has been a revival of interest in such a theory owing to the success of investigators (e.g., D. Fultz, 1953) in producing the ideal Hadley circulation in controlled laboratory experiments with rotating, heated fluids. To account for these laboratory results theoretical studies have been made by T. V. Davies (1953) and M. H. Rogers (1954) using an approach similar to that of Oberbeck; that is, they consider the convective motions to be "forced" by a fixed temperature distribution which is unmodified by the motion. H.-L. Kuo (1954), on the other hand, has considered the problem from the stability standpoint, in the manner of the treatment of the Bénard problem, and has determined the criterion for the existence of a "free" symmetric convection in which the velocity and temperature fields are interdependent.

The inadequacy of the symmetric model as an explanation of the general circulation was recognized early by H. von Helmholtz (1888) and, most pointedly, later, by Jeffreys (1926, 1933). However, aside from the work on energy conversions in cyclones by M. Margules (1903), and on low-level frontal waves at thermal discontinuities by H. Solberg (1928) and N. Kotschin (1932), for example, little in the way of a theoretical attack on the general non-symmetric problem was made until better observations of the global upper air flow revealed the true wave-like nature of the large-scale disturbances. At this point C.-G. Rossby (1939), for the first time, obtained wave solutions corresponding to the newly observed disturbances, following which, important studies of their stability properties were made by H.-L. Kuo (1949, 1951, 1953) and R. Fjørtoft (1950) with regard to the horizontal shear of zonal currents (the barotropic problem), and by J. Charney (1947), E. T. Eady (1949), R. Fjørtoft (1950), and H.-L. Kuo (1952) with regard to the horizontal temperature contrast (the baroclinic problem). The studies of barotropic instability showed that disturbances of all scales tend to damp rather than amplify at the expense of the zonal flow and therefore the existence of non-symmetric perturbations could not be explained as an instability of zonal currents which are induced by a Coriolis deflection of thermally direct symmetric overturnings. On the other hand, the studies of baroclinic instability revealed that, for the temperature contrasts observed in the

* A bibliography of articles referred to here, but not reproduced in this volume, is given at the end of this preface.

atmosphere, convective motions of a form corresponding to the wave cyclones and anticyclones would indeed grow and that this, in fact, is the main reason for their existence.

The works on the baroclinic problem had the limitation, however, that they were restricted, *ab initio*, to apply only to the conditions prevailing in the atmosphere, and also the stabilizing effects of nonconvective heat transfer and of viscosity were not included in as general a manner as, for example, in the studies of Bénard convection. For these reasons it was not possible to determine criteria for the separation between the symmetric and non-symmetric regimes or between various possible modes of non-symmetric flow such as are revealed by the laboratory experiments. Papers by E. N. Lorenz (1953), T. V. Davies (1956, 1959) and H.-L. Kuo (1956, 1957) represent the most recent contributions toward a more general theory which includes all of these possibilities. A main result is that under conditions of a relatively high rate of rotation and a low differential heating (i.e., the atmospheric case) a direct toroidal overturning cannot be realized because the system first becomes unstable for smaller-scale convective overturnings, which are the wave cyclones. The transfer of heat by these motions prevents the system from ever achieving the temperature contrast necessary to drive a purely symmetric circulation.

With the finding that the energy made available by heating is converted mainly into the kinetic energy of the non-symmetric wave components, the question of the maintenance of the symmetric components of the general circulation (i.e., the high energy zonal current and the low energy toroidal circulation) is brought to the fore. This question is answered in good measure by the barotropic stability studies listed above and by the studies of A. Eliassen (1952), R. Fjørtoft (1951), and H.-L. Kuo (1956), all of which show that the mean zonal and toroidal components tend to be forced as secondary effects of the thermally driven eddy motions.

The final paper included here, by N. A. Phillips (1956), represents the first attempt to treat the large-scale atmospheric convection in an approximation to its true non-linear form, with both baroclinic and barotropic processes occurring simultaneously. For this purpose numerical methods were used to integrate the fundamental equations. In almost all respects the results are in agreement with the picture which emerged from the linear stability studies.

In closing, it is fitting to take cognizance of the vital role played by experimental and observational studies in stimulating theoretical work of the type reproduced here. We shall make no attempt to list separately the pertinent papers in this regard; such references are given in the bibliographies of the individual theoretical papers.

The articles included in this volume are by no means the only important ones; but we do believe they represent an essential part of the basic source material for the subject treated and hope that their availability in a single volume will be of value to research workers and students.

BARRY SALTZMAN

Hartford, Connecticut
June, 1961

Supplementary Bibliography

DAVIES, T. V., 1953: The forced flow of a rotating viscous liquid which is heated from below. *Phil. Trans. Roy. Soc. A.*, *246*, 81–112.

ELIASSEN, A., 1952: Slow thermally or frictionally controlled meridional circulations in a circular vortex. *Astrophysica Norwegica*, *5*, 19–60.

FERREL, W., 1859–1860: The motions of fluids and solids relative to the earth's surface. *Math. Monthly*, *1* (140–148, 210–216, 300–307, 366–373, 397–406), 2 (89–97, 339–346, 374–390).

FJØRTOFT, R., 1950: Application of integral theorems in deriving criteria of stability for laminar flows and for the baroclinic circular vortex. *Geof. Publ.*, *17*, No. 6, 52 pp.

FULTZ, D., 1953: A survey of certain thermally and mechanically driven fluid systems of meteorological interest. *Fluid Models in Geophysics*, R. Long, ed., Johns Hopkins, 27–63.

HADLEY, G., 1735: Concerning the cause of the general trade wind. *Phil. Trans. Roy. Soc., London*, *39*, 58–62. (Reprinted by C. Abbe in *Smithsonian Misc. Coll.*, *51*, 1910.)

KOTSCHIN, N., 1932: Über die Stabilität von Margulesschen Diskontinuitätsflächen, *Beitr. Phys. fr. Atmos.*, *18*, 129–164.

KROPATSCHECK, F., 1935: Die Mechanik der grossen Zirkulation der Atmosphäre. *Beitr. Phys. fr. Atmos.*, *22*, 272–298.

KUO, H.-L., 1951: Dynamical aspects of the general circulation and the stability of zonal flow. *Tellus*, *3*, 268–284.

KUO, H.-L., 1952: Three-dimensional disturbances in a baroclinic zonal current. *J. Meteor.*, *9*, 260–278.

KUO, H.-L., 1953: On the production of mean zonal currents in the atmosphere by large disturbances. *Tellus*, *5*, 475–493.

LORENZ, E. N., 1953: A proposed explanation for the existence of two regimes of flow in a rotating symmetrically heated cylindrical vessel. *Fluid Models in Geophysics*, R. Long, ed., Johns Hopkins, 73–80.

MARGULES, M., 1903: Über die Energie der Stürme. *Jahrb. Zentralanst. f. Meteor. Geodyn.*, *40*, Vienna. (Translation by C. Abbe in *Smithsonian Misc. Coll.*, *51*, 533–595, 1910.)

ROGERS, M. H., 1954: The forced flow of a thin layer of viscous fluid on a rotating sphere. *Proc. Roy. Soc.*, *A*, *224*, 192–208.

SOLBERG, H., 1928: Integrationen der atmosphärischen Störungsgleichungen. *Geof. Publ.*, *5*, No. 9, 120 pp.

I. Uniform Heating from Below

Reprinted from *Philosophical Magazine*, Series 6, Vol. 32, 1916.

LIX. *On Convection Currents in a Horizontal Layer of Fluid, when the Higher Temperature is on the Under Side. By* Lord RAYLEIGH, *O.M., F.R.S.**

THE present is an attempt to examine how far the interesting results obtained by Bénard † in his careful and skilful experiments can be explained theoretically. Bénard worked with very thin layers, only about 1 mm. deep, standing on a levelled metallic plate which was maintained at a uniform temperature. The upper surface was usually free, and being in contact with the air was at a lower temperature. Various liquids were employed—some, indeed, which would be solids under ordinary conditions.

The layer rapidly resolves itself into a number of *cells*, the motion being an ascension in the middle of a cell and a descension at the common boundary between a cell and its neighbours. Two phases are distinguished, of unequal duration, the first being relatively very short. The limit of the first phase is described as the "semi-regular cellular regime"; in this state all the cells have already acquired surfaces *nearly* identical, their forms being nearly regular convex polygons of, in general, 4 to 7 sides. The boundaries

* Communicated by the Author.

† *Revue générale des Sciences*, vol. xii. pp. 1261, 1309 (1900); *Ann. d. Chimie et de Physique*, t. xxiii. p. 62 (1901). M. Bénard does not appear to be acquainted with James Thomson's paper "On a Changing Tesselated Structure in certain Liquids" (Proc. Glasgow Phil. Soc. 1881–2), where a like structure is described in much thicker layers of soapy water cooling from the surface.

are vertical, and the circulation in each cell approximates to that already indicated. This phase is brief (1 or 2 seconds) for the less viscous liquids (alcohol, benzine, &c.) at ordinary temperatures. Even for paraffin or spermacetti, melted at 100° C., 10 seconds suffice; but in the case of very viscous liquids (oils, &c.), if the flux of heat is small, the deformations are extremely slow and the first phase may last several minutes or more.

The second phase has for its limit a permanent regime of regular hexagons. During this period the cells become equal and regular and allign themselves. It is extremely protracted, if the limit is regarded as the complete attainment of regular hexagons. And, indeed, such perfection is barely attainable even with the most careful arrangements. The tendency, however, seems sufficiently established.

The theoretical consideration of the problem here arising is of interest for more than one reason. In general, when a system falls away from unstable equilibrium it may do so in several principal modes, in each of which the departure at time t is proportional to the small displacement or velocity supposed to be present initially, and to an exponential factor e^{qt}, where q is positive. If the initial disturbances are small enough, that mode (or modes) of falling away will become predominant for which q is a maximum. The simplest example for which the number of degrees of freedom is infinite is presented by a cylindrical rod of elastic material under a longitudinal compression sufficient to overbalance its stiffness. But perhaps the most interesting hitherto treated is that of a cylinder of fluid disintegrating under the operation of capillary force as in the beautiful experiments of Savart and Plateau upon jets. In this case the surface remains one of revolution about the original axis, but it becomes *varicose*, and the question is to compare the effects of different wave-lengths of varicosity, for upon this depends the number of detached masses into which the column is eventually resolved. It was proved by Plateau that there is no instability if the wave-length be less than the circumference of the column. For all wave-lengths greater than this there is instability, and the corresponding modes of disintegration may establish themselves if the initial disturbances are suitable. But if the general disturbance is very small, those components only will have opportunity to develop themselves for which the wave-length lies near to that of maximum instability.

It has been shown * that the wave-length of maximum

* Proc. Lond. Math. Soc. vol. x. p. 4 (1879); Scientific Papers, vol. i. p. 361. Also 'Theory of Sound,' 2nd ed. §§ 357, &c.

instability is 4·508 times the diameter of the jet, exceeding the wave-length at which instability first enters in the ratio of about 3 : 2. Accordingly this is the sort of disintegration to be expected when the jet is shielded as far as possible from external disturbance.

It will be observed that there is nothing in this theory which could fix the *phase* of the predominant disturbance, or the particular particles of the fluid which will ultimately form the centres of the detached drops. There remains a certain indeterminateness, and this is connected with the circumstance that absolute regularity is not to be expected. In addition to the wave-length of maximum instability we must include all those which lie sufficiently near to it, and the superposition of the corresponding modes will allow of a slow variation of phase as we pass along the column. The phase in any particular region depends upon the initial circumstances in and near that region, and these are supposed to be matters of chance *. The superposition of infinite trains of waves whose wave-lengths cluster round a given value raises the same questions as we are concerned with in considering the character of approximately homogeneous light.

In the present problem the case is much more complicated, unless we arbitrarily limit it to two dimensions. The cells of Bénard are then reduced to infinitely long strips, and when there is instability we may ask for what wave-length (width of strip) the instability is greatest. The answer can be given under certain restrictions, and the manner in which equilibrium breaks down is then approximately determined. So long as the two-dimensional character is retained, there seems to be no reason to expect the wave-length to alter afterwards. But even if we assume a natural disposition to a two-dimensional motion, the direction of the length of the cells as well as the phase could only be determined by initial circumstances, and could not be expected to be uniform over the whole of the infinite plane.

According to the observations of Bénard, something of this sort actually occurs when the layer of liquid has a general motion in its own plane at the moment when instability commences, the length of the cellular strips being parallel to the general velocity. But a little later, when the general motion has decayed, division-lines running in the perpendicular direction present themselves.

* When a jet of liquid is acted on by an external vibrator, the resolution into drops may be regularized in a much higher degree.

In general, it is easy to recognize that the question is much more complex. By Fourier's theorem the motion in its earlier stages may be analysed into components, each of which corresponds to rectangular cells whose sides are parallel to fixed axes arbitrarily chosen. The solution for maximum instability yields one relation between the sides of the rectangle, but no indication of their ratio. It covers the two-dimensional case of infinitely long rectangles already referred to, and the contrasted case of squares for which the length of the side is thus determined. I do not see that any plausible hypothesis as to the origin of the initial disturbances leads us to expect one particular ratio of sides in preference to another.

On a more general view it appears that the function expressing the disturbance which develops most rapidly may be assimilated to that which represents the free vibration of an infinite stretched membrane vibrating with given frequency.

The calculations which follow are based upon equations given by Boussinesq, who has applied them to one or two particular problems. The special limitation which characterizes them is the neglect of variations of density, *except in so far as they modify the action of gravity*. Of course, such neglect can be justified only under certain conditions, which Boussinesq has discussed. They are not so restrictive as to exclude the approximate treatment of many problems of interest.

When the fluid is inviscid and the higher temperature is below, all modes of disturbance are instable, even when we include the conduction of heat during the disturbance. But there is one class of disturbances for which the instability is a maximum.

When viscosity is included as well as conduction, the problem is more complicated, and we have to consider boundary conditions. Those have been chosen which are simplest from the mathematical point of view, and they deviate from those obtaining in Bénard's experiments, where, indeed, the conditions are different at the two boundaries. It appears, a little unexpectedly, that the equilibrium may be thoroughly stable (with higher temperature below), if the coefficients of conductivity and viscosity are not too small. As the temperature gradient increases, instability enters, and at first only for a particular kind of disturbance.

The second phase of Bénard, where a tendency reveals itself for a slow transformation into regular hexagons, is not touched. It would seem to demand the inclusion of the squares of quantities here treated as small. But the size of the hexagons (under the boundary conditions postulated) is determinate, at any rate when they assert themselves early enough.

An appendix deals with a related analytical problem having various physical interpretations, such as the symmetrical vibration in two dimensions of a layer of air enclosed by a nearly circular wall.

The general Eulerian equations of fluid motion are in the usual notation :—

$$\frac{\mathrm{D}u}{\mathrm{D}t}=\mathrm{X}-\frac{1}{\rho}\frac{dp}{dx}, \quad \frac{\mathrm{D}v}{\mathrm{D}t}=\mathrm{Y}-\frac{1}{\rho}\frac{dp}{dy}, \quad \frac{\mathrm{D}w}{\mathrm{D}t}=\mathrm{Z}-\frac{1}{\rho}\frac{dp}{dz}, \quad . \quad (1)$$

where

$$\frac{\mathrm{D}}{\mathrm{D}t}=\frac{d}{dt}+u\frac{d}{dx}+v\frac{d}{dy}+w\frac{d}{dz}, \quad . \quad . \quad . \quad (2)$$

and X, Y, Z are the components of extraneous force reckoned per unit of mass. If, neglecting viscosity, we suppose that gravity is the only impressed force,

$$\mathrm{X}=0, \qquad \mathrm{Y}=0, \qquad \mathrm{Z}=-g, \quad . \quad . \quad . \quad (3)$$

z being measured upwards. In equations (1) ρ is variable in consequence of variable temperature and variable pressure. But, as Boussinesq * has shown, in the class of problems under consideration the influence of pressure is unimportant and even the variation with temperature may be disregarded except in so far as it modifies the operation of *gravity*. If we write $\rho=\rho_0+\delta\rho$, we have

$$g\rho=g\rho_0(1+\delta\rho/\rho_0)=g\rho_0-g\rho_0\alpha\theta,$$

where θ is the temperature reckoned from the point where $\rho=\rho_0$ and α is the coefficient of expansion. We may now identify ρ in (1) with ρ_0, and our equations become

$$\frac{\mathrm{D}u}{\mathrm{D}t}=-\frac{1}{\rho}\frac{d\mathrm{P}}{dx}, \quad \frac{\mathrm{D}v}{\mathrm{D}t}=-\frac{1}{\rho}\frac{d\mathrm{P}}{dy}, \quad \frac{\mathrm{D}w}{\mathrm{D}t}=-\frac{1}{\rho}\frac{d\mathrm{P}}{dz}+\gamma\theta, \quad . \quad (4)$$

where ρ is a constant, γ is written for $g\alpha$, and P for $p+g\rho z$.

* *Théorie Analytique de la Chaleur*, t. ii. p. 172 (1903).

Also, since the fluid is now treated as incompressible,

$$\frac{du}{dx}+\frac{dv}{dy}+\frac{dw}{dz}=0. \quad . \quad . \quad . \quad . \quad . \quad (5)$$

The equation for the conduction of heat is,

$$\frac{\mathrm{D}\theta}{\mathrm{D}t}=\kappa\left(\frac{d^2\theta}{dx^2}+\frac{d^2\theta}{dy^2}+\frac{d^2\theta}{dz^2}\right), \quad . \quad . \quad . \quad . \quad (6)$$

in which κ is the diffusibility for temperature. These are the equations employed by Boussinesq.

In the particular problems to which we proceed the fluid is supposed to be bounded by two infinite fixed planes at $z=0$ and $z=\zeta$, where also the temperatures are maintained constant. In the equilibrium condition u, v, w vanish and θ being a function of z only is subject to $d^2\theta/dz^2=0$, or $d\theta/dz=\beta$, where β is a constant representing the temperature gradient. If the equilibrium is stable, β is positive; and if unstable with the higher temperature below, β is negative. It will be convenient, however, to reckon θ as the departure from the equilibrium temperature Θ. The only change required in equations (4) is to write ϖ for P, where

$$\varpi=\mathrm{P}-\rho\gamma\int\Theta dz. \quad . \quad . \quad . \quad . \quad . \quad (7)$$

In equation (6) $\mathrm{D}\theta/\mathrm{D}t$ is to be replaced by $\mathrm{D}\theta/\mathrm{D}t+w\beta$.

The question with which we are principally concerned is the effect of a small departure from the condition of equilibrium, whether stable or unstable. For this purpose it suffices to suppose u, v, w, and θ to be small. When we neglect the squares of the small quantities, $\mathrm{D}/\mathrm{D}t$ identifies itself with d/dt and we get

$$\frac{du}{dt}=-\frac{1}{\rho}\frac{d\varpi}{dx}, \quad \frac{dv}{dt}=-\frac{1}{\rho}\frac{d\varpi}{dy}, \quad \frac{dw}{dt}=-\frac{1}{\rho}\frac{d\varpi}{dz}+\gamma\theta, \quad . \quad (8)$$

$$\frac{d\theta}{dt}+\beta w=\kappa\left(\frac{d^2\theta}{dx^2}+\frac{d^2\theta}{dy^2}+\frac{d^2\theta}{dz^2}\right), \quad . \quad . \quad . \quad (9)$$

which with (5) and the initial and boundary conditions suffice for the solution of the problem. The boundary conditions are that $w=0$, $\theta=0$, when $z=0$ or ζ.

We now assume in the usual manner that the small quantities are proportional to

$$e^{ilx}e^{imy}e^{nt}, \quad . \quad . \quad . \quad . \quad . \quad . \quad . \quad (10)$$

so that (8), (5), (9) become

$$nu = -\frac{il\varpi}{\rho}, \quad nv = -\frac{im\varpi}{\rho}, \quad nw = -\frac{1}{\rho}\frac{d\varpi}{dz} + \gamma\theta, \quad . \quad (11)$$

$$ilu + imv + dw/dz = 0, \quad . \quad . \quad . \quad . \quad . \quad (12)$$

$$n\theta + \beta w = \kappa(d^2/dz^2 - l^2 - m^2)\theta, \quad . \quad . \quad . \quad (13)$$

from which by elimination of u, v, w, we derive

$$\frac{n}{l^2+m^2}\frac{d^2w}{dz^2} = nw - \gamma\theta. \quad . \quad . \quad . \quad . \quad (14)$$

Having regard to the boundary conditions to be satisfied by w and θ, we now assume that these quantities are proportional to $\sin sz$, where $s = q\pi/\zeta$, and q is an integer. Hence

$$\beta w + \{n + \kappa(l^2+m^2+s^2)\}\theta = 0, \quad . \quad . \quad . \quad (15)$$

$$n(l^2+m^2+s^2)w - \gamma(l^2+m^2)\theta = 0, \quad . \quad . \quad (16)$$

and the equation determining n is the quadratic

$$n^2(l^2+m^2+s^2) + n\kappa(l^2+m^2+s^2)^2 + \beta\gamma(l^2+m^2) = 0. \quad (17)$$

When $\kappa=0$, there is no conduction, so that each element of the fluid retains its temperature and density. If β be positive, the equilibrium is stable, and

$$n = \frac{\pm i\sqrt{\{\beta\gamma(l^2+m^2)\}}}{\sqrt{\{l^2+m^2+s^2\}}}, \quad . \quad . \quad . \quad . \quad (18)$$

indicating vibrations about the condition of equilibrium. If, on the other hand, β be negative, say $-\beta'$,

$$n = \frac{\pm\sqrt{\{\beta'\gamma(l^2+m^2)\}}}{\sqrt{\{l^2+m^2+s^2\}}}. \quad . \quad . \quad . \quad . \quad . \quad (19)$$

When n has the positive value, the corresponding disturbance increases exponentially with the time.

For a given value of l^2+m^2, the numerical values of n diminish without limit as s increases—that is, the more subdivisions there are along z. The greatest value corresponds with $q=1$ or $s=\pi/\zeta$. On the other hand, if s be given, $|n|$ increases from zero as l^2+m^2 increases from zero (great wave-lengths along x and y) up to a finite limit when l^2+m^2 is large (small wave-lengths along x and y). This case of no conductivity falls within the scope of a former investigation where the fluid was supposed from the beginning to be incompressible but of variable density *.

Returning to the consideration of a finite conductivity, we have again to distinguish the cases where β is positive and negative. When β is negative (higher temperature below) both values of n in (17) are real and one is positive. The equilibrium is unstable for all values of l^2+m^2 and of s. If β be positive, n may be real or complex. In either case the real part of n is negative, so that the equilibrium is stable whatever l^2+m^2 and s may be.

When β is negative $(-\beta')$, it is important to inquire for what values of l^2+m^2 the instability is greatest, for these are the modes which more and more assert themselves as time elapses, even though initially they may be quite subordinate. That the positive value of n must have a maximum appears when we observe it tends to vanish both when l^2+m^2 is small and also when l^2+m^2 is large. Setting for shortness $l^2+m^2+s^2=\sigma$, we may write (17)

$$n^2\sigma+n\kappa\sigma^2-\beta'\gamma(\sigma-s^2)=0, \quad . \quad . \quad . \quad (20)$$

and the question is to find the value of σ for which n is greatest, s being supposed given. Making $dn/d\sigma=0$, we get on differentiation

$$n^2+2n\kappa\sigma-\beta'\gamma=0\,; \quad . \quad . \quad . \quad . \quad . \quad (21)$$

and on elimination of n^2 between (20), (21)

$$n=\frac{\beta'\gamma s^2}{\kappa\sigma^2}. \quad . \quad . \quad . \quad . \quad . \quad . \quad . \quad (22)$$

Using this value of n in (21), we find as the equation for σ

$$\frac{2s^2}{\sigma}=1-\frac{\beta'\gamma s^4}{\kappa^2\sigma^4}. \quad . \quad . \quad . \quad . \quad . \quad . \quad (23)$$

When κ is relatively great, $\sigma=2s^2$, or

$$l^2+m^2=s^2. \quad . \quad . \quad . \quad . \quad . \quad . \quad . \quad (24)$$

A second approximation gives

$$l^2+m^2=s^2+\frac{\beta'\gamma}{8\kappa^2s^2}. \quad . \quad . \quad . \quad . \quad . \quad . \quad (25)$$

The corresponding value of n is

$$n=\frac{\beta'\gamma}{4\kappa s^2}\left\{1-\frac{\beta'\gamma}{8\kappa^2s^4}\right\}. \quad . \quad . \quad . \quad . \quad . \quad (26)$$

* Proc. Lond. Math. Soc. vol. xiv. p. 170 (1883); Scientific Papers, vol. ii. p. 200.

The modes of greatest instability are those for which s is smallest, that is equal to π/ζ, and

$$l^2+m^2=\frac{\pi^2}{\zeta^2}+\frac{\beta'\gamma}{8\kappa^2\pi^2/\zeta^2}. \quad . \quad . \quad . \quad . \quad (27)$$

For a two-dimensional disturbance we may make $m=0$ and $l=2\pi/\lambda$, where λ is the wave-length along x. The λ of maximum instability is thus approximately

$$\lambda=2\zeta. \quad . \quad . \quad . \quad . \quad . \quad . \quad . \quad . \quad (28)$$

Again, if $l=m=2\pi/\lambda$, as for square cells,

$$\lambda=2\sqrt{2}\,.\,\zeta, \quad . \quad . \quad . \quad . \quad . \quad . \quad . \quad (29)$$

greater than before in the ratio $\sqrt{2}:1$.

We have considered especially the cases where κ is relatively small and relatively large. Intermediate cases would need to be dealt with by a numerical solution of (23).

When w is known in the form

$$w=\mathrm{W}e^{ilx}e^{imy}\sin sz\,.\,e^{nt}, \quad . \quad . \quad . \quad . \quad (30)$$

n being now a known function of l, m, s, u and v are at once derived by means of (11) and (12). Thus

$$u=\frac{il}{l^2+m^2}\frac{dw}{dz}, \quad v=\frac{im}{l^2+m^2}\frac{dw}{dz}. \quad . \quad . \quad . \quad (31)$$

The connexion between w and θ is given by (15) or (16). When β is negative and n positive, θ and w are of the same sign.

As an example in two dimensions of (30), (31), we might have in real form

$$w=\mathrm{W}\cos x\,.\sin z\,.\,e^{nt}, \quad . \quad . \quad . \quad . \quad (32)$$

$$u=-\mathrm{W}\sin x\,.\cos z\,.\,e^{nt}, \quad v=0. \quad . \quad . \quad . \quad (33)$$

Hitherto we have supposed the fluid to be destitute of viscosity. When we include viscosity, we must add $\nu(\nabla^2u,\ \nabla^2v,\ \nabla^2w)$ on the right of equations (1), (8), and (11), ν being the kinematic coefficient. Equations (12) and (13) remain unaffected. And in (11)

$$\nabla^2=d^2/dz^2-l^2-m^2 \quad . \quad . \quad . \quad . \quad . \quad (34)$$

We have also to reconsider the boundary conditions at $z=0$ and $z=\zeta$. We may still suppose $\theta=0$ and $w=0$; but for a further condition we should probably prefer $dw/dz=0$, corresponding to a fixed solid wall. But this entails much complication, and we may content ourselves with the supposition $d^2w/dz^2=0$, which (with $w=0$) is satisfied by taking as before w proportional to $\sin sz$ with $s=q\pi/\zeta$. This is equivalent to the annulment of lateral *forces* at the wall. For (Lamb's 'Hydrodynamics,' §§ 323, 326) these forces are expressed in general by

$$p_{xz}=\frac{dw}{dx}+\frac{du}{dz}, \quad p_{yz}=\frac{dw}{dy}+\frac{dv}{dz}, \quad . \quad . \quad . \quad (35)$$

while here $w=0$ at the boundaries requires also $dw/dx=0$, $dw/dy=0$. Hence, at the boundaries, $d^2u/dx\,dz$, $d^2v/dy\,dz$ vanish, and therefore by (5), d^2w/dz^2.

Equation (15) remains unaltered :—

$$\beta w+\{n+\kappa(l^2+m^2+s^2)\}\theta=0, \quad . \quad . \quad . \quad (15)$$

and (16) becomes

$$\{n+\nu(l^2+m^2+s^2)\}(l^2+m^2+s^2)w-\gamma(l^2+m^2)\theta=0. \quad (36)$$

Writing as before $\sigma=l^2+m^2+s^2$, we get the equation in n

$$(n+\kappa\sigma)(n+\nu\sigma)\sigma+\beta\gamma(l^2+m^2)=0, \quad . \quad . \quad (37)$$

which takes the place of (17).

If $\gamma=0$ (no expansion with heat) the equations degrade, and we have two simple alternatives. In the first $n+\kappa\sigma=0$ with $w=0$, signifying conduction of heat with no motion. In the second $n+\nu\sigma=0$, when the relation between w and θ becomes

$$\beta w+\sigma(\kappa-\nu)\theta=0. \quad . \quad . \quad . \quad . \quad . \quad (38)$$

In both cases, since n is real and negative, the disturbance is stable.

If we neglect κ in (37), the equation takes the same form (20) as that already considered when $\nu=0$. Hence the results expressed in (22), (23), (24), (25), (26), (27) are applicable with simple substitution of ν for κ.

In the general equation (37) if β be positive, as γ is supposed always to be, the values of n may be real or complex. If real they are both negative, and if complex the real part is negative. In either case the disturbance dies down. As was to be expected, when the temperature is higher above, the equilibrium is stable.

In the contrary case when β is negative $(-\beta')$ the roots of the quadratic are always real, and one at least is negative. There is a positive root only when

$$\beta'\gamma(l^2+m^2)>\kappa\nu\sigma^3. \quad . \quad . \quad . \quad . \quad . \quad (39)$$

If κ, or ν, vanish there is instability; but if κ and ν are finite and large enough, the equilibrium for this disturbance is stable, although the higher temperature is underneath.

Inequality (39) gives the condition of instability for the particular disturbance (l, m, s). It is of interest to inquire at what point the equilibrium becomes unstable when there is no restriction upon the value of l^2+m^2. In the equation

$$\beta'\gamma(l^2+m^2)-\kappa\nu\sigma^3=\beta'\gamma(\sigma-s^2)-\kappa\nu\sigma^3=0, \quad . \quad (40)$$

we see that the left-hand member is negative when l^2+m^2 is small and also when it is large. When the conditions are such that the equation can only just be satisfied with some value of l^2+m^2, or σ, the derived equation

$$\beta'\gamma-3\kappa\nu\sigma^2=0 \quad . \quad . \quad . \quad . \quad . \quad . \quad (41)$$

must also hold good, so that

$$\sigma=3s^2/2, \qquad l^2+m^2=\tfrac{1}{2}s^2, \quad . \quad . \quad . \quad (42)$$

and

$$\beta'\gamma=27\kappa\nu s^4/4. \quad . \quad . \quad . \quad . \quad . \quad . \quad . \quad . \quad (43)$$

Unless $\beta'\gamma$ exceeds the value given in (43) there is no instability, however l and m are chosen. But the equation still contains s, which may be as large as we please. The smallest value of s is π/ζ. The condition of instability when l, m, and s are all unrestricted is accordingly

$$\beta'\gamma>\frac{27\pi^4\kappa\nu}{4\zeta^4} \quad . \quad . \quad . \quad . \quad . \quad . \quad . \quad (44)$$

If $\beta'\gamma$ falls below this amount, the equilibrium is altogether stable. I am not aware that the possibility of complete stability under such circumstances has been contemplated.

To interpret (44) more conveniently, we may replace β' by $(\Theta_2-\Theta_1)/\zeta$ and γ by $g(\rho_2-\rho_1)/\rho_1(\Theta_2-\Theta_1)$, so that

$$\beta'\gamma=\frac{g}{\zeta}\frac{\rho_2-\rho_1}{\rho_1}, \quad . \quad . \quad . \quad . \quad . \quad . \quad . \quad (45)$$

where Θ_2, Θ_1, ρ_2, and ρ_1 are the extreme temperatures and densities in equilibrium. Thus (44) becomes

$$\frac{\rho_2-\rho_1}{\rho_1}>\frac{27\pi^4\kappa\nu}{4g\zeta^3} \quad . \quad . \quad . \quad . \quad . \quad . \quad (46)$$

In the case of air at atmospheric conditions we may take in C.G.S. measure

$$\nu=\cdot 14, \quad \text{and} \quad \kappa=\tfrac{5}{2}\nu \text{ (Maxwell's Theory).}$$

Also $g=980$, and thus

$$\frac{\rho_2-\rho_1}{\rho_1} = \frac{\cdot 033}{\zeta^3}. \qquad (47)$$

For example, if $\zeta=1$ cm., instability requires that the density at the top exceed that at the bottom by one-thirtieth part, corresponding to about 9° C. of temperature. We should not forget that our method postulates a small value of $(\rho_2-\rho_1)/\rho_1$. Thus if $\kappa\nu$ be given, the application of (46) may cease to be legitimate unless ζ be large enough.

It may be remarked that the influence of viscosity would be increased were we to suppose the horizontal velocities (instead of the horizontal forces) to be annulled at the boundaries.

The problem of determining for what value of l^2+m^2, or σ, the instability, when finite, is a maximum is more complicated. The differentiation of (37) with respect to σ gives

$$n^2+2n\sigma(\kappa+\nu)+3\kappa\nu\sigma^2-\beta'\gamma=0, \qquad (48)$$

whence

$$n=\frac{\beta'\gamma s^2-2\kappa\nu\sigma^3}{\sigma^2(\kappa+\nu)}, \qquad (49)$$

expressing n in terms of σ. To find σ we have to eliminate n between (44) and (45). The result is

$$\sigma^6\kappa\nu(\kappa-\nu)^2+\sigma^4\beta'\gamma(\kappa+\nu)^2-\sigma^3 . 2\beta'\gamma s^2(\kappa^2+\nu^2)-\beta'^2\gamma^2 s^4=0, \qquad (50)$$

from which, in particular cases, σ could be found by numerical computation. From (50) we fall back on (23) by supposing $\nu=0$, and again on a similar equation if we suppose $\kappa=0$.

But the case of a nearly evanescent n is probably the more practical. In an experiment the temperature gradient could not be established all at once and we may suppose the progress to be very slow. In the earlier stages the equilibrium would be stable, so that no disturbance of importance would occur until n passed through zero to the positive side, corresponding to (44) or (46). The breakdown thus occurs for $s=\pi/\zeta$, and by (42) $l^2+m^2=\pi^2/2\zeta^2$. And since the evanescence of n is equivalent to the omission of d/dt in the original equations, the motion thus determined has the character of a *steady* motion. The constant multiplier is, however, arbitrary; and there is nothing to determine it so long as the squares of u, v, w, θ are neglected.

In a particular solution where w as a function of x and y has the simplest form, say

$$w = 2\cos x \,.\, \cos y, \quad . \quad . \quad . \quad . \quad . \quad (51)$$

the particular coefficients of x and y which enter have relation to the particular axes of reference employed. If we rotate these axes through an angle ϕ, we have

$$\begin{aligned} w &= 2\cos\{x'\cos\phi - y'\sin\phi\} \,.\, \cos\{x'\sin\phi + y'\cos\phi\} \\ &= \cos\{x'(\cos\phi - \sin\phi)\} \,.\, \cos\{y'(\cos\phi + \sin\phi)\} \\ &+ \sin\{x'(\cos\phi - \sin\phi)\} \,.\, \sin\{y'(\cos\phi + \sin\phi)\} \\ &+ \cos\{x'(\cos\phi + \sin\phi)\} \,.\, \cos\{y'(\cos\phi - \sin\phi)\} \\ &- \sin\{x'(\cos\phi + \sin\phi)\} \,.\, \sin\{y'(\cos\phi - \sin\phi)\}. \quad (52) \end{aligned}$$

For example, if $\phi = \frac{1}{4}\pi$, (52) becomes

$$w = \cos(y'\sqrt{2}) + \cos(x'\sqrt{2}). \quad . \quad . \quad . \quad (53)$$

It is to be observed that with the general value of ϕ, if we call the coefficients of x', y', l and m respectively, we have in every part $l^2 + m^2 = 2$, unaltered from the original value in (51).

The character of w, under the condition that all the elementary terms of which it is composed are subject to $l^2 + m^2 = \text{constant } (k^2)$, is the same as for the transverse displacement of an infinite stretched membrane, vibrating with one definite frequency. The limitation upon w is, in fact, merely that it satisfies

$$(d^2/dx^2 + d^2/dy^2 + k^2)w = 0. \quad . \quad . \quad . \quad . \quad . \quad (54)$$

The character of w in particular solutions of the membrane problem is naturally associated with the nodal system ($w = 0$), where the membrane may be regarded as held fast; and we may suppose the nodal system to divide the plane into similar parts or cells, such as squares, equilateral triangles, or regular hexagons. But in the present problem it is perhaps more appropriate to consider divisions of the plane with respect to which w is symmetrical, so that dw/dn is zero on the straight lines forming the divisions of the cells. The more natural analogy is then with the two-dimensional vibration of air, where w represents velocity-potential and the divisions may be regarded as fixed walls.

The simplest case is, of course, that in which the cells are squares. If the sides of the squares be 2π, we may take with axes parallel to the sides and origin at centre

$$w=\cos x+\cos y, \quad . \quad . \quad . \quad . \quad . \quad (55)$$

being thus composed by superposition of two parts for each of which $k^2=1$. This makes $dw/dx=-\sin x$, vanishing when $x=\pm\pi$. Similarly, dw/dy vanishes when $y=\pm\pi$, so that the sides of the square behave as fixed walls. To find the places where w changes sign, we write it in the form

$$w=2\cos\frac{x+y}{2}.\cos\frac{x-y}{2}, \quad . \quad . \quad . \quad . \quad (56)$$

giving $x+y=\pm\pi$, $x-y=\pm\pi$, lines which constitute the inscribed square (fig. 1). Within this square w has one sign (say $+$) and in the four right-angled triangles left over the $-$ sign. When the whole plane is considered, there is no want of symmetry between the $+$ and the $-$ regions.

Fig. 1.

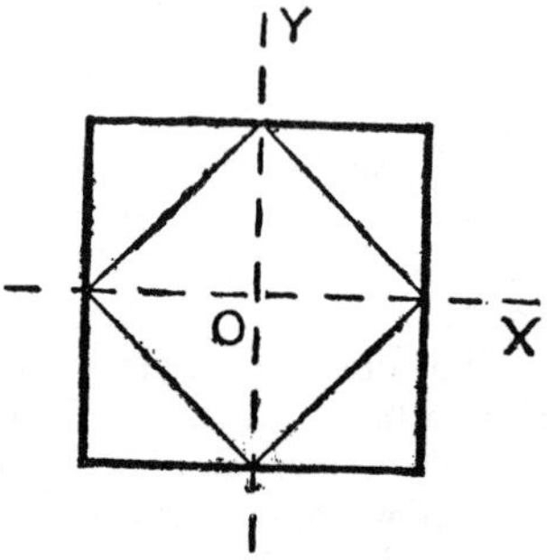

The principle is the same when the elementary cells are equilateral triangles or hexagons; but I am not aware that an analytical solution has been obtained for these cases. An experimental determination of k^2 might be made by observing the time of vibration under gravity of water contained in a trough with vertical sides and of corresponding section, which depends upon the same differential equation and boundary conditions*. The particular vibration in question is not the slowest possible, but that where there is a simultaneous rise at the centre and fall at the walls all round, with but one curve of zero elevation between.

In the case of the hexagon, we may regard it as deviating comparatively little from the circular form and employ the approximate methods then applicable. By an argument analogous to that formerly developed † for the boundary condition $w=0$, we may convince ourselves that the value of k^2 for the hexagon cannot differ much from that appropriate to a circle of the same area. Thus if a be the radius

* See Phil. Mag. vol. i. p. 257 (1876); Scientific Papers, vol. i. pp. 265, 271.

† Theory of Sound, § 209; compare also § 317. See Appendix.

of this circle, k is given by $J_0'(ka)=0$, J_0 being the Bessel's function of zero order, or $ka=3\cdot 832$. If b be the side of the hexagon, $a^2=3\sqrt{3}\,.\,b^2/2\pi$.

Appendix.

On the nearly symmetrical solution for a nearly circular area, when w satisfies $(d^2/dx^2+d^2/dy^2+k^2)w=0$ and makes $dw/dn=0$ on the boundary.

Starting with the true circle of radius a, we have w a function of r (the radius vector) only, and the solution is $w=J_0(kr)$ with the condition $J_0'(ka)=0$, yielding $ka=3\cdot 832$, which determines k if a be given, or a if k be given. In the problem proposed the boundary is only approximately circular, so that we write $r=a+\rho$, where a is the mean value and

$$\rho=\alpha_1\cos\theta+\beta_1\sin\theta+\ldots+\alpha_n\cos n\theta+\beta_n\sin n\theta. \quad . \quad (57)$$

In (57) θ is the vectorial angle and α_1 &c. are quantities small relatively to a. The general solution of the differential equation being

$$w=A_0J_0(kr)+J_1(kr)\{A_1\cos\theta+B_1\sin\theta\}$$
$$+\ldots+J_n(kr)\{A_n\cos n\theta+B_n\sin\theta\}, \quad . \quad . \quad (58)$$

we are to suppose now that A_1, &c., are small relatively to A_0. It remains to consider the boundary condition.

If ϕ denote the small angle between r and the normal dn measured outwards,

$$\frac{dw}{dn}=\frac{dw}{dr}\cos\phi-\frac{dw}{rd\theta}\sin\phi, \quad . \quad . \quad . \quad . \quad (59)$$

and

$$\tan\phi=\frac{dr}{rd\theta}=\frac{d\rho}{ad\theta}=\frac{n}{a}(-\alpha_n\sin n\theta+\beta_n\cos n\theta) \quad (60)$$

with sufficient approximation, only the general term being written. In formulating the boundary condition $dw/dn=0$ correct to the second order of small quantities, we require dw/dr to the second order, but $dw/d\theta$ to the first order only. We have

$$\frac{1}{k}\frac{dw}{dr}=A_0\{J_0'(ka)+k\rho\,J_0''(ka)+\tfrac{1}{2}k^2\rho^2J_0'''(ka)\}$$
$$+\{J_n'(ka)+k\rho\,J_n''(ka)\}\{A_n\cos n\theta+B_n\sin n\theta\},$$

$$\frac{dw}{ad\theta}=\frac{n}{a}J_n(ka)\{-A_n\sin n\theta+B_n\cos n\theta\}$$

and for the boundary condition, setting $ka=z$ and omitting the argument in the Bessel's functions,

$$A_0\{J_0'.\cos\phi+k\rho\, J_0''+\tfrac{1}{2}k^2\rho^2 J_0'''\}$$
$$+\{J_n'+k\rho\, J_n''\}\{A_n\cos n\theta+B_n\sin n\theta\}$$
$$-\frac{n^2}{az}J_n\{-A_n\sin n\theta+B_n\cos n\theta\}\{-\alpha_n\sin n\theta$$
$$+\beta_n\cos n\theta\}=0. \quad . \quad (61)$$

If for the moment we omit the terms of the second order, we have

$$A_0J_0'+kA_0J_0''\{\alpha_n\cos n\theta+\beta_n\sin n\theta\}$$
$$+J_n'\{A_n\cos n\theta+B_n\sin n\theta\}=0\,; \quad . \quad (62)$$

so that $$J_0'(z)=0, \quad \text{and}$$

$$kA_0J_0''.\alpha_n+J_n'.A_n=0, \qquad kA_0J_0''.\beta_n+J_n'.B_n=0. \quad . \quad (63)$$

To this order of approximation $z, =ka$, has the same value as when $\rho=0$; that is to say, the equivalent radius is equal to the mean radius, or (as we may also express it) k may be regarded as dependent upon the *area* only. Equations (63) determine A_n, B_n in terms of the known quantities α_n, β_n.

Since J_0' is a small quantity, $\cos\phi$ in (61) may now be omitted. To obtain a corrected evaluation of z, it suffices to take the mean of (61) for all values of θ. Thus

$$A_0\{2J_0'+\tfrac{1}{2}k^2J_0'''(\alpha_n^2+\beta_n^2)\}$$
$$+\{kJ_n''-n^2J_n/az\}\{\alpha_nA_n+\beta_nB_n\}=0,$$

or on substitution of the approximate values of A_n, B_n from (63),

$$J_0'=\tfrac{1}{2}k^2(\alpha_n^2+\beta_n^2)\left\{\frac{J_0''}{J_n'}\left(J_n''-\frac{n^2J_n}{z^2}\right)-\frac{J_0'''}{z}\right\}. \quad . \quad (64)$$

This expression may, however, be much simplified. In virtue of the general equation for J_n,

$$J_n''-\frac{n^2}{z^2}J_n=-\frac{J_n'}{z}-J_n\,;$$

and since here $J_0'=0$ approximately,

$$J_0''=-J_0, \qquad J_0'''=-z^{-1}J_0''=z^{-1}J_0.$$

Thus

$$J_0'(z)=\tfrac{1}{2}k^2J_0.\Sigma(\alpha_n^2+\beta_n^2)\left\{\frac{J_n}{J_n'}+\frac{1}{2z}\right\}, \quad . \quad (65)$$

the sign of summation with respect to n being introduced.

Let us now suppose that $a+da$ is the equivalent radius, so that $J_0'(ka+k\,da)=0$, that is the radius of the exact circle which corresponds to the value of k appropriate to the approximate circle. Then

$$J_0'(z)+k\,da\,J_0''(z)=0,$$

and

$$da=-\frac{J_0'}{kJ_0''}=k\Sigma(\alpha_n^2+\beta_n^2)\left\{\frac{J_n}{2J_n'}+\frac{1}{4z}\right\}. \quad . \quad (66)$$

Again, if $a+da'$ be the radius of the true circle which has the same *area* as the approximate circle

$$da'=\frac{1}{4a}\Sigma(\alpha_n^2+\beta_n^2), \quad . \quad . \quad . \quad . \quad (67)$$

and

$$da'-da=-\Sigma\frac{\alpha_n^2+\beta_n^2}{2a}\frac{zJ_n(z)}{2J_n'(z)}, \quad . \quad . \quad . \quad (68)$$

where z is the first root (after zero) of $J_0'(z)=0$, viz. 3·832.

The question with which we are mainly concerned is the sign of $da'-da$ for the various values of n. When $n=1$, $J_1(z)=-J_0'(z)=0$, so that $da=da'$, a result which was to be expected, since the terms in α_1, β_1 represent approximately a displacement merely of the circle, without alteration of size or shape. We will now examine the sign of J_n/J_n' when $n=2$, and 3.

For this purpose we may employ the sequence equations

$$J_{n+1}=\frac{2n}{z}J_n-J_{n-1}, \qquad J_n'=\tfrac{1}{2}J_{n-1}-\tfrac{1}{2}J_{n+1},$$

which allow J_n and J_n' to be expressed in terms of J_1 and J_0, of which the former is here zero. We find

$$J_2=-J_0, \qquad J_3=-4z^{-1}J_0, \qquad J_4=(1-24z^{-2})J_0;$$
$$J_1'=J_0, \qquad J_2'=2z^{-1}J_0, \qquad J_3'=(12z^{-2}-1)J_0.$$

Thus

$$\frac{J_1}{J_1'}=0, \qquad \frac{J_2}{J_2'}=-\frac{z}{2}, \qquad \frac{J_3}{J_3'}=\frac{4z}{z^2-12};$$

whence on introduction of the actual value of z, viz. 3·832, we see that J_2/J_2' is negative, and that J_3/J_3' is positive.

When $n>z$, it is a general proposition that $J_n(z)$ and $J_n'(z)$ are both positive *. Hence for $n=4$ and onwards, J_n/J_n' is positive when $z=3·832$. We thus arrive at the

* See, for example, Theory of Sound, § 210.

curious conclusion that when $n=2$, $da'>da$, as happens for all values of n (exceeding unity) when the boundary condition is $w=0$, but that when $n>2$, $da'<da$. The existence of the exceptional case $n=2$ precludes a completely general statement of the effect of a departure from the truly circular form; but if the terms for which $n=2$ are absent, as they would be in the case of any regular polygon with an even number of sides, regarded as a deformed circle, we may say that $da'<da$. In the physical problems the effect of a departure from the circular form is then to depress the pitch when the area is maintained constant ($da'=0$). But for an elliptic deformation the reverse is the case.

At first sight it may appear strange that an elliptic deformation should be capable of raising the pitch. But we must remember that we are here dealing with a vibration such that the phase at both ends of the minor axis is the opposite of that at the centre. A parallel case which admits of complete calculation is that of the rectangle regarded as a deformed square, and vibrating in the gravest *symmetrical* mode *. It is easily shown that a departure from the square form raises the pitch. Of course, the one-dimensional vibration parallel to the longer side has its pitch depressed.

Reprinted from *Philosophical Magazine*, Series 7, Vol. 2, 1926.

LXXVI. *The Stability of a Layer of Fluid heated below.*

By HAROLD JEFFREYS, *M.A., D.Sc., F.R.S.**

IT was shown by the late Lord Rayleigh † in 1916 that a liquid might be in stable equilibrium even if its density increased upwards, provided its viscosity was sufficiently great; and a detailed solution was obtained for the mode of decay or growth of disturbances in certain conditions. The results were in qualitative agreement with the experimental work of Bénard ‡, since repeated and extended by A. R. Low and Brunt §. The boundary conditions assumed by Rayleigh were somewhat artificial, and on account of the general interest of the question and the practical importance of some of its applications it is desirable to extend the work to allow for other possibilities.

The method adopted here is based on the principle of "exchange of stabilities." Let us consider for simplicity a system with a finite number of degrees of freedom. If we assume that in a free disturbance from the steady state all the departures vary with the time like $e^{\gamma t}$, where γ is a constant, γ will satisfy an algebraic equation with real coefficients. If then

* Communicated by the Author.

† Phil. Mag. xxxii. pp. 529–546 (1916).

‡ *Ann. d. Chimie et de Physique*, xxiii. p. 62 (1901).

§ 'Nature,' cxv. pp. 299–301 (1925).

the physical circumstances of the system vary continuously, all the roots of this equation will in general vary continuously. If the system is conservative, and passes from stability to instability, one of the admissible values of γ^2 changes sign by passing through zero. But the vanishing of a root of an algebraic equation implies that the constant term vanishes; and since γ is equivalent to $\partial/\partial t$, the departure from the steady state will satisfy a differential equation involving the independent variable only through its differential coefficients with regard to the time and not explicitly. Thus when the system is on the verge of becoming unstable the equations of motion will have a solution such that the departure from the steady state is different from zero and independent of the time. When instability is attained, the departure involved in this solution will be the one that will grow with the time.

The present system involves viscosity, and therefore is not conservative. It will still be true, however, that γ will involve an equation with real coefficients (possibly of infinite degree). If the rate of increase of temperature upwards is β (which will be taken as negative), it is fairly clear that when the kinematic viscosity ν is great enough any disturbance will die down exponentially with the time, so that every value of γ is real and negative. When ν diminishes algebraically, instability will arise when one of the values of γ first acquires a positive real part. If its imaginary part is also zero, the previous considerations will apply, and a steady departure from the state of equilibrium will be possible. But if as ν diminishes from ∞ to the critical value two of the values of γ coalesce and then become conjugate complexes, they may have finite imaginary parts when their real part vanishes, and the argument will break down. In this case the motion arising when instability develops will be an oscillation with gradually increasing amplitude. The impossibility of such a movement has not been proved in the present paper, but in Lord Rayleigh's discussion it was proved for a special type of boundary conditions, and here I shall only appeal to experiment to confirm that it is not the type of motion that actually does arise when equilibrium breaks down. I shall assume, then, that the uniformly stratified condition of the fluid first becomes unstable when the equations of the problem have a solution different from zero and independent of the time.

2. Let us assume that in the steady state the temperature is βz, the temperature on the floor being taken as zero; here

β is a constant and z the elevation above the floor. Take horizontal coordinates x and y; and let the components of velocity be u, v, and w. Let p be the pressure, V the temperature, ρ the density; and let suffix zero attached to any of them indicate its value at the same place in the undisturbed state, and an accent its departure from the undisturbed value. Let κ, ν, and α be the coefficients of thermometric conductivity, kinematic viscosity, and volume expansion. Then the equations of motion and of heat conduction are

$$\rho \frac{d}{dt}(u, v, w) = -\left(\frac{\partial}{\partial x}, \frac{\partial}{\partial y}, \frac{\partial}{\partial z}\right) p + \nu\rho\nabla^2(u, v, w) - (0, 0, g\rho), \quad \ldots \quad (1)$$

$$\frac{dV}{dt} = \kappa\nabla^2 V, \quad \ldots \quad (2)$$

and the equation of continuity is

$$\frac{d\rho}{dt} = -\rho\left(\frac{\partial u}{\partial x} + \frac{\partial v}{\partial y} + \frac{\partial w}{\partial z}\right). \quad \ldots \quad (3)$$

The equation of thermal expansion may be taken to be

$$\rho = \rho_c(1 - \alpha V), \quad \ldots \quad (4)$$

where ρ_c is the density at temperature zero; the fluid is supposed incompressible.

All these equations reduce to identities in the steady state except the equation of vertical motion, which gives

$$0 = -\frac{\partial p_0}{\partial z} - g\rho_0. \quad \ldots \quad (5)$$

Let us now neglect all squares of departures from the steady state. The d/dt reduces to $\partial/\partial t$ in (1), giving

$$\rho_0\left(\frac{\partial}{\partial t} - \nu\nabla^2\right)(u, v, w) = -\left(\frac{\partial}{\partial x}, \frac{\partial}{\partial y}, \frac{\partial}{\partial z}\right) p' - (0, 0, g\rho'). \quad \ldots \quad (6)$$

Forming the divergence of both sides of this equation, we may put ρ_c for ρ_0 when multiplied by a small quantity; then

$$\rho_c\left(\frac{\partial}{\partial t} - \nu\nabla^2\right)\left(\frac{\partial u}{\partial x} + \frac{\partial v}{\partial y} + \frac{\partial w}{\partial z}\right) = -\nabla^2 p' - g\frac{\partial \rho'}{\partial z}. \quad (7)$$

From (3) (4) and (2)

$$\frac{\partial u}{\partial x} + \frac{\partial v}{\partial y} + \frac{\partial w}{\partial z} = -\frac{1}{\rho_c}\frac{d\rho}{dt} = \alpha\frac{dV}{dt} = \alpha\kappa\nabla^2 V'. \quad . \quad (8)$$

Thus

$$\alpha\kappa\left(\frac{\partial}{\partial t}-\nu\nabla^2\right)\nabla^2 V' = -\frac{1}{\rho_c}\nabla^2 p' + g\alpha\frac{\partial V'}{\partial z}. \quad . \quad (9)$$

Also from (2)

$$\left(\frac{\partial}{\partial t}-\kappa\nabla^2\right)V' + \beta w = 0, \quad . \quad . \quad . \quad . \quad (10)$$

which determines w in terms of V'. Substituting in the equation of vertical motion we have

$$\left(\frac{\partial}{\partial t}-\kappa\nabla^2\right)\left(\frac{\partial}{\partial t}-\nu\nabla^2\right)V' = \frac{\beta}{\rho_0}\frac{\partial p'}{\partial z} - g\alpha\beta V'. \quad (11)$$

Eliminating p' between (9) and (11),

$$\left\{\kappa\alpha\frac{\partial}{\partial z}+\frac{1}{\beta}\left(\frac{\partial}{\partial t}-\kappa\nabla^2\right)\right\}\left(\frac{\partial}{\partial t}-\nu\nabla^2\right)\nabla^2 V'$$

$$= -g\alpha\left(\frac{\partial^2 V'}{\partial x^2}+\frac{\partial^2 V'}{\partial y^2}\right). \quad (12)$$

If the depth is h, the ratio of the term involving $\kappa\alpha$ to that on the right is of order $(\nu\kappa/gh^3)$ which is in general very small. The term in $\kappa\alpha$ will therefore be neglected. (This approximation was made *ab initio* by Rayleigh.) At the same time we shall introduce the condition of marginal stability that $\partial V/\partial t$ is zero. Then (12) simplifies to

$$\nabla^6 V' = -\frac{g\alpha\beta}{\kappa\nu}\left(\frac{\partial^2 V'}{\partial x^2}+\frac{\partial^2 V'}{\partial y^2}\right). \quad . \quad . \quad . \quad (13)$$

Suppose now that V' is proportional to $\sin lx \sin my$, the remaining factor being a function of z only. Put

$$(l^2+m^2)h^2 = a^2, \quad . \quad . \quad . \quad . \quad . \quad (14)$$

so that a is a pure number. Put also

$$z = h\zeta, \quad . \quad . \quad . \quad . \quad . \quad . \quad . \quad . \quad (15)$$

so that ζ is zero at the bottom and unity at the top. Then (13) becomes

$$\left(\frac{\partial^2}{\partial\zeta^2}-a^2\right)^3 V' = -\lambda a^2 V', \quad . \quad . \quad . \quad . \quad (16)$$

where

$$\lambda = -\frac{g\alpha\beta h^4}{\kappa\nu}. \quad . \quad . \quad . \quad . \quad . \quad (17)$$

3. *The boundary conditions.*

At the upper and lower boundaries some condition must be satisfied by the temperature. If the fluid is in contact with a perfect conductor V′ will be zero; if there is no conduction across the boundary $\partial V'/\partial z$ will be zero.

Three conditions must also be satisfied by the velocity components. If there is a rigid boundary, u, v, and w must all vanish. By 2(10) w is proportional to $\nabla^2 V'$. With our hypothesis as to the form of V′ the conditions satisfied by u and v reduce to one. Since these components are zero at all points of the boundary, $\frac{\partial u}{\partial x} + \frac{\partial v}{\partial y}$ is zero, whence by 2(3) $\partial w/\partial z$ is proportional to w, which is zero. Thus the conditions at a rigid boundary are that $\nabla^2 V'$ and $\frac{\partial}{\partial z}\nabla^2 V'$ are zero.

If in the undisturbed position of a free surface z is constant over it, in the disturbed state w for this value of z will be proportional to $\partial p'/\partial t$, which is zero for marginal stability. Thus $\nabla^2 V'$ is zero. Also $\partial u/\partial z$ and $\partial v/\partial z$ will be zero for all values of x and y over this surface. Hence by differentiating 2(8) with regard to z, we see that $\partial^2 w/\partial z^2$ is equal to $\frac{\partial}{\partial z}\alpha\kappa\nabla^2 V'$. Using the value of w from 2(10) we see that this implies that

$$\frac{\partial^2}{\partial z^2}\nabla^2 V' = \alpha\beta\frac{\partial}{\partial z}\nabla^2 V'.$$

The maximum values of the quantities involved in this equation, if not restricted to be surface values, would be in a ratio comparable with $1 : \alpha\beta h$. The latter quantity is the ratio, to the mean density, of the difference between the undisturbed densities at the top and bottom of the fluid, which we have already assumed to be small. Thus our condition will hold only if the quantity on the left, evaluated on the boundary, is only a small fraction of its maximum in the interior of the fluid. Only a trifling error will therefore be introduced if we replace the conditiou by the assertion that $\frac{\partial^2}{\partial z^2}\nabla^2 V'$ is zero at the boundary. Thus the conditions at a free surface are that $\nabla^2 V'$ and $\frac{\partial^2}{\partial z^2}\nabla^2 V'$ are zero.

Altogether three conditions must be satisfied at both the top and the bottom of the fluid, while the linear equation 2(16) is of the sixth order. Their consistency implies a relation between the numbers a and λ; for a given a the lowest of the values of λ that satisfy this relation (if there are more than one) would give the value of β appropriate to marginal instability if this were the only value of a admitted. Then the value of a that gives the lowest λ so determined will give the first type of disturbance that will grow, and the associated λ will give the value of β for marginal instability.

4. *Rayleigh's problem.*

The conditions adopted by Rayleigh at the boundary are equivalent to the vanishing of V', $\partial^2 V'/\partial z^2$, and $\partial^4 V'/\partial z^4$. His solution therefore corresponds to a fluid with a free surface at both top and bottom, with the temperature maintained constant over both. This is not a natural system, but admits a simple solution, all the conditions being satisfied if V' is proportional to $\sin s\zeta$, where s is a constant, and $\sin s=0$. Then 2(16) gives

$$(s^2+a^2)^3 = \lambda a^2, \quad . \quad . \quad . \quad . \quad . \quad . \quad . \quad (1)$$

and the lowest admissible value of λ is given by taking $s=\pi$. Then

$$\lambda = \frac{(\pi^2+a^2)^3}{a^2}. \quad . \quad . \quad . \quad . \quad . \quad (2)$$

We find that λ is least when

$$a = \frac{\pi}{\sqrt{2}} = 2{\cdot}22, \quad . \quad . \quad . \quad . \quad . \quad (3)$$

and then

$$\lambda = \frac{27}{4}\pi^4 = 651. \quad (4)$$

This result is equivalent to equations (42) and (44) of Rayleigh's paper.

5. *Solution by finite differences.*

The equation 2(16) could be formally solved in terms of exponential functions, but this method would be troublesome, since four of the coefficients of ζ in the indices would be complex, and the boundary conditions would lead to an equation for λ in the form of the vanishing of a determinant of the sixth order with many complex elements. The most convenient method seems to be that of L. F. Richardson, using central differences *. Let us denote by Z the factor

* Mathematical Gazette, July 1925.

of V′ that involves ζ. If the values of the dependent variable are given at equal intervals d of the independent variable, thus,

$$Z_{-3},\ Z_{-2},\ Z_{-1},\ Z_0,\ Z_1,\ Z_2,\ Z_3,\ \ldots\ldots,$$

the basis of the method is to replace differential coefficients by finite centred differences: thus for example those centred at $\zeta=0$ are

$$Z' = \frac{1}{2d}(Z_1-Z_{-1}),$$

$$Z'' = \frac{1}{d^2}(Z_1-2Z_0+Z_{-1}),$$

$$Z''' = \frac{1}{2d^3}(Z_2-2Z_1+2Z_{-1}-Z_{-2}),$$

$$Z^{iv} = \frac{1}{d^4}(Z_2-4Z_1+6Z_0-4Z_{-1}+Z_{-2}),$$

$$Z^{vi} = \frac{1}{d^6}(Z_3-6Z_2+15Z_1-20Z_0+15Z_{-1}-6Z_{-2}+Z_{-3}).$$

If the boundary condition at $\zeta=0$ is that Z, Z″, and Z‴ vanish, these show that the neighbouring values of Z are of the form

$$Z_2-4Z_1,\ -Z_1,\ 0,\ Z_1,\ Z_2,\ \ldots\ .$$

This is the condition for a conducting rigid boundary. For a non-conducting free surface Z′, Z″, and Z^{iv} vanish, and we must have the values

$$2Z_0-Z_2,\ Z_0,\ Z_0,\ Z_0,\ Z_2,\ \ldots\ .$$

The differential equation being of the sixth order, we must substitute for the derivatives from our central-difference formulæ at all points far enough from both ends for the sixth derivative to be formed by this process. The resulting equations should determine λ, and then the approximation may be improved by repeating the calculation for a larger number of intervals and using the principle that the error is of the form Ad^2+Bd^4.

6. *Case of two rigid conducting boundaries.*

The simplest distribution of values of the independent variable to take consists in assuming a value of Z at $\zeta=\frac{1}{2}$, say b, and allowing all others to be determined by the boundary conditions. Then we have $d=\frac{1}{2}$, and

ζ	-1	$-\frac{1}{2}$	0	$\frac{1}{2}$	1	$1\frac{1}{2}$	2
Z	$-4b$	$-b$	0	b	0	$-b$	$-4b$

Forming the difference equation for the middle value, we find

$$\lambda a^2 = 1024 + 192a^2 + 24a^4 + a^6. \quad . \quad . \quad . \quad (1)$$

To this approximation the minimum value of λ is 540, and occurs when $a=2{\cdot}33$.

Next consider the values of Z at intervals of $\frac{1}{3}$. The solution must be either symmetrical or antisymmetrical with regard to the median plane, and it is clear that the symmetrical solution will be the first to give instability, for it implies that the columns of warm and cold fluid extend throughout the whole depth. With these data only one value of Z needs to be assigned arbitrarily, and we have

ζ	$-\frac{2}{3}$	$-\frac{1}{3}$	0	$\frac{1}{3}$	$\frac{2}{3}$	1	$1\frac{1}{3}$	$1\frac{2}{3}$
Z	$-3b$	$-b$	0	b	b	0	$-b$	$-3b$

The difference equation at either $\frac{1}{3}$ or $\frac{2}{3}$ gives

$$\lambda a^2 = 2187 + 243a^2 + 27a^4 + a^6, \quad . \quad . \quad . \quad (2)$$

whence the minimum value of λ is 793, and occurs when $a=2{\cdot}69$.

Considering intervals of $\frac{1}{4}$, we now have two values of Z not fixed already, and we take

ζ	$-\frac{1}{2}$	$-\frac{1}{4}$	0	$\frac{1}{4}$	$\frac{1}{2}$	$\frac{3}{4}$	1	$1\frac{1}{4}$	$1\frac{1}{2}$
Z	$-8b+c$	$-3b$	0	$3b$	$4b+c$	$3b$	0	$-3b$	$-8b+c$

Two independent difference equations must hold at $\frac{1}{4}$ and $\frac{1}{2}$; they lead to two equations homogeneous in b and c. By elimination we have, after some reduction, the quadratic for λ,

$$\{10922\tfrac{2}{3} + (512-\lambda)a^2 + 32a^4 + a^6\}$$
$$\times\{169301\tfrac{1}{3} + (8704-\lambda)a^2 + 160a^4 + a^6\}$$
$$=(21845\tfrac{1}{3} + 1024a^2 + 16a^4)(60074\tfrac{2}{3} + 2048a^2 + 32a^4). \quad (3)$$

From the two examples already worked out, assuming that the error in the value of a that makes λ a minimum is proportional to d^2, we see that the true value of a should be nearly 3. Substituting this in (3) and solving for λ, we find that $\lambda=928$. The error of λ is proportional to the square of the small error of a, and therefore is probably unimportant. Thus we have found that when d takes the values $\frac{1}{2}$, $\frac{1}{3}$, $\frac{1}{4}$, the minimum values of λ found are respec-540, 793, and 928. Extrapolating on the hypothesis that the error is of the form Ad^2+Bd^4, we find that the true value of λ is about 1140.

A preliminary solution was constructed by forming the simplest polynomial that would satisfy the boundary conditions and then finding how far it failed to satisfy the differential equation. Other terms were then added to improve the approximation, which was fairly rapid: λ was found to be about 1200. The initial computations were, however, very laborious, and on the whole Richardson's method is much more satisfactory.

7. *Rigid conducting boundary at base: free non-conducting surface at top.*

The method of the last section applies, except that there will no longer be symmetry about the median planes. The first approximation assumes the values

ζ	-1	$-\frac{1}{2}$	0	$\frac{1}{2}$	1	$1\frac{1}{2}$	2
Z	$-3b$	$-b$	0	b	b	b	$2b$

The equation for λ turns out to be

$$\lambda a^2 = 384 + 192a^2 + 12a^4 + a^6, \quad . \quad . \quad . \quad (1)$$

and the appropriate values are $a=2{\cdot}08$, $\lambda=256$.

In the second approximation we take

$\zeta=$	$-\frac{2}{3}$	$-\frac{1}{3}$	0	$\frac{1}{3}$	$\frac{2}{3}$	1	$1\frac{1}{3}$	$1\frac{2}{3}$
Z=	$c-4b$	$-b$	0	b	c	c	c	$2c-b$

Writing $3f$ for a, and 81μ for λ, we have the equation for μ,

$$\{3+3f^2+3f^4+2(f^6-f^2\mu)\}\{39+5f^2+15f^4-2(f^6-f^2\mu)\}$$
$$=-(5-3f^2-3f^4)(11+9f^2+3f^4) \quad . \quad . \quad (2)$$

Substituting for f^2 in this the values 1·000, 0·885, 0·770 (the intermediate one being chosen because it makes the right side vanish), we find that μ takes the values 5·34, 5·31, 5·39. By interpolation the minimum of μ is 5·30, occurring when $f^2=0{\cdot}911$. Thus $a=2{\cdot}86$ and $\lambda=430$.

From the results obtained for $d=\frac{1}{2}$ and $d=\frac{1}{3}$ we may now extrapolate on the supposition that the error is proportional to d^2. We find that $a=3{\cdot}49$, $\lambda=571$.

As might be expected from the fact that variations of

temperature over the upper surface are now possible, instability sets in for a smaller temperature gradient than in either of the cases already considered. But at the same time the absence of the conducting upper surface delays the spread of heat horizontally; it is presumably to this that the higher value of a, corresponding to a shorter critical wave-length, is to be attributed.

8. *Non-conducting rigid boundaries at top and bottom.*

The boundary conditions in this case are that Z', Z'', and Z''' vanish at both boundaries. Returning now to the equation 2(16), which takes the form

$$\left(\frac{d^2}{d\zeta^2}-a^2\right)^3 Z=-\lambda a^2 Z,$$

we see that the equation and all the boundary conditions are satisfied by a constant value of Z, provided that

$$\lambda = a^4.$$

Hence instability arises first for a zero, that is, for infinite wave-length, and then for λ very small. In this case therefore there is no possibility of complete stability with the higher temperature below. The movement once initiated cannot be maintained, of course, because there is no means of supplying new energy to the fluid; if the hotter fluid is originally underneath, it will exchange places with that above, and the motion will then gradually die down.

The same would apply if the upper surface was free, so long as it is non-conducting. Conduction over either boundary excludes the possibility of variations of the temperature there, and solutions of the type just considered do not arise then; a conducting boundary is essential to the stability of the arrangement with the hotter fluid below.

9. The conditions of greatest physical interest are probably those discussed in 6 and 7. These are the ordinary cases of liquid heated below, the upper boundary being in the one case a conducting solid, and in the other a non-conducting free surface. I was led to the former by the suggestion of L. H. Adams * that viscosity would play an important part in determining the vertical distribution of temperature in the earth's crust just after the solidification of the exterior; for a high viscosity would tend to damp down eddy currents, and the underlying magma might therefore cool at all points

* J. Wash. Acad. Sci. xiv. pp. 459–472 (1924).

until the viscosity everywhere had reached the critical value needed to prevent such currents, so that the distribution of temperature would become such as to make the viscosity nearly independent of depth. Let us try, then, to estimate the viscosity needed. For a rock magma the thermometric conductivity is probably about 0·01 c.g.s.; α is about 2×10^{-5}. Let us find the value of ν needed to prevent eddy currents in a layer 100 km. thick with a temperature difference of 100° between the top and bottom, so that $\beta=-10^{-5}$. Then from 2(17)

$$\lambda = 2\times10^{23}/\nu,$$

while the critical value of λ is about 1140. Thus ν must be about 2×10^{20} cm.^{2}/sec. to prevent the development of eddy currents that would redistribute the temperature. This is far above any viscosity yet measured, and a fluid with such a viscosity would be experimentally indistinguishable from a solid. For the same value of β the critical value of ν varies as h^4, so that it would be very much reduced if we considered a smaller depth of fluid. If the substance acquires even a small permanent strength at these high viscosities, eddies would be prevented entirely, so that the temperature distribution when currents ceased would be determined by the melting-point. A further tendency to stability would be introduced if there was a concentration of heavier materials towards the bottom. On the whole, then, it seems likely that viscosity would not be the determining factor, though the present discussion does not close the question.

10. The non-conducting free surface above represents the ordinary heating of a fluid from below. There is a familiar domestic instance of complete stability in this case, namely, the burning of porridge when it is not kept stirred. The high viscosity of the material can prevent currents even when the free surface is at ordinary temperatures and the bottom is charring. Taking h equal to 3 cm., βh equal to -400°, κ and α equal to the corresponding quantities for water, say 0·0015 and 10^{-3} (both varying notably with temperature), we have

$$\lambda = 10^7/\nu,$$

while the critical value of λ is about 571. Thus stability would be maintained if ν were something like 1700 cm.^{2}/sec. The viscosity of Lyle's Golden Syrup is given by Kaye and Laby (1919) as 1400 c.g.s., so that 1700 for porridge at the stage when it burns is not unreasonable. (It is capable of being poured, so that we are dealing with a case of viscous stability and not of solidification.)

Of course the effect of stirring is to promote rapid mixing and thereby to reduce the difference of temperature between the top and the bottom, the supply of heat at the bottom remaining the same. The eddy currents introduced by stirring take the place of those caused purely by heating, so that the heat can be got rid of at a temperature gradient much less than that needed for instability due to heating alone.

195

Reprinted from *Proceedings of the Royal Society*, Series A, Vol. 118, Mar. 1, 1928.

Some Cases of Instability in Fluid Motion.

By Harold Jeffreys, F.R.S.

(Received October 24, 1927.)

1. In a recent paper* I obtained a numerical solution of some problems concerning the stability of a layer of incompressible fluid when the temperature decreases upwards. The results depended on the solution of the sixth-order differential equation

$$\left(\frac{d^2}{d\zeta^2} - a^2\right)^3 Z = -\lambda a^2 Z. \tag{1}$$

In this solution the co-ordinates were x, y and z, the last being taken vertically. The depth of the fluid is h, and

$$\zeta = z/h. \tag{2}$$

Z is the factor of the disturbance of temperature that involves Z. The other factor is supposed to be of the form sin lx sin my, and

$$a^2 = (l^2 + m^2)\, h^2. \tag{3}$$

Further

$$\lambda = -g\alpha\beta h^4/\kappa\nu \tag{4}$$

where g is gravity, α the coefficient of expansion of the fluid, β the undisturbed vertical gradient of temperature, κ the coefficient of thermometric conductivity, and ν that of kinematic viscosity. Here ζ, a, and λ are all positive numbers.

The previous solution was obtained by L. F. Richardson's method of finite differences.† An alternative method is to use the principle that the solution of (1) is a combination of exponential functions, and therefore has no singularities for finite values of the argument. Hence it must be expansible for $0 < \zeta < 1$ in a series of sines of multiples of $\pi\zeta$. On assuming such an expansion and substituting in the equation we might expect to be able to equate coefficients of corresponding terms. But the result is obviously that terms of different arguments do not combine at all, and the inference would be that the only solution is one where every term is zero, which is not the case. The reason for the error is that where r is great the coefficients of the terms in the sine-series will ordinarily decrease like r^{-1} or r^{-2}. The trigonometric series obtained by differentiating more than twice are therefore divergent. But the derivatives of the solution, like the solution itself, are linear combinations of exponentials,

* 'Phil. Mag.,' vol. 2, p. 833 (1926).

† 'Math. Gazette,' July, 1925.

and have valid expansions in sine-series. In fact the series obtained by differentiating the series for Z term by term are not the correct series for the derivatives of Z, and if we are to substitute in (1) and equate coefficients we must use the correct Fourier expansions.

We can, however, work from the other end. We can assume a trigonometric series for $d^6Z/d\zeta^6$, and then obtain forms for lower derivatives and for Z itself by integration. The constants introduced by the integrations give a polynomial of the fifth degree in Z, while the trigonometric portion gives a series converging like r^{-7} or r^{-8}—that is to say, very rapidly. The divergence of the derived series in the former attempt arises from the Fourier series for the polynomial; but in the present method we have the whole of the polynomial in finite terms and can conveniently deal with it separately.

We put then

$$\xi = \pi\zeta = \pi z/h, \tag{5}$$

so that $\xi = 0$ and π at the limits. Put also

$$a = \pi b\,; \qquad \lambda = \mu\pi^4. \tag{6}$$

Then (1) can be written

$$\left\{\frac{d^2}{d\xi^2} - b^2\right\}^3 Z + \mu\, b^2 Z = 0. \tag{7}$$

We now assume

$$\frac{d^6 Z}{d\xi^6} = \sum_{r=1}^{\infty} A_r \sin r\xi. \tag{8}$$

whence, on repeated integration

$$Z = B_0 + B_1(\tfrac{1}{2}\pi - \xi) + \frac{B_2}{2\,!}(\tfrac{1}{2}\pi - \xi)^2 + \frac{B_3}{3\,!}(\tfrac{1}{2}\pi - \xi)^3 + \frac{B_4}{4\,!}(\tfrac{1}{2}\pi - \xi)^4 + \frac{B_5}{5\,!}(\tfrac{1}{2}\pi - \xi)^5$$
$$- \sum_{r=1}^{\infty} \frac{A_r}{r^6} \sin r\xi. \tag{9}$$

Let us denote the polynomial by P. Then (7) is equivalent to

$$\Sigma \{(r^2 + b^2)^3 - \mu b^2\} \frac{A_r}{r^6} \sin r\xi + \left\{\left(\frac{d^2}{d\xi^2} - b^2\right)^3 + \mu b^2\right\} P = 0. \tag{10}$$

Put

$$\tfrac{1}{2}\pi - \xi = \eta. \tag{11}$$

$$\sum_{r=1}^{\infty} \lambda_r \sin r\xi = -\left\{\left(\frac{d^2}{d\xi^2} - b^2\right)^3 + \mu b^2\right\} P \tag{12}$$

$$= 3b^2(B_4 + B_5\eta) - 3b^4\left(B_2 + B_3\eta + \frac{B_4}{2\,!}\eta^2 + \frac{B_5}{3\,!}\eta^3\right)$$
$$+ (b^6 - \mu b^2)\left(B_0 + B_1\eta + \frac{B_2}{2\,!}\eta^2 + \frac{B_3}{3\,!}\eta^3 + \frac{B_4}{4\,!}\eta^4 + \frac{B_5}{5\,!}\eta^5\right.$$
$$= Q, \tag{13}$$

say. Then

$$A_r = \frac{r^6}{(r^2+b^2)^3 - \mu b^2}\lambda_r, \tag{14}$$

where

$$\tfrac{1}{2}\pi\ \lambda_r = \int_0^\pi Q \sin r\xi\, d\xi. \tag{15}$$

The A_r thus become determinate functions of the six B's. Also

$$\int_0^\pi \eta^n \sin r\xi\, d\xi = 0 \tag{16}$$

if n and r both odd or both even, and otherwise

$$= 2\int_0^{\frac{1}{2}\pi} \eta^n \sin r\xi\, d\xi$$

$$= \frac{2}{r}(\tfrac{1}{2}\pi)^n\left(1 - \frac{n(n-1)}{r^2}\left(\frac{2}{\pi}\right)^2 + \frac{n(n-1)(n-2)(n-3)}{r^4}\left(\frac{2}{\pi}\right)^4 - \ldots\right). \tag{17}$$

Hence

$$\begin{aligned}\tfrac{1}{4}\pi r\lambda_r = {} & \{3b^2B_4 - 3b^4B_2 + (b^6 - \mu b^2)B_0\} \\ & + (\tfrac{1}{2}\pi)^2\left\{1 - \frac{2}{r^2}\left(\frac{2}{\pi}\right)^2\right\}\left\{-\frac{3}{2!}b^4B_4 + (b^6-\mu b^2)\frac{B_2}{2!}\right\} \\ & + (\tfrac{1}{2}\pi)^4\left\{1 - \frac{12}{r^2}\left(\frac{2}{\pi}\right)^2 + \frac{24}{r^4}\left(\frac{2}{\pi}\right)^4\right\}(b^6-\mu b^2)\frac{B_4}{4!},\end{aligned} \tag{18}$$

when r is odd, and

$$\begin{aligned}\tfrac{1}{4}\pi r\lambda_r = {} & \tfrac{1}{2}\pi\{3b^2B_5 - 3b^4B_3 + (b^6 - \mu b^2)B_1\} \\ & + (\tfrac{1}{2}\pi)^3\left\{1 - \frac{6}{r^2}\left(\frac{2}{\pi}\right)^2\right\}\left\{-\frac{1}{2!}b^4B_5 + (b^6-\mu b^2)\frac{B_3}{3!}\right\} \\ & + (\tfrac{1}{2}\pi)^5\left\{1 - \frac{20}{r^2}\left(\frac{2}{\pi}\right)^2 + \frac{120}{r^4}\left(\frac{2}{\pi}\right)^2\right\}(b^6-\mu b^2)\frac{B_5}{5!},\end{aligned} \tag{19}$$

when r is even. From these expressions, together with (9) and (14), we can write down the formal solution of the differential equation. We see, as expected, that when r is great the coefficients in the trigonometric series included in Z decrease like r^{-7}. It also appears from the form of the coefficients that if the boundary conditions are such that the same derivatives of Z are zero at the top and bottom the even and odd B's enter the solution entirely separately, and the possible solutions break up into two sets, one symmetrical and the other anti-symmetrical about the median plane.

2. *Rayleigh's problem.**—In this the boundary conditions were that Z, Z″, and Z^{iv} vanished at the top and bottom. The trigonometric part

* 'Phil. Mag.,' vol. 32, p. 529 (1916).

contributes nothing to any of these derivatives when ξ is 0 or π, and the conditions for the symmetrical solutions are

$$B_0 + \frac{B_2}{2\,!}(\tfrac{1}{2}\pi)^2 + \frac{B_4}{4\,!}(\tfrac{1}{2}\pi)^4 = 0, \qquad (1)$$

$$B_2 + \frac{B_4}{2\,!}(\tfrac{1}{2}\pi)^2 = 0, \qquad (2)$$

$$B_4 = 0, \qquad (3)$$

whence all the B's, and thence by 1 (18) and (19) all the λ's are zero. The only possibility of a solution different from zero is therefore that one of the denominators in (14) may vanish, when the solution will reduce to a single trigonometric term. The lowest value of μ is then given by $r = 1$, and we have

$$\mu b^2 = (1 + b^2)^3, \qquad (4)$$

which is equivalent to 4 (2) of my previous paper and to equations (42) and (44) of Rayleigh's.

3. *Two boundaries where Z, Z'', and Z''' vanish.*—Here 2 (1) and (2) still hold, but (3) is replaced by

$$-\tfrac{1}{2}\pi B_4 + \Sigma\, A_r/r^3 = 0, \qquad (1)$$

while

$$B_0 = \tfrac{5}{24}(\tfrac{1}{2}\pi)^4 B_4\,; \qquad B_2 = -\tfrac{1}{2}(\tfrac{1}{2}\pi)^2 B_4. \qquad (2)$$

Substituting in 1 (18) and simplifying, we find

$$\tfrac{1}{4}\pi r \lambda_r = \{3b^2 + 3b^4/r^2 + (b^6 - \mu b^2)/r^4\}\, B_4, \qquad (3)$$

whence

$$A_r = \frac{4r}{\pi}\left(1 - \frac{r^6}{(r^2+b^2)^3 - \mu b^2}\right) B_4, \qquad (4)$$

and our required condition of consistency is

$$-\tfrac{1}{8}\pi^2 + \Sigma \frac{1}{r^2}\left(1 - \frac{r^6}{(r^2+b^2)^3 - \mu b^2}\right) = 0, \qquad (5)$$

the summation extending over odd positive values of r. But with this condition

$$\Sigma\, 1/r^2 = \tfrac{1}{8}\pi^2 \qquad (6)$$

and we have finally

$$\Sigma \frac{r^4}{(r^2+b^2)^3 - \mu b^2} = 0. \qquad (7)$$

For a given value of b, the lowest admissible value of μ is evidently larger than in Rayleigh's problem, and will make the first term of (7) negative, but all the others positive. We can improve the convergence as follows. Restore a and λ, thus obtaining the equation

$$\Sigma \frac{r^4\pi^4}{(r^2\pi^2+a^2)^3-\lambda a^2}=0, \tag{8}$$

and use the identity

$$\tanh \tfrac{1}{2}a = \Sigma \frac{4a}{r^2\pi^2+a^2}. \tag{9}$$

From the latter we derive the further identity

$$\left(1+\tfrac{1}{4}a\frac{d}{da}\right)\left(1+\tfrac{1}{2}a\frac{d}{da}\right)\left(\frac{1}{4a}\tanh\tfrac{1}{2}a\right)=\Sigma\frac{r^4\pi^4}{(r^2\pi^2+a^2)^3}. \tag{11}$$

Comparing (8) and (11) we have

$$\lambda a^2\,\Sigma\frac{r^4\pi^4}{(r^2\pi^2+a^2)^3\{(r^2\pi^2+a^2)^3-\lambda a^2\}}=-\mathrm{K}, \tag{12}$$

where K denotes the known function on the left of (11). The terms of the series diminish like r^{-8}, and the second is of order 3^{-8} compared with the first. We shall therefore have, very nearly,

$$\frac{\lambda a^2\pi^4}{(\pi^2+a^2)^3\{(\pi^2+a^2)^3-\lambda a^2\}}=-\mathrm{K},$$

whence

$$\lambda a^2=\frac{\mathrm{K}(\pi^2+a^2)^6}{\mathrm{K}(\pi^2+a^2)^3-\pi^4}=\frac{(\pi^2+a^2)^3}{1-\pi^4/(\pi^2+a^2)^3\mathrm{K}}. \tag{13}$$

Also

$$64\mathrm{K}=\frac{6}{a}\tanh\tfrac{1}{2}a+5\,\mathrm{sech}^2\tfrac{1}{2}a+a\,\mathrm{sech}^2\tfrac{1}{2}a\tanh\tfrac{1}{2}a. \tag{14}$$

Working out the values of λ for a number of values of a, we find

a	2·6	2·8	3·0	3·2
λ	1056	1053	1051	1075

Hence λ has a rather flat minimum in the neighbourhood of $a = 3{\cdot}0$, and its value is 1051 within at most a few units.

When this problem was treated by the method of finite differences, λ was found to take the values 540, 793 and 928 when the intervals d were $\frac{1}{2}$, $\frac{1}{3}$, $\frac{1}{4}$. Extrapolation to zero on the hypothesis that the error was of the form $\mathrm{A}d^2+\mathrm{B}d^4$ gave $\lambda = 1140$. But if only $d=\frac{1}{3}$ and $\frac{1}{4}$ are used, extrapolation on the hypothesis that the error varies as d^2 gives $\lambda = 1101$, which is nearer the accurate value.

4. *Two rigid conducting boundaries.*—The problem of the previous section was investigated under this title in my former paper, but I overlooked the fact that the full boundary conditions

$$V' = 0, \qquad \nabla^2 V' = 0, \qquad \frac{\partial}{\partial z}\nabla^2 V' = 0, \tag{1}$$

reduce, when V' is of the form $Z \sin lx \sin my$, to

$$Z = 0, \qquad \frac{d^2 Z}{dz^2} = 0, \qquad \frac{d^3 Z}{dz^3} - (l^2 + m^2)\frac{dZ}{dz} = 0, \tag{2}$$

and the last of these conditions does not reduce to $Z''' = 0$. If we use the substitutions 1 (2) and (3) it becomes

$$\frac{d^3 Z}{d\zeta^3} - a^2 \frac{dZ}{d\zeta} = 0, \tag{3}$$

and by 1 (6)

$$\frac{d^3 Z}{d\xi^3} - b^2 \frac{dZ}{d\xi} = 0. \tag{4}$$

The solution follows the same lines as in § 3. Equations 3 (2) (3) (4) still hold, but (1) is replaced by

$$-\tfrac{1}{2}\pi B_4 + b^2\left\{\tfrac{1}{2}\pi B_2 + (\tfrac{1}{2}\pi)^3\frac{B_4}{3\,!}\right\} + \sum_{r=1}^{\infty}\frac{A_r}{r^3} + b^2\sum_{r=1}^{\infty}\frac{A_r}{r^5} = 0. \tag{5}$$

On substitution for A_r and B_2 we find

$$-\tfrac{1}{8}\pi^2\{1 + \tfrac{1}{3}(\tfrac{1}{2}\pi)^2 b^2\} + \Sigma\frac{1}{r^2}\left(1 + \frac{b^2}{r^2}\right)\left\{1 - \frac{r^6}{(r^2+b^2)^3 - \mu b^2}\right\} = 0. \tag{6}$$

But

$$\Sigma\frac{1}{r^2} = \tfrac{1}{8}\pi^2, \qquad \Sigma\frac{1}{r^4} = \tfrac{1}{96}\pi^4 \tag{7, 8}$$

(only odd values of r arising) and therefore

$$\Sigma\frac{r^2(r^2+b^2)}{(r^2+b^2)^3 - \mu b^2} = 0, \tag{9}$$

which is equivalent to

$$\Sigma\frac{r^2\pi^2(r^2\pi^2+a^2)}{(r^2\pi^2+a^2)^3 - \lambda a^2} = 0. \tag{10}$$

Now if we write

$$K = \Sigma\frac{r^2\pi^2}{(r^2\pi^2+a^2)^2} \tag{11}$$

$$= \frac{1}{8}\left(\frac{1}{a} + \frac{d}{da}\right)\tanh\tfrac{1}{2}a = \frac{1}{8a}\tanh\tfrac{1}{2}a + \frac{1}{16}\operatorname{sech}^2\tfrac{1}{2}a \tag{12}$$

and subtract from (10), we have

$$\frac{\lambda a^2\pi^2}{(\pi^2+a^2)^2\{\lambda a^2 - (\pi^2+a^2)^3\}} = K + \lambda a^2\,\Sigma'\frac{r^2\pi^2}{(r^2\pi^2+a^2)^2\{(r^2\pi^2+a^2)^3 - \lambda a^2\}}, \tag{13}$$

where the summation on the right covers the values 3, 5, 7 . . . of r. On account of the high power of r involved these terms are very small for the lowest value of λ that satisfies the equation, and we have the first approximation

$$\lambda a^2 = (\pi^2 + a^2)^3 \Big/ \left\{1 - \frac{\pi^2}{(\pi^2 + a^2)^2 \mathrm{K}}\right\}, \tag{14}$$

where K is to be found from (12). On proceeding to calculation we find

a	2	3	3·2	3·4	4
λ	2166	1726	1717	1734	1984

By interpolation the least value of λ occurs when $a = 3{\cdot}17$, and is nearly 1717. We can now obtain a second approximation by substituting in the small terms in (13), and altering (14) accordingly. The new value of λ is 1709·5; the corresponding value of a is hardly changed. Since a is nearly equal to π, the wave-length in a two-dimensional disturbance is nearly $2h$. The cells in a vertical plane, bounded by the solid boundaries and by neighbouring upward and downward currents, are therefore nearly square.

5. *Rigid conducting boundary at base; non-conducting free surface at top.*—In the previous paper it was supposed that the conditions of this problem could be realized by taking Z, Z″, and Z‴ zero at $\zeta = 0$, and Z′, Z″ and Z^{iv} zero at $\zeta = 1$. These are not quite correct; the proper conditions are

$$\mathrm{Z} = 0, \quad \mathrm{Z}'' - a^2\mathrm{Z} = 0, \quad \frac{\partial}{\partial z}(\mathrm{Z}'' - a^2\mathrm{Z}) = 0 \quad \text{at } \zeta = 0.$$

$$\mathrm{Z}' = 0, \quad \mathrm{Z}'' - a^2\mathrm{Z} = 0, \quad \frac{\partial^2}{\partial z^2}(\mathrm{Z}'' - a^2\mathrm{Z}) = 0 \quad \text{at } \zeta = 1.$$

The conditions being dissimilar, the full set of odd and even powers of η is required in the solution, and six constants of integration have to be determined. The former solution is, however, probably not far wrong, and the necessary revision has not yet been undertaken.

6. *Effect of a Current.*—A. R. Low* has called attention to the fact that when instability occurs through heating below, but the liquid is already in steady flow, the form of the disturbance generated differs from that when the liquid is originally at rest. In the absence of a current the liquid forms into roughly regular hexagonal or pentagonal cells, rising in the centres and sinking around the edges. A current elongates the cells into strips, the greater dimension being along the stream. The reason for this can be seen easily. When there is no current the factor sin lx sin my in the disturbance of the temperature

* 'Nature,' vol. 115, pp. 299–301 (1925).

affects the differential equation 1 (1) only through the number a, that is, through $l^2 + m^2$. All disturbances with the same value of this quantity should begin to develop at the same time; the ultimate preponderance of the honeycomb structure, with cells as nearly symmetrical as possible, is to be attributed to terms of higher order in the differential equations. The cause making for motion is that an element of fluid hotter than normal tends to rise, and therefore to draw up from the bottom locally a column of warm and light fluid, thus intensifying the differences of pressure over horizontal surfaces. The action is resisted by conduction and viscosity, which tend to spread out the inequalities of temperature and velocity.

When there is a permanent current in the direction of x increasing, on the other hand, the bottom layer of the liquid is at rest, and the remainder is shearing over it. Thus a vertical column of warm fluid is distorted into a curved sloping one, and the possibility of a steady cellular motion disappears. But when the type of disturbance considered is such that the variables u, v, w, V are all independent of x, a shear parallel to x leaves the warm vertical planes unaltered, and the condition for instability is the same as in the absence of a current. To put the matter formally, we notice that in equations (1) to (3) of the previous paper, when a permanent current of velocity U exists, d/dt is equivalent to $\partial/\partial t + \mathrm{U}\partial/\partial x$, except in the equation of motion parallel to x, where we have

$$\frac{du}{dt} = \frac{\partial u}{\partial t} + \mathrm{U}\frac{\partial \mathrm{U}}{\partial x} + w\frac{\partial \mathrm{U}}{\partial z}, \tag{1}$$

u being now the departure of the x velocity from its mean value U. But if u, v, w, V are independent of x, $\partial/\partial x$ in all cases gives zero. In passing from (6) to (7), again, we formed the divergence of the equations of motion; but in our conditions

$$\frac{\partial}{\partial x}\left(w\frac{\partial \mathrm{U}}{\partial z}\right) = 0, \tag{2}$$

so that the terms involving U make no contribution to the further work. The same applies to the boundary conditions. Thus the effect of a steady current is to promote stability for all modes except those with $l = 0$; for these it has no effect. This explains why it causes the convective disturbance to occur in strips instead of in roughly symmetrical cells.

7. *Fluid between Two Rotating Cylinders.*—Prof. G. I. Taylor and Major A. R. Low have both suggested to me that there should be an analogy between the conditions in a layer of liquid heated below and in a liquid between two coaxial cylinders rotating at different rates. In Taylor's discussion of the latter

problem* the equations of motion are referred to cylindrical co-ordinates r, ϕ, z. The undisturbed velocity is V in the direction of ϕ increasing, where

$$V = Ar + B/r \tag{1}$$

and A and B are constants determined by the rates of rotation of the inner and outer cylinders. Symmetry about the axis is assumed for the disturbed motion.

Taylor takes the components of velocity to be u, $V + v$, w, and assumes

$$u = u_1 \cos \lambda z \, e^{\sigma t}, \tag{2}$$

$$v = v_1 \cos \lambda z \, e^{\sigma t}, \tag{3}$$

$$w = w_1 \sin \lambda z \, e^{\sigma t}, \tag{4}$$

where u_1, v_1, and w_1 are functions of r only. The relevant equations reduce to

$$\frac{u_1}{r} + \frac{\partial u_1}{\partial r} + \lambda w_1 = 0, \tag{5}$$

$$\nu \left(\nabla_1^2 - \frac{1}{r^2} - \lambda^2 - \frac{\sigma}{\nu} \right) v_1 = 2Au_1, \tag{6}$$

$$\frac{\nu}{\lambda} \frac{\partial}{\partial r} \left\{ \left(\nabla_1^2 - \lambda^2 - \frac{\sigma}{\nu} \right) w_1 \right\} = -2 \left(A + \frac{B}{r^2} \right) v_1 - \nu \left(\nabla_1^2 - \frac{1}{r^2} - \lambda^2 - \frac{\sigma}{\nu} \right) u_1. \tag{7}$$

Now if we are considering only marginal instability $\sigma = 0$. Also

$$\nabla_1^2 = \frac{\partial^2}{\partial r} + \frac{1}{r} \frac{\partial}{\partial r}. \tag{8}$$

In all cases fully worked out by Taylor the difference between the radii of the cylinders is a fraction, a quarter to a twentieth, of either radius separately. We can therefore in a first approximation ignore $1/r$ in comparison with $\partial/\partial r$ and reduce the equations to

$$\lambda w_1 + \frac{\partial u_1}{\partial r} = 0, \tag{9}$$

$$2\,Au_1 = \nu \left(\frac{\partial^2}{\partial r^2} - \lambda^2 \right) v_1, \tag{10}$$

$$\frac{\nu}{\lambda} \frac{\partial}{\partial r} \left\{ \left(\frac{\partial^2}{\partial r^2} - \lambda^2 \right) w_1 \right\} = -2 \left(A + \frac{B}{r^2} \right) v_1 - \nu \left(\frac{\partial^2}{\partial r^2} - \lambda^2 \right) u_1. \tag{11}$$

From (9) and (10) we obtain u_1 and w_1 in terms of v_1. Substituting in (11) we have on simplification

$$\left(\frac{\partial^2}{\partial r^2} - \lambda^2 \right)^3 v_1 = \frac{4A\,\lambda^2}{\nu^2} \left(A + \frac{B}{r^2} \right) v_1. \tag{12}$$

* 'Phil. Trans.,' A, vol. 223, p. 289 (1923).

If h be the distance between the inner and outer cylinders we put

$$\lambda h = a, \qquad r = h\zeta + \text{const.}, \tag{13}$$

and we have

$$\left(\frac{\partial^2}{\partial \zeta^2} - a^2\right)^3 v_1 = \frac{4\mathrm{A}a^2h^4}{\nu^2}\left(\mathrm{A} + \frac{\mathrm{B}}{r^2}\right) v_1. \tag{14}$$

The components of velocity at the inner and outer boundaries are all prescribed by the motion of the cylinders, and therefore $u_1 = v_1 = w_1 = 0$ there. Hence from (10) $\partial^2 v_1/\partial r^2 = 0$, and from (9)

$$\frac{\partial}{\partial r}\left(\frac{\partial^2}{\partial r^2} - \lambda^2\right) v_1 = 0. \tag{15}$$

The conditions are the same as those satisfied by the disturbance of temperature V′ in the thermal problem with rigid conducting boundaries at the top and bottom, namely, $\mathrm{V}' = 0$; $\nabla^2 \mathrm{V}' = 0$; $\frac{\partial}{\partial z} \nabla^2 \mathrm{V}' = 0$. But the differential equation (14) is not quite the same. Whereas in the thermal problem the coefficient of V′ on the right was a numerical constant $-\lambda a^2$, that of v_1 here involves r. A complete analogy is therefore not to be expected. Nevertheless if $\mathrm{A} + \mathrm{B}/r^2$ always has the same sign, that is, if the cylinders rotate in the same direction, the comparison indicates that instability should be possible if A and $\mathrm{A} + \mathrm{B}/r^2$ have opposite signs. This means that $r\mathrm{V}$ decreases with r, giving the result that the circulation must decrease outwards for instability. If, on the other hand, $\mathrm{A} + \mathrm{B}/r^2$ changes sign, A and $\mathrm{A} + \mathrm{B}/r^2$ have the same sign in an outer region, which is therefore stable; instability arises near the inner cylinder. Thus Taylor's results that the stronger currents occur in the inner region, and that the velocity needed for instability is greater when the cylinders rotate in opposite directions than in the same direction, are in accordance with what we should expect. A general qualitative correspondence therefore exists between the two problems; but quantitative agreement is not to be expected on account of the variability of $\mathrm{A} + \mathrm{B}/r^2$.

We may recall that Taylor's fundamental equations assume that the disturbed motion has cylindrical symmetry. He does not, however, prove theoretically that the first mode to become unstable will actually be symmetrical, and the question naturally arises why it has this property. A full discussion would have to start from the full equations of viscous motion in cylindrical co-ordinates. But we may notice that

$$\nabla^2 = \frac{1}{r}\frac{\partial}{\partial r}\left(r\frac{\partial}{\partial r}\right) + \frac{1}{r^2}\frac{\partial^2}{\partial \phi^2} + \frac{\partial^2}{\partial z^2}, \tag{16}$$

so that if we neglect $1/r$ in comparison with $\partial/\partial r$ we can take

$$\nabla^2 = \frac{\partial^2}{\partial r^2} + \frac{\partial^2}{r^2 \partial \phi^2} + \frac{\partial^2}{\partial z^2}, \tag{17}$$

which is analogous to the Cartesian form. The correspondence of co-ordinates is

Thermal problem.	Taylor's problem.
z	r
x	ϕ
y	z

The chief effect of the velocities is to make

$$\frac{d}{dt} \text{ equal to } \frac{\partial}{\partial t} + u\frac{\partial}{\partial r} + \frac{V+v}{r}\frac{\partial}{\partial \phi} + w\frac{\partial}{\partial z};$$

if the quantity operated on is small, this reduces to $\frac{\partial}{\partial t} + \frac{V}{r}\frac{\partial}{\partial \phi}$. The second term corresponds to the extra term $U\,\partial/\partial x$ in the thermal problem. Taylor's problem is, in fact, not analogous to the thermal problem with the fluid initially at rest, but to that with steady streaming parallel to the axis of x. In the latter, instability first arises for disturbances not involving x, and therefore, by analogy, the first instability in Taylor's problem is for a disturbance independent of ϕ, that is, a symmetrical one.

The analogy could be pushed further if $A + B/r^2$ was nearly constant; with Taylor's notation $\Omega_2/\Omega_1 = \mu$ must be nearly 1. Putting Ω_1 and Ω_2 both equal to Ω we have the condition for marginal instability

$$\frac{4Ah^4}{\nu^2}\Omega = -1709. \tag{18}$$

Taylor's first approximation when μ is nearly 1 is (equations (5.43) and (7.08) of his paper)

$$\frac{2\,\Omega_1^2 h^3 R_1^2 (1 - R_2^2\mu/R_1^2)}{\pi^4 \nu^2 (R_1 + R_2)} = \frac{1}{0{\cdot}0571\,(1+\mu)} \tag{19}$$

which is equivalent to

$$\frac{4Ah^4}{\nu^2}\Omega_1 = -\frac{\pi^4}{0{\cdot}0571} = -1706. \tag{20}$$

This is in good enough agreement with 1709, obtained by the methods of this paper.

A curious result emerges from (14) if the radii of the cylinders are made very great while h remains the same. The outer radius being R_2, we take the inner cylinder to be at rest and the outer to have a linear velocity V, so that

$$(R_1 + R_2) hA = R_2 V, \tag{21}$$

while

$$A + B/r^2 = Vp/hR_2 \tag{22}$$

where p is the distance from the inner plate. Then the coefficient of $a^2 v_1$ on the right of (14) is

$$\frac{2Vh^4}{h\nu^2}\frac{Vp}{hR_1} = \frac{2V^2h^2p}{\nu^2 R_1}, \tag{23}$$

which tends to zero for all values of p when R_1 is made great enough. Thus if the plates are flat the equation (14) takes the same form as for the thermal problem with no gradient of temperature. The system is then thoroughly stable, and we infer that instability cannot arise from the shearing of one flat plate over another.

[*Added January* 20, 1928.—This result, like the others of this paper, is to be read in conjunction with the first section of its predecessor ; that is, it depends on the postulate that the method of exchange of stabilities is applicable to problems of the types here considered. The postulate is certainly valid for the stability of steady states of holonomic conservative systems, and of many dissipative ones, but it has not been justified universally. The apparent simplicity of the method of the last paragraph, in comparison with the difficult discussions of the stability of steady motion by Orr and others, is therefore somewhat illusory ; to *prove* that the method is valid would probably be as difficult as Orr's work. The justification of the postulate, in fact, lies at present in the general agreement of its results with experiment.]

8. *The Effect of a General Rotation.*—Rotation of the solid boundaries about a vertical axis influences the treatment of the consequences of heating a fluid below by introducing terms $-2\omega v$, $+2\omega u$ into the two equations of horizontal motion. It is easy to see that in some cases they will seriously alter the results, since they may be larger than the viscosity terms. In the problem of the burning of porridge, which was used as an illustration in the previous paper, the kinematic viscosity was probably about 1000 cm²./sec., and the vertical dimensions a few centimetres. Hence $\nu\partial^2 u/\partial z^2$ was of order $1000u$, while $2\omega u$ is only about $10^{-4}u$, when ω arises from the earth's rotation, and the rotational (or geostrophic) terms are quite unimportant. But in a fluid of depth 10 km. with the same rotation the viscosity would have to be about 10^5 cm.²/sec. to make the viscous terms equal to the rotational ones. Thus rotation may have

an important influence on stability in meteorological phenomena. It is interesting to notice that the critical viscosity is actually comparable with the observed coefficient of eddy-viscosity (though this is only another way of expressing the well-known fact that the effects of surface friction extend up for a kilometre or more).

A qualitative discussion of the effects of rotation appears worth attempting. The tendency to instability in a non-rotating fluid heated below comes, as has been said, from the fact that a local heated mass of fluid tends to rise and draw up a column of new hot fluid from the bottom. Instability occurs when this effect is enough to overcome the tendency of conduction and viscosity to redistribute the temperature and the velocities horizontally. In a rotating fluid, however, we have as a first approximation the equations

$$\rho u = -\frac{1}{2\omega}\frac{\partial p}{\partial y} \tag{1}$$

$$\rho v = \frac{1}{2\omega}\frac{\partial p}{\partial x} \tag{2}$$

whence

$$\frac{\partial}{\partial x}(\rho u) + \frac{\partial}{\partial y}(\rho v) = 0 \tag{3}$$

showing that there is no accumulation of fluid within any vertical column, whatever the pressure distribution may be.* There is no indraught into the heated region, and the cause making for instability has disappeared except for the small amount due to flow across the isobars due to friction at solid boundaries. If the horizontal and vertical scales of the motion remain the same as before, the effects of viscosity and conduction remain much the same. Hence the effect of rotation is to maintain stability.

The vertical scale of the motion is practically fixed by the depth of the fluid, but the horizontal scale may vary. If it becomes so small that the terms like $\frac{\partial^2 u}{\partial x^2} + \frac{\partial^2 u}{\partial y^2}$ become greater than the rotational terms, the theory given for no rotation will again be a useful first approximation; but a much larger gradient of temperature will be needed for instability on account of the increase of a. In air, for instance, with $2\omega = 10^{-4}$ and $\nu = 0\cdot 2$, in c.g.s. units, such an approximation would work if the horizontal scale was of the order of 40 cm. But then we shall have

$$a^2 = (l^2 + m^2)\,h^2 = (h/40 \text{ cm.})^2,$$

* This consequence of the geostrophic relation was given by Proudman, 'Roy. Soc. Proc.,' A, vol. 92, p. 420 (1916), and experimentally verified by G. I. Taylor, 'Proc. Camb. Phil. Soc.,' vol. 20, pp. 326–329 (1921); *cf.* also 'Phil. Mag.,' vol. 38, pp. 1–8 (1919).

and if we keep Rayleigh's form as a good enough approximation at the present stage we have nearly

$$\lambda = a^4 = (h/40 \text{ cm.})^4.$$

But with our formula 1 (4) for λ and with values of the constants suitable for air this gives

$$-\frac{g\alpha\beta}{\kappa\nu} = \left(\frac{1}{40}\right)^4; \quad \beta = O\,(10^{-5} \text{ degrees C/cm.})$$
$$= O\,(1^\circ \text{ C/km.}).$$

The depth of the atmosphere, h, cancels during the work. It appears that even in such a case as this the lapse-rate of temperature does not need to become much greater than the adiabatic to produce instability. The small horizontal dimensions indicated are suggestive of tornadoes, dust devils, and waterspouts; but the apparent agreement depends on the initial absence of turbulence from the air before these phenomena develop.

On the other hand, if the air is turbulent and the eddy-conductivity and eddy-viscosity both of order 10^5 cm.^{2}/sec., rotation is no longer of primary importance, and we shall have roughly

$$\lambda = -\frac{g\alpha\beta h^4}{\kappa\nu} = O\,(1000),$$

giving

$$\beta = O\,(10^{-11} \text{ degree C./cm.}).$$

In presence of rotation, high viscosity and conductivity may actually make instability easier to produce, by preventing the effects of rotation from being dominant. The effect of heating from the bottom an atmosphere originally perfectly stagnant might therefore be to give first disturbances of the nature of tornadoes, but with increasing turbulence these would spread out and give movements on a larger horizontal scale, comparable with the height of the atmosphere, or with tropical cyclones and thunderstorms. Such considerations as these suggest the character of the effect of rotation on the instability, though further development will probably require increased knowledge of the factors that determine the amount of the eddy-viscosity.

Reprinted from *Proceedings of the Cambridge Philosophical Society*, Vol. 26, 1930.

The Instability of a Compressible Fluid heated below. By Mr HAROLD JEFFREYS, St John's College.

[*Received* 7 January, *read* 27 January 1930.]

The vertical gradient of temperature needed to produce convection currents in a layer of incompressible liquid has already been investigated in several instances*. For a compressible fluid instability cannot arise until the gradient exceeds the adiabatic one; it has been assumed usually that what matters is the excess of the actual gradient over the adiabatic. Thus the excess needed in a compressible fluid is to be found by the same formula as gives the gradient needed for instability in an incompressible fluid. It is desirable, however, to investigate the validity of this assumption.

The circulation Ω around a contour of particles in a moving fluid varies at a rate†

$$\frac{d\Omega}{dt} = \int_C \frac{1}{\rho}\left\{- dp - \tfrac{2}{3} d(\mu\delta) + \frac{\partial}{\partial x_k}(\mu\xi_{ik})\, dx_i + 2\frac{\partial \mu}{\partial x_k} du_k + 2\mu d\delta\right\}. \qquad \text{.........(1)}$$

Here δ is the rate of expansion, ξ_{ik} is the rotation tensor, and the other letters have their usual meanings; the summation convention is used. We are concerned with the possibility of steady motions such that each particle describes a closed path. We therefore consider the circulations around such paths. If they can remain steady, a steady motion is possible and instability is on the verge of arising.

In equilibrium, with the temperature and pressure functions of the height alone, every term in (1) vanishes and we have a steady state. Consider now a small disturbance satisfying the boundary conditions but involving circulation. The second term $\tfrac{2}{3}\int \frac{1}{\rho} d(\mu\delta)$ would vanish if ρ was constant; it therefore involves products of the variations of ρ with $\mu\delta$ and is a small quantity of the second order. Similarly, the last term involves products of the disturbances of μ/ρ and δ and is of the second order. The fourth term involves variations of the viscosity from place to place and hardly needs consideration. The third term is of the first order, and represents the ordinary effect of viscosity on the circulation; the tendency is ultimately to annihilate it unless other factors are available to restore it; and the only other factor that can make a first order

* *Proc. Roy. Soc.* A, 118, 195–208, 1928 and earlier papers.
† *Proc. Camb. Phil. Soc.* 24, 477–9, 1928.

contribution to $d\Omega/dt$ is given by the first term. We are concerned therefore with a balance between the first and third terms of (1).

Let the density associated with pressure p in the undisturbed state be ρ_0; then ρ_0 is a function of p alone. Also

$$\frac{1}{\rho}=\frac{1}{\rho_0}+\frac{\partial}{\partial\theta}\left(\frac{1}{\rho}\right)\theta_1 \quad \text{.....................(2),}$$

where θ is the temperature and θ_1 the departure of the disturbed temperature from that originally associated with the same value of p. Further,

$$\rho_0\frac{\partial}{\partial\theta}\left(\frac{1}{\rho}\right)=\alpha \quad \text{.......................(3),}$$

where α is the coefficient of volume expansion. Hence

$$\int_C\frac{dp}{\rho}=\int_C\frac{dp}{\rho_0}+\int_C\frac{\alpha\theta_1}{\rho_0}dp \quad \text{.................(4),}$$

and the first integral on the right is zero. The second is of the first order of small quantities on account of the factor θ_1. Also if we neglect small quantities

$$dp=-g\rho_0 dz \quad \text{.......................(5),}$$

where z is the height. To the first order then

$$\int_C\frac{dp}{\rho}=-\int_C g\alpha\theta_1 dz \quad \text{....................(6),}$$

where θ_1 can now be taken to be the disturbance of temperature at a given height. The rate of change of circulation is therefore connected with the velocities and the disturbance of temperature in the same way as for an incompressible fluid. A given disturbance of temperature has, to the first order of accuracy, the same effect on the motion of a compressible as on that of an incompressible fluid.

The equation of heat conduction is*

$$\rho c_p\frac{d\theta}{dt}+M\frac{d\delta'}{dt}=\frac{\partial}{\partial x}\left(k\frac{\partial\theta}{\partial x}\right)+\frac{\partial}{\partial y}\left(k\frac{\partial\theta}{\partial y}\right)+\frac{\partial}{\partial z}\left(k\frac{\partial\theta}{\partial z}\right)+P \quad \text{...(7),}$$

where c_p is the specific heat at constant pressure, δ' the excess expansion (not *rate* of expansion) due to change of pressure, k the conductivity, and P the rate of generation of heat per unit volume. M is given by

$$M=K\alpha\theta \quad \text{.........................(8),}$$

where K is the bulk-modulus. Also

$$\delta'=-p/K \quad \text{.........................(9),}$$

so that the left side is

$$\rho c_p\frac{d\theta}{dt}-\alpha\theta\frac{dp}{dt} \quad \text{.......................(10).}$$

* *Proc. Camb. Phil. Soc.* 26, 101–106, 1930.

For marginal instability d/dt can be replaced by $w d/dz$, and the quantity operated on can be given its undisturbed value. Hence (10) becomes

$$w\left\{\rho c_p \frac{d\theta_0}{dz} - \alpha\theta \frac{dp_0}{dz}\right\} = \rho_0 w \left(c_p \frac{d\theta_0}{dz} + g\alpha\theta\right) \quad \text{......(11)}.$$

If there is no supply of heat this must vanish, and

$$\frac{d\theta_0}{dz} = -\frac{g\alpha\theta}{c_p} = \beta_0 \quad \text{....................(12)},$$

say. This is the adiabatic temperature gradient. In the actual undisturbed state we have

$$\frac{d\theta_0}{dz} = \beta \quad \text{..........................(13)},$$

and (11) becomes $\rho_0 c_p (\beta - \beta_0) w$. On the right of (7), P is the rate of generation of heat through viscosity, and is of the second order. Also the right of (7) is unaltered if θ is replaced by θ_1 and we neglect variations of β and β_0. Hence (7) reduces to

$$\rho_0 c_p (\beta - \beta_0) w = \frac{\partial}{\partial x}\left(k \frac{\partial \theta_1}{\partial x}\right) + \frac{\partial}{\partial y}\left(k \frac{\partial \theta_1}{\partial y}\right) + \frac{\partial}{\partial z}\left(k \frac{\partial \theta_1}{\partial z}\right) \quad \text{...(14)},$$

which has the same form as for an incompressible fluid except that $\beta - \beta_0$ replaces β. This is the only place where the compressibility or the vertical gradient of temperature appears in the work, and the previous assumption that the results already obtained become valid for a compressible fluid if $\beta - \beta_0$ is written for β is therefore justified. The previous actual numerical results, however, can be applied directly only when the density does not vary greatly within the system; they would not apply, for instance, to the earth's atmosphere as a whole without further discussion.

180

Reprinted from *Proceedings of the Royal Society*, Series A, Vol. 125, Aug. 1, 1929.

On the Criterion for Stability of a Layer of Viscous Fluid Heated from Below.

By A. R. Low, M.A.

(Communicated by L. N. G. Filon, F.R.S.—Received May 22, 1929.)

1. An analogy has been drawn by the present writer* between Bénard's problem of the modes of instability of a layer of viscous fluid initially at rest under gravity between horizontal plane boundaries heated below and cooled above, and Prof. G. I. Taylor's problem of the modes of instability of a viscous fluid initially in steady cyclic motion under inertia forces between concentric circular cylinders rotating with constant unequal angular velocities.

Rayleigh obtained a solution of Bénard's problem for two boundaries with no tangential forces between boundary and fluid,† while in Taylor's problem‡ there are two boundaries with no slip.

Dr. Harold Jeffreys § reduced Bénard's problem to the solution of a linear differential equation of the sixth order with constant coefficients, but remarked that the eliminant of the arbitrary constants of integration from the six boundary conditions, three at each boundary, would be a determinant of the sixth order, many complex quantities being involved, and proceeded to obtain approximate values of the criterion for stability by a method of finite differences. Among other results he obtained a criterion for two boundaries of no slip maintained at different constant temperatures which is the analogue of Taylor's problem, but his critical value was only about two-thirds of the corresponding value found from Taylor's analysis.

The writer confidently expected a much closer numerical agreement, and Prof. Taylor suggested the work undertaken in the present paper, of verifying the result.

In the meantime, Dr. Jeffreys has devised a method of solving the differential equation by expressing the sixth derivative of the assumed solution as a Fourier series, had amended the boundary conditions and has discussed the writer's analogy which he has put on a formal mathematical basis. His new value of the criterion for stability agrees closely with the value calculated from Taylor's analogous condition, the figures being 1709·5 and 1706 respectively.

* 'Nature,' vol. 115, p. 289 (1925).

† Rayleigh, 'Collected Papers,' vol. 6, p. 432 (1916).

‡ G. I. Taylor, 'Phil. Trans.,' A, vol. 223, p. 289 (1923).

§ H. Jeffreys, 'Phil. Mag.,' vol. 2, pp. 833–844 (1926).

In the present paper the formal solution of Jeffreys' differential equation is obtained by the usual methods without prohibitive complication.

The critical values given by the vanishing of the eliminant are computed for three cases, two surfaces of free slip, one surface of free slip and one of no slip, and two surfaces of no slip, in all cases the boundaries being kept at constant temperatures. The figures are 651, 1108 and 1706*, the first being in agreement with Rayleigh and Jeffreys, the second being a new result and the third agreeing closely with the critical value as calculated by Jeffreys for Taylor's analogous problem.

2. Slight alterations have been made in the notation for the sake of lightening the analytical expressions. In the investigation, equilibrium with a uniform negative temperature gradient upward, defining the undisturbed temperature $T = \beta\zeta$ in terms of the height above the lower boundary, was found by Rayleigh to be stable until a certain numerical value of β depending on the depth of the layer and the physical constants of the fluid was reached. At this value of β a slight disturbance produces a departure from the equilibrium distribution of temperature T. This departure is assumed to have the form

$$\Delta T = Z \sin(2\pi\xi/\lambda) \sin(2\pi\eta/\mu).$$

ξ, η, ζ being the co-ordinates in space, Z a function of the vertical co-ordinate ζ only; further $1/\lambda^2 + 1/\mu^2 = b^2/4h^2$, defining b, h being the depth of the layer.

3. Jeffreys' differential equation, satisfied by Z throughout the fluid becomes, on putting $z = \pi b\zeta/h$,

$$\{(D^2 - 1)^3 + (p^2 + 1)^3\} Z = 0, \tag{1}$$

where $D = d/dz$, κ = thermometric conductivity, ν = kinematic viscosity,

$$(p^2 + 1)^3 = g\alpha\beta' h^4/\kappa\nu\pi^4 b^4 = E/E_0\pi^4 b^4.$$

($\beta' = -\beta$ is used to avoid negative constants), $\alpha\beta' h = (\rho_2 - \rho_1)/\rho$ = the relative increase of density from bottom to top, $E = g(\rho_2 - \rho_1)h/6$ = the apparent energy per unit volume stored against gravity by the top-heavy distribution of the fluid, $E_0 = \kappa\nu\rho/6h^2$, a quantity depending on the physical constants and of the dimensions of energy per unit volume.

This permits of the immediate interpretation of the criterion of instability as the apparent amount of energy per unit volume stored in the fluid, beyond which the equilibrium becomes unstable.

* Corrected value 1704·4.

4. Proceeding now to solve equation (1) it may be factorised as follows,

$$(D + \iota p)(D - \iota p)(D + \iota q e^{\iota\gamma})(D - \iota q e^{\iota\gamma})(D + \iota q e^{-\iota\gamma})(D - \iota q e^{-\iota\gamma}) Z = 0, \quad (2)$$

where

$$q^4 = p^4 + 3p^2 + 3, \qquad \tan 2\gamma = \sqrt{3}\,(p^2+1)/(p^2+3).$$

For brevity put $c = \cos\gamma$, $s = \sin\gamma$, $c' = \cos 2\gamma$, $c'' = \cos 3\gamma$, $c''' = \cos 4\gamma$, etc.

The general solution and its first four derivatives may be written

$$Z = A_1 e^{\iota pz} + A_2 e^{-\iota pz} + A_3 e^{q(c+\iota s)z} + A_4 e^{-q(c+\iota s)z} + A_5 e^{q(c-\iota s)z} + A_6 e^{-q(c-\iota s)z},$$

$$Z' = \iota p (A_1 e^{\iota pz} - A_2 e^{-\iota pz}) + q(c + \iota s)[A_3 e^{q(c+\iota s)z} - A_4 e^{-q(c+\iota s)z}]$$
$$+ q(c - \iota s)[A_5 e^{q(c-\iota s)z} - A_6 e^{-q(c+\iota s)z}],$$

$$Z'' = -p^2 (A_1 e^{\iota pz} + A_2 e^{-\iota pz}) + q^2 (c' + \iota s')[A_3 e^{q(c+\iota s)z} + A_4 e^{-q(c+\iota s)z}]$$
$$+ q^2 (c' - \iota s')[A_5 e^{q(c-\iota s)z} + A_6 e^{-q(c-\iota s)z}],$$

$$Z''' = -\iota p^3 (A_1 e^{\iota pz} - A_2 e^{-\iota pz}) + q^3 (c'' + \iota s'')[A_3 e^{q(c+\iota s)z} - A_4 e^{-q(c+\iota s)z}]$$
$$+ q^3 (c'' - \iota s'')[A_5 e^{q(c-\iota s)z} - A_6 e^{-q(c-\iota s)z}],$$

$$Z^{iv} = p^4 (A_1 e^{\iota pz} + A_2 e^{-pz}) + q^4 (c''' + \iota s''')[A_3 e^{q(c+\iota s)z} + [A_4 e^{-q(c+\iota s)z}]$$
$$+ q^4 (c''' - \iota s''')[A_5 e^{q(c-\iota s)z} + A_6 e^{-q(c-\iota s)z}].$$

5. Grouping conjugate factors and expressing the result as the sum of even and odd functions

$$Z = a_2 \cos pz + a_4 (e^{qcz} C_0 + e^{-qcz} C_0) + a_6 (e^{qcz} S_0 - e^{-qcz} S_0)$$
$$+ a_1 \sin pz + a_3 (e^{qcz} C_0 - e^{-qcz} C_0) + a_5 (e^{qcz} S_0 + e^{-qcz} S_0),$$

$$Z' = -a_2 p \sin pz + a_4 q (e^{qcz} C_1 - e^{-qcz} C_{-1}) + a_6 q (e^{qcz} S_1 + e^{-qcz} S_{-1})$$
$$+ a_1 p \cos pz + a_3 q (e^{qcz} C_1 + e^{-qcz} C_{-1}) + a_5 q (e^{qcz} S_1 - e^{-qcz} S_{-1}),$$

$$Z'' = -a_2 p^2 \cos pz + a_4 q^2 (e^{qcz} C_2 + e^{-qcz} C_{-2}) + a_6 q^2 (e^{qcz} S_2 - e^{-qcz} S_{-2})$$
$$- a_1 p^2 \sin pz + a_3 q^2 (e^{qcz} C_2 - e^{-qcz} C_{-2}) + a_5 q^2 (e^{qcz} S_2 + e^{-qcz} S_{-2}),$$

$$Z''' = a_2 p^3 \sin pz + a_4 q^3 (e^{qcz} C_3 - e^{-qcz} C_{-3}) + a_6 q^3 (e^{qcz} S_3 + e^{-qcz} S_{-3})$$
$$- a_1 p^3 \cos pz + a_3 q^3 (e^{qcz} C_3 + e^{-qcz} C_{-3}) + a_5 q^3 (e^{qcz} S_3 - e^{-qcz} S_{-3}),$$

$$Z^{iv} = a_2 p^4 \cos pz + a_4 q^4 (e^{qcz} C_4 + e^{-qcz} C_{-4}) + a_6 q^4 (e^{qcz} S_4 - e^{-qcz} S_{-4})$$
$$+ a_1 p^4 \sin pz + a_3 q^4 (e^{qcz} C_4 - e^{-qcz} C_{-4}) + a_5 q^4 (e^{qcz} S_4 + e^{-qcz} S_{-4}),$$

where

$$C_{\pm n} = \cos(\psi \pm n\gamma), \qquad S_{\pm n} = \sin(\psi \pm n\gamma), \qquad \psi = qsz,$$

further

$$\phi = pz, \qquad Q = qcz,$$

and at a boundary where $\zeta = h/2$, $z = \pi b\zeta/h = \pi b/2$

$$\psi = qsb\pi/2, \qquad \phi = pb\pi/2, \qquad Q = qcb\pi/2.$$

All the quantities involved are now real for real values of z.

Later it will be convenient to write these relations in the form

$$Z = a_2Z_2 + a_4Z_4 + a_6Z_6 + a_1Z_1 + a_3Z_3 + a_5Z_5,$$

$$Z' = a_2Z_2' + a_4Z_4' \ldots\ldots\ldots\ldots\ldots\ldots + a_5Z_5',$$

$$\ldots\ldots\ldots\ldots\ldots\ldots\ldots\ldots\ldots\ldots\ldots\ldots$$

$$Z^{iv} = a_2Z_2^{iv} + a_4Z_4^{iv} + \ldots\ldots\ldots\ldots\ldots + a_5Z_5^{iv}.$$

6. There must be six boundary conditions available to determine the six arbitrary coefficients. In the problems under consideration there are two dynamical conditions and one thermal condition at each boundary. Let u, v, w be the components of the motion of instability.

Considering first the dynamical conditions, the condition $w = 0$ leads to $\nabla^2 T = 0$. At a surface of free slip the conditions $\partial u/\partial\xi = \partial v/\partial\eta = 0$ lead to $\partial^2 w/\partial\zeta^2 = 0$, thence to $\partial^2\nabla^2 T/\partial\zeta^2 = 0$. At a surface of no slip the conditions $u = 0$, $v = 0$, $w = 0$ lead to $\partial u/\partial\xi = \partial v/\partial\eta = \partial w/\partial\zeta = \partial\nabla^2 T/\partial\zeta = 0$.

Transforming from ζ to z, these conditions become :—

At a fixed plane surface......	$Z'' - Z = 0$	(3)
With no slip................	$Z''' - Z' = 0$	(4)
With free slip	$Z^{iv} - Z'' = 0$	(5)

Conditions (3) and (5) were first given by Rayleigh, and condition (4) by Jeffreys.

Rayleigh assumed, as thermal conditions, that both boundaries were maintained at different constant temperatures, which is at once expressed by

$$Z = 0. \quad (1)$$

Conditions (3) and (1) apply to both surfaces. Condition (4) or condition (5) may apply to either surface. Denoting the groups of conditions (1 3 4) and (1 3 5) by a and b, there are three cases :—

aa (1 3 4) at both surfaces,
bb (1 3 5) at both surfaces,
ab (1 3 4) at one surface,
(1 3 5) at the other surface.

Problem *bb* was solved by Rayleigh, and his result was obtained by Dr. Jeffreys and in the present paper in different ways.

Problem *aa* was solved by Dr. Jeffreys to a close approximation, and in the present paper more exactly.

Problem *ab* is solved in the present paper.

It is to be noted that a free fluid surface (under gravity) is a surface of zero tangential forces, further since the velocities are small quantities, say of the first order, the differences of level at a free surface are, at most, small quantities of the second order, by Bernoulli's relation. Hence no distinction need be made between a free fluid surface and a horizontal rigid plane surface of free slip to the order of approximation employed.

7. Considering first Rayleigh's problem, (*bb*), two horizontal plane boundaries, maintained at constant unequal temperatures and with free slip between boundary surface and fluid, yield the conditions at both boundaries,

$$Z = 0, \qquad Z'' - Z = 0, \qquad Z^{iv} - Z'' = 0$$

reducing at once to

$$Z = 0, \qquad Z'' = 0, \qquad Z^{iv} = 0.$$

Where the same condition holds at both boundaries, the odd and even parts of the expressions can be made to disappear independently by taking the origin midway between the boundaries, where $\zeta = \pm h/2$, $z = \pm pb\pi/2$.

Eliminating a_2, a_4, a_6 and a_1, a_3, a_5 in separate groups, the conditions of consistency are obtained in the form of third order determinants equated to zero. Dividing the second row by q^2, the third row by q^4 and multiplying the first column by q^4, we get

$$\begin{vmatrix} q^4 \begin{matrix}\cos\\ \sin\end{matrix} \phi & e^{Q}C_0 \pm e^{-Q}C_0 & e^{Q}S_0 \mp e^{-Q}S_0 \\ -p^2q^2 \begin{matrix}\cos\\ \sin\end{matrix} \phi & e^{Q}C_2 \pm e^{-Q}C_{-2} & e^{Q}S_2 \mp e^{-Q}S_{-2} \\ p^4 \begin{matrix}\cos\\ \sin\end{matrix} \phi & e^{Q}C_4 \pm e^{-Q}C_{-4} & e^{Q}S_4 \mp e^{-Q}S_{-4} \end{vmatrix} = 0$$

the upper symbols being taken for the even solution, the lower symbols for the odd solution.

On reduction of the even solution we get,

$$(e^{2Q} + 2\cos 2\psi + e^{-2Q})\,(q^4 + 2q^2p^2\cos 2\gamma + p^4)\sin 2\gamma\cos\phi = 0.$$

The only physical solution is given by

$$\cos\phi = 0, \quad \phi = pb\pi/2 = (2n+1)\pi/2, \quad pb = 2n+1$$

where n is any integer.

Subject to this relation a minimum value has to be found for

$$(p^2+1)^3 b^4 = E/\pi^4 E_0 = (2n+1)^4 (p^2+1)^3/p^4.$$

Clearly pb must be as small as possible numerically so that $n = 0$, $pb = 1$, which together with the minimum condition gives readily

$$p^2 = 2, \qquad p = \sqrt{2}, \qquad b = 1/\sqrt{2}, \qquad E_{min.}/E_0 = 3^3 \,.\, 2^{-2} \,.\, \pi^4 = 651$$

in agreement with Rayleigh and Jeffreys. The type of unstable flow is shown diagrammatically in fig. 1A.

The writer was anticipated in obtaining this result by his colleague Capt. D. Brunt of the Meteorological Office, who had noted that $Z = \cos pz$ satisfied the differential equation (1) by virtue of satisfying $(D^2 + p^2)\, Z = 0$, $D^2 + p^2$ being an obvious factor, and further can be made to satisfy the boundary conditions $Z = 0$, $Z'' = 0$, $Z^{iv} = 0$ at $z = \pm\, pb\pi/2$ by making $pb = 1$, thus obtaining Rayleigh's solution in a simple way.

8. Taking the lower symbols for the odd conditions we get in a similar manner $Z = \sin \phi = \sin pz$, and at the boundaries,

$$\sin \phi = 0$$
$$pb\pi/2 = \phi = n\pi$$
$$pb = 2n.$$

The smallest integral value of n for which pb does not vanish is unity, hence

$$pb = 2 \qquad E_{min.}/E_0 = 3^3 2^2 \pi^4.$$

This is 16 times larger than for the even solution and is not the critical solution. These conditions are produced by two circuits in the motion of instability (fig. 1B) mirror images of each other in the median plane, which is then dynamically equivalent to a surface of free slip since the tangential forces over it evidently vanish by symmetry.

From paragraph 3 it is seen that E is proportional to $\beta' h^4$ (for a given fluid with fixed values of α, κ, ν) so that halving the effective depth increases the required temperature gradient 16 times. For a given temperature gradient β, the minimum value of E is therefore the same for odd and even solutions of depth h and $2h$, and with one and two circuits respectively, and the odd solution is transformable into the even solution by change of scale and origin.

Fig. 1A shows diagrammatically the configuration of the motion of instability for Rayleigh's case, with a single circuit of flow in depth, but with mirror image circuits on either side. The motion is further assumed to be two-dimensional for simplicity of representation as this does not affect the critical value of E (*cp.* Rayleigh, *loc. cit.*).

FIG. 1B shows the configuration which produces the conditions of the odd

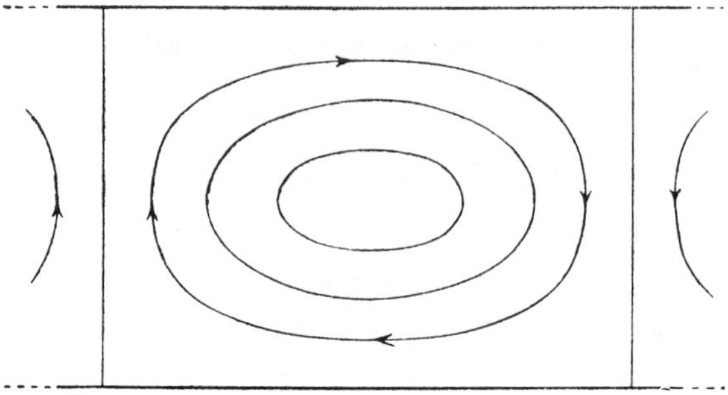

FIG. 1A.

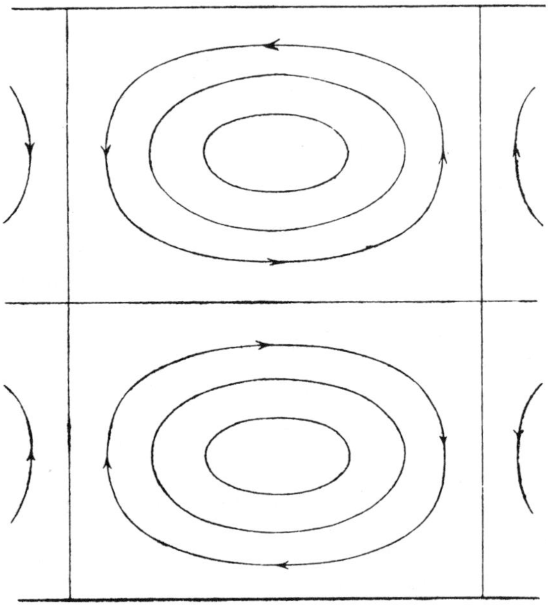

FIG. 1B.

solution, with twice the total depth, but with two circuits in depth so that the effective depth is unaltered. According to Rayleigh's commentary the former type would prevail in the long run as it has a larger increment in time for a given set of conditions, but the latter type is physically possible and would be set up by a suitable disturbance.

9. Considering next the case of two rigid boundaries with no slip; the conditions at both boundaries are

$$Z = 0, \quad Z'' = 0, \quad Z''' - Z' = 0 \quad (\text{case } aa).$$

Taking the origin midway between the boundaries and eliminating a_2, a_4, a_6 and a_1, a_3, a_5 in separate groups we get,

$$0 = \begin{vmatrix} q^2 \begin{matrix}\cos\\ \sin\end{matrix}\phi, & e^{Q}C_0 \pm e^{-Q}C_0, & e^{Q}S_0 \mp e^{-Q}S_0 \\ -p^2 \begin{matrix}\cos\\ \sin\end{matrix}\phi, & e^{Q}C_2 \pm e^{-Q}C_{-2}, & e^{Q}S_2 \mp e^{-Q}S_{-2} \\ \pm pq(q^2+1) \begin{matrix}\sin\\ \cos\end{matrix}\phi, & \begin{matrix} e^{Q}(q^2C_3 - C_1), \\ \mp e^{-Q}(q^2C_{-3} - C_{-1}), \end{matrix} & \begin{matrix} e^{Q}(q^2S_3 - S_1) \\ \pm e^{-Q}(q^2S_{-3} - S_{-1}) \end{matrix} \end{vmatrix},$$

taking as before the upper symbols for the even solution and the lower for the odd solution.

10. With the upper symbols, after reduction, we get,

$$\begin{aligned} \cos\phi\{[(q^4+q^2-p^2)\sin\gamma + p^2q^2\sin 3\gamma]\,(e^{2Q}-e^{-2Q}) \\ + [(q^4-q^2-p^2)\cos\gamma + p^2q^2\cos 3\gamma]\, 2\sin 2\psi\} \\ + \sin\phi\, qp\,(p^2+1)\,(e^{2Q}+e^{-2Q}+2\cos 2\psi)\sin 2\gamma = 0, \end{aligned}$$

whence

$$\begin{aligned} pb\pi/2 &= \phi \\ &= \tan^{-1}[\{(q^4+q^2-p^2)\sin\gamma + p^2q^2\sin 3\gamma + \varepsilon_1\}/\{qp(p^2+1)\sin 2\gamma\,(1+\varepsilon_2)\}]. \end{aligned}$$

where

$$\varepsilon_1 = [(q^4-q^2-p^2)\cos\gamma + p^2q^2\sin 3\gamma]\, 2\sin 2\psi/(e^{2Q}-e^{-2Q}),$$

$$\varepsilon_2 = 2\,(\cos 2\psi + e^{-2Q})/(e^{2Q}-e^{-2Q}).$$

It will be noted that b appears implicitly in Q, $\sin 2\psi$, and $\cos 2\psi$ and through them in ε_1, ε_2.

The convergence is, however, rapid owing to the magnitude of $e^{2Q} > 100$ near the minimum value of E, as appeared during the computations.

As p varies from zero to infinity, $-\tan\phi$ varies from infinity to $\sqrt{3}$, and $pb\pi/2 = \phi$ varies from $\pi/2 + n\pi$ to $2\pi/3 + n\pi$, where n has any integral value.

Putting $n = 0$ and plotting b as a function of p the pb curve lies between the hyperbolas $pb = 1$, and $pb = 4/3$.

The minimum value of $E/E_0 = (p^2+1)^3 b^4\pi^4$ subject to the condition $pb = 2\phi/\pi$, is most conveniently computed by assuming a series of values of p and tabulating the corresponding values of q, γ, and the first approximations for ϕ and b; then, using the values of b so found to evaluate ε_1, ε_2, second approximations are found for ϕ and b. Fig. 2A shows diagrammatically the flow for the two dimensional type of instability.

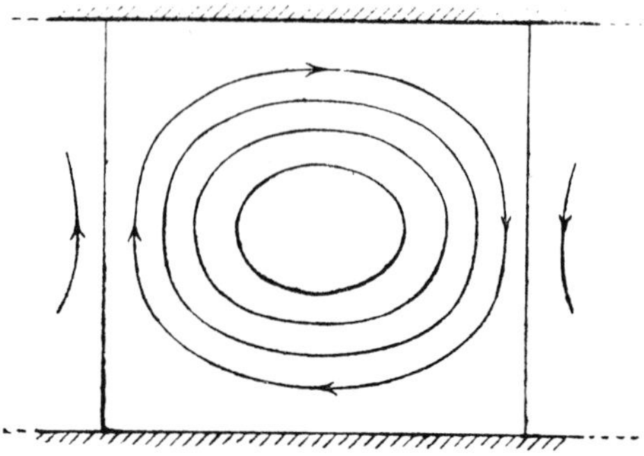

FIG. 2A.

The following values have been computed :—

EVEN SOLUTION.

1st approximation (neglecting ε_1, ε_2).

p	1·1	1·2	1·3	1·4	1·5
b..........	1·139	1·052	0·977	0·912	0·855
E/E_0	1767	1731	1726	1747	1788

2nd approximation.

b..........	1·137	1·049	0·974	0·914	0·852
E/E_0	1756	1716	1709	1726	1763

3rd approximation.

p	1·285	
b..........	0·9846	
E/E_0	1706*	minimum by interpolation.

11. Considering now the odd terms, the first approximation gives $\cot \phi' = -\tan \phi$ where the accent denotes the odd solution, whence $\phi' = \phi + \pi/2 + n\pi$. Putting $n = 0$ we get, for boundaries at $\pm h$

$$pb\pi = \phi' = \phi + \pi/2 > \pi$$
$$< \pi + \pi/6$$

or

$$1 < pb < 7/6,$$

the pb curve in this case lying between the hyperbolas $pb = 1$ and $pb = 7/6$.

* Corrected value 1704·4.

The value of Q is now $qbc\pi$ instead of $qbc\pi/2$ and e^{Q} is found to exceed 10^2, so that neglect of e^{-Q} in comparison with e^{Q} leads to an error of the order of

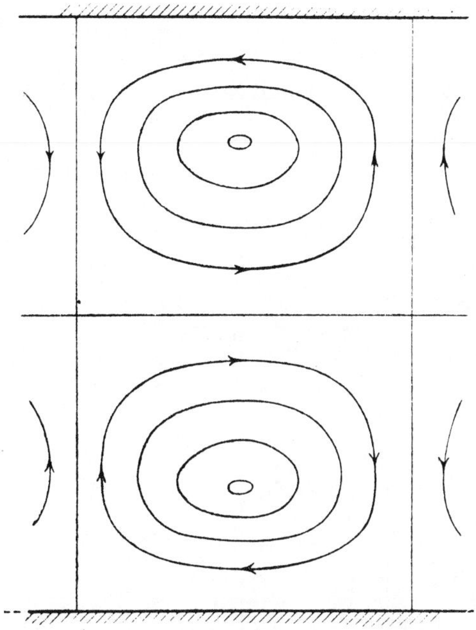

FIG. 2B.

10^{-4}, and the first approximation is sufficient for all practical purposes. The following values have been computed to the first approximation only.

ODD SOLUTION.

1*st approximation.*

b..........	1·025	0·944	0·874	0·815	0·762
E/E_0......	1180	1123	1108	1112	1130

The minimum value is nearly 1108, the corresponding value of p is 1·3.

Two vertically superposed circuits of flow, mirror images of each other in the median plane, produce the conditions of a free surface at steady temperature since clearly $Z = 0$ and tangential forces $= 0$ by symmetry. For comparison with the even solution the total depth is taken as $2h$, and the depth per circuit as h (fig. 2B).

The odd solution thus satisfies the conditions of case (ab) paragraph 6.

Using the values of p and b already found for minimum E/E_0 the coefficients a_1, a_2, a_3, a_4, a_5, a_6 have been computed, the relative values being—

$$a_2/75\cdot22 = a_4/4\cdot591 = -\,a_6/0\cdot0693$$

$$a_1/569\cdot0 = a_3/3\cdot064 = a_5/3\cdot507.$$

Putting a_1 and a_2 arbitrarily as unity, the curves of Z regarded as a function of ζ/h are drawn in figs. 3A and 3B. The first term which is simple harmonic and the other terms which are affected by exponential factors are plotted

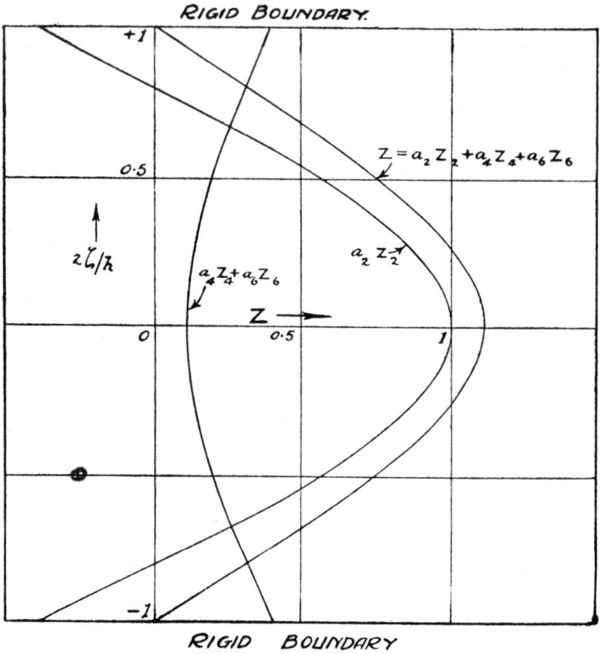

FIG. 3A.

separately. It is seen how rapidly the effect of the latter terms falls off as the distance from the solid boundary increases.

At the boundary their sum is equal and opposite to the simple harmonic term. At distance $h/2$ it has fallen, in the even case, to about 5 per cent. for one boundary and by addition to about 10 per cent. for both boundaries. At distance h it has fallen, in the odd case, to about 1 per cent. for each boundary but the values are of opposite sign and their sum vanishes at the surface separating the two circuits.

In the problems of paragraphs 7 and 8, we have $Z = \cos\phi$, $Z = \sin\phi$ respectively, but as these are elementary curves they have not been drawn.

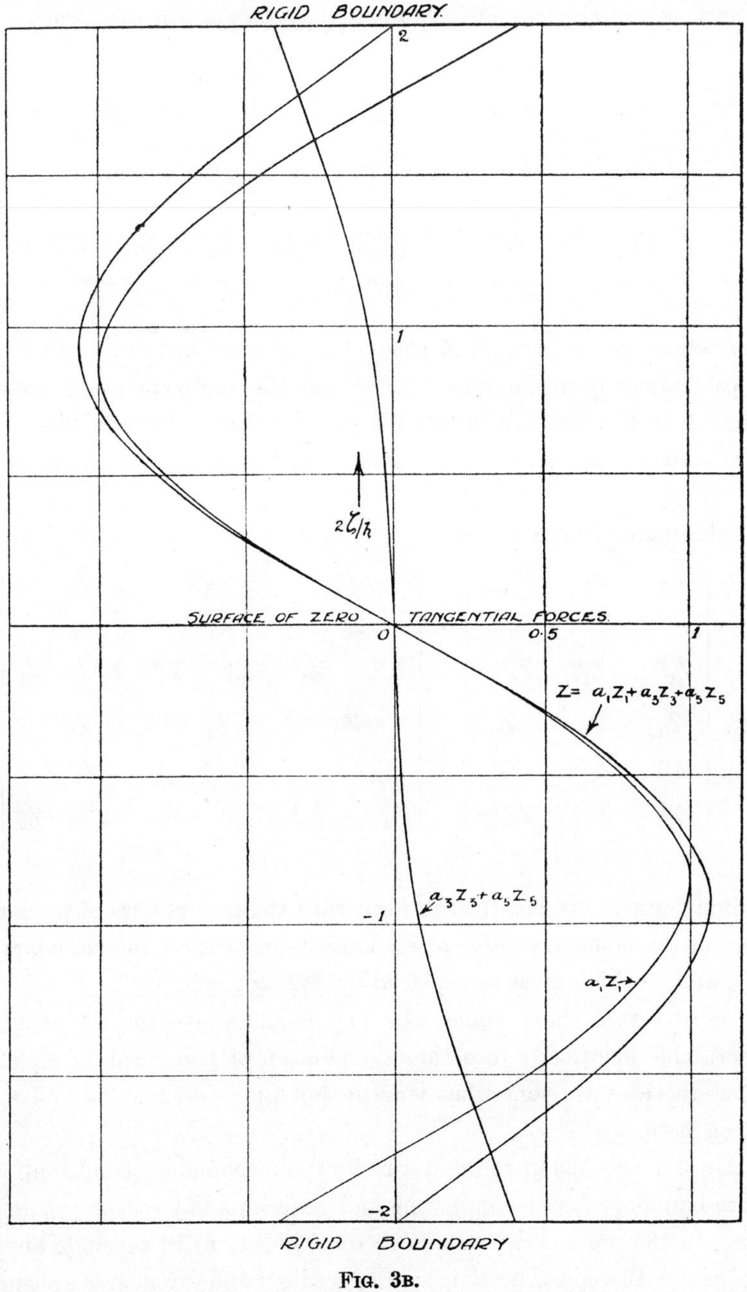
RIGID BOUNDARY
2
1
$2\zeta/h$
SURFACE OF ZERO TANGENTIAL FORCES.
0
0·5
1
$Z= a_1Z_1+a_3Z_3+a_5Z_5$
$a_3Z_3+a_5Z_5$
-1
a_1Z_1
-2
RIGID BOUNDARY

FIG. 3B.

12. The direct solution of the case *ab* with the origin midway between the rigid surface and the free surface, gives the eliminant in the form

$$\begin{vmatrix} Z_2 & Z_4 & Z_6 & 0 & 0 & 0 \\ 0 & 0 & 0 & Z_1 & Z_3 & Z_5 \\ Z_2'' & Z_4'' & Z_6'' & 0 & 0 & 0 \\ 0 & 0 & 0 & Z_1'' & Z_3'' & Z_5'' \\ Z_2'''-Z_2' & Z_4'''-Z_4' & Z_6'''-Z_6' & -Z_1'''+Z_1' & -Z_3'''+Z_3' & -Z_5'''+Z_5' \\ Z_2^{iv} & Z_4^{iv} & Z_6^{iv} & Z_1^{iv} & Z_3^{iv} & Z_6^{iv} \end{vmatrix} = 0.$$

Expressing this as the sum of products of pairs of 3rd order minors, one of each pair taken from columns 1, 2, 3 and the complementary minor from columns 4, 5, 6, there are in general ${}_6C_3 = 20$ pairs, but owing to the two rows of zeros in each set of three columns all but ${}_2C_1 = 2$ of the products are zero.

The eliminant reduces to

$$- \begin{vmatrix} Z_2 & Z_4 & Z_6 \\ Z_2'' & Z_4'' & Z_6'' \\ Z_2^{iv} & Z_4^{iv} & Z_6^{iv} \end{vmatrix} \times \begin{vmatrix} Z_1 & Z_3 & Z_5 \\ Z_1'' & Z_3'' & Z_5'' \\ Z_1''' - Z_1' & Z_3''' - Z_3' & Z_5''' - Z_5' \end{vmatrix}$$

$$+ \begin{vmatrix} Z_1 & Z_3 & Z_5 \\ Z_1'' & Z_3'' & Z_5'' \\ Z_1^{iv} & Z_3^{iv} & Z_5^{iv} \end{vmatrix} \times \begin{vmatrix} Z_2 & Z_4 & Z_6 \\ Z_2'' & Z_4'' & Z_6'' \\ Z_2''' - Z_2' & Z_4''' - Z_4' & Z_6''' - Z_6' \end{vmatrix} = 0$$

These four minors are identical in form with the four minors of paragraphs 7 and 9, but the boundary value of z is halved, and with it the boundary values of ϕ, ψ and q, which must be replaced by $\phi/2$, $\psi/2$, $q/2$.

On substituting these values the expression above for the eliminant is transformable identically into the odd solution of paragraph 9.

The reductions are somewhat lengthy but quite elementary and need not be given here.

13. Dr. Jeffreys has introduced a new type of boundary condition, namely, that the boundary is non-conducting and gives an analytical expression which becomes in the present notation $Z' = 0$. This seems to preclude any steady flow of heat with a constant temperature gradient and to render the phenomenon a transient one, unless it may be regarded as a limiting case of perfect transmission of heat from the boundary.

Assuming, in the first place, that the flow of heat is steady so that the heat reaching the boundary through the fluid equals the heat transmitted from the boundary to the ultimate sink, and that the latter quantity is proportional to the temperature difference between boundary and sink, while the former quantity, as before, is proportional to the temperature gradient in the fluid at the boundary, then we have

$$\partial T/\partial z = K(T - T_0),$$

where T is the steady boundary temperature and T_0 is the constant temperature of the sink.

In the disturbed state

$$\partial (T + \Delta T)/\partial z = K(T + \Delta T - T_0)$$

where $T + \Delta T$ is the disturbed temperature at the boundary.
Hence

$$\partial \Delta T/\partial z = K \Delta T,$$

which in the present notation reduces on dropping a common factor to

$$Z' = KZ.$$

If K becomes very large this condition approaches $Z = 0$, Rayleigh's boundary condition. If K becomes very small the condition approaches $Z' = 0$, Jeffreys's adiabatic condition.

Numbering this condition (2) in the scheme of para. 6, the possible combinations at a boundary surface are the old combinations (1 3 4) and (1 3 5) designated *a*, *b*, as in para. 6 and the new combinations (2 3 4), (2 3 5) which may be designed as *c*, *d*.

The possible pairs at two surfaces are *aa*, *bb*, *cc*, *dd*, *ab*, *ac*, *ad*, *bc*, *bd*, *cd*, ten in all. The odd and even solutions of *cc*, *dd* are separable and present no new difficulty.

Taking as before the plane of symmetry in the odd solutions as a surface of free slip and constant temperature subject to boundary conditions *b*, the odd solutions of *cc*, *dd*, give solutions of *cb*, *db*. Since the odd solution of *aa* transforms identically into the direct solution of *ab* (para. 12) it seems probable that the odd solutions of *cc*, *dd*, will be identical with the solutions of *cb*, *db*, but this has not been verified by direct transformation.

There remain three cases, *ac*, *ad*, *cd*. In cases *ac* and *cd* there are two conditions common to both boundaries, and the eliminants reduce to the sum of two products of complementary third order minors, as in case *ab* of para. 12.

The case *ad* has been considered by Jeffreys but the solution has not been completed. It is the least tractable of all, since there is only one condition common to both boundaries and the number of pairs of complementary minors reduces from ${}_3C_6$ only to ${}_2C_5 = 10$, of which two pairs have already been reduced above.

The third order minors are expressible in terms of the second order minors obtained from the matrix

$$\left\| \begin{matrix} e^{Q}C_0 \pm e^{-Q}C_0 & e^{Q}S_0 \mp e^{-Q}S_0 \\ e^{Q}C_1 \mp e^{-Q}C_{-1} & e^{Q}S_1 \pm e^{-Q}S_{-1} \\ e^{Q}C_2 \pm e^{-Q}C_{-2} & e^{Q}S_2 \mp e^{-Q}S_{-2} \\ e^{Q}C_3 \mp e^{-Q}C_{-3} & e^{Q}S_3 \pm e^{-Q}S_{-3} \\ e^{Q}C_4 \pm e^{-Q}C_{-4} & e^{Q}S_4 \mp e^{-Q}S_{-4} \end{matrix} \right\|$$

Denoting them by $\overline{01}$, $\overline{12}$, $\overline{23}$, $\overline{13}$, etc., for the upper signs and $\underline{01}$, $\underline{12}$, $\underline{23}$, $\underline{13}$ for the lower signs, we find on reduction,

$$\overline{01} = \overline{23} = \underline{12} = \underline{24} = (e^{2Q} - e^{-2Q}) \sin \gamma + 2 \sin 2\,\psi \cos \gamma,$$

$$\underline{01} = \underline{23} = \overline{12} = \overline{24} = (e^{2Q} - e^{-2Q}) \sin \gamma - 2 \sin 2\,\psi \cos \gamma,$$

$$\overline{02} = \overline{24} = \underline{13} = (e^{2Q} + e^{-2Q} + 2 \cos 2\psi) \sin 2\,\gamma,$$

$$\underline{02} = \underline{24} = \overline{13} = (e^{2Q} + e^{-2Q} - 2 \cos 2\psi) \sin 2\,\gamma,$$

$$\overline{03} = 14 = (e^{2Q} - e^{-2Q}) \sin 3\gamma + 2 \sin 2\psi \cos 3\gamma,$$

$$\underline{03} = \overline{14} = (e^{2Q} - e^{-2Q}) \sin 3\gamma - 2 \sin 2\psi \cos 3\gamma,$$

$$\overline{04} = (e^{2Q} + e^{-2Q} + 2 \cos 2\psi) \sin 4\gamma,$$

$$\underline{04} = (e^{2Q} + e^{-2Q} - 2 \cos 2\psi) \sin 4\gamma.$$

With these identities and recurrence relations, the eliminant of case *ad* can be expanded, and the minimum value found by computation, which may be lengthy.

The writer has not carried further this new problem which indeed lies outside the scope of his analogy and has been discussed here only on account of the attention given to it by Dr. Jeffreys.

14. The writer would acknowledge the advances made by Dr. Jeffreys in generalising Rayleigh's treatment of Bénard's problem, and in establishing formally the mathematical expression of the analogy with Taylor's problem.

The physical basis of the writer's analogy is the replacement of κ, measuring the diffusion of heat, by ν, measuring the diffusion of vorticity.

To render the analogous problems identical in mathematical detail the distribution through the fluids of the apparent energy of instability must be the same.

This is clearly so when the radii and angular velocities of the cylinders in Taylor's experiment are large compared with their differences since the energy is a function of ω and r of which the gradient may be considered linear throughout a small range of the variables, while the curvature of the boundaries has no sensible effect beyond setting up the inertia field. Jeffreys has given his demonstration of equivalence under these conditions.

But the numerical value of the criterion for instability is very nearly constant through the whole range of angular velocities in Taylor's first case where there is one circuit of unstable motion in the depth of the fluid, and it only begins to diverge when the second case with two circuits in depth has set in.

The physical explanation appears to be that the total apparent energy of the instability is the deciding factor, and that a departure from a linear gradient of energy per unit volume is of quite secondary importance.

If it were possible to impose an arbitrary variable gravitational field a general mathematical analogue of Taylor's problem could be constructed.

It is worth remarking that in Taylor's second case the larger circuit is giving out energy on a relatively large scale while the smaller circuit is absorbing energy on a smaller scale.

15. These solved problems of instability have the essential characteristic that the initial state of (rest or) steady motion, and the motion of instability have no common co-ordinate of velocity, as shown by the table.

	Steady state.	Motion of instability.
Rayleigh—3 dimensional case ..	0, 0, 0	u, v, w
2 dimensional case ..	u, 0, 0	0, v, w
Taylor	0, v, 0	u, 0, w

In such cases the motion of instability is in effect treated as steady.

Where the motion of instability and the initial steady motion involve a common velocity co-ordinate the former is no longer steady; the difficulties of the problem then become much greater, and have so far defeated all attempts at solution.

Reprinted from *Proceedings of the Royal Society*, Series A, Vol. 176, Nov. 1, 1940.

On maintained convective motion in a fluid heated from below

BY ANNE PELLEW AND R. V. SOUTHWELL, F.R.S.

(*Received* 1 *July* 1940)

This paper examines the stability in viscous liquid of a steady regime in which the temperature decreases with uniform gradient between a lower horizontal surface which is heated and an upper horizontal surface which is cooled. The problem has been treated both experimentally and theoretically by Bénard, Brunt, Jeffreys, Low and Rayleigh, and it is known that instability will occur at some critical value of $gh^3\Delta\rho/\rho k\nu$, h denoting the thickness of the fluid layer, $\Delta\rho/\rho$ the fractional excess of density in the fluid at the top as compared with the fluid at the bottom surface, k the diffusivity and ν the kinematic viscosity. The critical value depends upon the conditions at the top and bottom surfaces, which may be either 'free' or constrained by rigid conducting surfaces.

The theoretical problem is solved here under three distinct boundary conditions, and greater generality than before is maintained in regard to the 'cell pattern' which occurs in plan. In addition an approximate method is described and illustrated, depending on a stationary property akin to that of which Lord Rayleigh made wide application in vibration theory.

Within the assumptions of the approximate theory (i.e. with neglect of terms of the second order in respect of the velocities) a particular size is associated with every shape of cell (such that 'a^2' takes a preferred value), but no particular shape is more likely than another to occur in a layer of indefinite extent (§ 31). The explanation of the apparent preference for a hexagonal cell pattern (§ 5) must presumably be sought in a theory which takes account of second-order terms. This conjecture if correct goes some way towards explaining the rather indefinite nature of observed cell-formations (cf. Low 1930, figure 10).

THE PHYSICAL PROBLEM

1. When in a stationary fluid some layer has greater density than others which lie below it, its equilibrium is plainly unstable in the sense that even

a small disturbance may result in a completely changed regime. The difference in density may either be intrinsic, as when water condenses on the upper surface of a layer of oil, or it may be due to such causes as unequal salinity or temperature: in that event it will tend in time to be counteracted by diffusion, and convective (i.e. molar) motion of the fluid will not result if the diffusivity be sufficiently high. But diffusion may in turn be counteracted by some cause tending to maintain the inequality of density,—as when a fluid has its upper surface kept at constant temperature and heat is applied to it from below.* The question of stability in these circumstances has physical importance from several aspects. It appears to have been first studied by Lord Rayleigh (1916) in relation to experiments made by Bénard (1900).

In a theoretical treatment of the problem it is natural to assume that the top and bottom surfaces of the fluid are plane and horizontal so that its depth has a constant value h, and to take as the other boundary a vertical cylinder having any shape of horizontal cross-section. This cylindrical surface, or 'cell wall', may either be a material boundary (e.g. in experimental work) or it may be a surface of symmetry between adjacent cells of a 'convection pattern' occurring spontaneously in a fluid of infinite horizontal extent. In both instances we may impose the condition that *no heat is transmitted through the cell wall*, either because its material is thermally non-conducting† or in consequence of the predicated symmetry.

2. At the top or bottom surface, on the other hand, either of two conditions may be postulated: the material in contact with the fluid may be (thermally) either an insulator or conductor. In the first event no heat is transmitted, so the normal gradient of the temperature vanishes at the horizontal surface; in the second we may postulate that a uniform and specified temperature is maintained at every point. Here we shall impose the second condition at both surfaces, on the ground that only so can steady convective motion be *maintained*. Clearly, if one surface is a thermal insulator then all parts of the fluid must come in time (by conduction) to the temperature of the other, and a like regime of uniformly distributed temperature (manifestly stable) must result when both surfaces are non-conducting; so unless the temperature at each surface is kept constant at some cost in heat transmission, any instability discovered in analysis must

* The heat must of course be supplied from above if the fluid has a negative coefficient of thermal expansion (e.g. water close to its freezing point). Cf. § 20.

† Non-conducting material would almost certainly be used in experimental work. Heat transfer through the cell wall would entail prohibitive complication.

relate to some temporary distribution of temperature, and will be succeeded by some motion having (ultimately) the nature of a damped oscillation or subsidence.*

3. Not only the temperature but also the velocities have to satisfy appropriate conditions at the boundaries. When the fluid has viscosity, material boundaries (over which it cannot slip) will require all three components of velocity to vanish, surfaces of symmetry will entail a like number of conditions.† Detailed investigation shows (§ 11) that the problem can be formulated in terms either of the temperature (θ)‡ or of the vertical component of velocity (w), that both quantities are governed by equations of a like mathematical form, and that at every point of every boundary three conditions (in all) are imposed. Having determined θ we can deduce w and vice versa; and when w has been determined a supplementary calculation leads to the other two components of velocity, one further governing equation being involved together with one new condition at every boundary.

Review of previous mathematical investigations

4. Rayleigh's mathematical treatment proceeds primarily in terms of w, that of Jeffreys (1926) primarily in terms of the temperature (for which he employs the symbol V). Both assume that equations expressing the conditions of neutral stability are obtained when second-order terms are neglected and all time variations made zero, i.e. when the assumed regime entails steady velocity and temperature at any one point, the velocity being everywhere small. Jeffreys (§ 1) examines this assumption in some detail, showing that in effect it disregards the possibility that two exponential time-factors may coalesce and become conjugate complex quantities, so as to have finite imaginary parts when their real part vanishes. He cites Rayleigh as having disposed of this possibility in relation to boundary conditions of a special type, and himself makes appeal to experiment to confirm that it is not the type of motion that does in fact arise when equilibrium breaks down. In this paper (which follows Rayleigh in dealing primarily with w) a more detailed investigation (§§ 16–18) seems to establish

* It would seem that one of Jeffreys's results (case (2) of § 6) must be interpreted in this sense. Rayleigh's discussion (like this paper) is restricted to the case of two conducting surfaces.

† In the classical experiments of Bénard (cf. § 1) the bottom (heated) surface was a metallic plate, the upper (cooled) surface was usually free.

‡ More precisely, θ stands for the change of temperature due to convectional motion.

positively that *any oscillatory motion must of necessity decay*: consequently in seeking the conditions for maintained convective motion we may confine attention to modes associated with real exponential time-factors, and limiting conditions of stability are in fact obtained when all time variations are made zero.

Scope of the present paper

5. A point of novelty in the present paper is the standpoint adopted in regard to the shape of the cell wall (§ 1). Rayleigh's treatment is restricted to rectangular cells, on the ground that 'by Fourier's theorem the motion in its earlier stages may be analysed into components, each of which corresponds to rectangular cells whose sides are fixed axes arbitrarily chosen'. On the other hand he asserts that 'on a more general view...the disturbance which develops most rapidly may be assimilated to...the free vibration of an infinite stretched membrane vibrating with given frequency', and he makes some approach to a theory of the hexagonal cells which appear from Bénard's experiments to be the final and permanent regime, by treating the hexagon as a *slight* deviation from the circular form. He states in regard to cells having the forms of equilateral triangles or hexagons: 'I am not aware that an analytical solution has been obtained for these cases.' Jeffreys (1926, 1928) follows him in assuming rectangular cells for the purpose of a mathematical treatment. By contrast, in the analytical part of this paper the shape of the cell is left indefinite, its influence on the motion being represented by a parameter a^2 which can be interpreted on the basis of the 'membrane analogue' noticed by Rayleigh in the sentence cited above: a is proportional to the gravest natural frequency of a uniform membrane having the shape of the cell in plan and vibrating transversely under appropriate edge conditions. In this way the main problem is reduced to that of relating the 'characteristic number' $-\beta\gamma h^4/k\nu$ (§ 20) with a^2, and the separate problem of evaluating a^2 for any specified shape of cell is left for approximate treatment by 'relaxation methods'. A suitable technique has been evolved by D. G. Christopherson, who was led by this enquiry to discover an *exact* functional solution for the hexagonal cell. His work is cited in § 30.

6. Not only in regard to cell shape but also in the variety of the contemplated boundary conditions this investigation has a wider range than Rayleigh's. He for simplicity assumed that horizontal velocities can occur (although vertical motion is prevented) at both the top and bottom surfaces, whereas at a solid boundary such velocities are excluded by the requirement

of 'no slip'; consequently the conditions of his solution are unreal, unless (possibly) in relation to meteorology. Jeffreys dealt also with the cases (1) of two rigid and conducting boundaries and (2) of a bottom boundary rigid and conducting, with a free non-conducting surface at the top. For reasons stated earlier (§ 1 and footnote), case (2) would seem to relate to a merely temporary instability.

In this paper uniform and constant temperature is postulated at each of the horizontal surfaces, but these may either be free or in contact with rigid surfaces preventing slip. Solutions are obtained for a range of values for a^2 (§ 5), and are believed to be correct to five significant figures. The treatment though laborious is not difficult, and in a preliminary exploration it can be replaced by an alternative method (believed to be new) which is justified in § 34 by the proving of a stationary property analogous with that of which Lord Rayleigh made wide application in the theory of vibrations. Concluding sections of the paper deal with the supplementary determination of θ and of the horizontal component velocities u and v.

7. Grateful acknowledgement is made of help received in the preparation of diagrams from the Secretary and staff of the Aeronautical Research Committee.

General theory

The governing equations

8. In rectangular co-ordinates (Ox, Oy lying in the bottom horizontal plane and Oz being directed vertically upwards) the complete equations of motion are

$$\rho \frac{D}{Dt}(u, v, w) = \rho(X, Y, Z) - \left(\frac{\partial}{\partial x}, \frac{\partial}{\partial y}, \frac{\partial}{\partial z}\right)\mathbf{p} + \nu\rho\nabla^2(u, v, w) \tag{1}$$

in the customary notation (Lamb 1924, § 328); and in this problem we have

$$X = 0, \quad Y = 0, \quad Z = -g. \tag{2}$$

The equation of continuity is (Lamb 1924, § 7)

$$\frac{D\rho}{Dt} + \rho\left(\frac{\partial u}{\partial x} + \frac{\partial v}{\partial y} + \frac{\partial w}{\partial z}\right) = 0, \tag{3}$$

and the equation of thermal expansion is

$$\rho = \rho_0(1 - \alpha\boldsymbol{\theta}) \tag{4}$$

when the fluid (assumed incompressible) has density ρ_0 at the temperature from which $\boldsymbol{\theta}$ is measured, α denoting its coefficient of expansion. Finally, the equation of conduction for heat is

$$\frac{D\boldsymbol{\theta}}{Dt} = k\nabla^2\boldsymbol{\theta}, \tag{5}$$

k denoting the diffusivity for temperature.

9. In the initial (steady) state u, v, w vanish severally, so that the first two of (1) require that $\mathbf{p} = p_0$ shall be independent of x and y, and the third reduces to

$$0 = -g\rho - \frac{\partial p_0}{\partial z}, \tag{i}$$

p_0 denoting the initial (steady) pressure at (x, y, z). Equation (3) is then satisfied identically.

The temperature is steady and independent of x and y, so that (5) reduces to

$$0 = k\frac{\partial^2\boldsymbol{\theta}}{\partial z^2}. \tag{ii}$$

Therefore we may express the initial temperature θ_0 in the form

$$\theta_0 = \Theta_0 + \beta z, \tag{6}$$

β being a measure of the 'steady temperature gradient'. Then Θ_0 is the temperature at the bottom horizontal surface ($z = 0$), and at the top surface

$$z = h \text{ (say)}, \quad \theta_0 = \Theta_0 + \beta h = \Theta_1 \text{ (say)}. \tag{7}$$

Again, in the steady state we have from (4)

$$\rho = \rho_0(1 - \alpha\theta_0), \tag{iii}$$

or, if ρ_0 be now defined as the density corresponding with Θ_0,

$$\rho = \rho_0\{1 - \alpha(\theta_0 - \Theta_0)\} = \rho_0(1 - \alpha\beta z), \text{ by (6)}. \tag{iv}$$

Therefore according to (i)

$$\frac{\partial p_0}{\partial z} = -g\rho_0(1 - \alpha\beta z). \tag{8}$$

10. *Now let u, v, w, the velocities in the convective motion, be assumed sufficiently small to justify neglect of their squares and products:* then in (1) we

may replace D/Dt by $\partial/\partial t$. The consequent change of temperature will also be small, so that writing

$$\boldsymbol{\theta} = \theta_0 + \theta = \Theta_0 + \beta z + \theta \text{ by (6)} \tag{v}$$

for the temperature as modified by convection, we may neglect terms of the second order in u, v, w, θ. Substituting from (v) in (5), on this understanding we deduce that

$$-\beta w = \left[\frac{\partial}{\partial t} - k\nabla^2\right]\theta; \tag{9}$$

also we have from (4), ρ_0 being defined in (iv) of § 9,

$$\rho = \rho_0\{1 - \alpha(\boldsymbol{\theta} - \Theta_0)\} = \rho_0\{1 - \alpha(\beta z + \theta)\}. \tag{vi}$$

Comparing (vi) with (iv) we see that the increment in ρ which results from the convective motion is a fraction

$$-\frac{\alpha\theta}{1 - \alpha\beta z} \tag{vii}$$

of the steady value, and so (on the above convention) may be neglected when it is multiplied by u, v, w or θ. Similarly, writing

$$\mathbf{p} = p_0 + p \tag{viii}$$

for the pressure as modified by convection, we deduce from (1), in virtue of (8), the three equations

$$\left.\begin{aligned} \frac{\partial}{\partial t}(u, v, w) &= (0, 0, \gamma\theta) - \frac{1}{\rho}\left(\frac{\partial}{\partial x}, \frac{\partial}{\partial y}, \frac{\partial}{\partial z}\right)p + \nu\nabla^2(u, v, w), \\ \text{in which} \qquad \gamma &= g\alpha \end{aligned}\right\} \tag{10}$$

and θ and p have the meanings given above.

In (10) ρ stands for the density in the steady state as given by (iv) of § 9, so depends, strictly speaking, both on z and Θ_0. But a similar argument shows that its non-constant part may be neglected when (as here) it is associated with p, and thus in (10) without sensible inaccuracy we may treat ρ as constant. In other words, we may treat α as negligible except in association with g: i.e. we may (with Boussinesq and Rayleigh) disregard in this problem the change of density due to temperature, 'except in so far as it modifies the operation of *gravity*'.*

Consistently with this approximate treatment we may replace (3) by

$$\frac{\partial u}{\partial x} + \frac{\partial v}{\partial y} + \frac{\partial w}{\partial z} = 0, \tag{11}$$

* Rayleigh 1916, p. 436.

since the quantity which is then neglected, namely

$$\frac{1}{\rho}\frac{D\rho}{Dt},$$

vanishes with α when we substitute for ρ from (vi).

11. Eliminating u and v by combining (11) with the first and second of (10), we have

$$\left[\frac{\partial}{\partial t}-\nu\nabla^2\right]\frac{\partial w}{\partial z}=\frac{1}{\rho}\nabla_1^2 p, \tag{ix}$$

∇_1^2 standing for $\partial^2/\partial x^2+\partial^2/\partial y^2$, and ρ being again treated as constant. Then eliminating p between this equation and the third of (10), we find that

$$\left[\frac{\partial}{\partial t}-\nu\nabla^2\right]\nabla^2 w=\gamma\nabla_1^2\theta. \tag{12}$$

Another relation between w and θ has been given in (9) of § 10. If between (9) and (12) we eliminate θ, there results

$$\left[\left(\frac{\partial}{\partial t}-\nu\nabla^2\right)\left(\frac{\partial}{\partial t}-k\nabla^2\right)\nabla^2+\beta\gamma\nabla_1^2\right]w=0. \tag{13}$$

Eliminating w we obtain a like equation in θ.

12. If we can solve for w, then we can deduce θ from (12) combined with boundary conditions which have still to be discussed. We can also deduce u and v, since from the first and second of (10) we may eliminate p to obtain

$$\left[\frac{\partial}{\partial t}-\nu\nabla^2\right]\left(\frac{\partial v}{\partial x}-\frac{\partial u}{\partial y}\right)=0, \tag{x}$$

—an equation which can be solved by writing

$$u=-\frac{\partial\phi}{\partial x}-\frac{\partial\psi}{\partial y},\quad v=-\frac{\partial\phi}{\partial y}+\frac{\partial\psi}{\partial x},$$

where ϕ is unrestricted and

$$\left[\frac{\partial}{\partial t}-\nu\nabla^2\right]\nabla_1^2\psi=0. \tag{14}$$

Then equation (11) requires that

$$\frac{\partial w}{\partial z}=-\left(\frac{\partial u}{\partial x}+\frac{\partial v}{\partial y}\right)=\nabla_1^2\phi, \tag{15}$$

and (14) and (15), in combination with appropriate boundary conditions, serve to determine ϕ and ψ.

Separation of the variables. The membrane analogy

13. We are concerned (§ 1) with cells which are bounded by a vertical cylinder and by two horizontal surfaces, so an obvious first step to the solution of (13) is the separation of the variables x and y from z by the assumption that w has the form $f(x,y).F(z).\Phi(t)$, where $\nabla_1^2 f \propto f$ and $\Phi(t)$ is an exponential function. Accordingly we now impose the condition

$$h^2\nabla_1^2 w + a^2 w = 0, \tag{16}$$

in which h denotes the depth of a cell and a^2 is a 'characteristic number' not yet determined.

As remarked by Rayleigh (cf. § 5), an equation of the form of (16) governs the displacement (w) of a uniform membrane having the cell wall as boundary and vibrating freely in a 'normal mode'. If (§ 1) the cell wall is a material boundary on which the fluid cannot slip, then w must be kept zero at the boundary: if it is a surface of symmetry (as assumed by Rayleigh), then the normal gradient $\partial w/\partial n$ must vanish in virtue of that symmetry. In either event a like h must be real, since we have by Green's theorem, according to (16),

$$\begin{aligned} a^2\iint w^2\,dx\,dy &= -h^2\iint w\nabla_1^2 w\,dx\,dy \\ &= h^2\left[\iint\left\{\left(\frac{\partial w}{\partial x}\right)^2+\left(\frac{\partial w}{\partial y}\right)^2\right\}dx\,dy - \oint w\frac{\partial w}{\partial n}\,ds\right]: \end{aligned} \tag{17}$$

the line integral is zero and both of the surface integrals are necessarily positive, so a^2 is a positive quantity.

The boundary conditions

14. At every boundary physical conditions are imposed both on the temperature (θ) and on the fluid velocities (u, v, w); but every condition can be expressed in terms of either quantity, since θ is related with w both by (9) and (12).

Writing n for the normal to the cylindrical boundary drawn outwards, we have at every point of that boundary:

If this is a surface of symmetry (as assumed by Rayleigh)

$$\frac{\partial w}{\partial n} = 0 \quad\text{and}\quad \frac{\partial \theta}{\partial n} = 0; \tag{18}$$

if this is a non-conducting rigid surface on which the fluid cannot slip (e.g. in experiment: cf. § 1 and footnote)

$$w = 0 \quad \text{and} \quad \frac{\partial \theta}{\partial n} = 0 \quad \text{as before.} \tag{19}$$

The condition imposed on w serves to define the parameter a^2 of § 13. The condition $\partial\theta/\partial n = 0$, imposed at every point of the cell wall (i.e. for all values of z), requires according to (9) and (12) that

$$\beta\gamma \frac{\partial w}{\partial n} = k\gamma \frac{\partial}{\partial n} \nabla_1^2 \theta = k \frac{\partial}{\partial n}\left[\frac{\partial}{\partial t} - \nu \nabla^2\right] \nabla^2 w. \tag{20}$$

If w satisfies equation (16) this relation is satisfied identically when $\partial w/\partial n = 0$ at every point of the cell wall, consequently the second condition (18) is equivalent to the first. When the cell wall is a non-conducting rigid boundary at which $w = 0$, the second of (19) can be replaced by (20).

15. The top and bottom surfaces may be either free or constrained by rigid boundaries, but in either event are assumed in this paper (cf. § 2) to be maintained at constant temperature. At a free surface w and $\partial u/\partial z$, $\partial v/\partial z$ will vanish, therefore $\partial^2 w/\partial z^2$ in virtue of (11); at a rigid surface on which the fluid cannot slip, w must vanish with u and v, i.e. with $\partial w/\partial z$; on a surface kept at constant temperature we have $\boldsymbol{\theta} = \theta_0$ always, therefore $\theta = 0$. Accordingly at these surfaces we may have either of the following sets of boundary conditions:

If the surface is free

$$w = D^2 w = 0 \quad \text{and} \quad \theta = 0, \tag{21}$$

if the surface is defined by a rigid boundary

$$w = Dw = 0 \quad \text{and} \quad \theta = 0, \tag{22}$$

D denoting $\partial/\partial\zeta$, where $\zeta = z/h$.

As in § 14 we can express the condition $\theta = 0$ as a third condition to be satisfied by w. For since $\nabla_1^2\theta$ will vanish with θ, according to (12) we have

$$\left[\frac{\partial}{\partial t} - \nu \nabla^2\right] \nabla^2 w = 0 \tag{i}$$

at each surface, whether it be free or constrained by a rigid boundary. Also from (9), when $w = \theta = 0$, it follows that $\nabla^2\theta$ vanishes, therefore $\nabla^2\nabla_1^2\theta$; and so according to (12), at either type of boundary

$$\left[\frac{\partial}{\partial t} - \nu \nabla^2\right] \nabla^4 w = 0. \tag{ii}$$

This, however, is not a new condition, being a consequence of (i) and of the first of (21) or (22) according to the governing equation (13).

Combined with the first and second of (21), equations (i) and (ii) show that at a *free surface*

$$w = D^2w = D^4w = D^6w = \dots \text{ etc.} = 0. \tag{23}$$

At a rigid boundary, (i) replacing the third of (22), we have

$$w = Dw = \left[\frac{\partial}{\partial t} - \nu\nabla^2\right]\nabla^2 w = 0. \tag{24}$$

Either set of conditions, in combination with the governing equation (13), will serve to determine w; and until solutions in w have been obtained we need not again consider θ.

Nature of the exponential time factor $\Phi(t)$. The possibility of oscillatory convective motion

16. When $\Phi(t) \propto e^{\sigma t}$ as assumed in § 13, according to (9) and (12)

$$[\sigma - k\nabla^2]\,\theta = -\beta w, \quad [\sigma - \nu\nabla^2]\,\nabla^2 w = \gamma\nabla_1^2\theta. \tag{25}$$

Eliminating θ between these relations in the manner of § 11, we have

$$[\sigma^2\nabla^2 - (k+\nu)\,\sigma\nabla^4 + k\nu\nabla^6 + \beta\gamma\nabla_1^2]\,w = 0, \tag{26}$$

which is the form assumed by (13) when $\partial/\partial t \equiv \sigma$. We now examine the possibility that σ may take complex or imaginary values.

A complex or imaginary value of σ will be associated with a complex form of w in (26), and its conjugate σ', in association with w' the conjugate of w, will also satisfy that equation together with the boundary conditions (18) or (19), (23) or (24). Moreover according to (25) θ will be complex with w, and its conjugate θ', in association with σ' and w', will also satisfy equations (25) together with the boundary conditions imposed on θ: that is to say, corresponding with (25) we shall have the relations

$$[\sigma' - k\nabla^2]\,\theta' = -\beta w', \quad [\sigma' - \nu\nabla^2]\,\nabla^2 w' = \gamma\nabla_1^2\theta'. \tag{27}$$

Then from the first of (25) and second of (27), by cross-multiplication, there will result

$$\beta w[\sigma' - \nu\nabla^2]\,\nabla^2 w' + \gamma\nabla_1^2\theta'[\sigma - k\nabla^2]\,\theta = 0. \tag{28}$$

17. Now let the left-hand side of this equation be integrated throughout the volume of one cell. Having regard to the boundary conditions (18)–(22),

which are satisfied by w, w' and by θ, θ', and taking account of (16), with the aid of Green's transformation we find that

$$\iiint\left(w\nabla^2 w' + \frac{\partial w}{\partial x}\frac{\partial w'}{\partial x} + \frac{\partial w}{\partial y}\frac{\partial w'}{\partial y} + \frac{\partial w}{\partial z}\frac{\partial w'}{\partial z}\right) d(\text{vol.}) = \iint w\frac{\partial w'}{\partial \nu}\, dS = 0,$$

$$\iiint (w\nabla^4 w' - \nabla^2 w \nabla^2 w')\, d(\text{vol.}) = \iint\left(w\frac{\partial}{\partial \nu}\nabla^2 w' - \frac{\partial w}{\partial \nu}\nabla^2 w'\right) dS = 0,$$

$$\iiint\left(\theta\nabla_1^2\theta' + \frac{\partial \theta}{\partial x}\frac{\partial \theta'}{\partial x} + \frac{\partial \theta}{\partial y}\frac{\partial \theta'}{\partial y}\right) d(\text{vol.}) = \iint \theta\frac{\partial \theta'}{\partial n}\, ds\, dz = 0,$$

$$\iiint\left(\frac{\partial^2\theta}{\partial z^2}\nabla_1^2\theta' - \frac{\partial^2\theta}{\partial x\partial z}\frac{\partial^2\theta'}{\partial x\partial z} - \frac{\partial^2\theta}{\partial y\partial z}\frac{\partial^2\theta'}{\partial y\partial z}\right) d(\text{vol.})$$

$$= \iiint\left\{\frac{\partial}{\partial z}\left(\frac{\partial \theta}{\partial z}\nabla_1^2\theta'\right) - \frac{\partial}{\partial x}\left(\frac{\partial \theta}{\partial z}\frac{\partial^2\theta'}{\partial x\partial z}\right) - \frac{\partial}{\partial y}\left(\frac{\partial \theta}{\partial z}\frac{\partial^2\theta'}{\partial y\partial z}\right)\right\} d(\text{vol.})$$

$$= \iint\left[\frac{\partial \theta}{\partial z}\nabla_1^2\theta'\right]_0^1 dx\, dy - \iint \frac{\partial \theta}{\partial z}\frac{\partial}{\partial n}\left(\frac{\partial \theta'}{\partial z}\right) ds\, dz = 0,$$

where as in § 13 s denotes the boundary of a horizontal section of the cell wall and n the outward normal to that boundary. (Thus $ds\,dz = dS_c$, an element of the cell wall, and $dx\,dy = dS_h$, the element of a horizontal surface.) dS denotes, indifferently, either dS_c or dS_h, and ν denotes the outward-drawn normal to dS, in a surface integration extending to the whole cell boundary. Suffixes 0 and 1 relate respectively to the lower and upper boundary.

In virtue of these relations, the result of the integration performed on (28) may be written as

$$\beta\sigma' I_1 + \beta\nu I_2 + \gamma\sigma I_3 + k\gamma I_4 = 0, \tag{29}$$

where

$$\left.\begin{aligned}
&I_1 \text{ stands for the integral } \iiint\left(\frac{\partial w}{\partial x}\frac{\partial w'}{\partial x} + \frac{\partial w}{\partial y}\frac{\partial w'}{\partial y} + \frac{\partial w}{\partial z}\frac{\partial w'}{\partial z}\right) d(\text{vol.}),\\
&I_2 \text{ stands for the integral } \iiint \nabla^2 w\, \nabla^2 w'\, d(\text{vol.}),\\
&I_3 \text{ stands for the integral } \iiint\left(\frac{\partial \theta}{\partial x}\frac{\partial \theta'}{\partial x} + \frac{\partial \theta}{\partial y}\frac{\partial \theta'}{\partial y}\right) d(\text{vol.}),\\
&I_4 \text{ stands for the integral } \iiint\left(\nabla_1^2\theta\, \nabla_1^2\theta' + \frac{\partial^2\theta}{\partial x\partial z}\frac{\partial^2\theta'}{\partial x\partial z} + \frac{\partial^2\theta}{\partial y\partial z}\frac{\partial^2\theta'}{\partial y\partial z}\right) d(\text{vol.}).
\end{aligned}\right\} \tag{30}$$

18. If we had started (§ 16) by cross-multiplication between the second of (25) and first of (27), the relation corresponding with (29) would have been

$$\beta\sigma I_1+\beta\nu I_2+\gamma\sigma' I_3+k\gamma I_4 = 0, \tag{31}$$

as is evident from the symmetry of the expressions (30). Now writing

$$\left.\begin{aligned}\sigma &= p+iq\\ \sigma' &= p-iq\end{aligned}\right\} \tag{32}$$

in accordance with § 16, we have by addition of (29) and (31)

$$p(\beta I_1+\gamma I_3)+\beta\nu I_2+k\gamma I_4 = 0,$$

and by subtraction

$$q(\gamma I_3-\beta I_1) = 0, \tag{33}$$

in which the I's are all positive according to (30), since every integrand consists of one or more products of conjugate complex quantities.

Since ν and k are positive by definition, the first of (33) shows that p will be negative (i.e. the time factor $\Phi(t)$ will be one of decay) unless $\beta\gamma$ is negative; and if $\beta\gamma$ is negative q must be zero according to the second of (33), i.e. $\Phi(t)$ must be exponential with real index pt. Consequently, while oscillatory motions are not excluded by this investigation, they are permitted only in circumstances making for stability, i.e. in which they decay. Whenever *maintained* convective motion is possible, σ in § 16 must be real: therefore limiting conditions of stability are in fact obtained (§ 4) when all time variations are made zero.

Critical conditions. The simplified equations

19. Accordingly we now proceed on the assumption that $\sigma \equiv \partial/\partial t$ is zero, so that (13) and (26) are replaced by

$$[k\nu\nabla^6+\beta\gamma\nabla_1^2]\,w = 0,$$

or

$$[k\nu(D^2-a^2)^3-\beta\gamma h^4a^2]\,w = 0 \tag{i}$$

according to (16), D denoting $\partial/\partial\zeta$ as in § 15. Similarly equation (14) is now replaced by

$$\nabla^2\nabla_1^2\psi = 0, \tag{14)A}$$

and (24) by

$$w = Dw = (D^2-a^2)^2\,w = 0. \tag{24)A}$$

For convenience we shall write (i) in the form

$$[(D^2-a^2)^3+\lambda^3a^6]\,w = 0, \tag{34}$$

where

$$\lambda^3 = -\frac{\beta\gamma h^4}{k\nu a^4}. \tag{35}$$

Our immediate problem is to relate λ with a and thereby to find the lowest value of the 'characteristic number' $-\beta\gamma h^4/k\nu$ for which steady slow motion can occur.

20. The symbol λ was used by Jeffreys to denote this characteristic number: Rayleigh, using γ and ν in their present connotation, writes β' for $-\beta$, ζ for h, κ for k. Following Rayleigh we may obtain a physical interpretation by writing $(\Theta_1-\Theta_0)/h$ for β, $g(\rho_1-\rho_0)/\rho_0(\Theta_0-\Theta_1)$ for γ, where Θ_1, ρ_1 and Θ_0, ρ_0, as in § 9, stand for the temperatures and densities in the initial (steady) regime at the top and bottom surfaces respectively. Then the characteristic number is given by

$$\lambda^3 a^4 = \frac{-\beta\gamma h^4}{k\nu} = \frac{gh^3}{k\nu}\,\frac{\rho_1-\rho_0}{\rho_0}, \tag{36}$$

in which $(\rho_1-\rho_0)/\rho_0$ is the fractional excess of density in the fluid at the top as compared with the fluid at the bottom (heated) surface. When α and therefore γ is negative, to maintain convective motion heat must be supplied at the top surface,* but the characteristic number will still be given by (36).

21. We have shown that λ^3 must be positive, since it was proved in § 18 that p must be negative unless $\beta\gamma$ is negative, and the other factors of λ^3 (namely, k, ν and h^4) are positive. Using (34) we can proceed further: for on multiplying that equation by $(D^2-a^2)^2 w$ and then integrating with respect to ζ in the range $0 \leqslant \zeta \leqslant 1$ (i.e. between the lower and upper horizontal surfaces) we have

$$\lambda^3 a^6 \int_0^1 w.(D^2-a^2)^2 w\, d\zeta = -\int_0^1 (D^2-a^2)^2 w.(D^2-a^2)^3 w\, d\zeta, \tag{i}$$

D standing for $\partial/\partial\zeta$ as before; also

$$\int_0^1 [w.(D^2-a^2)^2 w - \{(D^2-a^2)w\}^2]\, d\zeta = \Big[w.D(D^2-a^2)w - Dw.(D^2-a^2)w \Big]_0^1, \tag{ii}$$

$$\int_0^1 [(D^2-a^2)^2 w.(D^2-a^2)^3 w + \{D(D^2-a^2)^2 w\}^2 + a^2\{(D^2-a^2)^2 w\}^2]\, d\zeta$$
$$= \Big[(D^2-a^2)^2 w.D(D^2-a^2)^2 w \Big]_0^1, \tag{iii}$$

and the quantities on the right of (ii) and (iii) vanish at both limits, in virtue

* Cf. footnote to § 1.

either of the boundary conditions (23) or (24) A. Consequently (i) is equivalent to

$$\lambda^3 a^6 \int_0^1 \{(D^2-a^2)\,w\}^2\,d\zeta = \int_0^1 [\{D(D^2-a^2)^2\,w\}^2 + a^2\{(D^2-a^2)^2\,w\}^2]\,d\zeta, \quad (37)$$

and both integrals in this equation are positive.

Exact solutions of the simplified equations

22. Having shown that λ is positive, we may solve (34) symbolically in the form

$$D^2 \equiv a^2\{1-\lambda\times(\omega_1,\omega_2,\omega_3)\}, \quad (38)$$

where $\omega_1, \omega_2, \omega_3 = 1, \quad \dfrac{-1\pm i\sqrt{3}}{2}$

are the three cube roots of unity, so that (39)

$$\omega_2^2 = \omega_3, \quad \omega_3^2 = \omega_2.$$

The most general solution can then be written in the form

$$w = A_1 \cosh 2\mu_1\zeta + A_2 \cosh 2\mu_2\zeta + A_3 \cosh 2\mu_3\zeta + B_1 \sinh 2\mu_1\zeta + B_2 \sinh 2\mu_2\zeta + B_3 \sinh 2\mu_3\zeta, \quad (40)$$

where A_1, A_2, A_3, B_1, B_2, B_3 are arbitrary and $4\mu_1^2$, $4\mu_2^2$, $4\mu_3^2$ are the three values of D^2 as given by (38). There are six arbitrary constants, therefore three conditions can be satisfied at each of the horizontal boundaries; but except for particular values of λ the solution will be nugatory in that all six constants are zero.

For convenience we shall now change the origin of ζ so that the lower and upper boundaries are defined by $\zeta = -\frac{1}{2}$, $\zeta = +\frac{1}{2}$ and the range of ζ is $-1 \leqslant 2\zeta \leqslant 1$. Then in (40) we can separate 'even' and 'odd solutions' in the two symmetrical cases, viz.

(*a*) that of *two free surfaces* (Rayleigh's case: cf. § 6), in which the boundary conditions (23) must be satisfied when $2\zeta = \pm 1$,

(*b*) that of *two rigid boundaries*, in which the conditions (24) A must be satisfied when $2\zeta = \pm 1$.

In our third case (*c*) *one surface is free, the other constrained by a rigid boundary*, so (23) must be satisfied at one and (24) A at the other of the limits $2\zeta = \pm 1$. Here, by reason of the asymmetry, all six terms will appear in (40); but we shall find that in fact solutions for case (*c*) can be based on those for case (*b*).

Case (a). Two free surfaces.

23. The solution for this case is simple. The 'even' solutions are derived from

$$w = A_1 \cosh 2\mu_1\zeta + A_2 \cosh 2\mu_2\zeta + A_3 \cosh 2\mu_3\zeta, \tag{41}$$

where by (23), since $\mu_1 \neq \mu_2 \neq \mu_3$,

$$A_1 \cosh \mu_1 = A_2 \cosh \mu_2 = A_3 \cosh \mu_3 = 0.$$

Hence we have solutions typified by

$$w = A \cosh in\pi\zeta = A \cos n\pi\zeta, \tag{42}$$

A being arbitrary and n having any (non-zero) integral value; and on substituting from (42) in (34) we deduce that

$$\lambda^3 = \left(1+\frac{n^2\pi^2}{a^2}\right)^3. \tag{43}$$

The 'odd' solutions are found in the same way to be typified by

$$w = -iB \sinh 2im\pi\zeta = B \sin 2m\pi\zeta, \tag{44}$$

B being arbitrary and m having any (non-zero) integral value; and we have

$$\lambda^3 = \left(1+\frac{4m^2\pi^2}{a^2}\right)^3. \tag{45}$$

Case (b). Two rigid boundaries.

24. Here again even and odd solutions can be separated and the even solutions are given by

$$w = A_1 \cosh 2\mu_1\zeta + A_2 \cosh 2\mu_2\zeta + A_3 \cosh 2\mu_3\zeta, \qquad (41)\ bis$$

but now, since (24) A must be satisfied when $2\zeta = \pm 1$, we have

$$A_1 \cosh \mu_1 + A_2 \cosh \mu_2 + A_3 \cosh \mu_3 = 0,$$

$$\mu_1 A_1 \sinh \mu_1 + \mu_2 A_2 \sinh \mu_2 + \mu_3 A_3 \sinh \mu_3 = 0,$$

$$(4\mu_1^2 - a^2)^2 A_1 \cosh \mu_1 + (4\mu_2^2 - a^2)^2 A_2 \cosh \mu_2 + (4\mu_3^2 - a^2)^2 A_3 \cosh \mu_3 = 0,$$

showing that A_1, A_2, A_3 will vanish severally unless

$$\begin{vmatrix} \cosh \mu_1, & \cosh \mu_2, & \cosh \mu_3, \\ \mu_1 \sinh \mu_1, & \mu_2 \sinh \mu_2, & \mu_3 \sinh \mu_3, \\ \omega_1^2 \cosh \mu_1, & \omega_2^2 \cosh \mu_2, & \omega_3^2 \cosh \mu_3 \end{vmatrix} = 0. \tag{46}$$

(The third line of the determinant has been simplified after substitution for μ_1^2, μ_2^2, μ_3^2 in accordance with their definitions in § 22.)

ω_1^2, ω_2^2, ω_3^2 having the values (39), since μ_1, μ_2, μ_3 are non-zero an equivalent condition is

$$\begin{vmatrix} 1, & 1, & 1, \\ \mu_1 \tanh \mu_1, & \mu_2 \tanh \mu_2, & \mu_3 \tanh \mu_3, \\ 0, & \sqrt{3}+i, & \sqrt{3}-i \end{vmatrix} = 0,$$

i.e.
$$2i\mu_1 \tanh \mu_1 + (\sqrt{3}-i)\,\mu_2 \tanh \mu_2 - (\sqrt{3}+i)\,\mu_3 \tanh \mu_3 = 0. \tag{47}$$

25. Now writing

$$2\mu_2 = (A - iB)\,a, \quad 2\mu_3 = (A+iB)\,a,$$

we have from the definition of μ_2, μ_3 in § 22

$$A^2 - B^2 = 1 + \tfrac{1}{2}\lambda, \quad 2AB = \frac{\sqrt{3}}{2}\lambda, \tag{48}$$

and hence by elimination of λ

$$A^2 - B^2 - \frac{2}{\sqrt{3}}AB = 1.$$

Moreover we have

$$2\mu_1 = ia\sqrt{(\lambda-1)} = ia\sqrt{\{(B+\sqrt{3}A)^2 - 4A^2\}}, \tag{49}$$

so (47) can be written in the form

$$-\sqrt{(\lambda-1)}\tan \tfrac{1}{2}a\sqrt{(\lambda-1)} = \frac{(A+\sqrt{3}B)\sinh aA + (\sqrt{3}A - B)\sin aB}{\cosh aA + \cos aB}. \tag{50}$$

In exactly the same way, starting with an odd solution in the form

$$w = B_1 \sinh 2\mu_1\zeta + B_2 \sinh 2\mu_2\zeta + B_3 \sinh 2\mu_3\zeta, \tag{51}$$

we obtain a condition similar to (47) but with hyperbolic cotangents replacing the hyperbolic tangents. Making the substitutions (48) we can transform this to

$$\sqrt{(\lambda-1)}\cot \tfrac{1}{2}a\sqrt{(\lambda-1)} = \frac{(A+\sqrt{3}B)\sinh aA - (\sqrt{3}A - B)\sin aB}{\cosh aA - \cos aB}, \tag{52}$$

which is similar to (50).

26. Solutions of (50) and of (52) can be obtained by plotting curves to represent the quantities on their left- and right-hand sides. From (48) we have

$$(A+\sqrt{3}B)^2 = 4A^2 - 3,$$

whence (since λ and therefore AB must be positive)

$$\sqrt{3}B = \sqrt{(4A^2-3)} - A \quad \text{and} \quad A^2 > 1.$$

Then we have

$$A+\sqrt{3}B = \sqrt{(4A^2-3)}, \quad \sqrt{3}A - B = \frac{1}{\sqrt{3}}\{4A - \sqrt{(4A^2-3)}\}, \tag{53}$$

also $$\lambda - 1 = \frac{4AB}{\sqrt{3}} - 1 = \frac{4A}{3}\{\sqrt{(4A^2-3)} - A\} - 1,$$

by (48). Hence, giving A a series of values in excess of unity, we can calculate, once for all, corresponding values of the coefficients B, $(A+\sqrt{3}B)$, $(\sqrt{3}A - B)$ and $\sqrt{(\lambda-1)}$. The sign of A is immaterial provided that AB is kept positive.

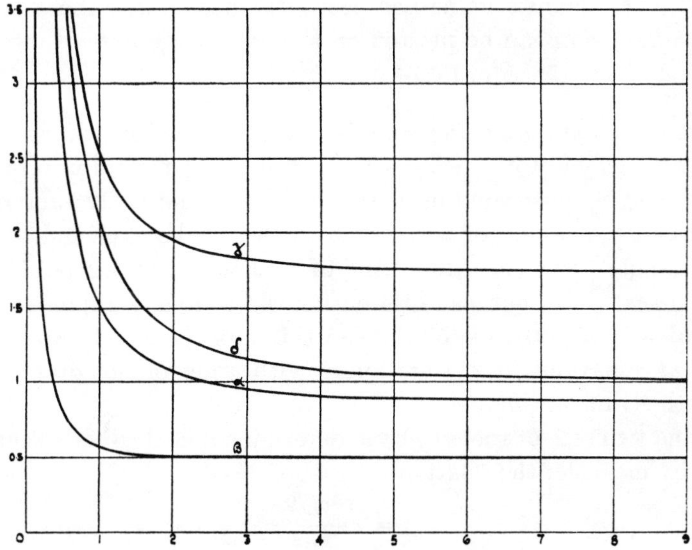

$\sqrt{(\lambda-1)} = 2x/a$

FIGURE 1

If now $2x$ stands for the quantity $a\sqrt{(\lambda-1)}$,

α stands for the ratio $A/\sqrt{(\lambda-1)}$,

β stands for the ratio $B/\sqrt{(\lambda-1)}$, (54)

γ stands for the ratio $(A+\sqrt{3}B/\sqrt{(\lambda-1)}$,

δ stands for the ratio $(\sqrt{3}A - B)/\sqrt{(\lambda-1)}$,

so that x, α, β, γ, δ now have new significance, these results may be recorded in the form of curves (figure 1) which present α, β, γ, δ as functions of

$\surd(\lambda - 1) = 2x/a$. Also equations (50) and (52) can be written in the equivalent forms

$$-\tan x = \frac{\gamma \sinh 2\alpha x + \delta \sin 2\beta x}{\cosh 2\alpha x + \cos 2\beta x} \tag{50)A}$$

and

$$\cot x = \frac{\gamma \sinh 2\alpha x - \delta \sin 2\beta x}{\cosh 2\alpha x - \cos 2\beta x}, \tag{52)A}$$

so can be solved with the aid of curves of $-\tan x$ and $\cot x$, drawn once for all on a base of x. Except when αx is small the expression on the right of either equation will be closely represented by

$$\gamma \tanh 2\alpha x \ (= \gamma, \text{ to six significant figures, when } \alpha x < 4),$$

and when some definite value has been attached to a, either this or the complete expression can be plotted on a base of x. Points of intersection will define roots of (50) A or (52) A.

27. Figure 2 exhibits some solutions obtained in this manner. First, two series of (asymptotic) curves for $-\tan x$ and for $\cot x$ were drawn; then curves of γ corresponding with $a = 2$, 3, 4 and 5. The intersections suggest restricted ranges of x in which roots may be expected to lie, and for those ranges curves of $-\tan x$ and of $\cot x$ were constructed to a much more open scale, also curves representing the complete expression on the right-hand side of (50) A or (52) A.* In this way roots of those equations, regarded as equations in x, were found with an error not greater than 1 in the sixth significant figure.

From the two sets of roots as thus determined, critical values of λ were deduced by means of the relation

$$\lambda = 1 + \frac{4x^2}{a^2}, \tag{55}$$

which is equivalent to the first of (54). Table 1 records the first three of these values as deduced from equation (50) A, table 2 the first three values as deduced from equation (52) A. The last three columns of each table record corresponding values of the 'characteristic number' of § 19, viz.

$$-\frac{\beta \gamma h^4}{k\nu} = \lambda^3 a^4. \tag{56}$$

Only five significant figures are given, since a fractional error of 10^{-6} in x would entail a fractional error of 6×10^{-6} in λ^3.

* For ranges in which $2\alpha x > 13$ the complete expressions on the right of (50) A and (52) A were found to agree with γ to six significant figures.

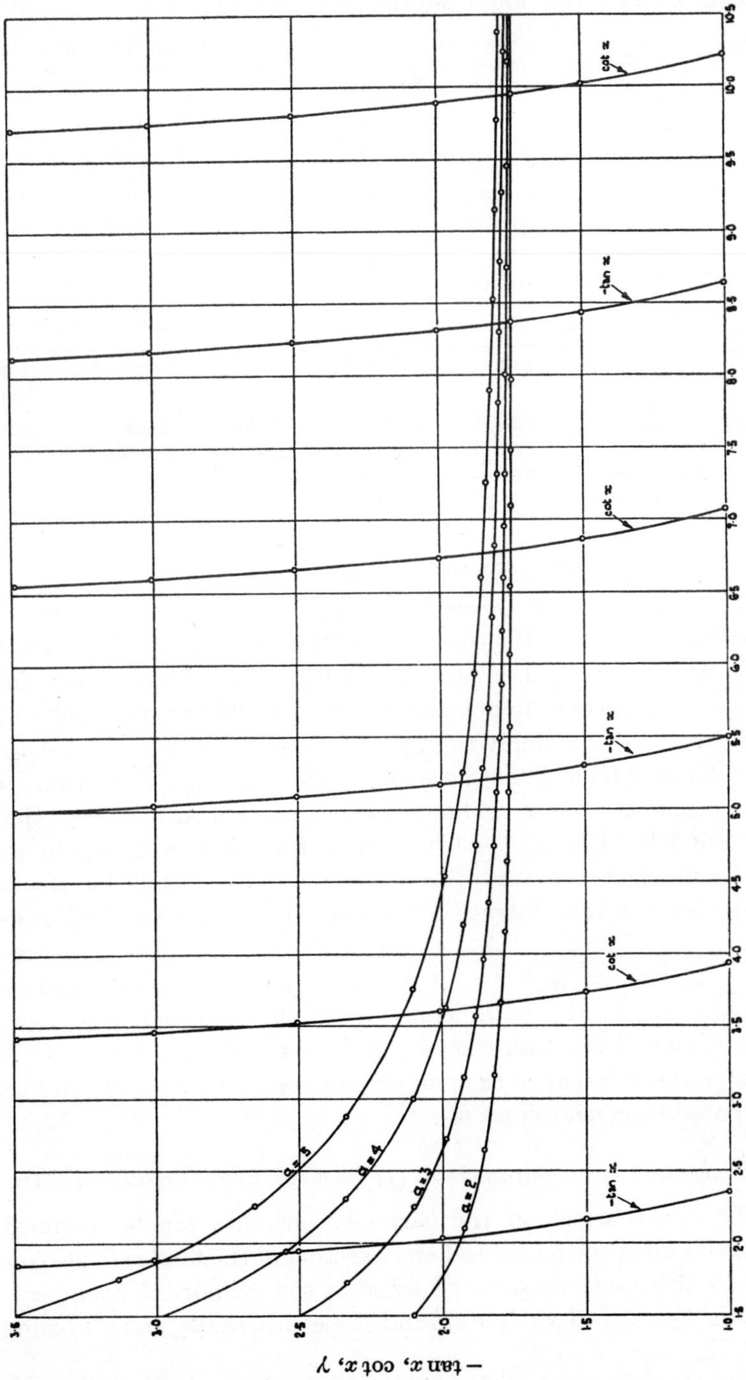

$x = \frac{1}{2}a\sqrt{(\lambda - 1)}$

FIGURE 2

TABLE 1. SYMMETRICAL MODES DEDUCED FROM EQUATION (50)

	λ			$-\beta\gamma h^4/k\nu = \lambda^3 a^4$		
	1st mode	2nd mode	3rd mode	1st mode	2nd mode 10 ×	3rd mode 100 ×
$a=2$	5·14367	28·3347	71·1343	2177·4	36398	57591
3	2·76447	13·1045	32·1418	1711·3	18228	26896
4	1·94349	7·77543	$18{\cdot}4953_5$	1879·3	12034	16197
5	1·57447	5·31047	12·1794	2439·4	93601	11292

TABLE 2. SKEW-SYMMETRICAL MODES DEDUCED FROM EQUATION (52)

	λ			$-\beta\gamma h^4/k\nu = \lambda^3 a^4$		
	1st mode	2nd mode	3rd mode	1st mode	2nd mode 10 ×	3rd mode 100 ×
$a=2$	14·3222	47·2691	99·9269	47006	168990	159650
3	6·85976	21·5295	44·9440	26146	80833	73536
4	4·25234	12·5214	25·6997	19684·5	50257	43453
5	3·04991	8·35258	16·7927	17731	36420	29597

Case (*c*). *One free surface, one rigid boundary.*

28. The 'odd' solutions in case (*b*) are expressions having the form of (51) which satisfy all three of the conditions (24) A when $2\zeta = \pm 1$. In addition, when $\zeta = 0$ they satisfy all three of the conditions (23), because then $\sinh \mu\zeta$, together with its second, fourth and all even derivatives, vanishes without restriction on μ. Accordingly from these odd solutions we can also deduce solutions for case (*c*) of § 22, where one of the horizontal surfaces is 'free', the other constrained by a rigid boundary. But whereas in case (*b*) the two surfaces are defined by $2\zeta = \pm 1$, in case (*c*) the origin of ζ must be in one surface, so the range is halved: this means that any odd solution of case (*b*) which applies to a cell of depth h will apply in case (*c*) to a cell of depth $h' = \frac{1}{2}h$.

Because the cell-depth h is related with a by (16), the other (horizontal) cell dimensions will also be different in case (*c*). We shall return to this question when we have dealt with the problem of affixing values to a. What matters for the moment is that no special consideration (on the lines of §§ 24–27) need be given to case (*d*).

Determination of the parameter a (1) *for a rigid cylindrical boundary*

29. The values which in any particular instance can be assumed by a will depend upon the depth and cross-section of the fluid cell, also on the condition which must be satisfied by w at the cylindrical boundary. In experiment the cell wall will be rigid and of specified shape, and the boundary

condition will be $w = 0$; then in the 'membrane analogy' (§ 13) the boundary lies in the cell wall and on it the transverse displacement must vanish. For any shape there will be an indefinite number of possible modes, each associated with some critical value of a: e.g. when the boundary is a circle of radius R the expression

$$w = A_n \cos(n\theta + \alpha_n) J_n(kr) \tag{57}$$

(A_n and α_n being arbitrary constants) will satisfy (16) if

$$k^2 = a^2/h^2, \tag{58}$$

and it will vanish at the boundary ($r = R$) provided that

$$J_n(kR) = 0. \tag{59}$$

The roots of (59) are known, and for each, using (58), we can calculate the corresponding value of a expressed as a fraction of h/R. Table 3 records, for $n = 0, 1, 2, 3$, the four lowest critical values of aR/h appropriate to a rigid circular cell wall. It is based on Table B of § 206 in Chap. IX of Lord Rayleigh's *Theory of Sound.*

TABLE 3. CRITICAL VALUES OF aR/h FOR CIRCULAR CELL

$n =$	0	1	2	3
First	2·404	3·832	5·135	6·379
Second	5·520	7·016	8·417	9·760
Third	8·654	10·173	11·620	13·017
Fourth	11·792	13·323	14·796	16·224

The result obtained in this instance, that a is proportional to the depth h divided by a length (R) which defines the size of the cell in plan, holds also in respect of other shapes and of other boundary conditions. Thus if the cell wall is a rigid square of side L, then a will be proportional to h/L.*

Determination of the parameter a (2) when the cylindrical boundary is a surface of symmetry

30. The boundary condition $$\frac{dw}{dn} = 0 \tag{18 bis}$$

must be satisfied at the cell wall when this is a surface of symmetry. Only three possibilities† demand attention, namely,

* Solutions appropriate to several shapes of boundary will be found in Chap. IX (on the Vibrations of Membranes) of Lord Rayleigh's *Theory of Sound.*

† I.e. of complete symmetry, which requires that n, the number of the sides, shall be expressible in the form $2 + 4/(N-2)$, N being integral.

(1) the boundary may be an equilateral triangle of side L,
(2) the boundary may be rectangular, of sides L_1 and L_2,
(3) the boundary may be a regular hexagon of side L,
and evidently the solutions in case (1) are included in those for case (3).

Case (2) is simple: for (18) will be satisfied (if the origin is taken at the centre of the rectangle) by

$$w = A_{mn} \cos\frac{m\pi x}{L_1} \cos\frac{n\pi y}{L_2} \tag{60}$$

(A_{mn} being constant) when m and n are *any even integers*; and this expression will also satisfy (16) provided that

$$a^2 = h^2\left(\frac{m^2}{L_1^2}+\frac{n^2}{L_2^2}\right). \tag{61}$$

The regular hexagon (case 3) has more interest in relation to our thermal problem, because it appears from Bénard's experiments (cf. § 5) that hexagonal cells characterize the permanent regime in a layer of unlimited extent. The necessity of approximate treatment in the manner of Rayleigh (§ 5) has been removed by the recent discovery of an exact solution (Christopherson 1940). The expression

$$w = \tfrac{1}{3}w_0\left\{\cos\frac{2n\pi}{3L}(\sqrt{3}x+y)+\cos\frac{2n\pi}{3L}(\sqrt{3}x-y)+\cos\frac{4n\pi y}{3L}\right\}, \tag{62}$$

or

$$\left.\begin{aligned} w = \tfrac{1}{3}w_0\Big\{&\cos\frac{2n\pi r}{3L}(\sqrt{3}\cos\theta+\sin\theta) \\ &+\cos\frac{2n\pi r}{3L}(\sqrt{3}\cos\theta-\sin\theta)+\cos\frac{4n\pi r}{3L}\sin\theta\Big\}, \\ \text{where} \quad & r\cos\theta = x, \quad r\sin\theta = y, \end{aligned}\right\} \tag{63}$$

is symmetrical with respect to the line $\theta = 0$, and it is not altered by an increase of θ to $\theta+\frac{1}{3}\pi$, therefore it is also symmetrical with respect to the lines $\theta = \frac{1}{3}\pi$, $\theta = \frac{2}{3}\pi$. Evidently w_0 is the value of w when $x = y = 0$, i.e. at the centre of the hexagon.

According to (62)

$$\begin{aligned} \frac{dw}{dn} &= \mp\frac{2n\pi}{3\sqrt{3}L}w_0\left\{\sin\frac{2n\pi}{3L}(\sqrt{3}x+y)+\sin\frac{2n\pi}{3L}(\sqrt{3}x-y)\right\} \\ &= -\frac{4n\pi}{3\sqrt{3}L}w_0\sin n\pi\cos\frac{2n\pi}{3L}y = 0 \text{ if } n \text{ is integral,} \end{aligned}$$

when $x = \pm\frac{\sqrt{3}}{2}L$. So when w is given by (62) then $dw/dn = 0$ (i.e. *the boundary condition is satisfied*) on the regular hexagon whose sides are defined by

$$\left(x \pm \frac{\sqrt{3}}{2}L\right)\left(\frac{x}{\sqrt{3}} + y \pm L\right)\left(\frac{x}{\sqrt{3}} - y + L\right) = 0 \tag{64}$$

and accordingly have length L. Moreover we have from (62)

$$\nabla_1^2 w = -\left(\frac{4n\pi}{3L}\right)^2 w,$$

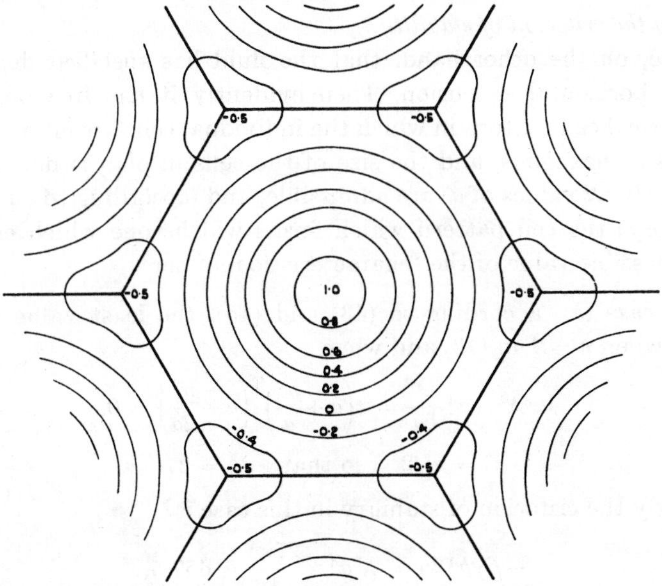

FIGURE 3

and this equation is equivalent to (16) when

$$\frac{aL}{h} = \frac{4n\pi}{3}, \tag{65}$$

n being integral. Accordingly for hexagonal surfaces of symmetry (65) gives the critical values of a.

Figure 3 shows the nature of this important solution, by curves representing contours of the ratio w/w_0.

The criterion of stability

31. In § 19 our problem was reduced to that of finding the least value of

$$-\beta\gamma h^4/k\nu = \lambda^3 a^4 \qquad (56)\ bis$$

for which, under particular conditions imposed at the horizontal surfaces, non-zero solutions of (34) exist, i.e. *steady* solutions of the governing equation (13). The criterion of thermal stability will be that $-\beta\gamma h^4/k\nu$ must not exceed this value.

When the cylindrical boundary is of specified shape and rigid (§ 29), a series of possible values can be attached to a, and hence a series of possible values of $\lambda^3 a^4$ can be determined with the aid of (43) and (45) in case (a) or of tables 1 and 2 in case (b). *The smallest value of $\lambda^3 a^4$ so found is to be inserted in the criterion of stability.*

Suppose, on the other hand, that the fluid has specified depth h but indefinite horizontal extension. Then evidently it has freedom to form a symmetrical cell pattern in which the individual cells are either triangles, rectangles or hexagons, and the size of the cells in plan is not restricted: consequently *all* values of a^2 are admissible, and (according to our approximate theory) the cell pattern which forms will be one which entails the smallest possible value of the 'characteristic number'.

32. In case (a), according to (43) and (45), the least value of $\lambda^3 a^4$ is obtained when $n = 1$ in (43) and when

$$4a^3\lambda^4 + a^4\frac{\partial\lambda^3}{\partial a} = 4\left(a + \frac{\pi^2}{a}\right)^2\left(a - \frac{\pi^2}{2a}\right) = 0,$$

i.e. when $a^2 = \pi^2/2$, so that $\lambda^3 = 27$.

Accordingly the criterion of stability in this case is*

$$-\beta\gamma h^4/k\nu = \lambda^3 a^4 \ngtr \frac{27\pi^4}{4} = 657{\cdot}5. \qquad (66)$$

In case (b), inspection of tables 1 and 2 (§ 27) shows that the smallest value of $\lambda^3 a^4$ corresponds (in column 4 of table 1) with a value of a in the neighbourhood of 3. A more detailed exploration led to results which are exhibited in figure 4: the least value of $\lambda^3 a^4$ is 1707·8, and it corresponds with a value of a in the neighbourhood of 3·13. Accordingly the criterion of stability in this case is

$$-\beta\gamma h^4/k\nu = \lambda^3 a^4 \ngtr 1707{\cdot}8, \qquad (67)$$

and if this limit is exceeded a cell pattern will form for which $a \approx 3{\cdot}13$.†

* Jeffreys (1926, § 4) and Low (1929, p. 181) both give the numerical value as 651.

† Jeffreys (1928, § 4) gives the figure 1709·5, corresponding with $a = 3{\cdot}17$. Low (1929, p. 188) obtained 1767, 1756, 1704·4 as successive approximations.

33. Case (c) has been noticed in § 28, where it was shown that any odd solution of case (b), applicable to a cell of depth h, also provides a solution of case (c), applicable to a cell of depth $h' = \frac{1}{2}h$. This means that the last three columns of table 2 record values of

$$-\frac{\beta\gamma h^4}{k} = -16\frac{\beta\gamma h'^4}{k\nu},$$

—that is, 16 times the characteristic number appropriate to case (c); also that the values of aR/h which are given in table 3, and the value given in (65) for aL/h, must now be interpreted as values of $aR/2h'$ and of $aL/2h'$ respectively. (Similarly in (61) h^2 must be replaced by $4h'^2$.)

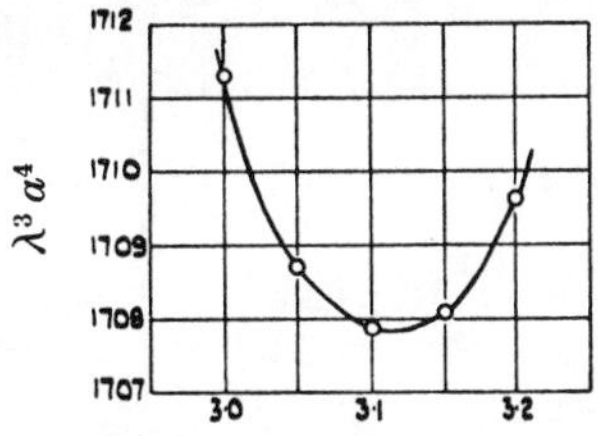

FIGURE 4

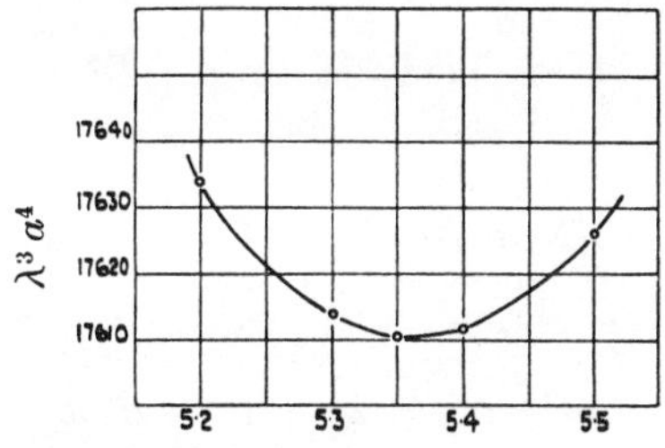

FIGURE 5

Calculations extending the range of table 2 (§ 27) showed that the smallest value assumed by $\lambda^3 a^4$ in relation to 'odd' modes corresponds with a value of a in the neighbourhood of 5, and a more detailed exploration gave results which are exhibited in figure 5 (corresponding with figure 4 for 'even' modes). The least value of $\lambda^3 a^4$ is 17610·5, and in relation to case (c), as we have just shown, this quantity stands for 16 times the characteristic number: consequently the criterion of stability in case (c) is*

$$\frac{-\beta\gamma h'^4}{k\nu} \not> \frac{17610 \cdot 5}{16} = 1100 \cdot 65, \tag{68}$$

and if this value is exceeded a cell-pattern will form for which a (*interpreted as above*) $\approx 5 \cdot 36$.

STATIONARY PROPERTY OF THE CHARACTERISTIC NUMBER

34. We now describe a method, analogous to the use of 'Rayleigh's principle' in vibration theory, which may be used as alternative to the exact treatment given above. It is based upon the integral equation (37) of § 21.

* Low (1929, p. 189) obtained 1180 as a first approximation.

Substituting in that equation the correct expression for w, we obtain the true value of λ^3 appropriate to the particular boundary conditions. When on the other hand w is replaced by $w+\delta w$, then the consequent alteration in λ^3 is given as concerns terms of the first order in δw by

$$\left.\begin{aligned} a^6\delta(\lambda^3) &= \frac{1}{(\text{Den.})}\left[\delta(\text{Num.})-\left(\frac{\text{Num.}}{\text{Den.}}\right)\delta(\text{Den.})\right] \\ &= \frac{1}{(\text{Den.})}[\delta(\text{Num.})-\lambda^3a^6\delta(\text{Den.})], \quad \text{by (37) again,} \\ \text{where} & \\ (\text{Num.}) \text{ stands for } & \int_0^1\{[D(D^2-a^2)^2w]^2+a^2[(D^2-a^2)^2w]^2\}\,d\zeta, \\ (\text{Den.}) \text{ stands for } & \int_0^1[(D^2-a^2)w]^2\,d\zeta, \\ \text{so that} & \\ \delta(\text{Num.}) &= 2\int_0^1\{[D(D^2-a^2)^2w][D(D^2-a^2)^2\delta w] \\ &\qquad +a^2[(D^2-a^2)^2w][(D^2-a^2)^2\delta w]\}\,d\zeta, \\ \delta(\text{Den.}) &= 2\int_0^1[(D^2-a^2)w][(D^2-a^2)\delta w]\,d\zeta. \end{aligned}\right\} \tag{69}$$

Integrating by parts, we may replace the last two of (69) by

$$\left.\begin{aligned} \delta(\text{Num.}) &= 2\left[\delta Z\frac{\partial Z}{\partial \zeta}\right]_0^1-2\int_0^1\delta Z.(D^2-a^2)Z\,d\zeta, \\ \delta(\text{Den.}) &= 2\left[\frac{\partial w}{\partial \zeta}(D^2-a^2)\delta w-w\frac{\partial}{\partial \zeta}(D^2-a^2)\delta w\right]_0^1+2\int_0^1 w\,\delta Z\,d\zeta, \\ \text{in which} \qquad & Z \text{ stands for } (D^2-a^2)^2w, \\ & \delta Z \text{ stands for } (D^2-a^2)^2\delta w, \end{aligned}\right\} \tag{70}$$

and then, if the limits of integration are the horizontal boundaries (at which either (23) or (24) A must be satisfied by w and therefore by δw), the first terms on the right of (70) vanish, leaving only the definite integrals. Consequently we may write the first of equations (69) as

$$a^6\delta(\lambda^3) = \frac{-2}{(\text{Den.})}\int_0^1\delta Z\{(D^2-a^2)Z+\lambda^3a^6w\}\,d\zeta,$$

and it follows that $\delta(\lambda^3)$ will vanish for all variations δZ, provided that *at every point in the fluid*

$$(D^2-a^2)Z+\lambda^3a^6w = (D^2-a^2)^3w+\lambda^3a^6w = 0, \qquad (34)\ \textit{bis}$$

as will be the fact when w is an exact solution.

We conclude that not only will λ^3 as calculated from (37) on the basis of an assumed form of w be exact, but it will moreover be stationary in respect of any small variations which are allowed by the boundary conditions, when the assumed form is correct. Consequently,

(*a*) any reasonably close approximation to the correct form for w will, when inserted in (37), lead to a very close estimate of λ^3,

(*b*) in regard to the smallest value of λ^3 an estimate obtained in this way will err, if at all, on the side of *excess*: that is to say, the limit of stability will be placed too high.

These conclusions hold in respect of all of our cases (*a*), (*b*) and (*c*), and without restriction on a, i.e. for all shapes of cylindrical boundary. Either of the conditions (23) or (24) A requires Z (and therefore δZ) to vanish; but between the boundaries δZ is unrestricted, since the solution of

$$(D^2-a^2)^2 w = Z \qquad (70)\ bis$$

can be made to satisfy one or other of the conditions

$$w = D^2 w = 0 \qquad (23)\ bis$$

or

$$w = Dw = 0 \qquad (24)\text{A}\ bis$$

at either boundary.

Application of the stationary property in case (b)

35. To apply the conclusion we assume a form for Z involving one or more arbitrary parameters; we deduce the corresponding form of w according to (70) and (23) or (24) A; and we then adjust the parameters so as to make the quantity

$$\frac{\int_0^1 \{(DZ)^2+a^2Z^2\}\,d\zeta}{a^2\int_0^1 \{(D^2-a^2)\,w\}^2\,d\zeta} = \lambda^3 a^4 \quad \text{according to (37)} \qquad (71)$$

as small as possible. What results will be a close but slightly excessive estimate of the characteristic number.

Suppose, for example, that the boundary conditions are those of case (*b*), that the origin is taken at the centre of the field, and that we are concerned with 'even' solutions (§ 24). Taking as the assumed form

$$Z = A(1+A_1\cos\pi\zeta+\cos 2\pi\zeta),$$

we obtain

$$w = A\left[\frac{1}{a^4}+\frac{A_1\cos\pi\zeta}{(\pi^2+a^2)^2}+\frac{\cos 2\pi\zeta}{(4\pi^2+a^2)^2}+Pa\cosh a\zeta+Qa^2\zeta\sinh a\zeta\right] \qquad (72)$$

as the solution of (70) which satisfies (24)A when $2\zeta = \pm 1$, P and Q being constants determined by the terminal conditions

$$\left.\begin{aligned} \frac{1}{a^4}-\frac{1}{(4\pi^2+a^2)^2}+Pa\cosh\frac{a}{2}+\tfrac{1}{2}Qa^2\sinh\frac{a}{2} &= \frac{w}{A} = 0,\\ -\frac{\pi A_1}{(\pi^2+a^2)^2}+Pa^2\sinh\frac{a}{2}+Qa^2\left(\sinh\frac{a}{2}+\frac{a}{2}\cosh\frac{a}{2}\right) &= \frac{Dw}{A} = 0.\end{aligned}\right\} \quad (73)$$

Then $\quad [D^2-a^2]\,w = -A\left(\frac{1}{a^2}+\frac{A_1\cos\pi\zeta}{\pi^2+a^2}+\frac{\cos 2\pi\zeta}{4\pi^2+a^2}-2a^3Q\cosh a\zeta\right),$

and it is easy to show that for the limits $2\zeta = \pm 1$

$$\int (DZ)^2\,d\zeta = \pi^2A^2\left(2+\frac{16}{3\pi}A_1+\frac{A_1^2}{2}\right),$$

$$a^2\int Z^2 d\zeta = a^2A^2\left(\frac{3}{2}+\frac{16}{3\pi}A_1+\frac{A_1^2}{2}\right),$$

$$\begin{aligned} a^2\int\{[D^2-a^2]\,w\}^2\,d\zeta = a^2A^2\Bigg\{&\frac{1}{a^4}-8Q\sinh\frac{a}{2}+2Q^2a^5(a+\sinh a)\\ &+\frac{A_1^2}{2(\pi^2+a^2)^2}+\frac{1}{2(4\pi^2+a^2)^2}+\frac{16A_1(3\pi^2+a^2)}{3\pi a^2(\pi^2+a^2)(4\pi^2+a^2)}\\ &-\frac{8\pi Qa^3}{(\pi^2+a^2)^2}A_1\cosh\frac{a}{2}+\frac{8Qa^4}{(4\pi^2+a^2)^2}\sinh\frac{a}{2}\Bigg\}.\end{aligned}$$

But from (73) we have (on elimination of P)

$$\tfrac{1}{2}Qa^2(a+\sinh a) = \frac{\pi A_1}{(\pi^2+a^2)^2}\cosh\frac{a}{2}+\frac{8\pi^2(2\pi^2+a^2)}{a^3(4\pi^2+a^2)^2}\sinh\frac{a}{2},$$

and on making use of this relation we find that

$$\begin{aligned} a^2&\int\{[D^2-a^2]\,w\}^2\,d\zeta\\ &= A^2\Bigg[\frac{1}{a^2}+\frac{a^2}{2(4\pi^2+a^2)^2}+\frac{A_1^2a^2}{2(\pi^2+a^2)^2}+\frac{16A_1(3\pi^2+a^2)}{3\pi(\pi^2+a^2)(4\pi^2+a^2)}\\ &\qquad-\frac{8a^3}{(a+\sinh a)}\left\{\frac{\pi A_1}{(\pi^2+a^2)^2}\cosh\frac{a}{2}+\frac{8\pi^2(2\pi^2+a^2)}{a^3(4\pi^2+a^2)^2}\sinh\frac{a}{2}\right\}^2\Bigg].\end{aligned}$$

Now, for any assumed value of a, we can deduce from (71) an expression of the form

$$\lambda^3a^4 = \frac{f+gA_1+hA_1^2}{l+mA_1+nA_1^2}, \quad (74)$$

in which f, g, h, l, m, n, are known numerical coefficients; and then the condition that $\lambda^3 a^4$ shall be stationary in respect of A_1 yields the quadratic equation

$$gl - mf + 2(hl - fn)\,A_1 + (hm - gn)\,A_1^2 = 0,$$

from which A_1 can be calculated and inserted in (74).

36. In this way values were obtained as under for comparison with the 'exact' values given in table 1 (§ 27):

TABLE 4

	$-\beta\gamma h^4/k = \lambda^3 a^4$	
	'Exact' values (table 1)	Values by approximate method
$a = 2$	2177·4	2177·6
3	1711·3	1711·4
4	1879·3	$1879{\cdot}3_5$
5	2439·4	2439·4

The accuracy of the approximate method is remarkable.

COMPLETION OF THE SOLUTION

37. It remains to complete the solution of the simplified equations of small motion (§ 19) when w has been determined in the form $f(x, y) \,.\, F(z)$, $\Phi(t)$ in § 13 now having a constant value since all time variations are assumed to vanish (§ 18). $f(x, y)$ is a solution of equation (16) which satisfies the boundary condition (18) or (19).

On this understanding we have from (12) as simplified

$$\gamma \nabla_1^2 \theta = -\nu \nabla^4 w = \nu \frac{h^2}{a^2} \nabla_1^2 \nabla^4 w \text{ by (16)},$$

and it follows that

$$\gamma\theta = \nu \frac{h^2}{a^2} \nabla^4 w + \chi, \quad \text{where} \quad \nabla_1^2 \chi = 0. \qquad \text{(i)}$$

Then according to (9) as simplified we have

$$\beta\gamma w = k\gamma \nabla^2 \theta = \nu k \frac{h^2}{a^2} \nabla^6 w + k \frac{\partial^2 \chi}{\partial z^2},$$

$$= -\beta\gamma \frac{h^2}{a^2} \nabla_1^2 w + k \frac{\partial^2 \chi}{\partial z^2}, \quad \text{by (13) as simplified,}$$

$$= \beta\gamma w + k \frac{\partial^2 \chi}{\partial z^2}, \quad \text{by (16) again.}$$

Consequently χ is linear in respect of z; and because at both horizontal surfaces, by (21) or (22) combined with (12),

$$\theta = 0 \quad \text{and} \quad \nabla^4 w = 0, \quad \text{therefore } \chi = 0 \text{ by (i)},$$

it follows that χ is zero everywhere, so that (i) may be replaced by

$$\gamma\theta = \nu\frac{h^2}{a^2}\nabla^4 w, \tag{ii}$$

$$= -\gamma\frac{h^2}{a^2}\nabla_1^2\theta \quad \text{according to (12).}$$

This means that if equation (16) is satisfied by w, θ will satisfy an equation of identical form: therefore for a particular value of a it will not (in general) be possible to satisfy simultaneously both of the boundary conditions (19). We can on the other hand satisfy both of (18), since according to (ii) and (16) we have

$$\gamma\theta = \frac{\nu}{h^2a^2}(D^2 - a^2)^2 w, \tag{75}$$

and when θ is calculated from this expression, on the cylindrical boundary $\partial\theta/\partial n$ will vanish with $\partial w/\partial n$.

We conclude from this investigation that the case of a rigid non-conducting boundary (§§ 1, 14) is not tractable on the basis of a separation of the variables (§ 13). When the cell wall is a surface of symmetry (§ 1), θ comes quite simply from (75).

38. Finally we have to calculate u and v in the case which has been shown to be tractable. When w satisfies (16), we have according to (15)

$$\phi = -\frac{h^2}{a^2}\frac{\partial w}{\partial z} + \phi', \tag{76}$$

ϕ' denoting a plane-harmonic function of x and y. Now at the cylindrical boundary, if this is a surface of symmetry, u and v must satisfy the condition

$$0 = u\cos(x, n) + v\cos(y, n),$$

$$= -\frac{\partial\phi}{\partial n} - \frac{\partial\psi}{\partial s} \quad \text{according to the first and second of (14),}$$

where according to the third of (14), since the motion is steady,

$$\nabla^2\nabla_1^2\psi = 0.$$

We shall satisfy both conditions if ψ = constant and if $\partial\phi/\partial n$ vanishes at every point in the boundary; and when $\partial w/\partial n = 0$ at the boundary, according to (76) this last condition requires that

$$\phi' = \text{const.}$$

Then we have from (14) and (76)

$$u = \frac{h^2}{a^2}\frac{\partial^2 w}{\partial z \partial x}, \quad v = \frac{h^2}{a^2}\frac{\partial^2 w}{\partial y \partial z}. \tag{77}$$

References

Bénard, H. 1900 *Rev. Gén. Sci. Pur. Appl.* **12**, 1261, 1309.
— 1901 *Ann. Chim. Phys.* **23**, 62.
Christopherson, D. G. 1940 *Quart. J. Math.* **11**, 63–65.
Jeffreys, H. 1926 *Phil. Mag.* **2**, 833–844.
— 1928 *Proc. Roy. Soc.* A, **118**, 195–208.
Lamb, H. 1924 *Hydrodynamics*, 5th ed. Camb. Univ. Press.
Low, A. R. 1929 *Proc. Roy. Soc.* A, **125**, 180–195.
— 1930 *Proc. 3rd Int. Congr. Appl. Mech.* (*Stockholm*).
Rayleigh, Lord 1916 *Phil. Mag.* **32**, 529–546. (Reprinted in *Collected Papers*, **6**, 432–436.)

II. Effects of Rotation

Reprinted from *Proceedings of the Royal Society*, Series A, Vol. 93, Mar. 1, 1917.

Motion of Solids in Fluids when the Flow is not Irrotational.

By G. I. Taylor, M.A.

(Communicated by Prof. H. Lamb, F.R.S. Received April 13, 1916.)

The chief interest in the results obtained in the following pages lies in the fact that a mathematical result has been obtained concerning the motion of solids in fluids which is verified accurately when recourse is had to experiment, with real solids moving in real fluids. This is so exceptional a circumstance that it is hoped that the interest which it gives to the mathematical work will serve to extenuate, to a certain extent, the clumsiness of the methods employed.

The problem solved is two-dimensional. An infinite cylindrical body of any cross-section moves in a uniformly rotating fluid with its generators parallel to the axis of rotation. The stream lines and the reaction between the solid and the fluid are found.

Suppose that a stream function ψ' has been found which represents the irrotational motion of an incompressible fluid when a cylindrical solid (or several cylindrical solids) of the required cross-section is moved in an assigned manner starting from rest in a fluid which has a given boundary or has a given irrotational motion at infinity. ψ' is a function of x and y, the co-ordinates of a point in a plane perpendicular to the axis of rotation, and o t, the time.

Since the motion is irrotational ψ' satisfies the relation $\nabla^2\psi' = 0$ everywhere, and $-\partial\psi'/\partial s = V_n'$ at the solid boundaries, where V_n' represents the velocity normal to the boundary of a point on the surface of a cylindrical solid moving in the fluid, and $\partial\psi'/\partial s$ represents the rate of change in ψ' measured in a direction along the solid boundary. These, together with the conditions at infinity, if the fluid is unenclosed, are the necessary and sufficient conditions for determining ψ'. The components of velocity of the fluid are then

$$u' = -\partial\psi'/\partial y \quad \text{and} \quad v' = \partial\psi'/\partial x.$$

Now consider the function

$$\psi = \psi' + \tfrac{1}{2}\omega(x^2+y^2), \tag{1}$$

where ω is a constant both in regard to space and to time. It satisfies the dynamical equations of motion, $D/Dt(\nabla^2\psi) = 0$ for $\nabla^2\psi = 2\omega$, which is constant; and it is the stream function of the fluid motion obtained when the whole system represented by ψ' is rotated with uniform angular velocity ω

about the origin. The boundary conditions of the rotating system are evidently satisfied if the cylindrical solids move relative to the rotating system in the same way that they moved relative to fixed axes in the case of the motion represented by ψ'. Hence it appears that the system consisting of the cylindrical solids and the fluid in which they move may be rotated uniformly without affecting the motion of the fluid relative to the rotating system, provided the cylinders are constrained to move, relative to the rotating system, in the same way that they moved, relative to fixed axes, when the system was not rotating.* If, however, the solids are free to move under the action of their own inertia and of the pressure of the fluid, the rotation will make a considerable difference to the relative motion of the solids and the fluid. It therefore becomes important to find the pressure at any point.

Let p' be the pressure at the point (x, y) in the irrotational case, and let p be the pressure when the whole system is rotated.

The equations for p and p' are

$$\left.\begin{aligned} -\frac{1}{\rho}\frac{\partial p'}{\partial x} &= \frac{\partial u'}{\partial t} + u'\frac{\partial u'}{\partial x} + v'\frac{\partial u'}{\partial y} \\ -\frac{1}{\rho}\frac{\partial p'}{\partial y} &= \frac{\partial v'}{\partial t} + u'\frac{\partial v'}{\partial x} + v'\frac{\partial v'}{\partial y} \end{aligned}\right\}, \tag{2}$$

$$\left.\begin{aligned} -\frac{1}{\rho}\frac{\partial p}{\partial x} &= \frac{\delta u}{\delta t} + u\frac{\partial u}{\partial x} + v\frac{\partial u}{\partial y} \\ -\frac{1}{\rho}\frac{\partial p}{\partial y} &= \frac{\delta v}{\delta t} + u\frac{\partial v}{\partial x} + v\frac{\partial v}{\partial y} \end{aligned}\right\}, \tag{3}$$

where u and v are the components of velocity in the rotational motion.

The symbol $\delta u/\delta t$ has been used to represent the rate of change, at a point fixed in space, in the component of velocity parallel to a fixed direction which momentarily coincides with the axis of x.

This is not the same thing as $\partial u/\partial t$. Since u may be regarded as being known in terms of the co-ordinates (x and y), referred to rotating axes, and t the time, $\partial u/\partial t$ represents the rate of change in the component of the velocity of the fluid which is parallel to the rotating axis of x at a point which moves with the axes. It is evident that $\partial u/\partial t = \partial u'/\partial t$ and $\partial v/\partial t = \partial v'/\partial t$.

To find the value of $\delta u/\delta t$ and $\delta v/\delta t$, consider the rate of change, at a point fixed in space, in the component of velocity parallel to a fixed direction which momentarily makes an angle β with the axis of x.

* It will be shown later that this proposition cannot be extended to the case of the three-dimensional motion.

The component of the velocity of the fluid parallel to this direction is $u\cos\beta+v\sin\beta$.

After a short interval of time, δt, the co-ordinates of the fixed point relative to the moving axes are

$$x+\omega y\,\delta t \quad\text{and}\quad y-\omega x\,\delta t.$$

The components of velocity parallel to the rotating axes (which now make an angle $\omega\delta t$ with their previous positions) are

$$u+\left(\frac{\partial u}{\partial t}+\omega y\frac{\partial u}{\partial x}-\omega x\frac{\partial u}{\partial y}\right)\delta t \quad\text{and}\quad v+\left(\frac{\partial v}{\partial t}+\omega y\frac{\partial v}{\partial x}-\omega x\frac{\partial v}{\partial y}\right)\delta t.$$

The component of velocity parallel to the fixed direction is therefore

$$\left[u+\left(\frac{\partial u}{\partial t}+\omega y\frac{\partial u}{\partial x}-\omega x\frac{\partial u}{\partial y}\right)\delta t\right]\cos(\beta-\omega\delta t)$$
$$+\left[v+\left(\frac{\partial v}{\partial t}+\omega y\frac{\partial v}{\partial x}-\omega x\frac{\partial v}{\partial y}\right)\delta t\right]\sin(\beta-\omega\delta t).$$

The rate of change in velocity parallel to the fixed direction is therefore

$$\left(\frac{\partial u}{\partial t}+\omega y\frac{\partial u}{\partial x}-\omega x\frac{\partial u}{\partial y}-\omega v\right)\cos\beta+\left(\frac{\partial v}{\partial t}+\omega y\frac{\partial v}{\partial x}-\omega x\frac{\partial v}{\partial y}+\omega u\right)\sin\beta.$$

Putting $\beta=0$ we find

$$\frac{\delta u}{\delta t}=\frac{\partial u}{\partial t}+\omega y\frac{\partial u}{\partial x}-\omega x\frac{\partial u}{\partial y}-\omega v$$

and putting $\beta=\tfrac{1}{2}\pi$,

$$\frac{\delta v}{\delta t}=\frac{\partial v}{\partial t}+\omega y\frac{\partial v}{\partial x}-\omega x\frac{\partial v}{\partial y}+\omega u.$$

Substituting these values in (3), subtracting equations (2) and substituting for u and v, it will be found that

$$-\frac{1}{\rho}\frac{\partial}{\partial x}(p-p')=-\omega^2x-2\omega v' \quad\text{and}\quad -\frac{1}{\rho}\frac{\partial}{\partial y}(p-p')=-\omega^2y+2\omega u'.$$

These equations may be integrated in the form

$$(p-p')/\rho=\tfrac{1}{2}\omega^2(x^2+y^2)+2\omega\psi'. \qquad (4)$$

At this stage it is easy to prove that the proposition proved on p. 100 cannot be extended to the case of three-dimensional motion.

Let u', v', w' be the components of the velocity of a fluid in irrotational motion. Suppose that the motion defined by

$$u=u'-\omega y, \qquad v=v'+\omega y, \qquad w=w',$$

is possible.

Proceeding as before, it will be found that the pressure equations can be reduced to

$$-\frac{1}{\rho}\frac{\partial}{\partial x}(p-p') = -\omega^2 x - 2\omega v',$$

$$-\frac{1}{\rho}\frac{\partial}{\partial y}(p-p') = -\omega^2 y + 2\omega u',$$

$$-\frac{1}{\rho}\frac{\partial}{\partial z}(p-p') = 0.$$

These are not consistent unless u' and v' are independent of z; that is, unless the motion is two-dimensional.

Let us now apply (4) to find the resultant force and couple which the fluid pressure exerts on a solid moving in a rotating fluid.

Let F_x', F_y', and G' be the resultant forces and couple due to fluid pressure on the solid in the case when the system is not rotating. F_x' and F_y' are supposed to act at the centre of gravity C of the area of the cross-section of the solid. Let F_x, F_y, and G be the corresponding quantities in the case when the system is rotating.

If χ represents the angle between the normal to the surface of the solid and the axis of x, then

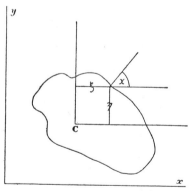

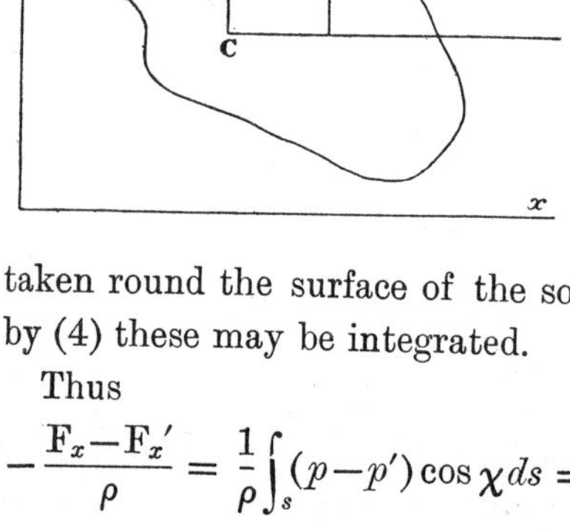

$$F_x - F_x' = -\int (p-p')\cos\chi\, ds,$$

$$F_y - F_y' = -\int_s (p-p')\sin\chi\, ds,$$

$$G - G' = \int_s (p-p')(\eta\cos\chi - \xi\sin\chi)\, ds,$$

where ξ and η are the co-ordinates of a point on the surface referred to axes parallel to the axes of x and y, and passing through C; and the integrals are taken round the surface of the solid. Substituting the value of $p-p'$ given by (4) these may be integrated.

Thus

$$-\frac{F_x - F_x'}{\rho} = \frac{1}{\rho}\int_s (p-p')\cos\chi\, ds = \frac{\omega^2}{2}\int (x^2+y^2)\cos\chi\, ds + 2\omega\int \psi'\cos\chi\, ds. \quad (5)$$

Now $\int_s y^2 \cos\chi\, ds$ vanishes since $\cos\chi\, ds = dy$. Also $\frac{\omega^2}{2}\int_s x^2\cos\chi\, ds = \omega^2 A x_0$, where A is the area of cross-section of the solid, and (x_0, y_0) are the co-ordinates of its centroid.

$2\omega\int_s \psi' \cos\chi ds$ may be integrated by parts. It then becomes

$$-2\omega\int_s y\frac{d\psi'}{ds}ds = -2\omega\int_s (y_0+\eta)\frac{d\psi'}{ds}ds = -2\omega\int_s \eta\frac{d\psi'}{ds}ds, \qquad (6)$$

since $\int_s y_0 \frac{d\psi'}{ds} ds$ evidently vanishes.

Now $-\partial\psi'/\partial s$ represents the velocity of the fluid normal to the surface of the solid. The boundary condition which must be satisfied by ψ' is

$$-\partial\psi'/\partial s = (\dot{x}_0 - \Omega\eta)\cos\chi + (\dot{y}_0+\Omega\xi)\sin\chi,$$

where Ω is the angular velocity of the body.

Substituting in (6) and remembering that $\cos\chi ds = d\eta$ and $\sin\chi\, ds = -d\xi$, it will be found that

$$2\omega\int_s \psi'\cos\chi ds = 2\omega\int_s \eta(\dot{x}_0-\Omega\eta)\,d\eta - 2\omega\int_s(\dot{y}_0+\Omega\xi)\,\eta\, d\xi.$$

The first of these integrals vanishes and the second may be written

$$-2\omega\dot{y}_0\int_s \eta d\xi - 2\omega\Omega\int_s \eta\xi d\xi,$$

Now $\int_s \eta d\xi = -\mathrm{A}$ and $\int_s \eta\xi d\xi = 0$, since C is the centroid of the area of cross-section.

Hence from (5) $\quad -(\mathrm{F}_x - \mathrm{F}_x')/\rho = \omega^2\mathrm{A}x_0 + 2\omega\mathrm{A}\dot{y}_0.$

Similarly it will be found that

$$-(\mathrm{F}_y - \mathrm{F}_y')/\rho = \omega^2\mathrm{A}y_0 - 2\omega\mathrm{A}\dot{x}_0.$$

It will be noticed that $\omega^2\mathrm{A}x_0$ and $\omega^2\mathrm{A}y_0$ are the components of a force $\omega^2\mathrm{AR}$ acting radially, R being the distance of C from the centre of rotation. Also $2\omega\mathrm{A}\dot{y}_0$ and $-2\omega\mathrm{A}\dot{x}_0$ are the components of a force $2\omega\mathrm{AQ}$ acting at right angles to the direction of motion of C relative to the rotating axes, Q being the relative velocity of C.

Now consider the couple $\mathrm{G}-\mathrm{G}'$ due to the rotation

$$\frac{\mathrm{G}-\mathrm{G}'}{\rho} = \int_s \frac{p-p'}{\rho}(\eta d\eta + \xi d\xi).$$

Substituting from (4),

$$\mathrm{G}-\mathrm{G}' = \frac{\omega^2}{2}\int_s \{(x_0+\xi)^2+(y_0+\eta)^2\}(\eta d\eta+\xi d\xi) + 2\omega\int_s \psi'(\eta d\eta + \xi d\xi).$$

Neglecting all terms which contain only powers of ξ or of η* and integrating the second integral by parts, this becomes

$$\frac{G-G'}{\rho} = \frac{\omega^2}{2}\left[2x_0\int_s \xi\eta\,d\eta + 2y_0\int_s \eta\xi\,d\xi + \int_s \xi^2\eta\,d\eta + \int_s \eta^2\xi\,d\xi\right]$$

$$-2\omega\int\frac{\xi^2+\eta^2}{2}\frac{d\psi'}{ds}\,ds.$$

Now $$\int_s \xi\eta\,d\eta = \int_s \eta\xi\,d\xi = 0,$$

and $$\int_s \xi^2\eta\,d\eta + \int_s \eta^2\xi\,d\xi = \tfrac{1}{2}\int_s d(\xi^2\eta^2) = 0;$$

also since $$-(\partial\psi'/\partial s)\,ds = (\dot{x}_0 - \Omega\eta)\,d\eta + (\dot{y}_0 + \Omega\xi)\,d\xi,$$

$(G-G')/\rho$ reduces to

$$2\omega\left[\dot{x}_0\int_s \tfrac{1}{2}\xi^2 d\eta - \dot{y}_0\int_s \tfrac{1}{2}\eta^2 d\xi - \Omega\int_s \xi^2\eta\,d\eta - \Omega\int_s \eta^2\xi\,d\xi\right] = 0.$$

The forces due to fluid pressure, which act on a body moving in an assigned manner in a rotating fluid, may therefore be regarded as being made up as follows:—

(1) The forces F_x', F_y', and the couple G′ which would act on the body if it moved in the same way relatively to the fluid at rest.

(2) A force equivalent to $\rho\omega^2$AR acting towards the centre of rotation through C.

(3) A force $2\rho\omega$AQ acting at C in a direction perpendicular to the relative motion of C and the rotating axes, and directed to the left if the rotation of the fluid is anti-clockwise.

We can therefore solve any problem on the motion of cylindrical solids in a rotating fluid if we can obtain a solution of a similar problem respecting the motion of the solids in a fluid at rest.

Now, consider the forces and the couple which it is necessary to apply to a solid body of mass M, in order that it may move in an assigned manner relatively to rotating axes. Suppose that a force F′ and a couple G′ must be applied at its centre of gravity, in order that it may move in the assigned manner relatively to fixed axes. The additional force which it is necessary to apply when the system is rotating uniformly with angular velocity ω may be shown to consist of a force $2M\omega Q$ perpendicular to the direction of the velocity Q of the centre of gravity relative to the rotating system, together with a force $M\omega^2R$ acting through the centre of gravity towards the centre of rotation.

* For they vanish when integrated round a closed contour.

It will be noticed that, if the position of the centre of gravity of the solid coincides with the centroid of its cross-section, and if the mass per unit length of the solid is equal to ρA, that is to say, if the mass and the centre of gravity of the solid are the same as those of the fluid displaced, then these forces are the same as those which act on the solid, owing to the additional pressures in the fluid due to its rotation.

These considerations lead to the conclusion that, if a solid of the same density as the fluid be moved along a certain path by certain assigned external forces, then a uniform rotation of the whole system, including the external force, makes no difference to the path which the solid pursues relative to the system.

This theorem applies only to the case of two-dimensional motion. In the case of a finite cylinder, for instance, it seems almost obvious that the pressures due to the rotation must fall off towards its ends. It is natural to suppose, therefore, that the reaction of the fluid would not be sufficient to hold a finite cylinder in its path when the whole system is rotated.

The case of a sphere moving in a rotating fluid presents considerable mathematical difficulties, but the initial motion has been investigated by Mr. J. Proudman, who has kindly consented to allow the author to make use of his results, though they are not yet published.* He finds that, if a sphere of volume V starts from rest in the rotating fluid and moves with uniform velocity along a straight line relative to the rotating system, it is acted on initially by a force $V\rho\omega^2R$ directed towards the centre of the rotation (which is at a distance R from the centre of the sphere) and by a force $\frac{1}{2}V\rho Q\omega$ acting in a direction perpendicular to its path. But in order that a sphere of the same density as the fluid, that is, one whose mass is $V\rho$, may move along a straight path relative to the rotating system, it must be acted on by a force $V\rho\omega^2R$ directed towards the centre of rotation and by a force $2V\rho\omega Q$ perpendicular to its path.

The forces due to fluid pressure are not sufficient to supply the second of these. If, therefore, the sphere were drawn through the rotating fluid by means of a string, it would not move in the direction the string was pulling it, but would be deflected to the left if the fluid were rotating clockwise, and to the right if were rotating anticlockwise. On the other hand, if a cylinder of the same density were drawn through the rotating fluid, the force necessary to hold it in its straight path would be supplied by the fluid pressure. The cylinder would therefore move straight through the fluid in the direction the string was pulling it.

* Since the above was written Mr. Proudman has published his results. They appeared in 'Roy. Soc. Proc.,' A, vol. 92, pp. 408–424 (1916).

These conclusions have been tested and completely verified by means of experiments made by the author in the Cavendish Laboratory with water in a rotating tank.

Experiments made with a Rotating Tank of Water.

A glass tank full of water was mounted so that it could be rotated about a vertical axis at various speeds by means of an electric motor. The speeds varied from 2 to 6 seconds per revolution. Two bodies were prepared, one cylindrical and the other spherical. The former consisted of a piece of thin-walled brass tube about 6 in. × $\frac{3}{4}$ in. stopped at the end with waxed cork, while the other was a spherical glass bulb. They were weighted until they would fall very slowly through water, and the positions of the weights were adjusted till they would stay almost at rest in any position in the water. The centres of gravity of the bodies were then coincident with the centres of gravity of the water displaced by them.

A simple mechanism was next devised to tow them through the tank from one end to the other. It consisted of a wood pulley about 4 inches in diameter, mounted on a vertical spindle which was driven into a wood bridge, fixed to the tank over the middle of it. This spindle coincided with the axis of rotation of the tank. Cotton was then wound round the pulley, passed through some small rings screwed into a board fixed to one end of the tank, and led horizontally along the tank to the cylinder or sphere, which was fixed at the other end.

The body was held in a holder while the tank and water were being brought to a state of uniform rotation. A device was arranged so that the holder could release the body and at the same moment the wood pulley on which the cotton was wound could be fixed in space. As the tank was then rotating round the pulley the cotton wound up round it, and pulled the bodies along the middle of the tank from one end to the other.

Result.—It was found that the cylinder moved straight through the middle of the tank. Even when the tank was rotating very rapidly the cylinder always passed over the central line. The sphere, however, was violently deviated to the left (the tank was rotating clockwise). When the tank was rotated quite slowly, about once in 6 seconds, the sphere would not quite touch the side, though it never came up to the stop at the other end from a direction less than 45° away from the central line. When the tank rotated more rapidly the complete path could never be seen, because the sphere always hit the side of the tank before it had gone more than a few inches in the direction along which the cotton was trying to pull it. After striking the side of the tank the sphere would follow the side along, touching all the time, till it got to a position close to the other end where the string was pulling in a direction making an angle of about 50° with the side of the tank. It would leave the side and approach the point towards which the cotton was pulling it along a curved path.

The accuracy with which the experiments just described verify the hydrodynamical theory of rotating fluids is at first sight most surprising. Besides the fact that there is apparently no other case in which experiments made with real solids moving in real fluids agree with the predictions of hydrodynamics, it is known that the stream lines of a real fluid round a circular cylinder in particular bear no resemblance to the stream lines used in the ordinary hydrodynamical theory. It will be noticed, however, that in order that there may be agreement between theory and experiment in the particular respect to which attention has been drawn, it is unnecessary that the actual flow pattern shall be the same as the flow pattern contemplated in the ordinary hydrodynamical theory. All that is necessary is that the flow pattern in the case of the cylinder shall be two-dimensional, while that in the case of the sphere shall be three-dimensional.

Experiments with Vortex Rings in a Rotating Fluid.

The theory explained on p. 105 leads to the conclusion that if a homogeneous solid, which is not cylindrical, be projected in a rotating fluid of the same density as itself it will be deviated, to the left if the rotation is clockwise, and to the right if the rotation is anti-clockwise, of the path it would pursue through the fluid if the whole system were not rotating. Now, a vortex ring affects the fluid round it in much the same way as a solid ring of the same dimensions as the cyclic portion of the flow system. If it is projected through a fluid at rest it travels along a straight line. We should expect, therefore, that if a vortex ring were projected through a rotating fluid it would follow a curved path relative to the fluid, being deviated to the left if the fluid were rotating clockwise.

This conclusion was tested experimentally and found to be correct. A small vortex box with a rubber top and a circular hole in the side was made. This was filled with a solution of fluoresceïn and placed in one end of the tank, which was filled with water and held fixed. On striking the rubber lightly a vortex ring was produced which travelled straight down the tank and struck the middle of the opposite end.

The same experiment was repeated when the tank and vortex box were rotating. On tapping the box, rings started out in the same direction as before, but were deflected in a curved path, so that they hit the side instead of the end of the tank. By tapping the box quite lightly and rotating the tank fairly rapidly the rings could be made to turn in such small circles that they came round and struck the vortex box again without touching the side of the tank on the way. They would, in fact, turn in a circle whose diameter was only about four times the diameter of the rings.

It was pointed out by Dr. F. W. Aston, to whom the writer was showing this experiment, that the rings appeared to remain parallel to a plane fixed in space, while the rest of the fluid rotated. He suggested that the gyroscopic action prevented the ring from being deviated from this plane, and that in order that the ring might move relative to the fluid in a direction perpendicular to its plane it would have to move through the fluid along a curved path.

Motion of a Circular Cylinder in a Fluid which has a Steady Rotational Motion at Infinity but does not Necessarily Rotate as a Whole.

The results given in the rest of this paper have no immediate practical interest. The author entered on the investigation with a view to getting an idea of how the instability which is known to exist in a uniformly shearing laminar flow would be likely to manifest itself, and to find out whether the characteristics of the motion of solids in rotating fluids, which have been discussed in the first part of this paper, have any counterpart in the case of solids moving a fluid whose undisturbed motion is a uniform laminar flow.

The problem of finding the motion of a circular cylinder in a rotationally moving fluid divides itself naturally into two parts, that of finding the stream function for a given motion of the cylinder, and that of finding the force which the pressure associated with that stream function exerts on the cylinder. The stream function for a certain type of rotational flow in which the vorticity is uniform will now be found.

Let (r, θ) be the polar co-ordinates of a point referred to axes through the centre of the cylinder, and let (x_0, y_0) be the co-ordinates of the centre of the cylinder referred to fixed axes, so that the equation $\theta = 0$ represents a line parallel to the axis of x at a distance y_0 from it.

Consider the stream function

$$\psi = \tfrac{1}{2}\zeta r^2 + (\mathrm{A}r + \mathrm{B}/r)\cos\theta + (\mathrm{C}r + \mathrm{D}/r)\sin\theta$$
$$+ (\mathrm{E}r^2 + \mathrm{F}/r^2)\cos 2\theta + (\mathrm{G}r^2 + \mathrm{H}/r^2)\sin 2\theta. \quad (7)$$

It satisfies the equation $\nabla^2\psi = 2\zeta$ everywhere.

If, therefore, the constants A, B, C, etc., be so chosen that the boundary condition

$$\partial\psi/r\partial\theta + \dot{x}_0\cos\theta + \dot{y}_0\sin\theta = 0 \quad (8)$$

is satisfied where $r = a$, a being the radius of the cylinder, then ψ is the stream function which represents the motion of a fluid which, if the cylinder were removed, would be moving in accordance with the velocities given by the stream function.

$$\psi_1 = \zeta r^2/2 + \mathrm{A}r\cos\theta + \mathrm{C}r\sin\theta + \mathrm{E}r^2\cos 2\theta + \mathrm{G}r^2\sin 2\theta. \qquad (9)$$

Now (8) must be satisfied for all values of θ; hence we may equate coefficients of $\cos\theta$, $\sin\theta$, $\cos 2\theta$, and $\sin 2\theta$, separately to zero. In this way the following relations between the constants are determined:—

$$\mathrm{A} + \mathrm{B}/a^2 - \dot{y}_0 = 0, \quad \mathrm{C} + \mathrm{D}/a^2 + \dot{x}_0 = 0, \quad \mathrm{E}a + \mathrm{F}/a^3 = 0, \quad \mathrm{G}a + \mathrm{H}/a^3 = 0. \qquad (10)$$

It will be noticed that ψ_1, the stream function of the fluid before the introduction of the cylinder, is expressed in terms of co-ordinates referred to moving axes. In order to find the motion of a cylinder in a fluid whose undisturbed motion before the introduction of the cylinder is known with reference to fixed axes, we must transform (9) so as to give ψ_1 in terms of co-ordinates x and y referred to the fixed axes used to fix the position of the cylinder. The transformation is performed by putting

$$r\cos\theta = x - x_0, \qquad r\sin\theta = y - y_0.$$

ψ_1 then becomes

$$\tfrac{1}{2}\zeta\{(x-x_0)^2+(y-y_0)^2\} + \mathrm{A}(x-x_0) + \mathrm{C}(y-y_0)$$
$$+\mathrm{E}\{(x-x_0)^2-(y-y_0)^2\} + 2\mathrm{G}(x-x_0)(y-y_0). \qquad (11)$$

If the motion of the fluid before the introduction of the cylinder be given by the function

$$\psi_1 = \tfrac{1}{2}\zeta(x^2+y^2) + \mathrm{A}'x + \mathrm{C}'y + \mathrm{E}'(x^2-y^2) + 2\mathrm{G}'xy, \qquad (12)$$

where A′, C′, E′, G′ are given constants, we find, by equating coefficients of x, y, x^2, xy, y^2 in (11) and (12), the following relations determining A, C, E, G, in terms of A′, C′, E′, G′, x_0 and y_0,

$$\left.\begin{array}{c} -\zeta x_0 + \mathrm{A} - 2\mathrm{E}x_0 - 2\mathrm{G}y_0 = \mathrm{A}', \qquad -\zeta y_0 + \mathrm{C} + 2\mathrm{E}y_0 - 2\mathrm{G}x_0 = \mathrm{C}', \\ \mathrm{E} = \mathrm{E}', \qquad \mathrm{G} = \mathrm{G}'. \end{array}\right\} \qquad (13)$$

Solving (10) and (13) we obtain the following values of A, B, C, D, E, F, G, H,

$$\left.\begin{array}{l} \mathrm{A} = \mathrm{A}' + \zeta x_0 + 2\mathrm{E}'x_0 + 2\mathrm{G}'y_0, \\ \mathrm{B} = -a^2(-\dot{y}_0 + \mathrm{A}' + \zeta x_0 + 2\mathrm{E}'x_0 + 2\mathrm{G}'y_0), \\ \mathrm{C} = \mathrm{C}' + \zeta y_0 - 2\mathrm{E}'y_0 + 2\mathrm{G}'x_0, \\ \mathrm{D} = -a^2(\dot{x}_0 + c' + \zeta y_0 - 2\mathrm{E}'y_0 + 2\mathrm{G}'x_0), \\ \qquad \mathrm{E} = \mathrm{E}', \qquad \mathrm{F} = -\mathrm{E}'a^4, \\ \qquad \mathrm{G} = \mathrm{G}', \qquad \mathrm{H} = -\mathrm{G}'a^4. \end{array}\right\} \qquad (14)$$

Hence the stream function is obtained for the motion of a cylinder in a fluid whose undisturbed motion may be expressed by a stream function of the form ψ_1. The two particular cases which are of the greatest interest are those of uniform rotation, for which $\psi_1 = \frac{1}{2}\omega(x^2+y^2)$, and uniformly shearing laminar flow, for which $\psi_1 = -\frac{1}{2}\alpha y^2$, α being the rate of shear. Before discussing these cases, however, it is necessary to find an expression in terms of ψ for the force on the cylinder.

In general there does not appear to be a simple pressure integral like Bernouilli's for the case of irrotational motion, or the expression given in equation (4) for the pressure in a rotating fluid. It is necessary to go back to the original equations of motion of the fluid.

If the rate of change in pressure along a direction which makes an angle χ with the axis of x be represented by the symbol dp/ds_χ, ds_χ representing an element of length in the direction χ, then the equation of motion is

$$-\frac{1}{\rho}\frac{dp}{ds_\chi} = \frac{\mathrm{D}}{\mathrm{D}t}(v_\chi),$$

where v_χ represents the component of velocity of the fluid in the direction χ. Its value may be found in terms of ψ by the equation

$$v_\chi = \partial\psi/\partial r \,.\, \sin(\chi-\theta) - \partial\psi/r\partial\theta \,.\, \cos(\chi-\theta). \tag{15}$$

Now $\frac{\mathrm{D}}{\mathrm{D}t}(v\ )$ may be written

$$\frac{\delta v_\chi}{\delta t} - \frac{\partial\psi}{r\partial\theta}\frac{\partial}{\partial r}(v_\chi) + \frac{\partial\psi}{\partial r}\frac{\partial}{r\partial\theta}(v_\chi), \tag{16}$$

where $\delta v_\chi/\delta t$ represents, as before, the rate of change in v_χ at a point fixed in space.

If δr, $\delta\theta$ are the changes in the co-ordinates of a fixed point in time δt,

$$\frac{\delta v_\chi}{\delta t} = \frac{\partial v_\chi}{\partial t} + \frac{\partial v_\chi}{\partial\theta}\frac{\delta\theta}{\delta t} + \frac{\partial v_\chi}{\partial r}\frac{\delta r}{\delta t}, \tag{17}$$

where $\partial v_\chi/\partial t$ represents the rate of change in v_χ at a point fixed relative to the moving axes. The value of $\partial v_\chi/\partial t$ may be obtained by differentiating the expression (15) with respect to time, which occurs in all terms which contain x_0, y_0, $\dot{x}_0$ or $\dot{y}_0$.

The values of δr and $\delta\theta$ may be found by resolving the velocity of c, the centre of the cylinder, along and perpendicular to r.

Thus

$$\delta r = -(\dot{x}_0\cos\theta + \dot{y}_0\sin\theta)\,\delta t, \qquad r\,\delta\theta = (\dot{x}_0\sin\theta - \dot{y}\cos\theta)\,\delta t\,;$$

substituting in (17),

$$\frac{\delta v_\chi}{\delta t} = \frac{\partial v_\chi}{\partial t} + (\dot{x}_0\sin\theta - \dot{y}_0\cos\theta)\frac{\partial v_\chi}{r\partial\theta} - (\dot{x}_0\cos\theta + \dot{y}_0\sin\theta)\frac{\partial v_\chi}{\partial r}\,;$$

substituting this in (16),

$$-\frac{1}{\rho}\frac{\partial p}{\partial s_\chi}=\frac{D}{Dt}(v_\chi)=\frac{\partial v_\chi}{\partial t}-\left(\frac{\partial \psi}{r\partial\theta}+\dot{x}_0\cos\theta+\dot{y}_0\sin\theta\right)\frac{\partial v_\chi}{\partial r}$$

$$+\left(\frac{\partial\psi}{\partial r}+\dot{x}_0\sin\theta-\dot{y}_0\cos\theta\right)\frac{\partial v_\chi}{r\partial\theta}.$$

Now $-\partial\psi/r\partial\theta-\dot{x}_0\cos\theta-\dot{y}_0\sin\theta$ represents the component, normal to the surface, of the relative velocity of the fluid and the cylinder. It must therefore vanish.

Hence $$-\frac{1}{\rho}\frac{\partial p}{\partial s_\chi}=\frac{\partial v_\chi}{\partial t}+\left(\frac{\partial\psi}{\partial r}+\dot{x}_0\sin\theta-\dot{y}_0\cos\theta\right)\frac{\partial v_\chi}{r\partial\theta}$$

and substituting for v_χ from (15),

$$-\frac{1}{\rho}\frac{\partial p}{\partial s}=\sin(\chi-\theta)\left[\frac{\partial^2\psi}{\partial r\partial t}+\left(\frac{\partial\psi}{\partial r}+\dot{x}_0\sin\theta-\dot{y}_0\cos\theta\right)\left(\frac{\partial^2\psi}{r\partial r\partial\theta}-\frac{\partial\psi}{r^2\partial\theta}\right)\right]$$

$$+\cos(\chi-\theta)\left[-\frac{1}{r}\frac{\partial^2\psi}{\partial\theta\partial t}+\left(\frac{\partial\psi}{\partial r}+\dot{x}_0\sin\theta-\dot{y}_0\cos\theta\right)\left\{-\frac{\partial\psi}{r\partial\theta}-\frac{1}{r}\frac{\partial}{r\partial\theta}\left(\frac{\partial\psi}{r\partial\theta}\right)\right\}\right].$$

If χ be put equal to $\frac{1}{2}\pi+\theta$, we obtain the variation in pressure round the cylinder in the form

$$-\frac{1}{\rho}\left[\frac{\partial p}{r\partial\theta}\right]_{r=a}=\left[\frac{\partial^2\psi}{\partial r\partial t}+\left(\frac{\partial\psi}{\partial r}+\dot{x}_0\sin\theta-\dot{y}_0\cos\theta\right)\frac{\partial}{\partial r}\left(\frac{1}{r}\frac{\partial\psi}{\partial\theta}\right)\right]_{r=a}. \quad (18)$$

If F_x and F_y represent the components of the resultant force acting on the cylinder due to fluid pressure,

$$F_x=-\int_0^{2\pi}p\cos\theta\,a\,d\theta,\qquad F_y=-\int_0^{2\pi}p\sin\theta\,a\,d\theta.$$

These may be integrated by parts.

F_x then becomes $a^2\int_0^{2\pi}\left[\frac{\partial p}{r\partial\theta}\right]_{r=a}\sin\theta\,d\theta$ and $F_y=-a^2\int_0^{2\pi}\left[\frac{\partial p}{r\partial\theta}\right]_{r=a}\cos\theta\,d\theta.$ (19)

By substituting the value obtained for $\left[\frac{\partial p}{r\partial\theta}\right]_{r=a}$ in (18) we can find the force exerted by fluid pressure when the cylinder has any assigned motion for which a stream function can be found.

This method will be applied to two particular cases: In Case (1) the general motion of the fluid is one of uniform rotation. This problem has been solved already in the first part of this paper, but it seems worth while to verify the calculation. In Case (2) the general motion of the fluid is one of uniform shearing.

Case 1.—The stream function of the general motion of the fluid is

$\psi_1 = \frac{1}{2}\omega(x^2+y^2)$. In this case, then, $\zeta = \omega$ and $A' = C' = E' = G' = 0$. The stream function of the motion round the cylinder is

$$\psi = \omega\frac{r^2}{2} + \left\{\omega x_0 r - \frac{a^2}{r}(-\dot{y}_0 + \omega x_0)\right\}\cos\theta + \left\{\omega y_0 r - \frac{a^2}{r}(\dot{x}_0 + \omega y_0)\right\}\sin\theta.$$

Substituting in (18) the value of $-\frac{1}{\rho}\left[\frac{\partial p}{r\partial\theta}\right]_{r=a}$ may be found, and substituting this value in (19) it will be found that

$$-F_x = \pi\rho a^2(\ddot{x}_0 + 4\omega\dot{y}_0 - 2\omega^2 x_0), \qquad F_y = \pi\rho a^2(\ddot{y}_0 + 4\omega\dot{x}_0 + 2\omega^2 y_0).$$

If these expressions be transformed by the transformation

$$x_0 = R\cos(\phi+\omega t), \qquad y_0 = R\sin(\phi+\omega t),$$

so that R, ϕ, are the polar co-ordinates of a point referred to axes which rotate with the fluid, it will be found that the forces F_x, F_y, may be resolved into components F_R along R, and F_ϕ perpendicular to it where

$$F_R = \pi\rho a^2\{-\ddot{R} + R\dot{\phi}^2 - 2R\omega\dot{\phi} - R\omega^2\},$$

$$F_\phi = \pi\rho a^2\{-R\ddot{\phi} - 2\dot{R}\dot{\phi} + 2\omega\dot{R}\}.$$

This agrees with the results obtained on p. 104, for the force whose components are F_R and F_ϕ may be regarded as being made up in the following way: (1) a force $\pi\rho a^2 \times$ (acceleration of the cylinder relative to the rotating axes); (2) a force $\pi\rho a^2\omega^2 R$ acting towards the centre of rotation; and (3) a force $2\pi\rho a^2\omega \times$ (velocity of the cylinder relative to the rotating axes) acting at right angles to the direction of relative motion. These are evidently the same as the three forces discussed on p. 104.

Case 2.—The general motion of the fluid is one of uniform shearing. The fluid moves parallel to the axis of x with velocity αy, which increases at a uniform rate as y increases. In this case $\psi_1 = -\frac{1}{2}\alpha y^2$, which may be written

$$\psi_1 = -\tfrac{1}{4}\alpha(x^2+y^2) + \tfrac{1}{4}\alpha(x^2-y^2).$$

Comparing this with (12) it appears that $\zeta = -\frac{1}{2}\alpha$ and $E' = \frac{1}{4}\alpha$, while $A' = C' = G' = 0$. Hence from (7) and (14)

$$\psi = -\alpha\frac{r^2}{4} + \frac{a^2\dot{y}_0}{r}\cos\theta - \left\{\alpha y_0 r + \frac{a^2}{r}(\dot{x}_0 - \alpha y_0)\right\}\sin\theta + \frac{\alpha}{4}\left(r^2 - \frac{a^4}{r^2}\right)\cos 2\theta.$$

Hence differentiating and putting $r = a$,

$$\left[\frac{\partial^2\psi}{\partial r\partial t}\right]_{r=a} = -\ddot{y}_0\cos\theta + \ddot{x}_0\sin\theta - 2\alpha\dot{y}_0\sin\theta,$$

$$\left[\frac{\partial\psi}{\partial r} + \dot{x}_0\sin\theta - \dot{y}_0\cos\theta\right]_{r=a} = \alpha(\cos 2\theta - \tfrac{1}{2}) - 2\dot{y}_0\cos\theta + 2(\dot{x}_0 - \alpha y_0)\sin\theta,$$

$$\left[\frac{\partial}{\partial r}\left(\frac{\partial\psi}{r\partial\theta}\right)\right]_{r=a} = \frac{1}{a}\{2\dot{y}_0\sin\theta + (\dot{x}_0 - \alpha y_0)\cos\theta - 2a\alpha\sin 2\theta\}.$$

Hence from (18)

$$-\frac{1}{\rho}\left[\frac{\partial p}{r\partial\theta}\right]_{r=a} = \ddot{x}_0 \sin\theta - \ddot{y}_0 \cos\theta - 2\alpha\dot{y}_0 \sin\theta$$

$$+\frac{2}{a}\{\dot{y}_0 \sin\theta + (\dot{x}_0 - \alpha y_0)\cos\theta - \alpha a \sin 2\theta\}$$

$$\times\{2(\dot{x}_0 - \alpha y_0)\sin\theta - 2\dot{y}_0\cos\theta + a\alpha(\cos 2\theta - \tfrac{1}{2})\}.$$

Hence from (19)

$$F_x = -\pi\rho a^2\{\ddot{x}_0 - \alpha\dot{y}_0\}, \qquad F_y = -\pi\rho a_2\{\ddot{y}_0 + 2\alpha(\dot{x}_0 - \alpha y_0)\}. \tag{20}$$

This result will now be applied to find the motion of a cylinder of the same density as the fluid when it is projected from the origin with velocity whose components are U and V.

The equations of motion of the cylinder are

$$\pi\rho a^2\ddot{x}_0 = -\pi\rho a^2\{\ddot{x}_0 - 2\alpha\dot{y}_0\}, \qquad \pi\rho a^2\ddot{y}_0 = -\pi\rho a^2\{\ddot{y}_0 + 2\alpha(\dot{x}_0 - \alpha y_0)\},$$

or

$$\ddot{x}_0 - \alpha\dot{y}_0 = 0, \qquad \ddot{y}_0 = -\alpha(\dot{x}_0 - \alpha y_0).$$

The first of these may be integrated in the form

$$\dot{x}_0 - \alpha y_0 = \text{constant}.$$

That is to say, the component parallel to the axis of x of the relative velocity of the cylinder and the fluid is constant and equal to U. The acceleration of the cylinder in the direction of the axis of x is constant and equal to $-\alpha V$. If $U = 0$, that is to say, if the cylinder is shot off in a direction perpendicular to the direction of shear, then the component of velocity parallel to the axis of y is constant, and the fluid pressure is just sufficient to give the cylinder the acceleration αV, which is necessary in order that the velocity of the cylinder relative to the fluid round it may remain constant. This property of uniformly shearing fluids appears to be analogous to a certain extent to the property of rotating fluids discussed on p. 105.

114

Reprinted from *Proceedings of the Royal Society*, Series A, Vol. 100, 1921.

Experiments with Rotating Fluids.

By G. I. Taylor, F.R.S.

(Received June 22, 1921.)

[Plate 2.]

It is well known that predictions about fluid motion based on the classic hydrodynamical theory are seldom verified in experiments performed with actual fluids. The explanation of this want of agreement between theory and experiment is to be found chiefly in the conditions at the surfaces of the solid boundaries of the fluid.

The classical hydrodynamical theory assumes that perfect slipping takes place, whereas in actual fluids the surface layers of the fluid are churned up into eddies. In the case of motions which depend on the conditions at the surface, therefore, no agreement is to be expected between theory and experiment. This class of fluid motion, unfortunately, includes all cases where a solid moves through a fluid which is otherwise at rest.

On the other hand, there are types of fluid motion which only depend to a secondary extent on the slip at the boundaries. For this reason theoretical predictions about waves and tides, or about the motion of vortex rings, are in much better agreement with observation than predictions about the motion of solids in fluids. Some time ago the present writer* made certain predictions about the motion of solids in rotating fluids, or rather about the differences which might be expected between the motion of solids in a rotating fluid and those in a fluid at rest. These predicted features of the motion did not depend on conditions at the boundaries. It was therefore to be anticipated that they might be verified by experiment. The experiments were carried out and the predictions were completely verified.

In view of the interest which attaches to any experimental verification of theoretical results in hydrodynamics, and more particularly to verifications of those concerning the motion of solids in fluids, it seems worth while to publish photographs showing the experiments in progress. In the second and third part of the paper further experiments are described in which theoretical predictions are verified in experiments with water.

Motion of Cylinder and Sphere in Rotating Fluid.

In these experiments a solid cylinder and a solid sphere, of the same density as water, were drawn through a rotating vessel containing water.

* 'Roy. Soc. Proc.,' A, vol. 93, p. 99 (1917).

The threads by means of which these solids were dragged, passed through small rings attached to the vertical wall of the circular rotating glass vessel in which the water was contained. The solids were initially attached to the opposite point of this vessel to that at which the rings were attached. Under these circumstances, if the vessel were not rotating, a symmetrical body like a sphere or cylinder would evidently pass along a diameter through the centre of the apparatus when towed by the threads.

When the vessel was rotating, however, the theoretical prediction* was that the cylinder would pass through the centre of the apparatus just as if the whole system were not rotating, while a sphere, or any symmetrical three-dimensional body, would be deflected and would pass to one side of the centre. The verification of this prediction was first made in an apparatus with which it was difficult to obtain photographs owing to the difficulty of throwing a light through the water towards a camera placed on the axis of rotation above the apparatus. A new apparatus was therefore devised, in which the vertical central spindle used in the previous apparatus was done away with.

Two dishes in the form of circular cylinders were made. Each had a thin plate-glass bottom, about 1 mm. thick. The diameter of one of them was made about 1/8 inch larger than the other, so that the smaller one would fit inside the larger one, leaving a space of about 1/16 inch all round. The inner dish was filled about two-thirds full of water, and the outer one was filled quite full. The inner cylinder would then float in the outer one. It was driven round a vertical axis by means of a jet of water projected at its outside surface. When the apparatus was set up so as to run truly, it was found that a very uniform rate of rotation would be obtained by this method. The whole apparatus stood in a trough with a plate glass bottom, in which the water which overflowed could be collected. This apparatus is shown in text-fig. 1.

In order to take instantaneous photographs, the apparatus was illuminated from underneath, and a camera with a lens of 15 inches focus was fixed about 6 feet above it. Two methods of illumination were used. In the first method the direct light from a spark between an aluminium wire and a hole in an aluminium plate was focussed, by means of a condenser, on the lens of the camera. In the second method use was made of diffused light, a mercury vapour spark being used to illuminate a ground-glass plate placed close under the apparatus. Plate 2, figs. 1, 2, 5 and 6, were taken by the first method, while figs. 3 and 4 were taken by the second. It is worth pointing out that the apparatus is very simple, and that it is easy to project all the

* *Loc. cit.*, p. 105.

experiments to be described in this paper on to a screen by means of a lantern.

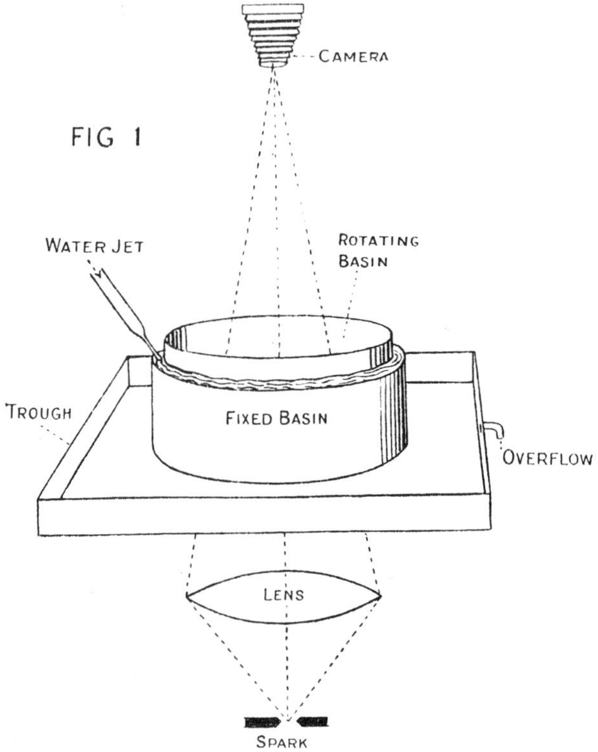

Fig. 1.—General Arrangement of Apparatus.

It was thought at first that it might be difficult to arrange to tow the solids through the rotating basin in such a way that no appreciable variation in the speed of rotation would occur. To avoid this difficulty, the threads used to tow the solids were led from the edge of the apparatus back to the centre, and were pulled upwards from that point. The method adopted for doing this was to fix a transparent celluloid bridge across the basin in such a position that its centre line ran from the initial position of the solid to the point towards which the threads were towing it. This transparent bridge shows up clearly as a broad band in figs. 1 and 2 (Plate 2). The threads passed through a small hole in the centre of the bridge, and were attached to a small wire ring, which rested on it in the middle.

To perform the experiment, the solid, which was usually made of wax or boxwood, was placed on small pins projecting from the side of the trough. The threads were then stretched across the basin to the opposite side, and led from there up to a ring close under the celluloid bridge. From this point they passed along the underside of the bridge to the centre, where they passed up through the central hole.

The tank was then set rotating, and, when the whole system had attained a constant speed, a steel pricker was inserted into the wire ring, and raised approximately vertically. The sketch (text-fig. 2) shows the apparatus in action. In the case of the cylinder two threads were used to ensure that

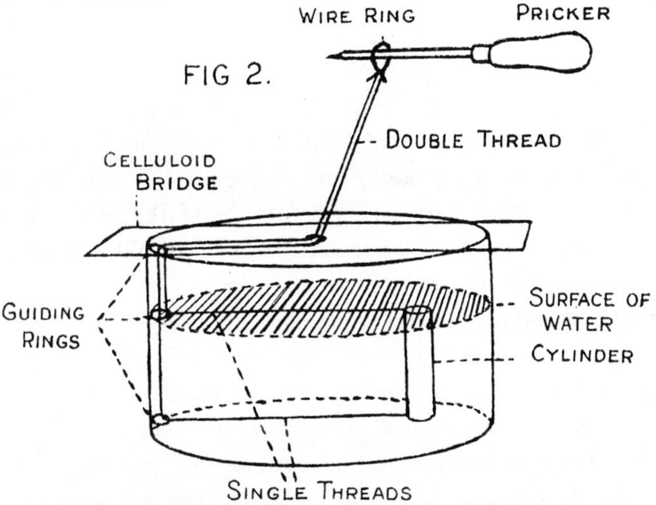

Fig. 2.—Rotating Tank arranged for Experiment with Cylinder.

the axis should remain vertical. This is the case shown in the sketch. With the sphere, only one thread was used.

The results in the two cases are shown in the photographs (Plate 2, figs. 1 and 2). In fig. 1 the cylinder is shown at the middle point of its path. Since its axis is nearly vertical it is seen end-on, and appears therefore as a black circle in the photograph. In the particular experiment shown in fig. 1, the axis of the cylinder had accidentally got tilted very slightly away from the vertical, so that both the upper and lower threads show as two distinct threads. The pricker and wire ring are seen at the bottom of the photograph; they are naturally rather out of focus. The lines in the photograph which are not straight are threads used for drawing the solids in other experiments. They have nothing to do with the present experiment. It will be seen that the predicted result is verified. The cylinder is moving practically straight across under the middle line of the celluloid bridge.

Fig. 2 shows the result in the case of the sphere. In this case it will be seen that the sphere is being deflected through a large angle, so that it is under the edge of the bridge instead of being under the middle, as it was in the case of the cylinder. It is not moving in the direction in which the thread is pulling it, but is being deflected to the right. In this case the liquid was rotating in the direction opposite to that of the hands of a clock. Again, this is the result which was predicted by theory.

Motion of Vortex Rings in a Rotating Fluid.

The difference between two- and three-dimensional fluid motion which has been discussed must apply to all fluid motions. It must therefore apply to the propagation of a vortex ring, as well as to the motions of a sphere and cylinder.

It is impossible, apparently, to produce a two-dimensional analogue of a vortex ring. If such a thing could be produced, it should, according to this theory, propagate itself in a straight line through a fluid, whether the fluid is rotating or not. In other words, since a rotation of the whole system should make no difference to any two-dimensional flow, it should make no difference to the two-dimensional analogue of a vortex ring.

The flow in a vortex ring, however, is three-dimensional, and a rotation of the whole system should affect it. For reasons explained in the paper already referred to,* it was anticipated on theoretical grounds that if a vortex ring can be propagated in a rotating fluid, it will not move in a straight line relative to the rotating system, but will move in a circle in the *opposite direction* to that in which the whole system is rotating.

In fig. 3 is shown a photograph of a vortex ring which has been projected from a small vortex box immersed in the water.† The basin was not rotating in this experiment. It will be seen that the ring, which is being projecte along a diameter of the basin, moves in a straight line, as was to be expected. A short wire was attached to the vortex box, so as to point in the direction in which the ring was aimed. This will be seen in the photograph (fig. 3).

Fig. 4 is a photograph of a vortex ring projected when the whole system is rotating. In this photograph, the predicted curved path traversed by the ring is shown up clearly by the track of coloured fluid left behind during its flight.

The jet which drives the apparatus can be seen on the right-hand side of

* *Loc. cit.*, p. 107.

† The liquid eventually used was not pure water, but an acid solution of ferrous sulphate. The rings consisted of a solution of permanganate of potash made up to the same density as the ferrous sulphate solution by mixing with a heavy neutral salt. The rings then dissolved after they had broken up and a large number could be projected without discolouring the solution. For the suggestion to use this solution I am indebted to Dr. A. A. Robb.

the photograph. It will be noticed that the basin is being driven in the counter-clockwise direction, and that the vortex ring is going round its circle in a clockwise direction, as predicted theoretically.

One point which the experiments bring out is that the direction of the axis of the ring appears to be fixed in space, so that the ring would go round in a circle once during each revolution of the system. It would therefore be possible to consider the motion as being a steady motion relative to axes whose directions are fixed in space, but whose origin moves and is situated at the centre of the path of the vortex ring.

Slow Motions in a Rotating Fluid.

The investigations described above naturally led to inquiries as to whether rotating liquids possess any other properties which can be predicted from hydrodynamical theory, The following striking peculiarity of rotating fluids was discovered in the course of this work. If any small motion is communicated to a fluid which is initially rotating steadily like a solid body, the resulting flow must be two-dimensional, though small oscillations about this state of slow motion are possible.* This may be proved as follows:—

Let u, v, w be the components of velocity of any particle of fluid relative to a system which is rotating uniformly with velocity ω about the axis of z.

The circulation round any circuit in the fluid is

$$I = \int \{(u-\omega y)\,dx + (v+\omega x)\,dy + w\,dz\},$$

the integral being taken round the circuit.

This may be divided into two parts

(*a*) $$I' = \int \{u\,dx + v\,dy + w\,dz\}$$

which may be called the circulation due to the relative motion, and

(*b*) $$\int (-\omega y\,dx + \omega x\,dy)$$

which can be expressed in the form $2\omega A$, where A is the area of the projection of the circuit on a plane perpendicular to the axis of rotation.

In a non-viscous fluid the circulation round any circuit which always consists of the same ring of particles, is constant. Hence it will be seen that $I = I' + 2\omega A$ is constant.

Evidently if the motion relative to the rotating system is small this means that the variations in A during the whole motion are small. The liquid must therefore move in such a way that the area of the projection of any ring of particles on a plane perpendicular to the axis of rotation is nearly constant.

* This is practically the same thing as the fact previously noted by Proudman, that small steady motions of a rotating fluid are two-dimensional.

Let us now enquire how this geometrical condition may be expected to reveal itself during the motion. First, we shall see what types of motion are possible in a fluid for which the areas of the projections on a given plane of all possible circuits of particles remain constant during the motion. This condition may be expressed mathematically by writing down an expression for the rate at which the area of the projection increases and equating it to 0. In this way it is found that

$$\int (v dx - u dy) = 0,$$

the integral being taken round the circuit.

This expression may be transformed by Stokes' Theorem into the form

$$\iint \left\{ l \frac{\partial u}{\partial z} + m \frac{\partial v}{\partial z} - n \left(\frac{\partial u}{\partial x} + \frac{\partial v}{\partial y} \right) \right\} dS = 0,$$

where dS is an element of surface of any surface which is bounded by the circuit in question and l, m, n are the direction cosines of the normal to that surface.

Since this relation holds for all possible circuits,

$$\partial u/\partial z = 0, \quad \partial v/\partial z = 0, \quad \text{and} \quad \partial u/\partial x + \partial v/\partial y = 0. \tag{1}$$

Hence, since the fluid is incompressible,

$$\partial w/\partial z = 0. \tag{2}$$

The conditions (1) show that any two particles which are originally in a line perpendicular to the given plane, will always remain in a line perpendicular to it. The condition (2) shows that they also remain at a constant distance apart throughout the motion.

If therefore any small motion be communicated to a rotating fluid the resulting motion of the fluid must be one in which any two particles originally in a line parallel to the axis of rotation remain so, except for possible small oscillations about that position. This property of rotating fluids is found to be true experimentally. It can be demonstrated in a very striking way by means of the apparatus described in the first part of this paper. The liquid is first made to rotate steadily as a solid body. A small motion is then communicated to it, and a few drops of coloured liquid are inserted. However carefully these drops are inserted the volume occupied by coloured water necessarily measures at least half a centimetre in every direction.

The slow movement of the fluid then draws this coloured portion of the fluid out into sheets. These sheets remain always parallel to the axis of rotation. They go on spreading almost indefinitely till they may perhaps be twenty or thirty times as long as the diameter of the basin, their thickness

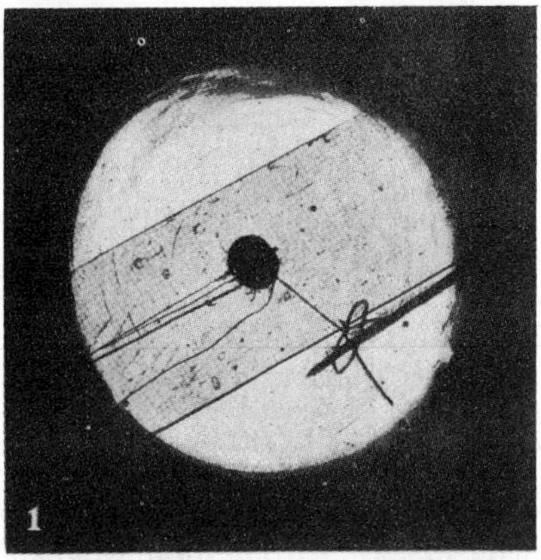

1

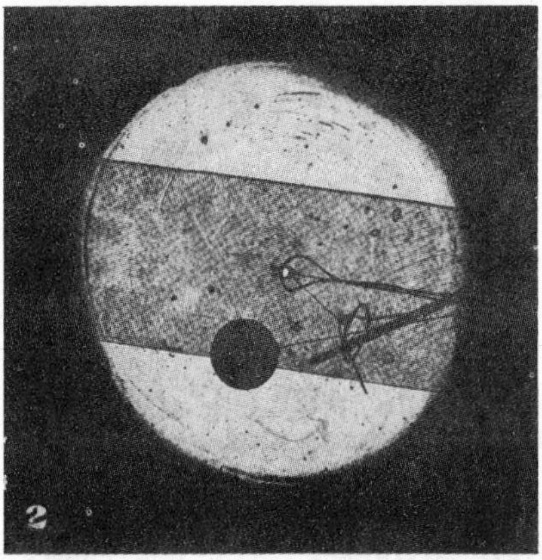

2

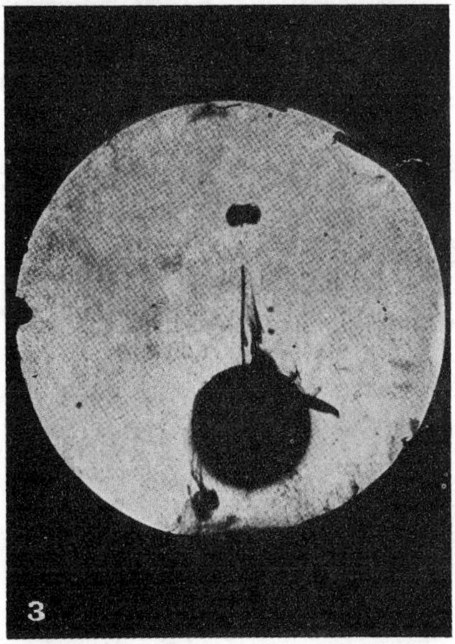

3

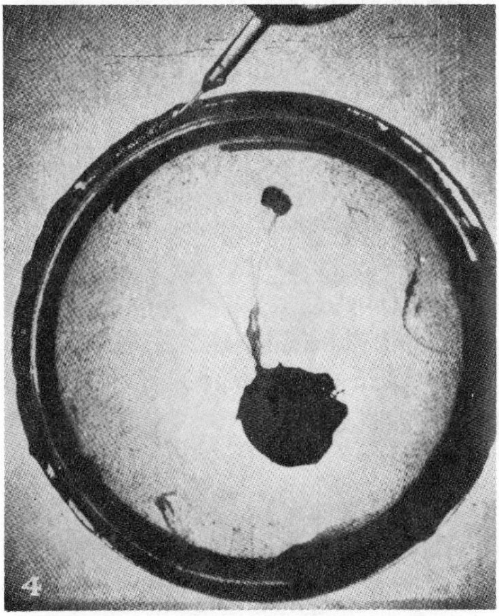

4

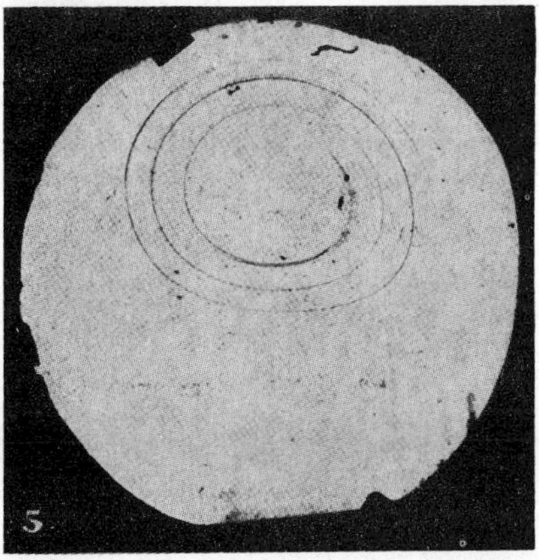

5

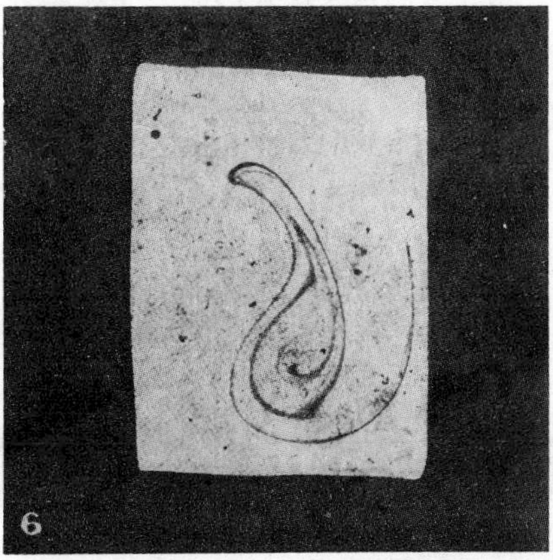

6

decreases correspondingly till they are only a small fraction of a millimetre thick.

The accuracy with which they remain parallel to the axis of rotation is quite extraordinary. After the motion has been going on for some time it is only possible to see that the colouring matter is not uniformly diffused through the liquid by placing one's eye on, or near, the axis of rotation. The portion of the fluid which is passing immediately beneath the eye then appears to be filled with fine lines which are, of course, in reality, thin sheets seen edgewise.

The photographs shown in figs. 5 and 6 were taken by a camera placed accurately on the axis of rotation of the basin. It will be seen that the lines are extremely fine. The sheets into which the originally diffuse patch of coloured liquid are drawn are therefore extremely thin, and are moreover accurately parallel to the axis of rotation. It appears therefore that in this case also the theoretical prediction is completely verified by experiments with real fluids.

In fig. 5 the small motion was communicated to the fluid by changing the speed of the rotating basin temporarily. Fig. 6 shows an experiment in which a rectangular boundary was placed in the rotating basin in order to alter the effect produced by a change of speed, and so produce a different pattern.

In a future paper the author hopes to discuss what happens in the case when the boundaries of the fluid move slowly in such a way that three-dimensional motion must take place.

DESCRIPTION OF PLATE.

Fig. 1.—Cylinder passing under centre of tank, seen from point above the tank and on the axis of rotation.

Fig. 2.—Sphere being deflected, seen from the same point as the cylinder shown in fig. 1.

Fig. 3.—Vortex ring being projected in a non-rotating tank. The large black disc is the vortex box, seen end-on. The wire seen projecting from the box indicates the direction of projection of the ring. The ring will be seen clear of the end of the wire.

Fig. 4.—Vortex ring projected in rotating tank. The curved path is shown by the trail of coloured liquid left by the ring in its flight. The jet which drives the inner basin is seen at the top of the photograph.

Fig. 5.—Sheet of coloured liquid seen from a point on the axis of rotation in a rotating liquid.

Fig. 6.—Another sheet of coloured liquid. In this case the liquid is contained in a rectangular boundary.

III. Uniform Heating from Below with Rotation

Reprinted (with corrections) from *Proceedings of the Royal Society*, Series A, Vol. 217, May 7, 1953.

The instability of a layer of fluid heated below and subject to Coriolis forces

By S. Chandrasekhar, F.R.S., *Yerkes Observatory*

(*Received* 29 *December* 1952)

This paper is devoted to examining the stability of a horizontal layer of fluid heated below, subject to an effective gravity (g) acting (approximately) in the direction of the vertical and the Coriolis force resulting from a rotation of angular velocity Ω about a direction making an angle ϑ with the vertical. It is shown that the effect of the Coriolis force is to inhibit the onset of convection, the extent of the inhibition depending on the value of the non-dimensional parameter $T = 4d^4\Omega^2 \cos^2 \vartheta/\nu^2$, where d denotes the depth of the layer and ν is the kinematic viscosity. Tables of the critical Rayleigh numbers (R_c) for the onset of convection are provided for the three cases (a) both bounding surfaces free, (b) both bounding surfaces rigid and (c) one bounding surface free and the other rigid. In all three cases $R_c \rightarrow \text{constant} \times T^{\frac{2}{3}}$ as $T \rightarrow \infty$; the corresponding dependence of the critical temperature gradient ($-\beta_c$) for the onset of convection, on ν and d, is $g\alpha\beta_c = \text{constant} \times \kappa(\Omega^4 \cos^4 \vartheta/d^4\nu)^{\frac{1}{3}}$ (κ is the coefficient of thermometric conductivity and α is the coefficient of volume expansion). The question whether thermal instability can set in as oscillations of increasing amplitude (i.e. as 'over-stability') is examined for case (a), and it is shown that if $\kappa/\nu < 1{\cdot}478$ this possibility does not arise; but if $\kappa/\nu > 1{\cdot}478$, over-stability is the first type of instability to arise for all T greater than a certain determinate value. It further appears that these latter possibilities should be considered in meteorological and astrophysical applications of the theory.

1. Introduction

The manner of the onset of convection by thermal instability in a layer of fluid heated below has been the subject of both experimental (Bénard 1901; Graham 1934; Chandra 1938) and theoretical (Rayleigh 1916; Jeffreys 1926, 1928; Low 1929; Pellew & Southwell 1940) investigations. And there have been several attempts to apply the results of these investigations to a number of meteorological (cf. Brunt 1939) and astrophysical (cf. Wasiutynski 1946) problems. In connexion with these latter meteorological applications, it was pointed out by Jeffreys (1928) that the rotation of the earth can have a pronounced inhibiting effect on the onset of instability in the earth's atmosphere, and that this effect should be considered before the results valid only in the absence of rotation are applied. In spite of the obvious strength of the arguments advanced by Jeffreys, the effect of rotation of the solid boundaries on thermal instability does not seem to have received a quantitative treatment. It is the object of this paper to provide such a treatment.

2. The equations of the problem

Consider a horizontal layer of fluid of depth d, confined between two parallel planes $z = 0$ and $z = d$, subject to an effective gravity g, acting (approximately) in the direction of the vertical and the Coriolis force resulting from a rotation of angular velocity Ω, about a direction specified by a unit vector $\mathbf{\upsilon}$. The equations of motion and heat conduction appropriate to the problem on hand are

$$\rho \frac{\partial u_i}{\partial t} + \rho \frac{\partial}{\partial x_j} u_i u_j = -\frac{\partial p}{\partial x_i} + \rho\nu \nabla^2 u_i - g\rho\lambda_i + 2\rho\Omega\epsilon_{ijk} u_j \upsilon_k, \tag{1}$$

and
$$\frac{\partial T}{\partial t}+u_j\frac{\partial T}{\partial x_j}=\kappa\nabla^2 T, \tag{2}$$

where, in order to use the tensor notation and the summation convention, we have introduced a unit vector $\boldsymbol{\lambda}$ which is in the direction of the vertical. Also, in the foregoing equations ρ denotes the density, p the pressure, T the temperature and ν and κ are the coefficients of kinematic viscosity and thermometric conductivity, respectively.

As is permissible in investigations of this kind (cf. Rayleigh 1916), we shall allow for the variation of density due to thermal expansion only in so far as it modifies gravity. Thus, in equation (1) we shall replace ρ which occurs as a factor of g by

$$\rho=\rho_0(1-\alpha\Delta T), \tag{3}$$

where α denotes the coefficient of volume expansion, ρ_0 the density corresponding to a mean temperature T_0 and ΔT is the deviation of the local temperature from T_0:

$$\Delta T=T-T_0; \tag{4}$$

and we regard ρ occurring elsewhere in equation (1) as a constant equal to ρ_0. On these assumptions, equation (1) can be written in the form

$$\frac{\partial u_i}{\partial t}+\frac{\partial}{\partial x_j}u_iu_j=-\frac{\partial}{\partial x_i}\left(\frac{p}{\rho_0}+g\lambda_jx_j\right)+\gamma\Delta T\lambda_i+\nu\nabla^2u_i+2\Omega\epsilon_{ijk}u_jv_k, \tag{5}$$

where
$$\gamma=g\alpha. \tag{6}$$

With the variation of density due to thermal expansion allowed for in this manner we, from now on, treat u_i as a solenoidal vector:

$$\frac{\partial u_i}{\partial x_i}=0. \tag{7}$$

Now suppose that a constant mean adverse temperature gradient $-\beta\,(\beta>0)$ is maintained in the direction $\boldsymbol{\lambda}$ by an external agency; then we can write (cf. equation (4))

$$T=T_0-\beta\lambda_jx_j+\theta,\quad \Delta T=-\beta\lambda_jx_j+\theta, \tag{8}$$

where θ denotes the instantaneous deviation of the temperature from the local mean value, $T_0-\beta\lambda_jx_j$. Inserting (8) in equations (2) and (5), we obtain

$$\frac{\partial u_i}{\partial t}+\frac{\partial}{\partial x_j}u_iu_j=-\frac{\partial\varpi}{\partial x_i}+\gamma\theta\lambda_i+\nu\nabla^2u_i+2\Omega\epsilon_{ijk}u_jv_k \tag{9}$$

and
$$\frac{\partial\theta}{\partial t}-\beta\lambda_ju_j+u_j\frac{\partial\theta}{\partial x_j}=\kappa\nabla^2\theta, \tag{10}$$

where, for brevity, we have written

$$\varpi=\frac{p}{\rho_0}+g\lambda_jx_j-\tfrac{1}{2}\beta\gamma\lambda_i\lambda_jx_ix_j. \tag{11}$$

Since our interest in equations (10) and (11) is primarily for deriving the condition for motions to ensue from an initial static situation, we may treat u_i and θ as quantities of the first order of smallness and ignore all products and squares of them. Equations (10) and (11) then reduce to

$$\frac{\partial u_i}{\partial t} = -\frac{\partial \varpi}{\partial x_i} + \gamma\theta\lambda_i + \nu\nabla^2 u_i + 2\Omega\epsilon_{ijk} u_j v_k, \tag{12}$$

and

$$\frac{\partial \theta}{\partial t} = \beta w + \kappa\nabla^2\theta, \tag{13}$$

where $w\,(= \lambda_j u_j)$ is the component of the velocity in the direction of the vertical.

We can eliminate ϖ from equation (12) by taking its curl. Thus, on making use of the solenoidal property of u_i, we find

$$\frac{\partial \omega_i}{\partial t} = \gamma\epsilon_{ijk}\frac{\partial \theta}{\partial x_j}\lambda_k + \nu\nabla^2\omega_i + 2\Omega v_j \frac{\partial u_i}{\partial x_j}, \tag{14}$$

where

$$\omega_i = \epsilon_{ijk}\frac{\partial u_k}{\partial x_j} \tag{15}$$

denotes the vorticity. Multiplying equation (14) by λ_i, we get

$$\frac{\partial \zeta}{\partial t} = \nu\nabla^2\zeta + 2\Omega v_j \frac{\partial w}{\partial x_j}, \tag{16}$$

where

$$\zeta = \lambda_j\omega_j = \frac{\partial v}{\partial x} - \frac{\partial u}{\partial y} \tag{17}$$

is the z-component of the vorticity. (In equation (17) u and v are the components of the velocity in two directions at right angles to the vertical.)

Next, taking the curl of equation (14) and remembering that in view of the solenoidal character of $\mathbf{u}$,

$$\operatorname{curl}\boldsymbol{\omega} = -\nabla^2\mathbf{u}, \tag{18}$$

we obtain

$$-\frac{\partial}{\partial t}\nabla^2 u_i = \gamma\left(\lambda_j\frac{\partial^2\theta}{\partial x_i\,\partial x_j} - \lambda_i\nabla^2\theta\right) - \nu\nabla^4 u_i + 2\Omega v_j\frac{\partial \omega_i}{\partial x_j}. \tag{19}$$

Resolving this equation in the direction of $\boldsymbol{\lambda}$, we get

$$-\frac{\partial}{\partial t}\nabla^2 w = \gamma\left(\lambda_i\lambda_j\frac{\partial^2\theta}{\partial x_i\,\partial x_j} - \nabla^2\theta\right) - \nu\nabla^4 w + 2\Omega v_j\frac{\partial \zeta}{\partial x_j}. \tag{20}$$

Equation (20) together with equations (13) and (16) are the basic equations of this theory. In seeking solutions of these equations we must satisfy certain boundary conditions on the planes $z = 0$ and $z = d$, between which the fluid is confined. Thus, we must certainly require that

$$\theta = 0 \quad\text{and}\quad w = 0 \qquad\text{for}\qquad z = 0 \quad\text{and}\quad z = d, \tag{21}$$

since the temperature on the bounding surfaces is kept constant and there can also be no motion normal to them. Additional boundary conditions follow from the equation of continuity; but these depend on whether the particular bounding surface considered is free or rigid. Thus, if a bounding surface is rigid and no slip occurs on it, the components of the velocity, u and v, at right angles to the vertical, must vanish identically (i.e. for all x and y) on the surface. From the equation of continuity and the definition of ζ, it now follows that

$$\frac{\partial w}{\partial z} = 0 \quad \text{and} \quad \zeta = 0 \quad \text{on a rigid surface.} \tag{22}$$

On the other hand, if a bounding surface is free, then we must require that the tangential viscous stresses

$$p_{xz} = \rho\nu\left(\frac{\partial u}{\partial z} + \frac{\partial w}{\partial x}\right) \quad \text{and} \quad p_{yz} = \rho\nu\left(\frac{\partial v}{\partial z} + \frac{\partial w}{\partial y}\right) \tag{23}$$

vanish on it; from this and the fact that w vanishes on a bounding surface, we conclude that $\partial u/\partial z$ and $\partial v/\partial z$ must vanish identically on a free surface. From the equation of continuity and the definition of ζ it now follows that

$$\frac{\partial^2 w}{\partial z^2} = 0 \quad \text{and} \quad \frac{\partial \zeta}{\partial z} = 0 \quad \text{on a free surface.} \tag{24}$$

3. The equations governing marginal stability with instability setting in as convection

We shall first derive the criterion for instability in case it sets in as a stationary pattern of convection. In §8 we shall examine whether it can also set in, in the alternative manner of 'over-stability' i.e. by oscillations of increasing amplitude.

When instability sets in as convection, the equations governing marginal stability are those which are obtained by setting $\partial/\partial t = 0$ in equations (13), (16) and (20). The equations are

$$\nu\nabla^4 w - 2\Omega v_j \frac{\partial \zeta}{\partial x_j} = \gamma\left(\lambda_i\lambda_j \frac{\partial^2 \theta}{\partial x_i \partial x_j} - \nabla^2\theta\right), \tag{25}$$

$$\nu\nabla^2\zeta = -2\Omega v_j \frac{\partial w}{\partial x_j} \tag{26}$$

and

$$\kappa\nabla^2\theta = -\beta w. \tag{27}$$

Operating equation (25) by ∇^2 and making use of equations (26) and (27), we obtain

$$\nabla^6 w + \frac{4\Omega^2}{\nu^2} v_i v_j \frac{\partial^2 w}{\partial x_i \partial x_j} = -\frac{\beta\gamma}{\kappa\nu}\left(\lambda_i\lambda_j \frac{\partial^2}{\partial x_i \partial x_j} - \nabla^2\right) w. \tag{28}$$

The boundary conditions with respect to which equations (26) and (28) must be solved are the same as before (equations (21), (22) and (23)).

4. The reduction to a characteristic value problem when both $\mathbf{\Omega}$ and $\mathbf{g}$ act in the same direction

In case the axis of rotation ($\mathbf{v}$) coincides with the direction of the vertical ($\boldsymbol{\lambda}$) we may set

$$\boldsymbol{\lambda} = \mathbf{v} = (0, 0, 1), \tag{29}$$

and equations (25), (26) and (28) reduce to

$$\nabla^4 w - \frac{2\Omega}{\nu}\frac{\partial \zeta}{\partial z} = -\frac{\gamma}{\nu}\left(\frac{\partial^2\theta}{\partial x^2} + \frac{\partial^2\theta}{\partial y^2}\right), \tag{30}$$

$$\nabla^2\zeta = -\frac{2\Omega}{\nu}\frac{\partial w}{\partial z} \tag{31}$$

and

$$\nabla^6 w + \frac{4\Omega^2}{\nu^2}\frac{\partial^2 w}{\partial z^2} = \frac{\beta\gamma}{\kappa\nu}\left(\frac{\partial^2 w}{\partial x^2} + \frac{\partial^2 w}{\partial y^2}\right). \tag{32}$$

By analogy with the classical Rayleigh-Jeffreys problem, we may expect that in the present case also, convection when it first sets in will have a cellular pattern with the cell walls being surfaces of symmetry. We may then separate the variables by assuming that w, θ and ζ have the forms

$$w = f(x,y)\,W(z), \quad \theta = f(x,y)\,\Theta(z) \quad \text{and} \quad \zeta = f(x,y)\,Z(z), \tag{33}$$

where

$$d^2\left(\frac{\partial^2 f}{\partial x^2}+\frac{\partial^2 f}{\partial y^2}\right) = -a^2 f. \tag{34}$$

This manner of separating the variables is essentially equivalent to analyzing a disturbance which may initiate instability into normal modes and characterizing a mode by its wave-number a/d.

Returning to equations (30) to (32) and substituting for w, θ and ζ in accordance with equations (33) and (34), we find that they can be reduced to the forms

$$(\mathrm{D}^2-a^2)^2\,W - \frac{2\Omega}{\nu}\,d^3\mathrm{D}Z = \frac{\gamma}{\nu}\,a^2 d^2\Theta, \tag{35}$$

$$(\mathrm{D}^2-a^2)\,Z = -\frac{2\Omega}{\nu}\,d\,\mathrm{D}W \tag{36}$$

and

$$(\mathrm{D}^2-a^2)^3\,W + T\mathrm{D}^2W = -Ra^2W, \tag{37}$$

where

$$R = \frac{g\alpha\beta}{\kappa\nu}\,d^4 \tag{38}$$

is the Rayleigh number and

$$T = \frac{4\Omega^2}{\nu^2}\,d^4 \tag{39}$$

is the square of a Reynolds number in terms of which the effect of rotation is to be measured. In reducing the equations to the form (35) to (37) we have assumed that z is measured in units of the depth of the layer (d) from its mid-point so that the boundaries are at $z = \pm\frac{1}{2}$; further $\mathrm{D} = \mathrm{d}/\mathrm{d}z$, where z is measured from the new origin in the new unit.

According to equation (35) the boundary condition $\theta = 0$ for $z = \pm\frac{1}{2}$ requires that

$$(\mathrm{D}^2-a^2)^2\,W - \frac{2\Omega}{\nu}\,d^3\mathrm{D}Z = 0 \quad \text{for} \quad z = \pm\tfrac{1}{2}. \tag{40}$$

The further boundary conditions are (cf. equations (21) to (23))

$$\left.\begin{array}{llllll} & W = 0 & \text{for} & z = \pm\frac{1}{2} & \\ \text{and} \quad \textit{either} & \mathrm{D}W = 0 & \text{and} & Z = 0 & \text{(on a rigid surface)} \\ \textit{or} & \mathrm{D}^2W = 0 & \text{and} & \mathrm{D}Z = 0 & \text{(on a free surface).} \end{array}\right\} \tag{41}$$

Since the boundary condition (40) involves Z it is clear that we cannot treat equation (37) without regard to equation (36); we are, therefore, effectively dealing with a system of equations of order eight.

Equations (40) and (41) provide eight boundary conditions, and the requirement that a solution of equations (36) and (37) satisfy these conditions will determine, for a given a^2, a sequence of possible characteristic values for the Rayleigh number R;

the minimum of the lowest of these characteristic numbers as a function of a^2 will determine the critical Rayleigh number, R_c, at which instability through convection will first set in.

Equations (36) and (37) being ordinary linear differential equations with constant coefficients there is, of course, no difficulty of principle in solving the characteristic value problem associated with these equations. But since the problem will have to be solved for many assigned values of a^2 and T, it is evident that a direct solution of the problem will involve a prohibitive amount of numerical work. However, it will appear that we can develop a convenient variational procedure for solving the problem, similar to the ones which the writer has recently used in the solution of related problems (cf. Chandrasekhar 1952*a*, *b* and 1953*a*, *b*).

5. A variational procedure for solving the characteristic value problem associated with equations (36) and (37)

First we shall obtain an integral expression for R. Letting (cf. equation (40))

$$F = (\mathrm{D}^2 - a^2)^2 W - \frac{2\Omega}{\nu} d^3 \mathrm{D}Z, \tag{42}$$

we can rewrite the differential equations governing W and Z in the forms

$$(\mathrm{D}^2 - a^2) F = -Ra^2 W \tag{43}$$

and

$$(\mathrm{D}^2 - a^2) Z = -\frac{2\Omega}{\nu} d \mathrm{D}W. \tag{44}$$

The boundary condition (40) requires that

$$F = 0 \quad \text{for} \quad z = \pm\tfrac{1}{2}. \tag{45}$$

Now multiply equation (43) by F and integrate over the range of z. After an integration by parts, the left-hand side of the equation gives

$$\int_{-\frac{1}{2}}^{+\frac{1}{2}} F(\mathrm{D}^2 - a^2) F \,\mathrm{d}z = -\int_{-\frac{1}{2}}^{+\frac{1}{2}} [(\mathrm{D}F)^2 + a^2 F^2] \,\mathrm{d}z, \tag{46}$$

the integrated part vanishing on account of (45); and the right-hand side of the equation requires us to consider

$$\int_{-\frac{1}{2}}^{+\frac{1}{2}} WF \,\mathrm{d}z = \int_{-\frac{1}{2}}^{+\frac{1}{2}} W(\mathrm{D}^2 - a^2)^2 W \,\mathrm{d}z - \frac{2\Omega}{\nu} d^3 \int_{-\frac{1}{2}}^{+\frac{1}{2}} W \mathrm{D}Z \,\mathrm{d}z. \tag{47}$$

After two integrations by parts, the first of the two integrals on the right-hand side of (47) becomes (cf. Chandrasekhar 1952*a*, equations (65) and (66))

$$\int_{-\frac{1}{2}}^{+\frac{1}{2}} W(\mathrm{D}^2 - a^2)^2 W \,\mathrm{d}z = \int_{-\frac{1}{2}}^{+\frac{1}{2}} [(\mathrm{D}^2 - a^2) W]^2 \,\mathrm{d}z, \tag{48}$$

while the second, after an integration by parts, gives (cf. equations (41) and (44))

$$\begin{aligned} -\frac{2\Omega}{\nu} d^3 \int_{-\frac{1}{2}}^{+\frac{1}{2}} W \mathrm{D}Z \,\mathrm{d}z &= \frac{2\Omega}{\nu} d^3 \int_{-\frac{1}{2}}^{+\frac{1}{2}} Z \mathrm{D}W \,\mathrm{d}z \\ &= -d^2 \int_{-\frac{1}{2}}^{+\frac{1}{2}} Z(\mathrm{D}^2 - a^2) Z \,\mathrm{d}z. \end{aligned} \tag{49}$$

Remembering that on a bounding surface either Z or DZ must vanish, we obtain after a further integration by parts that

$$-\frac{2\Omega}{\nu}d^3\int_{-\frac{1}{2}}^{+\frac{1}{2}} W\,\mathrm{D}Z\,\mathrm{d}z = d^2\int_{-\frac{1}{2}}^{+\frac{1}{2}}[(\mathrm{D}Z)^2+a^2Z^2]\,\mathrm{d}z. \tag{50}$$

Thus the result of multiplying equation (43) by F and integrating over z is

$$R = \frac{\displaystyle\int_{-\frac{1}{2}}^{+\frac{1}{2}}[(\mathrm{D}F)^2+a^2F^2]\,\mathrm{d}z}{\displaystyle a^2\int_{-\frac{1}{2}}^{+\frac{1}{2}}\{[(\mathrm{D}^2-a^2)\,W]^2+d^2[(\mathrm{D}Z)^2+a^2Z^2]\}\,\mathrm{d}z} = \frac{I_1}{a^2I_2} \quad \text{(say)}. \tag{51}$$

This formula expresses R as a ratio of two positive definite integrals.

Consider now the effect on R of variations δW and δZ in W and Z compatible with the boundary conditions on W and Z. To the first order, we have

$$\delta R = \frac{1}{a^2I_2}\left(\delta I_1 - \frac{I_1}{I_2}\delta I_2\right) = \frac{1}{a^2I_2}(\delta I_1 - a^2R\,\delta I_2), \tag{52}$$

where δI_1 and δI_2 are the corresponding variations in I_1 and I_2:

$$\delta I_1 = 2\int_{-\frac{1}{2}}^{+\frac{1}{2}}[(\mathrm{D}F)\,(D\,\delta F)+a^2F\,\delta F]\,\mathrm{d}z \tag{53}$$

and

$$\delta I_2 = 2\int_{-\frac{1}{2}}^{+\frac{1}{2}}[(\mathrm{D}^2-a^2)\,W]\,[(\mathrm{D}^2-a^2)\,\delta W]\,\mathrm{d}z + 2d^2\int_{-\frac{1}{2}}^{+\frac{1}{2}}[(\mathrm{D}Z)\,(\mathrm{D}\,\delta Z)+a^2Z\,\delta Z]\,\mathrm{d}z. \tag{54}$$

Making use of the boundary conditions which F, δF, W, δW, Z and δZ satisfy, we can reduce the expressions for δI_1 and δI_2 by one, or more, integration by parts. Thus

$$\delta I_1 = -2\int_{-\frac{1}{2}}^{+\frac{1}{2}}\delta F(\mathrm{D}^2-a^2)\,F\,\mathrm{d}z \tag{55}$$

and

$$\begin{aligned}\delta I_2 &= 2\int_{-\frac{1}{2}}^{+\frac{1}{2}}W(\mathrm{D}^2-a^2)^2\,\delta W\,\mathrm{d}z - 2d^2\int_{-\frac{1}{2}}^{+\frac{1}{2}}\delta Z(\mathrm{D}^2-a^2)\,Z\,\mathrm{d}z\\ &= 2\int_{-\frac{1}{2}}^{+\frac{1}{2}}W(\mathrm{D}^2-a^2)^2\,\delta W\,\mathrm{d}z + \frac{4\Omega}{\nu}d^3\int_{-\frac{1}{2}}^{+\frac{1}{2}}\delta Z\,\mathrm{D}W\,\mathrm{d}z\\ &= 2\int_{-\frac{1}{2}}^{+\frac{1}{2}}W\left\{(\mathrm{D}^2-a^2)^2\,\delta W - \frac{2\Omega}{\nu}d^3\,\mathrm{D}\,\delta Z\right\}\mathrm{d}z\\ &= 2\int_{-\frac{1}{2}}^{+\frac{1}{2}}W\delta F\,\mathrm{d}z.\end{aligned} \tag{56}$$

Now combining equations (52), (55) and (56), we obtain

$$\delta R = -\frac{2}{a^2I_2}\int_{-\frac{1}{2}}^{+\frac{1}{2}}\delta F\{(\mathrm{D}^2-a^2)\,F + Ra^2W\}\,\mathrm{d}z, \tag{57}$$

where it may be recalled that equation (42) defining F and equation (44) relating Z and W, have been explicitly used in the reductions.

From equation (57) it follows that $\delta R \equiv 0$ *for all small arbitrary variations* δF provided

$$(\mathrm{D}^2 - a^2) F + Ra^2 W = 0, \tag{58}$$

i.e. if the differential equation governing W is satisfied. It is evident that the converse of this proposition is also true. Moreover, it follows from (57) that the true solution of the problem leads to a minimum value of R when evaluated according to formula (51). This last fact enables us to formulate the following variational procedure for solving equations (36) and (37) (for any assigned a^2) and satisfying the boundary conditions of the problem.

Assume for F an expression involving one or more parameters A_k and which vanishes for $z = \pm\frac{1}{2}$. With the chosen form of F, determine W and Z as solutions of the equations

$$(\mathrm{D}^2 - a^2)^2 W - \frac{2\Omega}{\nu} d^3 \mathrm{D}Z = F \tag{59}$$

and

$$(\mathrm{D}^2 - a^2) Z = -\frac{2\Omega}{\nu} d \mathrm{D}W, \tag{60}$$

and satisfying a total of six boundary conditions on W and Z at $z = \pm\frac{1}{2}$; since equations (59) and (60) are together of order six, there will be enough constants of integration in the general solution to satisfy all the boundary conditions. Then evaluate R according to formula (51) and minimize it with respect to the parameters A_k. In this way we shall obtain the 'best' value of R for the chosen form of F. We shall see in the following section that even with the simplest trial function for F we reach quite high accuracy in the deduced values of R.

Finally, we may note that according to equations (59) and (60) the equation which must be solved in following the variational procedure is

$$(\mathrm{D}^2 - a^2)^3 W + T\mathrm{D}^2 W = (\mathrm{D}^2 - a^2) F, \tag{61}$$

where T is defined as in equation (39); it is evident that Z satisfies an equation of exactly the same form.

6. The critical Rayleigh number for the onset of convection as a function of T for three different types of boundary conditions

In determining the critical Rayleigh number for the onset of convection as a function of T we shall consider three types of boundary conditions: (*a*) both bounding surfaces free, (*b*) both bounding surfaces rigid and (*c*) one bounding surface free and the other rigid.

(*a*) *Both bounding surfaces free*

In this case the solution of equations (36) and (37) satisfying the boundary conditions (cf. equations (40) and (41))

$$W = \mathrm{D}^2 W = \mathrm{D}Z = (\mathrm{D}^2 - a^2)^2 W - \frac{2\Omega}{\nu} d^3 \mathrm{D}Z = 0 \quad (z = \pm\tfrac{1}{2}), \tag{62}$$

or, equivalently,

$$W = \mathrm{D}^2 W = \mathrm{D}^4 W = \mathrm{D}Z = 0 \quad (z = \pm\tfrac{1}{2}), \tag{63}$$

can be explicitly written down. Thus

$$W = \cos n\pi z \quad \text{and} \quad Z = -\frac{2\Omega d}{\nu}\frac{n\pi}{n^2\pi^2+a^2}\sin n\pi z, \tag{64}$$

where n is an integer, clearly represent a solution of equations (36 and (37) satisfying the boundary conditions (63), provided only

$$R = \frac{1}{a^2}[(n^2\pi^2+a^2)^3+n^2\pi^2T]. \tag{65}$$

It can be readily verified that the solution obtained by inspection in this manner is the unique solution of the problem under the present conditions.

Letting $a^2 = n^2\pi^2x$, we can rewrite equation (65) in the form

$$R = n^4\pi^4\frac{1}{x}\left[(1+x)^3+\frac{T}{n^4\pi^4}\right]. \tag{66}$$

From this equation it follows that for a given x (i.e. a^2) instability through convection first sets in for the lowest mode $n = 1$. The corresponding expression for R is

$$R = \pi^4\frac{1}{x}\left[(1+x)^3+\frac{T}{\pi^4}\right]. \tag{67}$$

As a function of x, R given by equation (67) attains its minimum when

$$2x^3+3x^2 = 1+T/\pi^4. \tag{68}$$

It is of interest to note that this cubic equation for determining the wave-number a at which instability first sets in as convection is the same (except that T/π^4 replaces Q/π^2) as the one which occurs in the problem of the inhibition of convection by a magnetic field when the fluid is similarly confined between two free surfaces (cf. Chandrasekhar 1952a, equation (85)).

With x determined as a solution of equation (68), (67) will give the required critical Rayleigh number, R_c. Values of R_c determined in this fashion for some values of T are given in table 1. The inhibiting effect of the Coriolis force on the onset of convection is apparent from this table.

TABLE 1. CRITICAL RAYLEIGH NUMBERS FOR THE CASE WHEN BOTH BOUNDING SURFACES ARE FREE

T	a	R_c	R_c/R_0	T	a	R_c	R_c/R_0
10	2·270	677	1·030	10000	5·698	5377	8·178
100	2·594	826	1·257	30000	6·961	10205	15·52
500	3·278	1275	1·938	100000	8·626	21309	32·41
1000	3·710	1676	2·549	300000	10·45	42573	64·75
2000	4·221	2299	3·497	1000000	12·86	92224	140·3
5000	5·011	3670	5·581				

For T/π^4 sufficiently large, the required root of equation (68) tends to

$$x_{\text{min.}} \to \left(\frac{T}{2\pi^4}\right)^{\frac{1}{3}} \quad (T\to\infty); \tag{69}$$

the corresponding limiting expression for R_c is found to be

$$R_c \to 3\pi^4 \left(\frac{T}{2\pi^4}\right)^{\frac{2}{3}} = 8{\cdot}6956 T^{\frac{2}{3}} \quad (T \to \infty). \tag{70}$$

Substituting for R and T in accordance with their definitions (equations (38) and (39)), we find that the formula which determines the critical temperature gradient $(-\beta_c)$ for convection, when the Coriolis force is dominant, is

$$g\alpha\beta_c \to 21{\cdot}911(\Omega^4/d^4\nu)^{\frac{1}{3}}\kappa \quad (T \to \infty). \tag{71}$$

The changed dependence of β_c on ν and d is particularly noteworthy; we shall return to a discussion of this later in this section.

(*b*) *Both bounding surfaces rigid*

We shall obtain the solution in this case by an application of the variational procedure described in § 5. But first we may observe that it follows from the identity of the boundary conditions to be satisfied in this case at $z = \pm\frac{1}{2}$, that the proper solutions of equations (36) and (37) fall into two non-combining groups of even and odd solutions, respectively, such that when W is even, Z is odd, and conversely. And it also follows that the solutions with W even and Z odd give the lower values of R; we must accordingly choose such solutions.

As a simple trial function for F which satisfies the boundary condition $F = 0$ at $z = \pm\frac{1}{2}$, we shall assume

$$F = \cos\pi z + A(1 + \cos 2\pi z), \tag{72}$$

where A is a variational parameter. With F given by (72) the equation to be solved for W is (cf. equation (61))

$$(\mathrm{D}^2 - a^2)^3 W + T\mathrm{D}^2 W = -[c_1 \cos\pi z + A(c_0 + c_2\cos 2\pi z)], \tag{73}$$

where

$$c_n = n^2\pi^2 + a^2. \tag{74}$$

The solution of equation (73) appropriate to the problem on hand is readily found to be

$$W = c_1\gamma_1\cos\pi z + A(c_0\gamma_0 + c_2\gamma_2\cos 2\pi z) + \sum_{i=1}^{3} B_i \cosh q_i z, \tag{75}$$

where the B_i's ($i = 1, 2, 3$) are constants of integration, the q_i^2's are the three roots of the cubic equation

$$(q^2 - a^2)^3 + Tq^2 = 0, \tag{76}$$

and

$$\gamma_n = (c_n^3 + n^2\pi^2 T)^{-1}. \tag{77}$$

The corresponding solution for Z is

$$Z = -\frac{2\Omega}{\nu} d\left\{\pi\gamma_1 \sin\pi z + 2\pi A\gamma_2 \sin 2\pi z + \sum_{i=1}^{3} \frac{B_i q_i}{q_i^2 - a^2}\sinh q_i z\right\}. \tag{78}$$

The boundary conditions $W = Z = \mathrm{D}W = 0$ at $z = \pm\frac{1}{2}$ now require that

$$\left.\begin{aligned}
\sum_{i=1}^{3} B_i \cosh\tfrac{1}{2}q_i &= A(c_2\gamma_2 - c_0\gamma_0),\\
\sum_{i=1}^{3} B_i q_i \sinh\tfrac{1}{2}q_i &= \pi c_1\gamma_1,\\
\sum_{i=1}^{3} \frac{B_i q_i}{q_i^2 - a^2}\sinh\tfrac{1}{2}q_i &= -\pi\gamma_1.
\end{aligned}\right\} \tag{79}$$

With the constants of integration, B_i, determined by these equations, the solutions for W and Z (equations (75) and (77)) become determinate, and we can evaluate R by formula (51) or more conveniently by

$$R = \frac{\int_{-\frac{1}{2}}^{+\frac{1}{2}} [(\mathrm{D}F)^2 + a^2F^2]\,\mathrm{d}z}{a^2 \int_{-\frac{1}{2}}^{+\frac{1}{2}} WF\,\mathrm{d}z}, \tag{80}$$

since the transformations used in going from (47) to (51) can be used in the reverse fashion; they depend, apart from definitions, only on the boundary conditions of the problem.

The evaluation and reduction of the integrals occurring in the numerator and the denominator of the expression giving R is straightforward though very lengthy. We find

$$\int_{-\frac{1}{2}}^{+\frac{1}{2}} [(\mathrm{D}F)^2 + a^2F^2]\,\mathrm{d}z = \tfrac{1}{2}c_1\left[1 + \frac{32}{3\pi}A + \frac{4\pi^2+3a^2}{\pi^2+a^2}A^2\right] \tag{81}$$

and

$$\begin{aligned}\int_{-\frac{1}{2}}^{+\frac{1}{2}} WF\,\mathrm{d}z = \tfrac{1}{2}\gamma_1\Bigg[c_1 + 4\pi^2\Bigg\{&\frac{F\coth\frac{1}{2}q}{\pi^2+q^2} \\ &+ \frac{\sigma}{\Gamma_1^2+Y^2}[(\Gamma_1 H - YG)\sinh\alpha_1 - (\Gamma_1 G + YH)\sin\alpha_2]\Bigg\}\Bigg] \\ &+ \left[\frac{2}{3\pi}(3c_0\gamma_0 + 4c_1\gamma_1 + c_2\gamma_2) + 2\pi(c_0\gamma_0 - c_2\gamma_2)\right\{\frac{f\coth\frac{1}{2}q}{\pi^2+q^2} \\ &+ \frac{\sigma}{\Gamma_1^2+Y^2}[(\Gamma_1 h - Yg)\sinh\alpha_1 - (\Gamma_1 g + Yh)\sin\alpha_2]\Bigg\} \\ &+ 8\pi^3\gamma_1\left\{\frac{F}{q(4\pi^2+q^2)} + \frac{MG+NH}{\Gamma_2^2+Y^2}\right\}\Bigg]A \\ &+ \left[(c_0\gamma_0 + \tfrac{1}{2}c_2\gamma_2) + 8\pi^2(c_0\gamma_0 - c_2\gamma_2)\left\{\frac{f}{q(4\pi^2+q^2)} + \frac{Mg+Nh}{\Gamma_2^2+Y^2}\right\}\right]A^2,\end{aligned} \tag{82}$$

where the various symbols have the following meanings:

Denoting by x and $X \pm \mathrm{i}Y$ $(Y > 0)$ the roots of the cubic equation

$$x^3 + Tx + Ta^2 = 0, \tag{83}$$

we first define

$$\left.\begin{aligned} &q = \sqrt{(a^2+x)}, \quad k = \frac{1}{x}, \quad \kappa_1 = \frac{X}{X^2+Y^2}, \quad \kappa_2 = -\frac{Y}{X^2+Y^2}, \\ &\alpha_1 = \{\tfrac{1}{2}\sqrt{[(a^2+X)^2+Y^2]} + \tfrac{1}{2}(a^2+X)\}^{\frac{1}{2}}, \\ &\alpha_2 = \{\tfrac{1}{2}\sqrt{[(a^2+X)^2+Y^2]} - \tfrac{1}{2}(a^2+X)\}^{\frac{1}{2}}, \\ &\Gamma_n = n^2\pi^2 + a^2 + X, \quad \sigma = (\cosh\alpha_1 - \cos\alpha_2)^{-1} \\ \text{and}\quad &\delta = \{\sigma q[(\alpha_1\kappa_2 + \alpha_2\kappa_1 - k\alpha_2)\sinh\alpha_1 + (\alpha_1\kappa_1 - \alpha_2\kappa_2 - k\alpha_1)\sin\alpha_2] \\ &\qquad - (\alpha_1^2+\alpha_2^2)\,\kappa_2\coth\tfrac{1}{2}q\}^{-1}. \end{aligned}\right\} \tag{84}$$

With these definitions (see also equations (74) and (77)) the various quantities introduced in (82) are

$$\left.\begin{aligned} f &= \delta\kappa_2(\alpha_1^2+\alpha_2^2),\\ g &= +\delta q(\alpha_1\kappa_1-\alpha_2\kappa_2-k\alpha_1),\\ h &= -\delta q(\alpha_1\kappa_2+\alpha_2\kappa_1-k\alpha_2),\\ F &= \delta\sigma\{[\alpha_2+c_1(\alpha_1\kappa_2+\alpha_2\kappa_1)]\sinh\alpha_1+[\alpha_1+c_1(\alpha_1\kappa_1-\alpha_2\kappa_2)]\sin\alpha_2\},\\ G &= +\delta\{[\alpha_1+c_1(\alpha_1\kappa_1-\alpha_2\kappa_2)]\coth\tfrac{1}{2}q-q\sigma(1+c_1k)\sinh\alpha_1\},\\ H &= -\delta\{[\alpha_2+c_1(\alpha_1\kappa_2+\alpha_2\kappa_1)]\coth\tfrac{1}{2}q+q\sigma(1+c_1k)\sin\alpha_2\},\\ M &= -\alpha_2(\Gamma_2+2\alpha_1^2)/(\alpha_1^2+\alpha_2^2),\\ N &= +\alpha_1(\Gamma_2-2\alpha_2^2)/(\alpha_1^2+\alpha_2^2). \end{aligned}\right\} \quad (85)$$

Returning to equations (80) to (82), we observe that the resulting formula for R is in the form of a ratio of two quadratic expressions in A; and the value of A which leads to the lowest value of R can be determined. By repeating such calculations for various initially assigned values of a^2 we can determine R_c. The results of such calculations are summarized in table 2. The values of R_c given under the column 'first approximation' are those obtained when A is put equal to zero in equations (81) and (82); they therefore correspond to a choice of a trial function (namely, $F = \cos\pi z$) which has no variational parameter in it. The values given under the column 'second approximation' are those obtained by including A in the calculations and minimizing R with respect to it. The extent of the agreement between the values given in the two columns is a measure of the accuracy reached in these calculations.

Finally, we may remark that the asymptotic behaviour of R_c for large T is the same as in case (*a*).

TABLE 2. CRITICAL RAYLEIGH NUMBERS AND RELATED CONSTANTS FOR THE CASE WHEN BOTH BOUNDING SURFACES ARE RIGID

T	a	A	first approximation	second approximation	R_c/R_0
10	3·10	+0·0958	1720	1713	1·003
100	3·15	+0·0959	1764	1756	1·028
500	3·30	+0·0949	1948	1940	1·136
1000	3·50	+0·0941	2159	2151	1·260
2000	3·75	+0·0898	2538	2530	1·482
5000	4·25	+0·0756	3476	3469	2·031
10000	4·80	+0·0555	4717	4712	2·759
30000	5·80	+0·0043	8326	8326	4·876
100000	7·20	−0·0589	16743	16725	9·793
1000000	10·90	−0·1475	71587	71103	41·63

(c) *One bounding surface free and the other rigid*

In this case the conditions to be satisfied on the two bounding surfaces are different. However, the solution for this case can be reduced to that of case (*b*) by considering odd (instead of even) solutions for W. For, it is evident that an odd solution for W satisfying the boundary conditions appropriate for case (b) vanishes at $z = 0$ and satisfies here the boundary conditions appropriate to a free surface. A similar remark applies also to Z. Consequently, a solution with W odd and Z even, suitable for case (b), and applicable to a cell depth d, provides a solution for case (c) applicable to a cell depth $d' = \frac{1}{2}d$ and a Rayleigh and a Taylor number which are sixteen times smaller.

In accordance with the foregoing remarks we shall assume for F the trial function

$$F = \sin 2\pi z + A(\sin \pi z + \sin 3\pi z), \tag{86}$$

where, as before, A is a variational parameter. On carrying through the calculations with this trial function, we find:

$$\int_{-\frac{1}{2}}^{+\frac{1}{2}} [(DF)^2 + a^2F^2]\,dz = \tfrac{1}{2}c_2\left[1 + \frac{128}{15\pi}A + \frac{2(5\pi^2+a^2)}{4\pi^2+a^2}A^2\right] \tag{87}$$

and

$$\begin{aligned}\int_{-\frac{1}{2}}^{+\frac{1}{2}} WF\,dz = \tfrac{1}{2}\gamma_2\Bigg[c_2 + 16\pi^2\Bigg\{&\frac{F'\tanh\frac{1}{2}q}{4\pi^2+q^2}\\ &+\frac{\sigma}{\Gamma_2^2+Y^2}[(\Gamma_2H' - YG')\sinh\alpha_1 + (\Gamma_2G' + YH')\sin\alpha_2]\Bigg\}\Bigg]\\ +\Bigg[\frac{4}{15\pi}(5c_1\gamma_1 + 8c_2\gamma_2 + 3c_3\gamma_3) + 4\pi(c_1\gamma_1 - c_3\gamma_3)\Bigg\{&\frac{f'\tanh\frac{1}{2}q}{4\pi^2+q^2}\\ &+\frac{\sigma}{\Gamma_2^2+Y^2}[(\Gamma_2h' - Yg')\sinh\alpha_1 + (\Gamma_2g' + Yh')\sin\alpha_2]\Bigg\}\\ +32\pi^3\gamma_2\left\{\frac{qF'}{(\pi^2+q^2)(9\pi^2+q^2)} + \frac{M'G'+N'H'}{(\Gamma_1^2+Y^2)(\Gamma_3^2+Y^2)}\right\}\Bigg]A\\ +\Bigg[\tfrac{1}{2}(c_1\gamma_1 + c_3\gamma_3) + 16\pi^2(c_1\gamma_1 - c_3\gamma_3)\Bigg\{&\frac{qf'}{(\pi^2+q^2)(9\pi^2+q^2)}\\ &+\frac{M'g'+N'h'}{(\Gamma_1^2+Y^2)(\Gamma_3^2+Y^2)}\Bigg\}\Bigg]A^2,\end{aligned} \tag{88}$$

where

$$\left.\begin{aligned} f' &= \delta'\kappa_2(\alpha_1^2+\alpha_2^2),\\ g' &= +\delta'q(\alpha_1\kappa_1 - \alpha_2\kappa_2 - k\alpha_1),\\ h' &= -\delta'q(\alpha_1\kappa_2 + \alpha_2\kappa_1 - k\alpha_2),\\ F' &= \delta'\sigma'\{[\alpha_2 + c_2(\alpha_1\kappa_2 + \alpha_2\kappa_1)]\sinh\alpha_1 - [\alpha_1 + c_2(\alpha_1\kappa_1 - \alpha_2\kappa_2)]\sin\alpha_2\},\\ G' &= \delta'\{+[\alpha_1 + c_2(\alpha_1\kappa_1 - \alpha_2\kappa_2)]\tanh\tfrac{1}{2}q - q\sigma'(1+c_2k)\sinh\alpha_1\},\\ H' &= \delta'\{-[\alpha_2 + c_2(\alpha_1\kappa_2 + \alpha_2\kappa_1)]\tanh\tfrac{1}{2}q + q\sigma'(1+c_2k)\sin\alpha_2\},\\ M' &= \alpha_2\{(\Gamma_1\Gamma_3 - Y^2) - 2\alpha_1^2(\Gamma_1+\Gamma_3)\},\\ N' &= \alpha_1\{(\Gamma_1\Gamma_3 - Y^2) + 2\alpha_2^2(\Gamma_1+\Gamma_3)\}.\end{aligned}\right\} \tag{89}$$

In (89) the various symbols (α_1, α_2, etc.,) have the same meanings as in case (b) (equations (74), (77) and (84)), except that now

$$\left.\begin{aligned}\sigma' &= (\cosh\alpha_1 + \cos\alpha_2)^{-1}\\ \text{and}\quad \delta' &= \{\sigma'q[(\alpha_1\kappa_2 + \alpha_2\kappa_1 - k\alpha_2)\sinh\alpha_1 - (\alpha_1\kappa_1 - \alpha_2\kappa_2 - k\alpha_1)\sin\alpha_2]\\ &\qquad - (\alpha_1^2+\alpha_2^2)\kappa_2\tanh\tfrac{1}{2}q\}^{-1}.\end{aligned}\right\} \tag{90}$$

The corresponding formula for R is

$$R = \frac{\int_{-\frac{1}{2}}^{+\frac{1}{2}} [(DF)^2 + a^2F^2]\,dz}{16a^2 \int_{-\frac{1}{2}}^{+\frac{1}{2}} WF\,dz}. \tag{91}$$

The results of calculations based on the foregoing formulae are given in table 3. It may be remarked here that for sufficiently large T, the values of R_c for this case approach one-quarter of that for cases (*a*) and (*b*).

Table 3. Critical Rayleigh numbers and related constants for the case when one of the bounding surfaces is free and the other is rigid

$16T$	$2a$	A	first approximation	second approximation	R_c/R_0
100	5·36	+0·2042	1120	1108	1·006
500	5·40	+0·2026	1148	1136	1·032
1000	5·58	+0·2026	1181	1169	1·062
3000	5·95	+0·1981	1303	1291	1·173
10000	6·80	+0·1807	1650	1638	1·488
30000	8·00	+0·1395	2369	2359	2·143
100000	9·85	+0·0656	4050	4046	3·676
300000	12·00	−0·0115	7230	7229	6·568
1000000	14·85	−0·0825	14532	14510	13·18
3000000	18·10	−0·1256	28506	28406	25·81

(*d*) *General discussion and numerical illustrations*

The results of the calculations for all three cases are illustrated in figures 1 and 2. The proportionalities $a \propto T^{\frac{1}{6}}$ and $R \propto T^{\frac{2}{3}}$ as $T \to \infty$, are apparent from these figures. However, the principal result which emerges from the calculations is that the Coriolis force has, depending on the value of T and the boundary conditions, an inhibiting effect on the onset of convection; and that this inhibiting effect is the greater, the larger the angular velocity Ω and the lower the kinematic viscosity ν. In a general way the reason for this inhibiting effect is clear. The vortex lines have a tendency to be dragged with the fluid, the attachment of the fluid to the vortex lines being the stronger, the lower the viscosity and the larger the angular velocity; and in the limit of zero viscosity, the attachment is a permanent one. Consequently, as Ω increases or ν decreases, motions at right angles to $\mathbf{\Omega}$ become increasingly 'difficult' and this will prevent an 'easy' closing in of the stream lines required for convection. This also explains why when instability finally sets in, it does so for a value of a which is increasingly large; for, a large value of a means that the cells are elongated in the direction of $\mathbf{\Omega}$ and motions in this direction are not hindered.

In the limit $T \to \infty$, the relation giving the critical temperature gradient $(-\beta_c)$ at which convection sets in, changes from

$$g\alpha\beta_c = \text{constant } \kappa\nu d^{-4}, \tag{92}$$

when $\Omega = 0$, to

$$g\alpha\beta_c = \text{constant } \kappa(\Omega^4/d^4\nu)^{\frac{1}{3}}, \tag{93}$$

when $\Omega/\nu \rightarrow \infty$. The fact that the dependence of β_c on d changes from a d^{-4}- to a $d^{-\frac{4}{3}}$-law is likely to be a decisive factor in determining the character of the convection which prevails in planetary and stellar atmospheres.

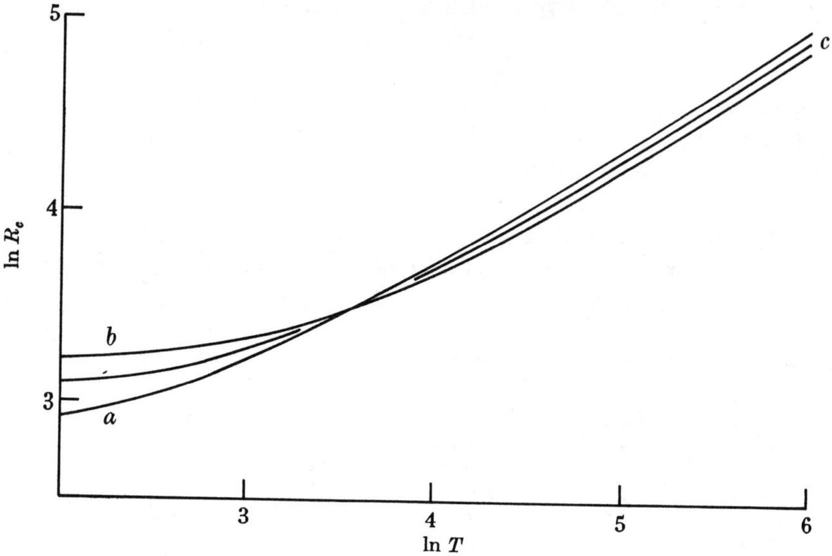

FIGURE 1. The variation of the critical Rayleigh number, R_c, for the onset of convection as a function of T $(= 4\Omega^2 d^4 \cos^2 \vartheta/\nu^2)$ for the three cases: (a) both bounding surfaces free, (b) both bounding surfaces rigid and (c) one bounding surface free and the other rigid.

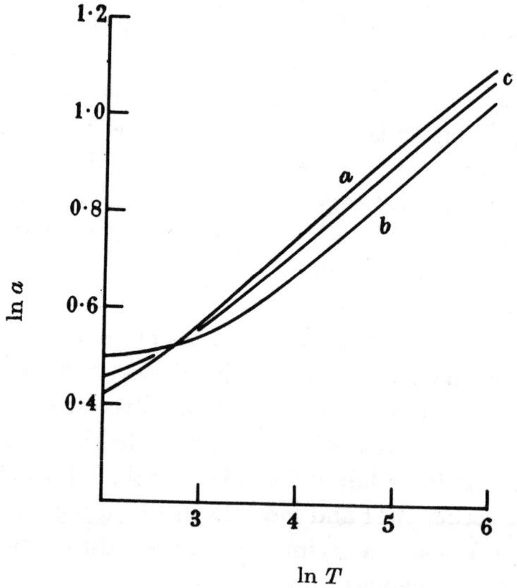

FIGURE 2. The dependence of the wave number a (in the unit $1/d$) of the disturbance at which convection first sets in as a function of T. The three curves refer to the same three cases as figure 1.

In order to see how effective rotation will be in practical cases, we shall consider numerical values suitable for a discussion of the earth's atmosphere. We have

$$\Omega = 7{\cdot}3 \times 10^{-5}/\mathrm{s} \quad \text{and} \quad \nu = 0{\cdot}15\,\mathrm{cm}^2/\mathrm{s}. \tag{94}$$

With these values

$$T = 9{\cdot}4 \times 10^{-5} d^4. \tag{95}$$

The solution for case (*c*) given in table 3 would appear to be the most suitable for applying to the earth's atmosphere. And according to table 3, it is only for $T > 10^6$ that we get inhibiting factors exceeding 10. From equation (95) it would, therefore, follow that for all atmospheric layers, of height in excess of 10 m, the effect of the earth's rotation on the onset of convection is likely to be a determining factor.

As a second example, we shall consider numerical values appropriate for the sun's atmosphere. We have (cf. Chandrasekhar 1952*a*, equation (165))

$$\Omega = 2{\cdot}9 \times 10^{-6}/\mathrm{s} \quad \text{and} \quad \nu = 5 \times 10^3\,\mathrm{cm}^2/\mathrm{s}. \tag{96}$$

With these values

$$T = 10^{-18} d^4. \tag{97}$$

Accordingly, for all layers on the sun, of vertical extent exceeding 10 km, the solar rotation is again likely to be a determining factor.

7. The case when $\boldsymbol{\Omega}$ and $\mathbf{g}$ act in different directions

We shall now briefly consider the case when $\boldsymbol{\Omega}$ and $\mathbf{g}$ act in different directions.

Let $\boldsymbol{\Omega}$ be inclined at an angle ϑ to the vertical. Also let the direction of the x-axis be so chosen that $\boldsymbol{\Omega}$ lies in the xz-plane. Then

$$\boldsymbol{\lambda} = (0, 0, 1) \quad \text{and} \quad \boldsymbol{\upsilon} = (\sin\vartheta, 0, \cos\vartheta), \tag{98}$$

and equations (25), (26) and (28) become

$$\nabla^4 w - \frac{2\Omega}{\nu}\left(\cos\vartheta\frac{\partial}{\partial z} + \sin\vartheta\frac{\partial}{\partial x}\right)\zeta = -\frac{\gamma}{\nu}\left(\frac{\partial^2\theta}{\partial x^2} + \frac{\partial^2\theta}{\partial y^2}\right), \tag{99}$$

$$\nabla^2\zeta = -\frac{2\Omega}{\nu}\left(\cos\vartheta\frac{\partial}{\partial z} + \sin\vartheta\frac{\partial}{\partial x}\right)w, \tag{100}$$

$$\nabla^6 w + \frac{4\Omega^2}{\nu^2}\left(\cos\vartheta\frac{\partial}{\partial z} + \sin\vartheta\frac{\partial}{\partial x}\right)^2 w = \frac{\beta\gamma}{\kappa\nu}\left(\frac{\partial^2 w}{\partial x^2} + \frac{\partial^2 w}{\partial y^2}\right). \tag{101}$$

If we seek solutions of these equations which are independent of x and are of the forms

$$w = W(z)\cos\frac{ay}{d}, \quad \zeta = Z(z)\cos\frac{ay}{d} \quad \text{and} \quad \theta = \Theta(z)\cos\frac{ay}{d}, \tag{102}$$

then equations (99) to (101) can be reduced to equations (35) to (37) with the only difference that in the definition of T (equation (39)), $\Omega\cos\vartheta$ replaces Ω. Consequently, if we restrict ourselves to an onset of convection in the form of infinitely extended 'rolls' (instead of cells) the discussion of the criterion for instability can be carried out exactly as in §§ 4 to 6; and the critical Rayleigh numbers can be deduced from those given in tables 1 to 3 by interpreting Ω to mean the component of $\boldsymbol{\Omega}$ in the direction of the vertical. It may be recalled here that a similar situation was encountered in treating the problem of convection in the presence of a magnetic field when the impressed field (H) is along a direction different from the vertical (Chandrasekhar 1952*a*, §7). The question as to what will happen then was left, as now, with similar remarks. However, both these problems require a more careful examination than they have received. The need for such an examination becomes clear when we consider the joint effects of **H** and **Ω** on the onset of convection. It is not difficult to solve this latter problem when all three vectors **g**, **H** and **Ω** are co-planar; when they are not a curious situation arises, and the questions raised by separating the variables in the manner (102) cannot be evaded. But the consideration of these questions is beyond the scope of this paper: they will be taken up in a separate paper devoted to that purpose.

8. The onset of thermal instability by oscillations of increasing amplitude

For the classical Rayleigh-Jeffreys problem it was shown by Pellew & Southwell (1940) that whenever the temperature gradient is adverse (i.e. whenever β in equation (8) is positive) the linearized form of the equations of motion and heat conduction (i.e. equations (13) and (20) without the Ω-term) allow solutions of the form e^{pt}, where p is of necessity a real number. Consequently, by setting $p = \partial/\partial t = 0$ in the relevant equations, we shall obtain the equations governing the marginal state which separates the stable from the unstable states. In other words, in the absence of rotation, the principle of the exchange of stabilities is valid and instability when it sets in, can only be as convection. However, it will appear that when Coriolis forces are acting, the principle of the exchange of stabilities is not generally true and that the alternative manner in which instability can arise, namely, by oscillations of increasing amplitude (i.e. by 'over-stability' in the sense of Eddington) is a very definite possibility.

We start from the general time-dependent equations (13), (16) and (20). If all the physical quantities vary with time like e^{pt}, the equations reduce to

$$\left.\begin{aligned}(p-\kappa\nabla^2)\,\theta = \beta w, \quad (p-\nu\nabla^2)\,\zeta = 2\Omega v_j \frac{\partial w}{\partial x_j}\\ \text{and}\qquad (p-\nu\nabla^2)\,\nabla^2 w = \gamma\left(\nabla^2-\lambda_i\lambda_j\frac{\partial^2}{\partial x_i\,\partial x_j}\right)\theta-2\Omega v_j\frac{\partial \zeta}{\partial x_j}.\end{aligned}\right\} \qquad (103)$$

In the further discussion of these equations we shall restrict ourselves to the case when **Ω** acts in the same direction as **g**, namely, (0, 0, 1). Then equations (103) become

$$(p-\kappa\nabla^2)\,\theta = \beta w, \quad (p-\nu\nabla^2)\,\zeta = 2\Omega\frac{\partial w}{\partial z} \qquad (104)$$

and

$$(p-\nu\nabla^2)\,\nabla^2 w = \gamma\left(\frac{\partial^2}{\partial x^2}+\frac{\partial^2}{\partial y^2}\right)\theta-2\Omega\frac{\partial \zeta}{\partial z}. \qquad (105)$$

By operating equation (105) by $(p-\kappa\nabla^2)(p-\nu\nabla^2)$ and making use of equations (104), we obtain

$$(p-\nu\nabla^2)^2(p-\kappa\nabla^2)\,\nabla^2 w = \beta\gamma(p-\nu\nabla^2)\left(\frac{\partial^2}{\partial x^2}+\frac{\partial^2}{\partial y^2}\right)w-4\Omega^2(p-\kappa\nabla^2)\frac{\partial^2 w}{\partial z^2}. \qquad (106)$$

We shall now suppose that the variables can be separated, as in §4, by the substitutions (33) and (34). Making these substitutions, we find that equation (106) can be reduced to the form

$$[pd^2-\nu(D^2-a^2)]^2\,[pd^2-\kappa(D^2-a^2)]\,(D^2-a^2)\,W$$
$$=-\beta\gamma d^4a^2[pd^2-\nu(D^2-a^2)]\,W-4\Omega^2d^4[pd^2-\kappa(D^2-a^2)]\,D^2W, \quad (107)$$

where D has now the same meaning as in equation (35) and the subsequent ones; in particular, the same convention regarding the origin of z and the unit in which it is measured is adopted.

A solution of equation (107) must be sought which satisfies the boundary conditions (21) to (23). However, by letting

$$W=\cos\pi z \quad\text{and}\quad Z=-\frac{2\Omega d\pi}{pd^2+\nu(\pi^2+a^2)}\sin\pi z, \quad (108)$$

we can satisfy the equation relating W and Z and the boundary conditions appropriate to a free surface at $z=\pm\frac{1}{2}$. Accordingly, we have an explicit solution for this case. A straightforward discussion of the solution for any other set of boundary conditions (as for cases (*b*) and (*c*) in §7) is likely to be troublesome. It will not be attempted in this paper.

For W given by (108), equation (107) becomes

$$[pd^2+\nu(\pi^2+a^2)]^2\,[pd^2+\kappa(\pi^2+a^2)]\,(\pi^2+a^2)+4\Omega^2d^4\pi^2[pd^2+\kappa(\pi^2+a^2)]$$
$$=\beta\gamma d^4a^2[pd^2+\nu(\pi^2+a^2)]. \quad (109)$$

Letting

$$q=\frac{pd^2}{\pi^2} \quad\text{and}\quad y=\frac{a^2}{\pi^2}+1, \quad (110)$$

we can rewrite equation (109) in the form

$$y(q+\kappa y)\,(q+\nu y)^2+T_1\nu^2(q+\kappa y)=R_1\kappa\nu(y-1)\,(q+\nu y), \quad (111)$$

where

$$T_1=T/\pi^4 \quad\text{and}\quad R_1=R/\pi^4. \quad (112)$$

Equation (111) is a cubic equation for q; it is more convenient to write it in the form

$$q^3+Bq^2+Cq+D=0, \quad (113)$$

where

$$\left.\begin{aligned} B&=(\kappa+2\nu)\,y,\\ C&=\nu(\nu+2\kappa)\,y^2+\frac{T_1}{y}\nu^2-R_1\frac{y-1}{y}\kappa\nu,\\ D&=\kappa\nu^2[y^3+T_1-R_1(y-1)]. \end{aligned}\right\} \quad (114)$$

and (the last line)

In the problem of the inhibition of convection by a magnetic field a similar cubic equation was encountered (Chandrasekhar 1952*a*, §8 equation (132)). The criteria derived there for distinguishing the two types of instabilities which can arise, can be directly applied to the present problem. Thus, $D<0$ is a necessary and sufficient condition for the principle of the exchange of stabilities to be valid, while

$$D>0 \quad\text{and}\quad BC-D<0 \quad (115)$$

are the conditions that equation (113) has a complex root with a positive real part. In the latter case, by letting $BC-D\to 0$ through negative values, we shall have a situation in which a complex root of equation (113), having a positive real part, tends to a purely imaginary limit. The inequalities (115) are, therefore, the necessary and sufficient conditions for the occurrence of over-stability.

With the coefficients B, C and D given by (114), the conditions (115) are equivalent to

$$R_1(y-1) < y^3 + T_1 \tag{116}$$

and

$$\kappa\nu^2[y^3+T_1-R_1(y-1)] > \nu(\nu+2\kappa)(\kappa+2\nu)\,y^3+\nu^2(\kappa+2\nu)\,T_1-\kappa\nu(\kappa+2\nu)\,R_1(y-1). \tag{117}$$

Rearranging this last inequality, we find

$$R_1(y-1) > \frac{2}{\kappa(\kappa+\nu)}[(\kappa+\nu)^2 y^3+\nu^2 T_1]. \tag{118}$$

The inequalities (116) and (118) can now be combined in the form

$$y^3+T_1 > R_1(y-1) > \frac{2}{\kappa(\kappa+\nu)}[(\kappa+\nu)^2 y^3+\nu^2 T_1]. \tag{119}$$

The outer inequalities in the foregoing can be rearranged to give

$$(\kappa-\nu)\,T_1 > (\kappa+\nu)\,y^3. \tag{120}$$

According to (120) a sufficient condition for the principle of the exchange of stabilities to be valid would be $\kappa<\nu$, since in this case (120) can never be satisfied. However, this condition ($\kappa<\nu$) is not met either under terrestrial or under astrophysical conditions. A more detailed examination of the conditions (119) is therefore necessary.

If the conditions (119) should be met and we have a case of over-stability, the Rayleigh number at which this will happen (for the given a^2) will be determined by the condition

$$BC = D, \tag{121}$$

or (cf. equations (112) and (118))

$$R = \pi^4\frac{2(\kappa+\nu)}{\kappa}\frac{1}{x}\left[(1+x)^3+\frac{\nu^2}{(\kappa+\nu)^2}\frac{T}{\pi^4}\right], \tag{122}$$

where for comparison with equation (67) we have replaced y by $x+1$. The lowest Rayleigh number at which over-stability *can* set in, can be obtained by minimizing the expression on the right-hand side of equation (122) with respect to x. It is evident that the results given in table 1 are sufficient to determine this new (R, T)-relation: for, we have only to interpret 'T' in this table as signifying $\nu^2T/(\kappa+\nu)^2$ while the values under 'R_c' should be multiplied by $2(\kappa+\nu)/\kappa$ to be in accord with equation (122). Let the curve in the (R, T)-plane derived in this fashion be called the 'over-stability curve' in contrast to the 'convection curve' representing the (R_c, T)-relation for the onset of convection (this latter is the curve labelled a in figure 1). With the two curves—the convection curve and the over-stability curve—drawn in the (R, T)-plane it is not a difficult matter to decide which of the two types of instabilities can occur, and if both can occur, which will be the first.

Now the convection curve starts on the R-axis at the point

$$R_c\,(\text{con.}) = 6{\cdot}75\pi^4 \quad (T = 0), \tag{123}$$

and for $T \to \infty$ becomes asymptotic to the curve (cf. equation (70))

$$R_c\,(\text{con.}) = 8{\cdot}6956 T^{\frac{2}{3}} \quad (T \to \infty); \tag{124}$$

while the over-stability curve starts on the R-axis at the point

$$R_c\,(\text{o.s.}) = 6{\cdot}75\pi^4 \frac{2(\kappa+\nu)}{\kappa} \quad (T = 0), \tag{125}$$

and for $T \to \infty$ becomes asymptotic to the curve

$$R_c\,(\text{o.s.}) = 8{\cdot}6956 \frac{2\nu^{\frac{4}{3}}}{\kappa(\kappa+\nu)^{\frac{1}{3}}} T^{\frac{2}{3}} \quad (T \to \infty). \tag{126}$$

From a comparison of equations (123) and (125) it follows that the *over-stability curve always starts above the convection curve.* Accordingly, from the asymptotic behaviours (124) and (126) we may conclude that the two curves will not intersect if

$$\frac{2\nu^{\frac{4}{3}}}{\kappa(\kappa+\nu)^{\frac{1}{3}}} > 1, \tag{127}$$

i.e. if

$$\frac{\kappa}{\nu}\left(1+\frac{\kappa}{\nu}\right)^{\frac{1}{3}} < 2. \tag{128}$$

Hence, if we denote by $(\kappa/\nu)^*$ the value of (κ/ν) which makes (128) an equality, the over-stability curve will always lie above the convection curve and will have no intersection with it, if (and only if)

$$(\kappa/\nu) < (\kappa/\nu)^* = 1{\cdot}4780. \tag{129}$$

And if this condition is fulfilled, over-stability cannot arise and the only mode of instability which the system is capable of is by convection. On the other hand if $(\kappa/\nu) > (\kappa/\nu)^*$ the two curves will intersect. Let $T = T^*$ at the point of intersection. Then for $T < T^*$ the over-stability curve lies above the convection curve and for these values of T, over-stability cannot arise and instability when it sets in, must be as convection. But for $T > T^*$ the over-stability curve lies above the convection curve and the conditions (119) can be met; accordingly, under these circumstances, as the Rayleigh number is increased the instability which will be the first to arise is over-stability; convection will become possible only at a higher Rayleigh number.

Now, for air at ordinary temperatures (κ/ν) is nearly equal to the critical value $(\kappa/\nu)^*$; in fact, it appears that it just barely satisfies the condition (129) (cf. Brunt 1939, p. 421, table IX). However, the margin by which (129) is satisfied is so narrow that we must conclude that in the earth's atmosphere thermal instability can, on occasions, arise as over-stability: a possibility which may have some meteorological interest. On the other hand, under astrophysical conditions $\kappa \gg \nu$; in fact, under typical solar atmospheric conditions $\kappa/\nu \sim 10^{10}$ (cf. Chandrasekhar 1952*a*, equation

(165)). And when κ/ν is as large as this, over-stability can set in at far lower Rayleigh numbers than can convection. For $\kappa/\nu \sim 10^{10}$, equation (122) will predict

$$R_c \simeq 13{\cdot}5\pi^4 = 1315$$

for $510 < T < 10^{22}$. It would, therefore, appear that under stellar atmospheric conditions thermal instability can manifest itself far more easily as over-stability than as convection. But this does not mean that turbulence as normally understood will follow conditions of over-stability even as it is presumed to follow conditions of cellular convection. The question obviously requires careful examination.

Finally, it may be noted that when over-stability arises, the frequency of oscillation at marginal stability will be given by

$$p' = \frac{\pi^2}{d^2}\sqrt{C} = \frac{\pi^2}{d^2}\sqrt{\frac{D}{B}} \quad (BC = D). \tag{130}$$

The corresponding velocity of wave propagation is

$$V = \frac{dp'}{\pi} = \frac{\pi}{d}\sqrt{C} = \frac{\pi}{d}\sqrt{\frac{D}{B}}. \tag{131}$$

9. Concluding remarks

The present paper has shown the importance of including the effect of Coriolis forces in treating problems of thermal instability which occur in nature. The extension of the analysis of this paper to the problem of the thermal instability of a rotating fluid sphere will be of particular interest for geophysics and geomagnetism. It appears that the methods which have recently been developed for the solution of problems of thermal instability in a fluid sphere (Chandrasekhar 1952*b*, 1953*b*) can be extended to include the effects of rotation.

A problem of a different kind which this paper suggests is to take into account the simultaneous effects of rotation and of an impressed magnetic field. The consideration of this problem is likely to be instructive in exhibiting the conflicting tendencies to which a conducting fluid is subject in its attempt to attach itself simultaneously to the vortex lines and the lines of magnetic force. The writer hopes to consider these matters in the near future.

In concluding this paper I should like to record my indebtedness to Miss Donna Elbert for her very valuable assistance in having carried out all the numerical calculations involved in the preparation of this paper.

References

Bénard, H. 1901 *Ann. Chim. (Phys.)*, **23**, 62.
Brunt, D. 1939 *Physical and dynamical meteorology*. Cambridge University Press.
Chandra, K. 1938 *Proc. Roy. Soc.* A, **164**, 231.
Chandrasekhar, S. 1952*a* *Phil. Mag.* (7), **43**, 501.
Chandrasekhar, S. 1952*b* *Phil. Mag.* (7), **43**, 1317.
Chandrasekhar, S. 1953*a* *Proc. Roy. Soc.* A, **216**, 293.
Chandrasekhar, S. 1953*b* *Phil. Mag.* (7), **44**, 233.

Graham, A. 1934 *Phil. Trans.* A, **232**, 285.
Jeffreys, H. 1926 *Phil. Mag.* (7), **2**, 833.
Jeffreys, H. 1928 *Proc. Roy. Soc.* A, **118**, 195.
Low, A. R. 1929 *Proc. Roy. Soc.* A, **125**, 180.
Pellew, A. & Southwell, R. V. 1940 *Proc. Roy. Soc.* A, **176**, 312.
Rayleigh, Lord 1916 *Phil. Mag.* (6), **32**, 529; also *Scientific papers*, **6**, 432.
Wasiutynski, J. 1946 *Astrophys. Norveg.* **4**.

Reprinted (with corrections) from *Proceedings of the Royal Society*, Series A, Vol. 231, Aug. 22, 1955.

The instability of a layer of fluid heated below and subject to Coriolis forces. II

By S. Chandrasekhar, F.R.S and Donna D. Elbert
University of Chicago

(*Received* 5 *April* 1955)

The theory described in an earlier paper (Chandrasekhar 1953*b*) is extended in a manner which enables the determination of the critical Rayleigh number for the onset of thermal instability of a layer of fluid heated below and subject to rotation via a marginal state of purely oscillatory motions. Numerical results are derived for the case when the ratio of the kinematic viscosity to the thermometric conductivity has a value (= 0·025) equal to that for mercury at ordinary temperatures. A comparison of the theoretical results obtained in this paper with those of experiments will be found in the following paper by Fultz & Nakagawa.

1. Introduction

In an earlier paper (Chandrasekhar 1953*b*; this paper will be referred to hereafter as I) it was shown that the effect of Coriolis acceleration on the instability of a horizontal layer of fluid heated below is to inhibit the onset of instability; and that the extent of the inhibition depends on the value of the non-dimensional parameter

$$T = \frac{4\Omega^2 \cos^2 \vartheta}{\nu^2} d^4, \tag{1}$$

where ν denotes the kinematic viscosity, d the depth of the layer considered, Ω the angular velocity of rotation and ϑ the inclination of the direction of $\mathbf{\Omega}$ to the vertical. It was further shown that the instability can, depending on circumstances, set in either as convection and a stationary pattern of motions or as over-stability and an oscillatory pattern of motions.

In I the critical Rayleigh numbers (R_c) for the onset of instability as convection for various values of T were derived for the three cases: (*a*) both bounding surfaces free, (*b*) both bounding surfaces rigid and (*c*) one bounding surface free and the other rigid. In all three cases

$$R_c \rightarrow \text{constant} \times T^{\frac{2}{3}} \quad (T \rightarrow \infty). \tag{2}$$

while the wave number a (in units of $1/d$) of the disturbance which manifests itself at marginal stability increases with T according to the law

$$a \rightarrow \text{constant} \times T^{\frac{1}{6}} \quad (T \rightarrow \infty). \tag{3}$$

But it was also shown in I that if the ratio (ϖ) of the kinematic viscosity (ν) to the thermometric conductivity (κ) is less than a certain critical value ϖ^* (say) then for all T greater than a determinate T^* (depending on ϖ) the type of instability which should set in first is over-stability and not convection. For the particular case of a layer of fluid confined between two free surfaces the precise value of ϖ^* was determined and shown to be equal to 0·67659 (= 1/1·4780; cf. I, equation (129)); further, it was shown that for this case the (R_c, T)-relation for the onset of over-stability can be deduced from the corresponding relation for the onset of convection

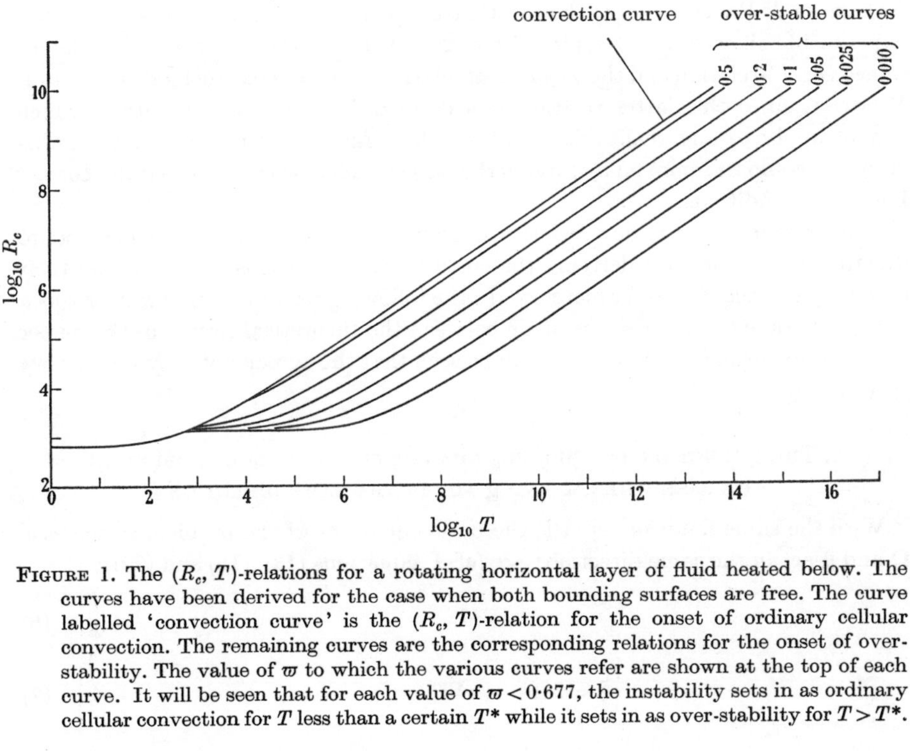

FIGURE 1. The (R_c, T)-relations for a rotating horizontal layer of fluid heated below. The curves have been derived for the case when both bounding surfaces are free. The curve labelled 'convection curve' is the (R_c, T)-relation for the onset of ordinary cellular convection. The remaining curves are the corresponding relations for the onset of over-stability. The value of ϖ to which the various curves refer are shown at the top of each curve. It will be seen that for each value of $\varpi < 0·677$, the instability sets in as ordinary cellular convection for T less than a certain T^* while it sets in as over-stability for $T > T^*$.

by suitable changes in the scales of R and T (cf. the remarks in I following equation (122)). In figure 1 the (R_c, T)-relations derived in this manner for various values of ϖ are illustrated. More particularly, the asymptotic behaviours of the curves shown in figure 1 are given by

$$\left.\begin{aligned} R_c\,(\text{convection}) &\to 8{\cdot}6956\,T^{\frac{2}{3}} \\ \text{and} \qquad R_c\,(\text{over-stability}) &\to 8{\cdot}6956\,\frac{2\varpi^{\frac{4}{3}}}{(1+\varpi)^{\frac{1}{3}}}\,T^{\frac{2}{3}}. \end{aligned}\right\} \tag{4}$$

In the case of water $\varpi = 6$; and this is so much greater than 0·67659 that we should expect (even though the value 0·67659 was derived for an unrealizable set of boundary conditions) that thermal instability in a layer of water in rotation should set in as convection. Experiments by Nakagawa & Frenzen (1955) not only confirmed this expectation but also provided a quantitative verification of the theory developed in I. On the other hand, for mercury $\varpi = 0{\cdot}025$; and this is so much less than 0·67659 that we should expect that in this case the instability should set in as oscillations of increasing amplitude. And the effect should be easily detectable, since according to (4)

$$\frac{R_c\,(\text{over-stability})}{R_c\,(\text{convection})} = \frac{1}{69} \quad (T \to \infty;\ \varpi = 0{\cdot}025). \tag{5}$$

Consequently, the (R_c, T)-relation for mercury should lie well below the theoretical curve derived in I for the onset of convection. Preliminary experiments by Fultz, Nakagawa & Frenzen (1954) showed that this is indeed the case. However, later experiments showed a systematic discrepancy between the experimentally determined (R_c, T)-relation and the theoretical relation for $\varpi = 0{\cdot}025$ included in figure 1. However, since this latter relation was derived for boundary conditions which cannot apply to any realizable situation, the possibility remained that the discrepancy could be removed by solving the basic problem with the physically correct boundary conditions.

The present paper is devoted to the solution of the general problem and to describing a method for deriving the correct (R_c, T)-relations and obtaining their explicit numerical forms for mercury. In the following paper by Fultz & Nakagawa (1955) a detailed comparison is made between the theoretical results of this paper and their experimental results. It will be seen that the agreement they find is very satisfactory.

2. The reduction to a double characteristic value problem in the case when $\mathbf{\Omega}$ and $\mathbf{g}$ act in the same direction

With the same notation as in I, the basic equations of the problem in the case $\mathbf{\Omega}$ and $\mathbf{g}$ act in the same direction† are (cf. I, equations (13), (16) and (20)):

$$\frac{\partial \theta}{\partial t} = \beta w + \kappa \nabla^2 \theta, \tag{6}$$

$$\frac{\partial \zeta}{\partial t} = 2\Omega \frac{\partial w}{\partial z} + \nu \nabla^2 \zeta \tag{7}$$

and

$$-\frac{\partial}{\partial t} \nabla^2 w = 2\Omega \frac{\partial \zeta}{\partial z} - \nu \nabla^4 w - \gamma \left(\frac{\partial^2}{\partial x^2} + \frac{\partial^2}{\partial y^2} \right) \theta. \tag{8}$$

If all the physical quantities are assumed to vary with time like e^{ipt}, the equations become

$$(\kappa \nabla^2 - ip)\,\theta = -\beta w, \tag{9}$$

$$(\nu \nabla^2 - ip)\,\zeta = -2\Omega \frac{\partial w}{\partial z} \tag{10}$$

and

$$(\nu \nabla^2 - ip)\,\nabla^2 w - 2\Omega \frac{\partial \zeta}{\partial z} = -\gamma \left(\frac{\partial^2}{\partial x^2} + \frac{\partial^2}{\partial y^2} \right) \theta. \tag{11}$$

† It would appear (cf. Chandrasekhar 1954*a*; see especially the discussion on p. 1190) that the results for the case when $\mathbf{\Omega}$ and $\mathbf{g}$ do not act in the same direction can be obtained by simply interpreting Ω in the definition of T to mean the component of $\mathbf{\Omega}$ in the direction of the vertical.

We shall now suppose that the variables (x, y and z) can be separated as in I, §4, by the substitutions I, equations (33) and (34). Making these substitutions and measuring z in units of the depth of the layer, d, from its mid-point (so that the boundaries are at $z = \pm\frac{1}{2}$) we find that equations (9) to (11) can be reduced to the forms

$$\left[(\mathrm{D}^2-a^2)-\mathrm{i}\frac{pd^2}{\kappa}\right]\Theta = -\frac{\beta}{\kappa}d^2W, \tag{12}$$

$$\left[(\mathrm{D}^2-a^2)-\mathrm{i}\frac{pd^2}{\nu}\right]Z = -\frac{2\Omega}{\nu}d\mathrm{D}W \tag{13}$$

and

$$\left[(\mathrm{D}^2-a^2)-\mathrm{i}\frac{pd^2}{\nu}\right](\mathrm{D}^2-a^2)W-\frac{2\Omega}{\nu}d^3\mathrm{D}Z = \frac{\gamma}{\nu}a^2d^2\Theta, \tag{14}$$

where $\mathrm{D} = \mathrm{d}/\mathrm{d}z$. Now letting

$$\sigma = \frac{pd^2}{\nu}, \quad \frac{\nu}{\kappa} = \varpi \quad \text{and} \quad \varpi\sigma = \frac{pd^2}{\kappa}, \tag{15}$$

we can combine equations (12) and (14) in the manner

$$(\mathrm{D}^2-a^2-\mathrm{i}\varpi\sigma)F = -Ra^2W, \tag{16}$$

where

$$F = (\mathrm{D}^2-a^2-\mathrm{i}\sigma)(\mathrm{D}^2-a^2)W-\frac{2\Omega}{\nu}d^3\mathrm{D}Z \tag{17}$$

and

$$R = \frac{\beta\gamma}{\kappa\nu}d^4 = \frac{g\alpha\beta}{\kappa\nu}d^4, \tag{18}$$

denotes, as usual, the Rayleigh number. The remaining equation

$$(\mathrm{D}^2-a^2-\mathrm{i}\sigma)Z = -\frac{2\Omega}{\nu}d\mathrm{D}W, \tag{19}$$

can be further combined with equation (17) to give

$$[(\mathrm{D}^2-a^2-\mathrm{i}\sigma)^2(\mathrm{D}^2-a^2)+T\mathrm{D}^2]W = (\mathrm{D}^2-a^2-\mathrm{i}\sigma)F, \tag{20}$$

where

$$T = \frac{4\Omega^2}{\nu^2}d^4 \tag{21}$$

is, what has now come to be called, the Taylor number.

Solutions of equations (16), (17) and (19) must now be sought which satisfy the boundary conditions (cf. I, equations (40) and (41))

$$\left.\begin{array}{lll} & W = F = 0 \quad \text{for} \quad z = \pm\frac{1}{2} & \\ \textit{either} & \mathrm{D}W = 0 \quad \text{and} \quad Z = 0 & \text{(on a rigid surface),} \\ \textit{or} & \mathrm{D}^2W = 0 \quad \text{and} \quad \mathrm{D}Z = 0 & \text{(on a free surface).} \end{array}\right\} \tag{22}$$

and (the last two lines of (22) apply)

These equations provide eight boundary conditions and the requirement that a solution of equations (16), (17) and (19) satisfy these conditions will determine for given a^2 and σ (which can be complex) a sequence of possible values for R. These characteristic values of R will in general be complex. But the physical interpretation of R requires it to be real. Hence, for a given a^2 the condition that R be real implies a relation between the real and the imaginary parts of σ. Since we are at present seeking only to specify the critical Rayleigh number for the onset of instability via purely oscillatory motions, it will suffice to consider only real values of σ. The solution of the problem, therefore, resolves itself to solving the following *double characteristic value problem*:

For an assigned a^2, σ (assumed to be real) is to be determined by the condition that the characteristic value of R is real. In general, there will be a sequence of possible values for σ (for any given a^2) which will make R real. We are, however, interested only in the particular σ which gives the lowest positive value for R. Let $R_c(a^2)$ and $\sigma_c(a^2)$ denote the corresponding values of R and σ. The meaning to be attached to these values is this: As the Rayleigh number is gradually increased, a disturbance in the horizontal plane characterized by the wave number a (in the unit $1/d$) first becomes unstable by over-stability when it reaches the value $R_c(a^2)$; and $\sigma_c(a^2)$ is the frequency (in the unit ν/d^2) of the oscillations which are set up in the marginal state. Consequently, to determine the critical Rayleigh number for the onset of over-stability we must determine the minimum of the function $R_c(a^2)$. And this minimum is required for various initially assigned values of T.

It should be apparent from the foregoing that an exact solution of the double characteristic-value problem presents a numerical problem of considerable magnitude. However, in this case, as in similar problems which have been treated (Chandrasekhar 1952*a*, *b*, 1953*a*, *b*, 1954*a*) we can devise a variational method for solving the problem. This method is described in the following section; but even with the simplification provided by the variational method the numerical work which is required to complete the solution of the problem remains considerable.

3. The variational method

Equations (16), (17), (19) and (20) can be treated in the same manner as in I, §5. Thus multiplying equation (16) by F and integrating over the range of z, we obtain after an integration by part, the equation

$$\int_{-\frac{1}{2}}^{+\frac{1}{2}} [(DF)^2 + (a^2 + i\varpi\sigma) F^2]\, dz = Ra^2 \int_{-\frac{1}{2}}^{+\frac{1}{2}} WF\, dz. \tag{23}$$

The right-hand side of this equation requires us to consider (cf. equation (17))

$$\int_{-\frac{1}{2}}^{+\frac{1}{2}} WF\, dz = \int_{-\frac{1}{2}}^{+\frac{1}{2}} W\left\{(D^2 - a^2)^2 W - i\sigma(D^2 - a^2) W - \frac{2\Omega}{\nu} d^3 DZ\right\} dz. \tag{24}$$

After several integrations by part we find that

$$\int_{-\frac{1}{2}}^{+\frac{1}{2}} WF\, dz = \int_{-\frac{1}{2}}^{+\frac{1}{2}} \{[(D^2 - a^2) W]^2 + i\sigma[(DW)^2 + a^2 W^2]\}\, dz + \frac{2\Omega}{\nu} d^3 \int_{-\frac{1}{2}}^{+\frac{1}{2}} Z DW\, dz, \tag{25}$$

the integrated parts always vanishing on account of boundary conditions. Now making use of equations (19), we find after a further integration by parts that

$$\int_{-\frac{1}{2}}^{+\frac{1}{2}} WF\, dz = \int_{-\frac{1}{2}}^{+\frac{1}{2}} \{[(D^2 - a^2) W]^2 + d^2[(DZ)^2 + a^2 Z^2]\}\, dz + i\sigma \int_{-\frac{1}{2}}^{+\frac{1}{2}} \{(DW)^2 + a^2 W^2 + d^2 Z^2\}\, dz. \tag{26}$$

Thus, the result of multiplying equation (16) by F and integrating over z is

$$R = \frac{\int_{-\frac{1}{2}}^{+\frac{1}{2}} [(\mathrm{D}F)^2 + (a^2 + \mathrm{i}\varpi\sigma) F^2] \, \mathrm{d}z}{a^2 \int_{-\frac{1}{2}}^{+\frac{1}{2}} \{[(\mathrm{D}^2 - a^2) W]^2 + d^2[(\mathrm{D}Z)^2 + a^2 Z^2] + \mathrm{i}\sigma[(\mathrm{D}W)^2 + a^2 W^2 + d^2 Z^2]\} \, \mathrm{d}z} = \frac{I_1}{a^2 I_2} \quad \text{(say)}. \tag{27}$$

Now it can be readily verified that the variation δR in R given by equation (27) due to variations δW and δZ in W and Z compatible only with the boundary conditions on W, Z and F, is given by

$$\delta R = -\frac{2}{a^2 I_2} \int_{-\frac{1}{2}}^{+\frac{1}{2}} \delta F\{(\mathrm{D}^2 - a^2 - \mathrm{i}\varpi\sigma) F + R a^2 W\} \, \mathrm{d}z. \tag{28}$$

Accordingly, $\delta R \equiv 0$ for all small arbitrary variations δF provided

$$(\mathrm{D}^2 - a^2 - \mathrm{i}\varpi\sigma) F + R a^2 W = 0, \tag{29}$$

i.e. if the differential equation governing W is satisfied. On this account, formula (27) provides the basis for the following variational procedure for solving equations (16), (17) and (19) (for any assigned a^2 and σ) and satisfying the boundary conditions of the problem:

Assume for F an expression involving one or more parameters A_k and which vanishes for $z = \pm\frac{1}{2}$. With the chosen form of F determine W and Z as solutions of equations (17) and (19) (or equivalently (19) and (20)) and satisfying a total of six boundary conditions on W and Z; since equations (17) and (19) are together of order six, there will be just enough constants of integration to satisfy the necessary boundary conditions. Next evaluate R in accordance with equation (27). Then determine the constants A_k by the condition that R is extremal with respect to variations of these constants. With the A_k's determined in this fashion formula (27) provides the best value of R for the chosen form of F.

4. The critical Rayleigh number for the onset of over-stability as a function of T for three different types of boundary conditions and for $\varpi = 0{\cdot}025$.

(*a*) *Both bounding surfaces rigid*

As the simplest trial function for F which vanishes at $z = \pm\frac{1}{2}$ we shall assume

$$F = \cos \pi z. \tag{30}$$

This is a trial function with no variational parameters. Nevertheless, from our earlier experience with problems of this kind (cf. I, for example) we may be confident that already this trial function will lead to values of R which are accurate to within 1 %.

With F given by (30) the equation to be solved for W is (cf. equation (20))

$$[(\mathrm{D}^2 - a^2 - \mathrm{i}\sigma)^2 (\mathrm{D}^2 - a^2) + T\mathrm{D}^2] W = -(\pi^2 + a^2 + \mathrm{i}\sigma) \cos \pi z. \tag{31}$$

The solution of this equation appropriate to the problem on hand is

$$W = c_1\gamma_1 \cos \pi z + \sum_{j=1}^{3} B_j \cos q_j z, \tag{32}$$

where

$$\left.\begin{aligned} c_n &= n^2\pi^2 + a^2 + i\sigma, \\ \gamma_n &= [c_n^2(n^2\pi^2 + a^2) + n^2\pi^2 T]^{-1}, \end{aligned}\right\} \tag{33}$$

the B_j's are constants of integration and the q_j^2's ($j = 1, 2, 3$) are the roots of the cubic equation

$$(q^2 - a^2 - i\sigma)^2 (q^2 - a^2) + Tq^2 = 0. \tag{34}$$

The corresponding solution for Z is (cf. equation (19))

$$Z = -\frac{2\Omega}{\nu} d \left\{ \pi\gamma_1 \sin \pi z + \sum_{j=1}^{3} B_j q_j k_j \sinh q_j z \right\}, \tag{35}$$

where

$$k_j = (q_j^2 - a^2 - i\sigma)^{-1}. \tag{36}$$

The boundary conditions, $W = Z = DW = 0$, at $z = \pm\frac{1}{2}$ now require

$$\left.\begin{aligned} &\sum_{j=1}^{3} B_j \cosh \tfrac{1}{2}q_j = 0, \\ &\sum_{j=1}^{3} B_j q_j \sinh \tfrac{1}{2}q_j = \pi c_1 \gamma_1, \\ &\sum_{j=1}^{3} B_j q_j k_j \sinh \tfrac{1}{2}q_j = -\pi\gamma_1. \end{aligned}\right\} \tag{37}$$

On solving these equations, we find that

$$B_1 = -\pi\gamma_1\{q_2(1 + c_1 k_2) \coth \tfrac{1}{2}q_3 - q_3(1 + c_1 k_3) \coth \tfrac{1}{2}q_2\} \Delta_1 \operatorname{cosech} \tfrac{1}{2}q_1, \tag{38}$$

where

$$\Delta_1^{-1} = \{q_2 q_3(k_2 - k_3) \coth \tfrac{1}{2}q_1 + q_3 q_1(k_3 - k_1) \coth \tfrac{1}{2}q_2 + q_1 q_2(k_1 - k_2) \coth \tfrac{1}{2}q_3\}; \tag{39}$$

and B_2 and B_3 are given by similar expressions which can be obtained by cyclically permuting the q_j's and the k_j's in equation (38).

With W and F given by equations (30) and (32), we readily find that

$$\int_{-\frac{1}{2}}^{+\frac{1}{2}} [(DF)^2 + (a^2 + i\varpi\sigma) F^2] \, dz = \tfrac{1}{2}(\pi^2 + a^2 + i\varpi\sigma) \tag{40}$$

and

$$\int_{-\frac{1}{2}}^{+\frac{1}{2}} WF \, dz = \tfrac{1}{2}c_1\gamma_1 + 2\pi \sum_{j=1}^{3} \frac{B_j}{q_j^2 + \pi^2} \cosh \tfrac{1}{2}q_j. \tag{41}$$

On substituting for the B_j's in accordance with equation (38) in equation (41), we find after some reductions in which use is made of the identity

$$\prod_{j=1}^{3} (n^2\pi^2 + q_j^2) = \gamma_n^{-1}, \tag{42}$$

that

$$\begin{aligned} \int_{-\frac{1}{2}}^{+\frac{1}{2}} WF \, dz = \tfrac{1}{2}c_1\gamma_1 - 2\pi^2\gamma_1^2\Delta_1 \prod_{j=1}^{3} \coth \tfrac{1}{2}q_j \\ \times \{q_1(q_2^2 - q_3^2)(q_1^2 + \pi^2)(1 + c_1 k_1) \tanh \tfrac{1}{2}q_1 \\ + q_2(q_3^2 - q_1^2)(q_2^2 + \pi^2)(1 + c_1 k_2) \tanh \tfrac{1}{2}q_2 \\ + q_3(q_1^2 - q_2^2)(q_3^2 + \pi^2)(1 + c_1 k_3) \tanh \tfrac{1}{2}q_3\}. \end{aligned} \tag{43}$$

For the chosen form of F (namely, $\cos \pi z$) the variational formula for R is

$$R = \frac{1}{2a^2} \frac{\pi^2 + a^2 + i\varpi\sigma}{\int_{-\frac{1}{2}}^{+\frac{1}{2}} WF \, dz}, \tag{44}$$

where the integral in the denominator is given by equation (43).

In the calculations based on the foregoing formulae, which we shall now present, the value

$$\varpi = 0{\cdot}025 \tag{45}$$

was adopted; for mercury at ordinary temperatures (with $\kappa = 4{\cdot}7 \times 10^{-2}\,\text{cm}^2/\text{s}$ and $\nu \doteq 1{\cdot}2 \times 10^{-3}\,\text{cm}^2/\text{s}$) has approximately this value of ϖ. Some details regarding the method by which the corresponding (R_c, T)-relation was derived may be of interest:

TABLE 1. CRITICAL RAYLEIGH NUMBERS AND RELATED CONSTANTS FOR THE ONSET OF OVER-STABILITY IN CASE BOTH BOUNDING SURFACES ARE RIGID AND $\varpi = 0{\cdot}025$

T	a	σ	R_c	p/Ω
10^4	3·08	$4{\cdot}45 \times 10^1$	$4{\cdot}39 \times 10^3$	0·8902
10^6	4·09	$5{\cdot}82 \times 10^2$	$9{\cdot}51 \times 10^3$	1·1646
5×10^7	8·10	$2{\cdot}43 \times 10^3$	$6{\cdot}29 \times 10^4$	0·6862
2×10^8	10·28	$3{\cdot}92 \times 10^3$	$1{\cdot}38 \times 10^5$	0·5541
10^9	13·46	$6{\cdot}81 \times 10^3$	$3{\cdot}54 \times 10^5$	0·4310
10^{10}	19·7	$1{\cdot}50 \times 10^4$	$1{\cdot}42 \times 10^6$	0·2992
10^{11}	28·75	$3{\cdot}27 \times 10^4$	$5{\cdot}83 \times 10^6$	0·2069
10^{12}	41·7	$7{\cdot}18 \times 10^4$	$2{\cdot}44 \times 10^7$	0·1435

TABLE 2. CRITICAL RAYLEIGH NUMBERS AND WAVE NUMBERS OF THE UNSTABLE MODES AT MARGINAL STABILITY FOR THE ONSET OF CONVECTION IN CASE BOTH BOUNDING SURFACES ARE RIGID

T	a	R_c	T	a	R_c
10	3·10	$1{\cdot}713 \times 10^3$	10^4	4·80	$4{\cdot}712 \times 10^3$
10^2	3·15	$1{\cdot}756 \times 10^3$	3×10^4	5·80	$8{\cdot}326 \times 10^3$
5×10^2	3·30	$1{\cdot}940 \times 10^3$	10^5	7·20	$1{\cdot}672 \times 10^4$
10^3	3·50	$2{\cdot}151 \times 10^3$	10^6	10·80	$7{\cdot}110 \times 10^4$
2×10^3	3·75	$2{\cdot}530 \times 10^3$	10^8	24·5	$1{\cdot}528 \times 10^6$
5×10^3	4·25	$3{\cdot}469 \times 10^3$	10^{10}	55·5	$3{\cdot}459 \times 10^7$

For a chosen value of a, R was evaluated in accordance with equations (43) and (44) for various assigned values of σ; and the value of σ for which R is real was deduced by interpolation. Thus for

$$T = 10^{10} \quad \text{and} \quad a = 19{\cdot}8 \tag{46}$$

it was found that

$$\left.\begin{aligned} R &= 1{\cdot}983 \times 10^6 - 5{\cdot}882 \times 10^5 i \quad \text{for} \quad \sigma = 1{\cdot}420 \times 10^4, \\ R &= 1{\cdot}322 \times 10^6 + 9{\cdot}510 \times 10^4 i \quad \text{for} \quad \sigma = 1{\cdot}500 \times 10^4 \\ \text{and} \quad R &= 1{\cdot}414 \times 10^6 + 3{\cdot}29 \times 10^3 i \quad \text{for} \quad \sigma = 1{\cdot}489 \times 10^4. \end{aligned}\right\} \tag{47}$$

From these values, it can be estimated that

$$R = 1{\cdot}418 \times 10^6 \quad \text{for} \quad \sigma = 1{\cdot}4886 \times 10^4. \tag{48}$$

By repeating such calculations for other a's, the minimum of R as a function of a may be determined. Thus, in the example considered, it was found that:

$$\left.\begin{array}{llll} \text{for} & a = 19{\cdot}6, & \sigma = 1{\cdot}503\times 10^4, & R = 1{\cdot}41765\times 10^6; \\ \text{for} & a = 19{\cdot}7, & \sigma = 1{\cdot}496\times 10^4, & R = 1{\cdot}4175 \times 10^6; \\ \text{for} & a = 19{\cdot}8, & \sigma = 1{\cdot}489\times 10^4, & R = 1{\cdot}4177 \times 10^6. \end{array}\right\} \tag{49}$$

Consequently, it may be concluded that for $T = 10^{10}$ the critical Rayleigh number for the onset of over-stability is $1{\cdot}4175\times 10^6$ when $a = 19{\cdot}7$ and $\sigma = 1{\cdot}496\times 10^4$. Earlier experience with similar problems suggests that the value of R_c derived in this manner may be trusted to within 1 %.

In table 1 the results of such calculations are summarized. For comparison, in table 2 the corresponding results derived in I (together with some additional ones) for the onset of instability as convection are given.

(b) *One bounding surface free and the other rigid*

In this case the conditions to be satisfied on the two bounding surfaces are different. However, the solution for this case can be reduced to that of case (a) by considering odd (instead of even) solutions for W. For, it is evident that an odd solution for W satisfying the boundary conditions for case (a) vanishes at $z = 0$ and satisfies here the conditions appropriate to a free surface. A similar remark applies to Z. Consequently, a solution with W odd and Z even suitable for case (a) and applicable to a cell depth d provides a solution for case (b) and applicable to a cell depth $d' = \frac{1}{2}d$ and Rayleigh and Taylor numbers which are sixteen times smaller.

In accordance with the foregoing remarks we shall assume for the trial function

$$F = \sin 2\pi z. \tag{50}$$

On carrying through the calculations with this trial function we find

$$\int_{-\frac{1}{2}}^{+\frac{1}{2}} [(\mathrm{D}F)^2 + (a^2 + i\varpi\sigma) F^2]\,\mathrm{d}z = \tfrac{1}{2}(4\pi^2 + a^2 + i\varpi\sigma) \tag{51}$$

and

$$\begin{aligned}\int_{-\frac{1}{2}}^{+\frac{1}{2}} WF\,\mathrm{d}z = \tfrac{1}{2}c_2\gamma_2 - 8\pi^2\gamma_2^2\Delta_2 \prod_{j=1}^{3} \tanh \tfrac{1}{2}q_j & \\ \times \{q_1(q_2^2-q_3^2)(q_1^2+4\pi^2)(1+c_2k_1)\coth\tfrac{1}{2}q_1 & \\ + q_2(q_3^2-q_1^2)(q_2^2+4\pi^2)(1+c_2k_2)\coth\tfrac{1}{2}q_2 & \\ + q_3(q_1^2-q_2^2)(q_3^2+4\pi^2)(1+c_2k_3)\coth\tfrac{1}{2}q_3\}, &\end{aligned} \tag{52}$$

where

$$\Delta_2^{-1} = \{q_2q_3(k_2-k_3)\tanh\tfrac{1}{2}q_1 + q_3q_1(k_3-k_1)\tanh\tfrac{1}{2}q_2 + q_1q_2(k_1-k_2)\tanh\tfrac{1}{2}q_3\}, \tag{53}$$

and the remaining symbols have the same meanings as in case (a). The corresponding formula for R, now, is

$$R = \frac{1}{32a^2}\frac{4\pi^2 + a^2 + i\varpi\sigma}{\int_{-\frac{1}{2}}^{+\frac{1}{2}} WF\,\mathrm{d}z}. \tag{54}$$

The results of calculations based on the foregoing formulae (again for $\varpi = 0{\cdot}025$) are summarized in table 3. And for comparison, in table 4 the corresponding results derived in I (together with some additional ones) for the onset of convection are given.

(c) *Both bounding surfaces free*

The complete solution for this case has already been given in I. However, for the sake of completeness the results for this case are summarized in tables 5 and 6.

TABLE 3. CRITICAL RAYLEIGH NUMBERS AND RELATED CONSTANTS FOR THE ONSET OF OVER-STABILITY IN CASE ONE BOUNDING SURFACE IS FREE AND THE OTHER IS RIGID AND $\varpi = 0{\cdot}025$

T	a	σ	R_c	p/Ω
10^7	5·85	$1{\cdot}44 \times 10^3$	$1{\cdot}71 \times 10^4$	0·9126
3×10^9	15·58	$1{\cdot}04 \times 10^4$	$4{\cdot}81 \times 10^5$	0·3801
10^{12}	40·5	$7{\cdot}46 \times 10^4$	$1{\cdot}87 \times 10^7$	0·1492

TABLE 4. CRITICAL RAYLEIGH NUMBERS AND WAVE NUMBERS OF THE UNSTABLE MODES AT MARGINAL STABILITY FOR THE ONSET OF CONVECTION IN CASE ONE BOUNDING SURFACE IS FREE AND THE OTHER IS RIGID

T	a	R_c	T	a	R_c
0	2·68	$1{\cdot}101 \times 10^3$	$1{\cdot}875 \times 10^4$	6·00	$7{\cdot}229 \times 10^3$
6·25	2·68	$1{\cdot}108 \times 10^3$	$6{\cdot}25 \times 10^4$	7·42	$1{\cdot}451 \times 10^4$
$3{\cdot}125 \times 10^1$	2·70	$1{\cdot}136 \times 10^3$	$1{\cdot}875 \times 10^5$	9·05	$2{\cdot}841 \times 10^4$
$6{\cdot}25 \times 10^1$	2·79	$1{\cdot}169 \times 10^3$	$6{\cdot}25 \times 10^5$	11·05	$6{\cdot}081 \times 10^4$
$1{\cdot}875 \times 10^2$	2·98	$1{\cdot}291 \times 10^3$	10^6	12·00	$8{\cdot}228 \times 10^4$
$6{\cdot}25 \times 10^2$	3·40	$1{\cdot}638 \times 10^3$	10^8	26·55	$1{\cdot}718 \times 10^6$
$1{\cdot}875 \times 10^3$	4·00	$2{\cdot}359 \times 10^3$	10^{10}	58·25	$3{\cdot}758 \times 10^7$
$6{\cdot}25 \times 10^3$	4·93	$4{\cdot}046 \times 10^3$			

TABLE 5. CRITICAL RAYLEIGH NUMBERS AND RELATED CONSTANTS FOR THE ONSET OF OVER-STABILITY IN CASE BOTH BOUNDING SURFACES ARE FREE AND $\varpi = 0{\cdot}025$

T	a	σ	R_c	p/Ω
0	2·233	—	$1{\cdot}348 \times 10^3$	imaginary
$1{\cdot}681 \times 10^4$	2·270	$1{\cdot}014 \times 10^2$	$1{\cdot}388 \times 10^3$	1·564
$1{\cdot}681 \times 10^5$	2·594	$3{\cdot}079 \times 10^2$	$1{\cdot}694 \times 10^3$	1·502
$8{\cdot}405 \times 10^5$	3·278	$6{\cdot}184 \times 10^2$	$2{\cdot}613 \times 10^3$	1·349
$1{\cdot}681 \times 10^6$	3·710	$8{\cdot}168 \times 10^2$	$3{\cdot}436 \times 10^3$	1·260
$3{\cdot}362 \times 10^6$	4·220	$1{\cdot}067 \times 10^3$	$4{\cdot}713 \times 10^3$	1·164
$8{\cdot}405 \times 10^6$	5·011	$1{\cdot}503 \times 10^3$	$7{\cdot}523 \times 10^3$	1·037
$1{\cdot}681 \times 10^7$	5·698	$1{\cdot}932 \times 10^3$	$1{\cdot}102 \times 10^4$	0·9424
$5{\cdot}043 \times 10^7$	6·961	$2{\cdot}851 \times 10^3$	$2{\cdot}092 \times 10^4$	0·8029
$1{\cdot}681 \times 10^8$	8·626	$4{\cdot}330 \times 10^3$	$4{\cdot}368 \times 10^4$	0·6680
$5{\cdot}043 \times 10^8$	10·45	$6{\cdot}308 \times 10^3$	$8{\cdot}728 \times 10^4$	0·5618
$1{\cdot}681 \times 10^9$	12·86	$9{\cdot}497 \times 10^3$	$1{\cdot}891 \times 10^5$	0·4633
$1{\cdot}681 \times 10^{10}$	19·02	$2{\cdot}062 \times 10^4$	$8{\cdot}501 \times 10^5$	0·3181
$1{\cdot}681 \times 10^{11}$	28·02	$4{\cdot}458 \times 10^4$	$3{\cdot}889 \times 10^6$	0·2175
$1{\cdot}681 \times 10^{12}$	41·20	$9{\cdot}620 \times 10^4$	$1{\cdot}793 \times 10^7$	0·1484
$1{\cdot}681 \times 10^{13}$	60·52	$2{\cdot}074 \times 10^5$	$8{\cdot}296 \times 10^7$	0·1012
$1{\cdot}681 \times 10^{14}$	88·87	$4{\cdot}470 \times 10^5$	$3{\cdot}845 \times 10^8$	0·0690
$1{\cdot}681 \times 10^{15}$	130·46	$9{\cdot}632 \times 10^5$	$1{\cdot}784 \times 10^9$	0·0470
$1{\cdot}681 \times 10^{16}$	191·51	$2{\cdot}075 \times 10^6$	$8{\cdot}276 \times 10^9$	0·0320

TABLE 6. CRITICAL RAYLEIGH NUMBERS AND WAVE NUMBERS OF THE UNSTABLE MODES AT MARGINAL STABILITY FOR THE ONSET OF CONVECTION IN CASE BOTH BOUNDING SURFACES ARE FREE

T	a	R_c	T	a	R_c
0	2·233	$6{\cdot}575 \times 10^2$	3×10^5	10·45	$4{\cdot}257 \times 10^4$
10	2·270	$6{\cdot}771 \times 10^2$	10^6	12·86	$9{\cdot}222 \times 10^4$
10^2	2·594	$8{\cdot}263 \times 10^2$	10^7	19·02	$4{\cdot}147 \times 10^5$
5×10^2	3·278	$1{\cdot}275 \times 10^3$	10^8	28·02	$1{\cdot}897 \times 10^6$
10^3	3·710	$1{\cdot}676 \times 10^3$	10^9	41·20	$8{\cdot}746 \times 10^6$
2×10^3	4·221	$2{\cdot}299 \times 10^3$	10^{10}	60·52	$4{\cdot}047 \times 10^7$
5×10^3	5·011	$3{\cdot}670 \times 10^3$	10^{11}	88·87	$1{\cdot}876 \times 10^8$
10^4	5·698	$5{\cdot}377 \times 10^3$	10^{12}	130·46	$8{\cdot}701 \times 10^8$
3×10^4	6·961	$1{\cdot}021 \times 10^4$	10^{13}	191·51	$4{\cdot}037 \times 10^9$
10^5	8·626	$2{\cdot}131 \times 10^4$			

(*d*) *The asymptotic behaviour of the solutions and general discussion*

The results of the calculations of the preceding sections are illustrated in figure 2. It appears that in all cases

$$R \propto T^{\frac{2}{3}} \quad \text{and} \quad a \propto T^{\frac{1}{6}} \quad (T \to \infty), \tag{55}$$

though in the over-stable case the validity of these asymptotic relations strictly requires that $\varpi^2 T \to \infty$. (The distinction between $\varpi^2 T \to \infty$ and $T \to \infty$ is important if $\varpi \ll 1$ and we let $\varpi \to 0$.) In addition, in the over-stable case, we have

$$\sigma \propto T^{\frac{2}{3}} \quad (\varpi^2 T \to \infty). \tag{56}$$

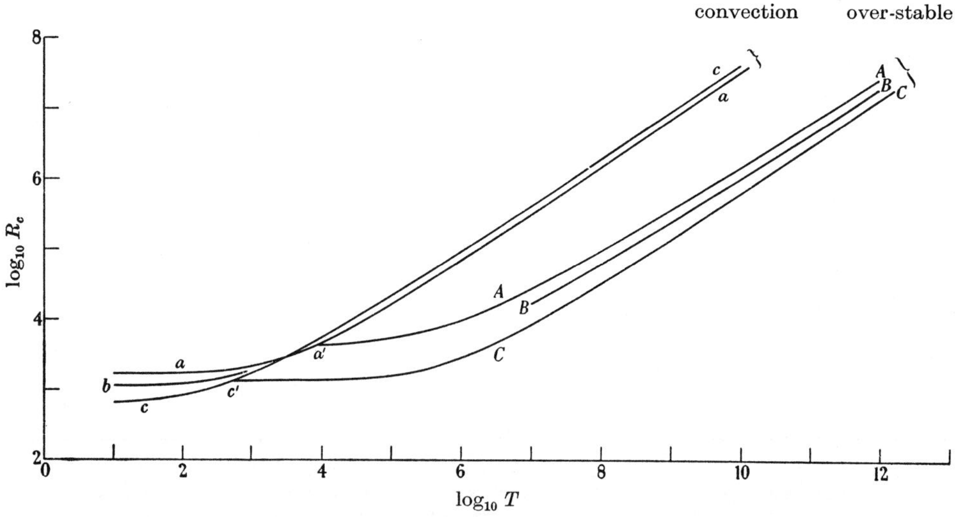

FIGURE 2. The (R_c, T)-relations for the three cases (*a*) both bounding surfaces rigid, (*b*) one bounding surface rigid and the other free and (*c*) both bounding surfaces free. The curves labelled *aa*, *b* and *cc* are the relations for the onset of ordinary cellular convection for the three cases, respectively. The curves labelled *a′AA*, *BB* and *c′CC* are the corresponding relations for the onset of over-stability for $\varpi = 0{\cdot}025$. At *a′* (respectively *c′*) we have a change from one type of instability to another as T increases.

The explicit form of the foregoing relations in case both bounding surfaces are free, are (cf. I, equations (69), (70), (122) and (125)):

$$\left.\begin{array}{l} R_c \to 3(\tfrac{1}{2}\pi^2 T)^{\frac{2}{3}} \\ a \to (\tfrac{1}{2}\pi^2 T)^{\frac{1}{6}} \end{array}\right\} \text{ for the onset of convection as } T \to \infty \qquad (57)$$

and

$$\left.\begin{array}{l} R_c \to \dfrac{6\varpi^{\frac{4}{3}}}{(1+\varpi)^{\frac{1}{3}}}(\tfrac{1}{2}\pi^2 T)^{\frac{2}{3}} \\ a \to \left(\dfrac{\varpi}{1+\varpi}\right)^{\frac{1}{3}} (\tfrac{1}{2}\pi^2 T)^{\frac{1}{6}} \\ \sigma \to \left(\dfrac{2}{1+2\varpi}\right)^{\frac{1}{2}} \left(\dfrac{1+\varpi}{\varpi}\right)^{\frac{1}{3}} (\tfrac{1}{2}\pi^2 T)^{\frac{1}{3}} \end{array}\right\} \begin{array}{l}\text{for the onset of over-}\\ \text{stability as } \varpi^2 T \to \infty.\end{array} \qquad (58)$$

A quantity of some interest is the frequency (p) of the oscillations at marginal stability in units of Ω. This is essentially given by $\sigma/\sqrt{T}$; for, according to the definitions of these quantities (cf. equations (15) and (21))

$$p/\Omega = 2\sigma/\sqrt{T}. \qquad (59)$$

This ratio is included in tables 1, 3 and 5.

An asymptotic relation for p/Ω can be derived from

$$\sigma\left(1+\frac{a^2}{\pi^2}\right)^{\frac{1}{2}} \to \sqrt{\frac{T}{1+2\varpi}} \quad (T \to \infty), \qquad (60)$$

which follows from I, equations (114) and (130). (Note that (60) is valid for $T \to \infty$, not merely for $\varpi^2 T \to \infty$.) From (60) it follows (in agreement with equations (58)) that

$$\sigma a \to \frac{\pi}{\sqrt{(1+2\varpi)}}\sqrt{T} \quad (\varpi^2 T \to \infty); \qquad (61)$$

or, according to equation (59),

$$pa \to \frac{2\pi}{\sqrt{(1+2\varpi)}}\Omega \quad (\varpi^2 T \to \infty). \qquad (62)$$

An alternative form of this last relation is

$$p\frac{d}{\lambda} \to \frac{\Omega}{\sqrt{(1+2\varpi)}} \quad (\varpi^2 T \to \infty), \qquad (63)$$

where λ denotes the wavelength of the disturbance which manifests itself at marginal instability. In contrast to the foregoing relations, it should be noted that in the limit $\varpi = 0$ (cf. I, unnumbered equation on the top of p. 326)

$$R_c = 13{\cdot}5\pi^4, \quad a = \tfrac{1}{2}\pi \quad \text{and} \quad p = (\tfrac{8}{3})^{\frac{1}{2}}\,\Omega. \qquad (64)$$

The relations (60) to (64) are applicable to the case of two free bounding surfaces; for other boundary conditions analogous relations hold with somewhat different numerical factors.

5. Concluding remarks

The experimental confirmation by Fultz & Nakagawa (1955) of the theoretical deductions of this paper is of particular importance, since it establishes firmly that in a fluid in rotation thermal instability need not always result in a stationary system of currents; it may result in a system of oscillatory motions. Indeed, the setting up of such oscillatory motions will be the rule (not the exception) if the thermometric conductivity, as compared with the kinematic viscosity, is sufficiently high. This latter condition will be met by all liquid metals such as mercury or molten iron. The phenomenon is therefore one which is very relevant to the manner of heat transfer in the earth's core. However, the presence of the magnetic field in the earth's core is likely to complicate matters very considerably. For, in a liquid metal while the presence of a magnetic field has an inhibiting effect on the onset of thermal instability (cf. Chandrasekhar 1952*a*, 1954*a* and the experimental confirmation of the theoretical deductions of these papers by Nakagawa 1955) it does not alter the basic character of the motions which ensue. The joint effects of a magnetic field and rotation must therefore be considered. A preliminary investigation of these latter effects (Chandrasekhar 1954*b*) has shown that the behaviour of a fluid under these conditions is likely to be excessively complicated. The matter is clearly one which merits a careful investigation both from the experimental and the theoretical points of view.

The research reported in this paper has in part been supported by the Geophysics Research Directorate of the Air Force Cambridge Research Center, Air Research Development Command, under Contract AF 19(604)–299 with the University of Chicago.

References

Chandrasekhar, S. 1952*a* *Phil. Mag.* (7), **43**, 501.
Chandrasekhar, S. 1952*b* *Phil. Mag.* (7), **43**, 1317.
Chandrasekhar, S. 1953*a* *Proc. Roy. Soc.* A, **216**, 293.
Chandrasekhar, S. 1953*b* *Proc. Roy. Soc.* A, **217**, 306.
Chandrasekhar, S. 1954*a* *Phil. Mag.* (7), **45**, 1177.
Chandrasekhar, S. 1954*b* *Proc. Roy. Soc.* A, **225**, 173.
Fultz, D. & Nakagawa, Y. 1955 *Proc. Roy. Soc.* A, **231**, 211.
Fultz, D., Nakagawa, Y. & Frenzen, P. 1954 *Phys. Rev.* **94**, 1471.
Nakagawa, Y. 1955 *Nature, Lond.*, **175**, 417.
Nakagawa, Y. & Frenzen, P. 1955 *Tellus.* (In the Press.)

IV. Horizontally Non-uniform Heating with Rotation (The Planetary Atmosphere)

Reprinted from C. Abbe's translation in *Smithsonian Miscellaneous Collection*, 1891. The article originally appeared in *Sitzungsberichte der Königlichen Preussischen Akademie der Wissenschaften*, 1888.

XII.

ON THE PHENOMENA OF MOTION IN THE ATMOSPHERE.*

(FIRST COMMUNICATION.)

By Prof. A. Oberbeck, *of the University of Greifswald, Germany.*

I.

The meteorological observations of the last ten years have given a series of notable laws that principally relate to the connection between the currents of air and the pressure of the air in the neighborhood of the earth's surface.

Of course one can only hope to obtain a complete insight into the complicated mechanism of the motion of the air when one understands more accurately the condition of the atmosphere in its higher strata. But difficulties that are perhaps never to be overcome oppose the observation of these strata. On the other hand, the completion of this and many other gaps in the theory of the motion of the air is certainly to be expected from a comprehensive mechanics of the atmosphere. The Treatise on Meteorology, by A. Sprung, Hamburg, 1885, gives a summary of what has hitherto been accomplished in this field, from which summary it is seen that only special individual problems have found a satisfactory solution.

The principal features of a rational mechanics of the atmosphere are given in the memoir by W. Siemens, "The conservation of energy in the earth's atmosphere."† It appears to me worth while to follow out mathematically the questions there treated of and to develop a theory of the motions of the air as general as possible. The results thus far attained by me, are collected in this present memoir.

On account of the magnitude and difficulty of the problem to be solved, I have at first confined myself to the determination of the currents of the air. A corresponding investigation of the distribution of pressure will follow hereafter. Moreover the phenomena of motion

* Read before the Royal Prussian Academy of Sciences, at Berlin, March 15, 1888. Translated from the *Sitzungsberichte Königl. Preus. Akad. der Wissenschaften.* 1888, pp. 383–395.

† See *Berlin Sitzungsberichte*, 1886, pp. 261–275.

will here be considered as "steady motion." On the other hand I have labored so to arrange the calculation that it can be applied to any condition of the atmosphere and to the general currents between the poles and the equator, or the atmospheric circulation, as well as also to individual cyclones or anticyclones.

In order to test the applicability of the formula thus obtained, the first of the problems just mentioned is completely solved.

I begin with an enumeration of the factors upon which the movement of the atmosphere depends, and with a description of the manner in which I have introduced these into the calculation.

II

(1) Since the ultimate cause of the motion of the air is to be sought in the effect of gravity and in the differences of temperature in the atmosphere, therefore the attraction of the earth must enter into the equations of motion as the moving force. But it is entirely sufficient here to consider the earth as a homogeneous sphere.

(2) The temperature of the atmosphere is to be considered as a function of the locality, but entirely independent of the time. The last condition is necessary if one confines himself to steady motions. For the temperature T, the analytical condition

$$\Delta T = \frac{\partial^2 T}{\partial x^2} + \frac{\partial^2 T}{\partial y^2} + \frac{\partial^2 T}{\partial z^2} = 0$$

must be satisfied.

This equation, as is well known, follows from the assumption that the heat is distributed through the medium in question according to the laws of the conduction of heat. Although I am by no means of the opinion that the conduction of heat principally determines the flow of heat from the earth's surface through the atmosphere into the planetary space, still it is very probable that the totality of all the phenomena here coming into consideration (conduction, radiation from the earth's surface with partial absorption in the atmosphere, vertical convection currents, etc.) will bring about a distribution of temperature analogous to that due to the conduction of heat.

(3) According to the rules of mechanics, the influence of the rotation of the earth can be expressed by a deflecting force, so that after its introduction the earth can be considered as at rest.

(4) Friction is furthermore to be considered, since without it the atmospheric currents under the continuous influence of accelerating forces would attain to indefinitely great velocities. In my opinion, the attempts made hitherto to give a correct theory of the motions of the air, especially one that can be developed analytically, have failed because of the insufficient or incorrect introduction of friction. I have adhered to the simplest assumption, namely, that the same law of friction holds good for atmospheric currents that has also been shown

to be correct in the motion of liquids.* But I would not hereby assert that the same numerical coefficient is to be used as is given by the laboratory experiments on the internal friction of the air made under the exclusion of all attendant disturbing circumstances. More likely is it that along with the greater horizontal currents there will arise small vertical currents of a local nature which will increase the friction. The air can either be held fast at the earth's surface or glide with more or less resistance. This fact, as is well known, is expressed in the boundary equations of condition by a number, the coefficient of slip, whose value may lie between zero and infinity.

(5.) The density of the air must be considered as dependent upon the temperature, since the effective cause of the currents results from this. But I have not objected to use, as the equation of continuity, that simpler expression that obtains for incompressible liquids. The error introduced hereby can be eliminated if, at places where the density is less than the average, one increases to a corresponding extent the velocity found for that locality, but considers the velocity as diminished at locations where the density exceeds the average.

(6) A hydro-dynamic problem is only perfectly definite when the fluid occupies a definite space, and its behavior is known for all limiting boundary surfaces. I have therefore assumed that the atmosphere is bounded both by the earth's surface and by a second spherical surface concentric therewith. The distance of the two spherical surfaces, which I will briefly designate as the height of the atmosphere, can remain undetermined. But this is quite small in comparison with the earth's radius. The above assumption just made however, only expresses the idea that for a given altitude above the earth's surface the radial or vertical currents are very small, or rather that when they are present they exert an inappreciably small influence on the remaining motions. This is certainly the case, since at very large altitudes the density is very small. Since moreover it is assumed that the air can glide without resistance on the upper spherical surface, therefore in my opinion no limitation of the motions of the atmosphere, contradictory to the real phenomena, results from the introduction of such an upper boundary surface.

III.

The following notation will be used for the principal equations of the problem. The position of a point in the atmosphere is determined by the rectangular coördinates x, y, z. The center of the earth is the origin of coördinates and the earth's axis in the direction of the North Pole is the positive axis of z. The positive directions of the two other axes are to be so chosen that the axis of y as seen from the North Pole must be turned through an angle of $90°$ in the direction of the motion of the hands of a watch in order to be made to coincide with the axis of x.

*[The term friction as here used therefore includes viscosity and slip, but excludes the resistance due to wave motion and to vortex motion and all the resistances implied in turbulent flow of fluids.—*C. A.*]

Let there be furthermore—
u, v, w, the components of velocity;
p, the pressure;
μ, the density;
k, the coefficient of friction;
G, the acceleration of gravity;
R, the radius of the earth;
r, the distance of any point from the center of the earth;
ε, the angular velocity of the earth.
Then we have—

$$\left.\begin{aligned}
\frac{du}{dt}&=GR^2\frac{\partial\frac{1}{r}}{\partial x}-\frac{1}{\mu}\frac{\partial p}{\partial x}+\frac{k}{\mu}\Delta u+2\varepsilon v,\\
\frac{dv}{dt}&=GR^2\frac{\partial\frac{1}{r}}{\partial y}-\frac{1}{\mu}\frac{\partial p}{\partial y}+\frac{k}{\mu}\Delta v-2\varepsilon u,\\
\frac{dw}{dt}&=GR^2\frac{\partial\frac{1}{r}}{\partial z}-\frac{1}{\mu}\frac{\partial p}{\partial z}+\frac{k}{\mu}\Delta w,\\
&\frac{\partial u}{\partial x}+\frac{\partial v}{\partial y}+\frac{\partial w}{\partial z}=0.
\end{aligned}\right\} \quad \ldots\ldots (1)$$

Since according to the law of Mariotte and Gay-Lussac

$$\frac{p}{\mu}=\frac{p_0}{\mu_0}(1+\alpha T)$$

we may put

$$\frac{1}{\mu}\cdot\frac{\partial p}{\partial x}=\frac{p_0}{\mu_0}(1+\alpha T)\frac{\partial \log p}{\partial x}.$$

The zero point of temperature is arbitrary. It is most appropriate to assume for it the average temperature of the atmosphere.

If c is the Newtonian value of the velocity of sound, then we have

$$\frac{p_0}{\mu_0}=c^2$$

After the introduction of these expressions into the above principal equations, imagine the latter divided throughout by $1+\alpha T$. Excepting in that member in which the gravity occurs, one can omit from consideration the influence of the factor $\frac{1}{1+\alpha T}$. In the term just mentioned one can, as a first approximation, put $(1-\alpha T)$ for the value of this factor. Furthermore let

$$\frac{k}{\mu}=\varkappa$$

The first of the equations of motion now becomes

$$\frac{du}{dt} = (1-\alpha T)\,GR^2 \frac{\partial \frac{1}{r}}{\partial x} - c^2 \frac{\partial \log p}{\partial x} + \varkappa \Delta u + 2\varepsilon v.$$

If the temperature of the atmosphere depended only on the altitude above the earth's surface and were therefore only a function of r, then would these equations be fulfilled by putting u, v, w respectively $= 0$; the atmosphere would then be in equilibrium. Therefore put

$$T = T_0 + T_1$$

wherein T_0 is a function of r only, but T_1 is also a function of the longitude and latitude; therefore

$$T_0 \frac{\partial \frac{1}{r}}{\partial x} = -\frac{\partial}{\partial x}\int \frac{T_0}{r^2}\,dr$$

$$T_1 \frac{\partial \frac{1}{r}}{\partial x} = \frac{\partial \frac{T_1}{r}}{\partial x} - \frac{1}{r}\frac{\partial T_1}{\partial x}$$

Finally one may put

$$p = p_1 \,.\, (1 + \nu).$$

The quantity ν in this latter equation expresses those changes of pressure that are caused by the phenomena of motion. Since ν is small in comparison with unity, therefore instead of $\log(1+\nu)$ the quantity ν itself can be substituted. By this means the first principal equation becomes

$$\frac{du}{dt} = GR^2 \frac{\partial}{\partial x}\left\{\frac{1-\alpha T_1}{r} + \alpha \int \frac{T_0}{r^2}\,dr\right\} - c^2 \frac{\partial \log p_1}{\partial x} - c^2 \frac{\partial \nu}{\partial x} + \varkappa \Delta u + 2\varepsilon v$$

After transforming the two other principal equations in the same manner we can put

$$c^2 \log p_1 = \text{constant} + GR^2 \left\{\frac{1-\alpha T_1}{r} + \alpha \int \frac{T_0}{r^2}\,dr\right\} \quad . \quad . \quad (2)$$

This equation gives the diminution of pressure at larger altitudes above the earth's surface, and can for smaller differences of altitude easily be transformed into the ordinary equation of barometric hypsometry.

The following system of equations relating to the phenomena of motion proper now remains:

$$\left.\begin{aligned}
\frac{du}{dt}&=\frac{\alpha GR^2}{r}\cdot\frac{\partial T_1}{\partial x}-c^2\frac{\partial \nu}{\partial x}+\varkappa\Delta u+2ev,\\
\frac{dv}{dt}&=\frac{\alpha GR^2}{r}\cdot\frac{\partial T_1}{\partial y}-c^2\frac{\partial \nu}{\partial y}+\varkappa\Delta v-2eu,\\
\frac{dw}{dt}&=\frac{\alpha GR^2}{r}\cdot\frac{\partial T_1}{\partial z}-c^2\frac{\partial \nu}{\partial z}+\varkappa\Delta w,\\
&\frac{\partial u}{\partial x}+\frac{\partial v}{\partial y}+\frac{\partial w}{\partial z}=0.
\end{aligned}\right\} \quad \dots\dots\dots (3)$$

One can now compute first those components of the current that depend only on temperature differences; after that those that are brought about by the rotation of the earth. If we put $u=u_1+u_2$; $v=v_1+v_2$; $w=w_1+w_2$; $\nu=\nu_1+\nu_2+\nu_3$, then will the following two systems of equations be those that are first to be discussed:

$$c^2\frac{\partial \nu_1}{\partial x}=\frac{\alpha GR^2}{r}\cdot\frac{\partial T_1}{\partial x}+\varkappa\Delta u_1$$

$$c^2\frac{\partial \nu_1}{\partial y}=\frac{\alpha GR^2}{r}\cdot\frac{\partial T_1}{\partial y}+\varkappa\Delta v_1$$

$$c^2\frac{\partial \nu_1}{\partial z}=\frac{\alpha GR^2}{r}\frac{\partial T_1}{\partial z}+\varkappa\Delta w_1$$

and

$$c^2\frac{\partial \nu_2}{\partial x}=2\,\varepsilon v_1+\varkappa\Delta u_2;$$

$$c^2\frac{\partial \nu_2}{\partial y}=-2\,\varepsilon u_1+\varkappa\Delta v_2;$$

$$c^2\frac{\partial \nu_2}{\partial z}=\varkappa\Delta w_2.$$

Thus there still remain the following equations which are no longer linear and which will serve principally in the computation of the variations in pressure produced by the motion:

$$c^2\frac{\partial \nu_3}{\partial x}+u\frac{\partial u}{\partial x}+v\frac{\partial u}{\partial y}+w\frac{\partial u}{\partial z}=2\,\varepsilon v_2;$$

$$c^2\frac{\partial \nu_3}{\partial y}+u\frac{\partial v}{\partial x}+v\frac{\partial v}{\partial y}+w\frac{\partial v}{\partial z}=-2\,\varepsilon u_2;$$

$$c^2\frac{\partial \nu_3}{\partial z}+u\frac{\partial w}{\partial x}+v\frac{\partial w}{\partial y}+w\frac{\partial w}{\partial z}=0.$$

The first two systems of equations are linear. When therefore T_1 consists of a sum of terms we shall obtain corresponding sums for the component velocities. The solution will be quite simple when T_1 is developed into a series of spherical harmonics.

If we put

$$T_1 = \Sigma \left\{ A_n r^n + \frac{A'_n}{r^{n+1}} \right\} p_n$$

and for brevity

$$\beta = \alpha G R^2,$$

and indicate by Q any term of the series with its corresponding constant then the solutions of the first two systems of equations are as follows :

$$\left.\begin{aligned} u_1 &= \frac{\beta}{\varkappa} \left\{ E \frac{\partial Q}{\partial x} + \frac{\partial (QF)}{\partial x} \right\} \\ v_1 &= \frac{\beta}{\varkappa} \left\{ E \frac{\partial Q}{\partial y} + \frac{\partial (QF)}{\partial y} \right\} \\ w_1 &= \frac{\beta}{\varkappa} \left\{ E \frac{\partial Q}{\partial z} + \frac{\partial (QF)}{\partial z} \right\} \\ c^2 \nu_1 &= \beta \{ \Delta (QF) + aQ \} \end{aligned}\right\} \quad . \; . \; . \; . \; . \; . \; . \quad (4)$$

In this E and F are functions of r only, and must satisfy the differential equations

$$\left.\begin{aligned} &\left(\frac{d^2 E}{dr^2} + \frac{2}{r} \frac{dE}{dr} \right) \frac{\partial Q}{\partial r} + 2 \frac{dE}{dr} \frac{\partial^2 Q}{\partial r^2} = \frac{\partial Q}{\partial r} \left(-\frac{1}{r} + a \right) \\ &\left(\frac{d^2 F}{dr^2} + \frac{2}{r} \frac{dF}{dr} \right) Q + \frac{\partial Q}{\partial r} \left(2 \frac{dF}{dr} + \frac{dE}{dr} \right) = 0 \end{aligned}\right\} \quad . \; . \quad (5)$$

The constant a must be added in order to obtain the number of constants needed in the consideration of the boundary conditions. The terms depending upon the earth's rotation are

$$\left.\begin{aligned} u_2 &= \frac{2\varepsilon\beta}{\varkappa^2} \left\{ -\left(J \frac{\partial Q}{\partial y} + \frac{\partial (QH)}{\partial y} \right) + \frac{\partial K}{\partial x} \right\} \\ v_2 &= \frac{2\varepsilon\beta}{\varkappa^2} \left\{ +J \frac{\partial Q}{\partial x} + \frac{\partial (QH)}{\partial x} + \frac{\partial K}{\partial y} \right\} \\ w_2 &= \frac{2\varepsilon\beta}{\varkappa^2} \cdot \frac{\partial K}{\partial z} \\ c^2 \nu_2 &= \frac{2\varepsilon\beta}{\varkappa} \Delta K \end{aligned}\right\} \quad . \; . \; . \quad (6)$$

Here also J and H are functions of r only, and must satisfy the differential equations

$$\left.\begin{aligned} &\left(\frac{d^2 J}{dr^2} + \frac{2}{r} \frac{dJ}{dr} \right) \frac{\partial Q}{\partial r} + 2 \frac{dJ}{dr} \frac{\partial Q}{\partial r} = \frac{\partial Q}{\partial r} (E - b) \\ &\left(\frac{d^2 H}{dr^2} + \frac{2}{r} \cdot \frac{dH}{dr} \right) Q + 2 \frac{dH}{dr} \cdot \frac{\partial Q}{\partial r} = Q (F + b). \end{aligned}\right\} \quad . \; . \; . \quad (7)$$

The constant b must also here be added for the same reason as above given.

The function K is to be computed from the equation

$$\Delta K+\frac{dJ}{dr}\left(\frac{\partial Q}{\partial y}\cdot\frac{x}{r}-\frac{\partial Q}{\partial x}\cdot\frac{y}{r}\right)=0 \quad . \quad . \quad . \quad . \quad . \quad . \qquad (8)$$

From this last equation it follows that the introduction of the function K can be omitted when the temperature of the atmosphere is assumed symmetrical with reference to the earth's axis. In this case $w_2=0$ and the [atmospheric] movement resulting from the rotation of the earth consists exclusively in a movement of rotation depending on the geographical latitude and the altitude above the earth's surface.

In order to present in the ordinary manner the currents of air for a given point in the atmosphere, the following components are to be introduced instead of u, v, w:

V, the vertical component computed positively upwards;

N and O, the two horizontal components, of which the first indicates movement toward the north, the latter, movement toward the east;

θ, the complement of the geographical latitude of a given place;

ψ, the longitude counted from an arbitrary meridian;

then we have

$$\left.\begin{aligned} V&=+(u\cos\psi+v\sin\psi)\sin\theta+w\cos\theta \\ N&=-(u\cos\psi+v\sin\psi)\cos\theta+w\sin\theta \\ O&=-u\sin\psi+v\cos\psi. \end{aligned}\right\} \quad . \quad . \quad . \quad . \qquad (9)$$

The formulæ (4, 6, and 9) contain the general solution of the problem so far as this is at present intended to be given, assuming the distribution of temperature to be given and that the functions E, F, J, H, K are determined in accordance with the boundary conditions.

IV.

When one attempts to represent the distribution of temperature on the earth's surface by a series of harmonic functions then the most important term is a harmonic function of the second order. Therefore as a first-approximation we put

$$T_1=\left(Ar^2+\frac{A'}{r^3}\right)(1-3\cos^2\theta).$$

This function, with a proper determination of the constants, expresses the great contrast in temperature between the equator and the pole. If now one would take into account the variation with the seasons one must next introduce harmonic functions of the first order. The consideration of the various peculiarities of the earth's surface will of course demand further terms that depend on the geographical longitude also.

I have at first limited myself to the computation for the above given distribution of temperature, and put

$$Q = Ar^2 (1-3 \cos^2 \theta)$$
$$Q' = \frac{A'}{r^3} (1-3 \cos^2 \theta).$$

The functions E, F, H, J are now to be computed with the help of this Q, and the corresponding E', F', H', and J' with the help of this Q'.

We first obtain the general expressions:

$$V = \frac{\alpha GR^2}{\varkappa}(1-3 \cos^2 \theta) \left[A \left\{ r^2 \frac{dF}{dr} + 2r\,(F+E) \right\} + \frac{A'}{r^4} \left\{ r\frac{dF'}{dr} - 3\,(E'+F') \right\} \right]$$

$$N = -\frac{\alpha GR^2}{\varkappa}\, 6 \cos \theta . \sin \theta \left\{ Ar(F+E) + \frac{A'}{r^4}(F'+E') \right\}$$

$$O = \frac{\alpha GR^2 2\varepsilon}{\varkappa^2} \sin \theta \left[(1-3 \cos^2 \theta) \left\{ Ar \left(r\frac{dH}{dr} + 2\,(H+J) \right) + \frac{A}{r^4}\left(r\frac{dH'}{dr} - 3\,(H'+J') \right) \right\} + 6 \cos^2 \theta \left\{ Ar\,(H+J) + \frac{A'}{r^4}(H'+J') \right\} \right]$$

The actual computation, having due reference to the boundary conditions, of the functions here introduced, gives results that are difficult to be discussed. But this is simplified when we make use of the circumstance that the atmosphere fills a very thin shell in comparison with the terrestrial sphere, wherefore the distances from the earth's surface are all small in comparison with the earth's radius. If we put

$$r = R\,(1+\sigma)$$

then is σ small with respect to unity. If we introduce these quantities in the above given equations and put

$$r\frac{dF}{dr} + 2\,(E+F) = Rf(\sigma), \qquad F+E = R\varphi(\sigma);$$

$$r\frac{dF'}{dr} - 3\,(E'+F') = Rf'\,(\sigma), \qquad F'+E' = R\varphi'\,(\sigma);$$

$$r\frac{dH}{dr} + 2(H+J) = R^3 g\,(\sigma), \qquad H+J = R^3\gamma(\sigma)$$

$$r\frac{dH'}{dr} - 3\,(H'+J') = R^3 g'\,(\sigma), \qquad H'+J' = R\nu^3\gamma'\,(\sigma);$$

then by restricting ourselves to the terms of the lowest order, we can obtain simple expressions for these functions. Primarily we find that the functions f and f', φ and φ', g and g', γ and γ' are identical.

Moreover the two constants A and A', which occur in the combination

$$A\ R^2 + \frac{A'}{R^3}$$

can be expressed in terms of the temperatures of the earth's surface at the equator, T_a, and at the pole, T_p. We have

$$\frac{1}{3}\ (T_a - T_p) = A\ R^2 + \frac{A'}{R^3}$$

Finally we put

$$C = \frac{\alpha\ G\ R^2}{\varkappa}\ \tfrac{1}{3}\ (T_a - T_p)$$

$$D = \frac{\alpha\ G\ R^4}{\varkappa^2}\ 2\varepsilon . \tfrac{1}{3}\ (T_a - T_p).$$

The numerical value of these two last constants can not be given, since, as before remarked, the coefficient of friction, $\varkappa$, will not agree with that determined from laboratory experiments. In any case D is considerably larger than C, since in D the fourth power of the radius of the earth occurs, but in C only the second power. The components of motion of the atmosphere are, therefore:

$$V = C\ (1 - 3\cos^2\theta) . f\ (\sigma)$$
$$N = -C . 6\cos\theta\sin\theta . \varphi\ (\sigma)$$
$$O = D\sin\theta \left\{ (1 - 3\cos^2\theta)\ g\ (\sigma) + 6\cos^2\theta . \gamma\ (\sigma) \right\}$$

If we take $R.h$ for the altitude of the atmosphere as above defined, then the four functions, f, φ, g, γ, are to be so determined that they satisfy the prescribed boundary conditions for $\sigma = 0$ and $\sigma = h$. I have executed this computation for the most general case, namely, that in which at the upper limit slipping occurs without friction, but at the lower limit sliding with friction. Undoubtedly however the condition of the atmosphere on the earth's surface is much more nearly that of adhesion than that of free slipping, so that I will here communicate only the solutions for this latter case. For this case the motion at the earth's surface is everywhere zero. But for this motion one can easily substitute the motion at a slight altitude, that is to say, for small values of σ. For the four functions we find the following expressions:

$$f\ (\sigma) = \frac{\sigma}{8} (h - \sigma)\ (3h\sigma - 2\sigma^2)$$

$$\varphi(\sigma) = \frac{\sigma}{48} \left\{ 6h^2 - 15h\sigma + 8\sigma^2 \right\}$$

$$g\ (\sigma) = \frac{\sigma}{480} \left\{ -9h^5 + 15h^2\sigma^3 - 15h\sigma^4 + 4\sigma^5 \right\}$$

$$\gamma(\sigma) = \frac{\sigma}{960} \left\{ 20h^2\sigma^2 - 25h\sigma^3 + 8\sigma^4 \right\}$$

According to this solution the following gives a picture of the atmospheric circulation, which in its principal points agrees with that of W. Siemens.

(1) *Currents on a spheroid without rotation.*

These currents consist of currents in the meridian, and of vertical movements.

(*a*) The meridional current in the northern hemisphere is southerly below, but northerly above, since the function φ changes its sign when σ increases from zero to h. It attains its largest value at 45°, and disappears at the equator and at the poles.

(*b*) The vertical circulation is zero at the earth's surface and at the upper limit of the atmosphere. From the equator to 35° 16′ north and south latitudes the flow of air is positive—that is to say, ascending—but in higher latitudes it is descending. Its velocity at the poles is twice as great as that at the equator.

By the comparison of the expressions for $f(\sigma)$ and $\varphi(\sigma)$, it appears that the former function contains the fourth powers of the small quantities h and σ; the latter function contains their third powers. Therefore, the vertical flow is to the horizontal flow, so far as magnitude is concerned, as h is to 1, or as the altitude of the earth's atmosphere is to the radius of the earth. From this we can scarcely assume that we should be successful in the direct observation of the vertical current. The great effect of the vertical current arises from this, that it rises or sinks over a very extensive area.

(2) *Currents in consequence of the rotation of the earth.*

Under the assumption here made as to the distribution of temperature on the earth's surface, these currents consist exclusively of movements along the parallel circles of latitude. As in the case of the two terms in the component O, so here we distinguish the two following.

(*a*) The movement depending on the function $g(\sigma)$. Since this function is invariably negative; therefore to begin with at the equator the motion is directed toward the west. It changes its sign at latitude 35° 16′, and then becomes a motion directed toward the east.

(*b*) The second current is zero at the equator; becomes a maximum at 54° 44′, and is exclusively directed toward the east. Both currents disappear at the poles.

The two motions (*a*) and (*b*) differ from each other fundamentally in that $\gamma(\sigma)$ differs from zero first when σ has larger values. It is therefore a current that only occurs in the higher strata of the atmosphere. But thereby the function g is of a higher order than γ for the small quantities h and σ. Therefore at great altitudes the current (*b*) must greatly exceed the current (*a*) in velocity.

The components 1*a* and 2*a* combine at the earth's surface to form the regular movement of the air that we designate as the lower trade wind.

On the ocean where this system of winds can freely develop in the manner here assumed, without the influence of continents, their course is in good agreement with the conclusions of theory. Thus, on the northern hemisphere, between 0° and 35° latitude, east and northeast winds prevail; at 35° nearly north or in general only feeble winds; in higher latitudes northwest and west winds.

It results from the preceding that the two currents (1*a*) and (1*b*) are of the same order of magnitude and give moderate winds in the lower strata of atmosphere. Since now the current (2*b*), in comparison with (2*a*) is of a different order of magnitude, therefore the former is by far the most intense of all currents of air, but only in the upper strata of the atmosphere.

In so far as this component combines with the upper current (1*a*), it forms in the tropics the southwest or upper trade wind. In higher latitudes the purely westerly current prevails. So far as is known to me, the observations of the highest clouds which show prevailing west winds agree herewith. That the just-mentioned rotation-currents attain a great velocity has its reason in this that they can circulate around the whole earth without being hindered by the friction of a lower opposite current, as for instance is the case with the meridional currents. I consider it probable (as also W. Siemens has already announced) that in this powerful upper current we have to seek for the principal source of the energy found in the wind system of the lower strata.

XIII.

ON THE PHENOMENA OF MOTION IN THE ATMOSPHERE.*

(SECOND COMMUNICATION.)

By Prof. A. OBERBECK, *of Greifswald.*

I.

A comparison of the highest and lowest atmospheric temperatures at the surface of the earth shows permanent differences of 70°C. If the pressure were uniform everywhere these would correspond to differences of density of the air of more than 20 per cent. Since, however, pressure and density mutually influence each other one should therefore expect minima of pressure at places of highest temperature and maxima of pressure at places of low temperature of a corresponding intensity.

Instead of this the average differences of pressure on the earth's surface attain only 6 or 7 per cent., and even the largest rapidly passing barometric variations scarcely exceed 10 per cent. We explain the relatively small value of these differences of pressure by the formation of corresponding currents; a lower current at the earth's surface in the direction of the increasing temperature and an opposite upper current. Still the above-mentioned rule as to the connection between temperature and pressure must be true in general. But this is by no means always the case. While the equatorial zone of highest temperature shows a feeble minimum of pressure there occurs a maximum of pressure between the twentieth and fortieth degree of latitude from which toward either pole, and especially markedly in the southern hemisphere, the atmospheric pressure very decidedly sinks.

It appears to me not to be doubted that we can explain this remarkable phenomenon only by the influence of the rotation of the earth upon the currents of air that originate in temperature differences. In a previous memoir † I have endeavored to carry out an analytical treatment of these phenomena of motion under certain assumptions which

* Read before the Royal Prussian Academy of Sciences at Berlin, November 8, 1888. Translated from the *Sitzungsberichte Königl. Preus. Akad. der Wissenschaften* zu Berlin. 1888, pp. 1129–1138.

† [See the previous number (XII) of this collection of Translations.—*C. A.*]

are there given in detail. In that memoir the pressures were not explained; this is done in the present treatise. I have arrived thus at the result that the distribution of pressure just described finds its explanation completely in the currents of the atmosphere, and that from the observed values of the pressure a conclusion can be drawn as to the intensity of the atmospheric currents.*

II.

In conformity with the notation of my first memoir the temperature of the atmosphere will be expressed by

$$T = T_0 + T_1$$

where T_0 depends only upon r, the distance of the point in question from the center of the earth, while T_1 is a function of r and of θ, the polar distance.

Let the pressure at the given point be

$$p = p_0(1+\nu)$$

In this expression p_0 also depends only upon r, while ν is a function of r and θ. So far as the observations of atmospheric pressure show, ν can be considered as a small numerical quantity in comparison with unity. For determining p_0 the following equation holds good:

$$c^2 \log p_0 = \text{constant} + GR^2\left(\frac{1}{r} + \alpha \int \frac{T_0}{r^2} dr\right)$$

from which the diminution of pressure as a function of the altitude above the earth's surface can be computed when the law of the diminution of temperature with the altitude, that is to say, the value of T_0 as a function of r is known.

Let us further put

$$\nu = \nu_0 + \nu_1 + \nu_2 + \nu_3$$

in which

$$\nu_0 = -\frac{GR^2 \alpha T_1}{r}$$

while ν_1, ν_2, ν_3 shall indicate the values determined in the previous memoir (pages 180 and 181).

The first two terms of this summation $\nu_0 + \nu_1$ give those changes in pressure which result directly from the differences of temperature on the earth's surface; that is to say, without considering the rotation of the earth.

If the temperature diminishes uniformly on both hemispheres from the equator toward the poles; or, in other words, if the temperature

* [Ferrel had published similar conclusions in 1859 but Oberbeck's independent confirmation is none the less valuable.—*C. A.*]

depends only on the geographical latitude (and not also on the longitude), then the motion of the air can only consist in vertical and meridional currents, and which (corresponding to the above given component velocities u_1, v_1, w_1) consist of one lower current toward the equator and of one upper current toward the poles. The distribution of pressure $\nu_0+\nu_1$ existing in connection with this furnishes (by means of the equation (4), page 182 of the previous memoir) the anticipated result that on the surface of the earth the pressure increases from the equator toward the pole, while at a medium altitude the differences of pressure disappear, but that finally, at greater altitudes, the pressure is greatest at the equator and least at the poles.

Since as above remarked, the actual distribution of pressure in nowise agrees with the above, it must be concluded that the influence of the term $\nu_0+\nu_1$ on the pressure can only be slight.

From the previous developments it results that the term ν_2 disappears under the assumption of a uniform distribution of temperature symmetrical with the earth's axis, so that as was already indicated in the first memoir, ν_3 will be the most important term.

III.

In the computation of this quantity ν_3 the system of equations previously given is to be used, namely:

$$c^2\frac{\partial \nu_3}{\partial x}+u\frac{\partial u}{\partial x}+v\frac{\partial u}{\partial y}+w\frac{\partial u}{\partial z}=2\varepsilon v_2$$

$$c^2\frac{\partial \nu_3}{\partial y}+u\frac{\partial v}{\partial x}+v\frac{\partial v}{\partial y}+w\frac{\partial v}{\partial z}=-2\varepsilon u_2$$

$$c^2\frac{\partial \nu_3}{\partial z}+u\frac{\partial w}{\partial x}+v\frac{\partial w}{\partial y}+w\frac{\partial w}{\partial z}=0$$

Since according to the accordant opinion of meteorologists, as also according to my previous deductions, it is very probable that the intensity of the rotatory currents of the atmosphere materially exceeds that of the meridional currents, therefore I have only introduced into the further computation the rotation currents, whose components are designated by u_2 and v_2.

Since we have to do with a movement of rotation about the axis of z therefore we can put

$$u_2=-\chi y,\ v_2=+\chi x,\ w_2=0,$$

and these values can also be used for u, v, and w, in the above-given system of equations.

The relative angular velocity χ is to be deduced from the expression for the easterly component O (see equation (9), page 183). This is a function of θ and of r or also of σ the altitude above the earth's surface. The first system of equations is therefore transformed into the following:

$$c^2\frac{\partial \nu_3}{\partial x} = (2\varepsilon+\chi)\,\chi x,$$

$$c^2\frac{\partial \nu_3}{\partial y} = (2\varepsilon+\chi)\,\chi y,$$

$$c^2\frac{\partial \nu_3}{\partial z} = 0.$$

Since χ is a function of r and θ, or of ρ and z if we put

$$z = r\cos\theta$$

$$\rho = r\sin\theta;$$

therefore, we can not find one function ν_3 that shall satisfy the three equations. If χ were independent of z we should find

$$c^2\nu_3 = \text{constant} + \int(2\varepsilon+\chi)\,\chi\rho\, d\rho.$$

Since however this is not the case we must therefore conclude that the above-given system of equations still needs a supplement; that therefore a movement of rotation of a fluid to the exclusion of all other movements can only exist when the angular velocity in the direction of the axis of rotation is everywhere the same. If this is not the case then further currents occur perpendicular to the rotary motion. In our case these latter would consist of vertical and meridional movements. Their components may be designated by $u_3\ v_3\ w_3$. These are to be introduced into the above system of equations as was done in the corresponding fundamental equations (3) of the first memoir which now become

$$\left.\begin{aligned} c^2\frac{\partial \nu_3}{\partial x} &= (2\varepsilon+\chi)\,\chi x + \varkappa\,\Delta u_3 \\ c^2\frac{\partial \nu_3}{\partial y} &= (2\varepsilon+\chi)\,\chi y + \varkappa\Delta v_3 \\ c^2\frac{\partial \nu_3}{\partial z} &= \varkappa\Delta w_3 \\ \frac{\partial u_3}{\partial x} + \frac{\partial v_3}{\partial y} + \frac{\partial w_3}{\partial z} &= 0. \end{aligned}\right\} \quad \ldots\ldots\ldots \quad (2)$$

If the component motions indicated by the subscript 3 that directly depend on the movements subscript 1 are materially less in intensity than the movements of rotation, then in any computation of the pressure their introduction ought not to be omitted. The former memoir gave a rather complicated value for the angular velocity χ. I have introduced a simplified expression for this in that, while retaining the dependence upon the polar distance θ, as there given, I have temporarily introduced a constant average value instead of the dependence upon the distance above the surface of the earth. According to this, one can put

$$\chi = \chi_1 \cos^2 \theta - \chi_2 \tag{3}$$

or with a slight difference

$$\chi = \frac{1}{R^2} \left\{ \chi_1 z^2 - \chi_2 r^2 \right\} \tag{4}$$

In these equations χ_1 and χ_2 are considered as constants. Therefore, as before found, the movement of rotation of the air in higher latitudes is positive, that is to say, has the same sign as the axial rotation of the earth. For a specific latitude the average value is 0, and at the equator the movement has the opposite sign.

Further computation shows that the relative angular velocity χ is small in comparison with that of the earth ε, so that the simpler equations to be solved are as follows:

$$\left.\begin{aligned} c^2 \frac{\partial \nu_3}{\partial x} &= 2\varepsilon\chi x + \varkappa \Delta u_3 \\ c^2 \frac{\partial \nu_3}{\partial y} &= 2\varepsilon\chi y + \varkappa \Delta v_3 \\ c^2 \frac{\partial \nu_3}{\partial z} &= \varkappa \Delta w_3 \\ \frac{\partial u_3}{\partial x} + \frac{\partial v_3}{\partial y} + \frac{\partial w_3}{\partial z} &= 0 \end{aligned}\right\} \quad \cdots \cdots \tag{5}$$

In solving these we first determine a function $\mathfrak{F}$ that is of such form as to satisfy the conditions $\frac{\partial \mathfrak{F}}{\partial x} = 2\varepsilon\chi x$, $\frac{\partial \mathfrak{F}}{\partial y} = 2\varepsilon\chi y$.

These conditions give

$$\mathfrak{F} = \frac{\varepsilon r^2}{R^2} \left\{ \chi_1 z^2 - \frac{\chi_2}{2} r^2 \right\} \tag{6}$$

Furthermore we put

$$u_3 = \frac{\partial L}{\partial x}, \quad v_3 = \frac{\partial L}{\partial y}, \quad w_3 = \frac{\partial L}{\partial z} + M \quad \cdots \cdots \tag{7}$$

where L and M are two new functions of x, y, and z, we can then write the system of equations as follows:

$$c^2 \frac{\partial \nu_3}{\partial x} = \frac{\partial \mathfrak{F}}{\partial x} + \varkappa \frac{\partial}{\partial x}(\Delta L)$$

$$c^2 \frac{\partial \nu_3}{\partial y} = \frac{\partial \mathfrak{F}}{\partial y} + \varkappa \frac{\partial}{\partial y}(\Delta L)$$

$$c^2 \frac{\partial \nu_3}{\partial z} = \frac{\partial \mathfrak{F}}{\partial z} + \varkappa \frac{\partial}{\partial z}(\Delta L) - \frac{\partial \mathfrak{F}}{\partial z} + \varkappa \Delta M.$$

The equation of continuity now becomes

$$\varDelta L = -\frac{\partial M}{\partial z} \quad \ldots \ldots \ldots \quad (8)$$

The three first equations lead to the two following:

$$c^2 \nu_3 = \text{Constant} + \mathfrak{F} - \varkappa \frac{\partial M}{\partial z} \quad \ldots \ldots \quad (9)$$

$$\varDelta M = \frac{1}{\varkappa} \cdot \frac{\partial \mathfrak{F}}{\partial z} \quad \ldots \ldots \ldots \quad (10)$$

If the functions L and M are so determined that they satisfy the boundary conditions then the problem is to be considered as solved and equation (9) gives the desired distribution of pressure. As boundary conditions I have retained those previously laid down, viz, adhesion to the earth's surface, slipping on an upper boundary surface at an altitude $R.\,h$ above the earth whereby h is to be considered as a small number in comparison with unity.

For further calculation it is expedient to introduce the vertical and meridional components of the current or V and N. These are connected with L and M by the equations

$$\left.\begin{aligned} V &= \frac{\partial L}{\partial r} + M \cos \theta \\ N &= -\frac{1}{r}\frac{\partial L}{\partial \theta} + M \sin \theta \end{aligned}\right\} \quad \ldots \ldots \ldots \quad (11)$$

The equation of continuity now becomes

$$\frac{\partial V}{\partial r} + \frac{2}{r} V = \frac{1}{r} \left\{ \cot \theta \,.\, N + \frac{\partial N}{\partial \theta} \right\} \quad \ldots \ldots \ldots \quad (12)$$

The elimination of L gives the further equation

$$\frac{\partial (Nr)}{\partial r} + \frac{\partial V}{\partial \theta} = r \frac{\partial M}{\partial r} \sin \theta + \frac{\partial M}{\partial \theta} \cos \theta \quad \ldots \ldots \quad (13)$$

The calculation gives the following values:

$$V = \frac{2\varepsilon}{\varkappa} R^3 \left\{ \chi_1 + 2\chi_2 - 6\,(4\chi_1 + \chi_2) \cos^2 \theta + 35 \chi_1 \cos^4 \theta \right\} . f(\sigma) \quad . \quad (14)$$

$$N = \frac{2\varepsilon}{\varkappa} R^3 \sin \theta \cos \theta \left\{ -\chi_1 - 2\chi_2 + 7\chi_1 \,.\, \cos^2 \theta \right\} . \, \varphi(\sigma) \quad \ldots \quad (15)$$

In these $f(\sigma)$ and $\varphi(\sigma)$ have a signification similar to that in the previous memoir, namely,

$$\left.\begin{aligned} f(\sigma) &= \frac{\sigma^2}{48} (h - \sigma)(3h - 2\sigma) \\ \varphi(\sigma) &= \frac{\sigma}{48} \left\{ 6h^2 - 15h\sigma + 8\sigma^2 \right\} \end{aligned}\right\} (16)$$

Moreover, σ is determined by the same equation as before,

$$r = R\,(1+\sigma)$$

Finally, from the equation (9)

$$c^2 \nu_3 = \text{const} + \mathfrak{F} - \varkappa \frac{\partial M}{\partial z}$$

there results the following:

$$c^2 \nu_3 = \text{const} + \varepsilon R^2 \left\{ \left(\frac{3\chi_1}{7} + \chi_2 \right) \cos^2 \theta - \chi_1 \cos^4 \theta \right\} \quad . \quad . \quad (17)$$

This last equation allows of a direct comparison with the above-mentioned observations of the distribution of pressure.

IV.

The average values of the pressure of the air in the Southern Hemisphere are given in the following table (under the column of observations) as a function of the latitude.*

Air pressure at the earth's surface.

Latitude.	Observed.	Computed.
°	*mm.*	*mm.*
0	758.0	758.0
S. 10	759.1	758.9
20	761.7	760.5
30	763.5	762.0
40	760.5	760.5
50	753.2	755.3
60	743.4	747.1
70	738.0	738.0
80	......	730.9
S. 90	......	727.2

These pressures are fairly represented by an expression of the form

$$p = p_a + a \cos^2 \theta - b \cos^4 \theta.$$

If we determine the constants a and b from the observed values for two different polar distances, for which I have used $\theta = 50°$ and $\theta = 20°$, then we obtain

$$p = 758 + 31.295 \cos^2 \theta - 61.094 \cos^4 \theta.$$

By the means of this formula the values given in the second column, under "computed," have been obtained.

* See A. Sprung, *Lehrbuch der Meteorologie*, p. 193; J. van Bebber, *Handbuch der Witterungskunde*, II, p. 136. [These figures are taken originally from Ferrel, "Meteorological Researches," I, 1880.—*C. A.*]

Furthermore, if we make the very probable assumption that the variations in pressure here considered depend exclusively on the movement of rotation, that therefore

$$p = p_a(1 + \nu_3)$$

where p_a represents the pressure at the equator, then is

$$\nu_3 = \frac{p - p_a}{p_a}.$$

Therefore

$$\nu_3 = \frac{\cos^2\theta}{758}\left\{31.295 - 61.094\cos^2\theta\right\}$$

$$= 0.0413\cos^2\theta - 0.0806\cos^4\theta \quad . \quad . \quad . \quad . \quad . \quad (19)$$

But the computation of ν_3 had already given

$$\nu_3 = \frac{\varepsilon R^2}{c^2}\cos^2\theta\left\{\frac{3\chi_1}{7} + \chi_2 - \chi_1\cos^2\theta\right\}$$

wherein the appended constant can be omitted.

Hence, the two expressions for ν_3 can be put equal to each other, and for the computation of the motion of rotation we obtain the two equations

$$\frac{\varepsilon\ R^2}{c^2}\chi_1 = 0.0806$$

$$\frac{\varepsilon\ R^2}{c^2}\left(\frac{3\chi_1}{7} + \chi_3\right) = 0.0413$$

If in these we put

$$R = 6379600^{\text{m}};\ c = 280^{\text{m}};$$
$$\varepsilon = 0.00007292$$

then we shall obtain

$$\chi_1 = 0.0292\ \varepsilon$$
$$\chi_2 = 0.0836\ \chi_1.$$

Hence, the relative angular velocity of the rotary motion of the air is

$$\chi = 0.0292\ \varepsilon\left\{\cos^2\theta - 0.0836\right\} \quad . \quad . \quad . \quad . \quad . \quad . \quad . \quad . \quad (20)$$

This is small in comparison with ε, the angular velocity of the earth, therefore it nowhere leads to improbably large movements of the atmosphere. If we form the product $\chi_1 R$, we obtain for it the value 13.58 metres per second. But the true linear velocity corresponding to the rotatory motion is

$$O = \chi.\ R.\ \sin\theta.$$

The maximum value of this occurs at S. latitude 56° 27′ and amounts to 4.59 metres per second. From the S. pole to 16° 49′ S. latitude the average value of the rotatory motion is positive, that is to say, directed toward the east; thence to the equator the value is negative, therefore directed toward the west.

These results can easily be combined with the conclusions of my previous memoir, according to which the motion of rotation can be considered as the sum of two terms that are of entirely different natures. Of the second term it was remarked especially that the current corresponding to it first attains sensible values at great altitudes. This therefore becomes at that altitude materially larger than the above deduced average value. The first term gave a movement entirely confined to the lower strata of the atmosphere: it is directed toward the east from the pole down to 35° latitude, but directed toward the west exclusively in the equatorial zone and less in velocity than the first component movement. The numerical computation leads to the same conclusion, since χ_2 is small in comparison with χ_1 Since from 35° of latitude down to the neighborhood of the equator there are two currents of opposite signs flowing over each other, therefore the place where the average movement of rotation is 0° will lie nearer to the equator than to 35°.

Therefore the conclusion of W. Siemens, which gave the first stimulus to the present investigation, has to be subjected to a modification only in so far as we must consider that the westward movement of the upper regions and higher latitudes has a predominance over the easterly movement of the lower regions and lower latitudes, because the former loses a much smaller fraction than the latter of its living force in consequence of friction.

The vertical and meridional components V and N are to be added to the corresponding components that were computed in my first memoir. The vertical component is positive at the equator and at the pole, it therefore gives an ascending current at both places, whereas V is negative throughout a broad central zone. *Therefore at the equator the ascending current is strengthened, at the pole the descending current is enfeebled.*

The meridional component N is zero at the surface of the earth at the equator; it is negative, *i. e.*, it is directed toward the south from thence to about 24° latitude; thence to the pole, where it is again zero, it has a northerly direction. Therefore in the tropics it strengthens the equatorial current and in higher latitudes it enfeebles it. Perhaps this explains the occurrence of northwest winds which frequently occur in the southern hemisphere between 50° and 60° south latitude.

Finally it may be remarked that the formula above used for the distribution of pressure agrees still better with the observations if a third term with a 6th power of cos θ is introduced. This term would also find its explanation by the analytical development, since the newly found meridional current should properly be again evaluated, in order to further compute the movements of rotation that are to be added to the first approximation, and which will bring about a corresponding change in the formula for pressure.

In other words, by a series of approxim ations one seeks the true solution in a manner similar, for instance, to that used in the computation of mutual inductive effects of two conductors, in which computation we imagine the total influence developed into a series of individual influences of the first conductor upon the second and then again of the second upon the first, and so on. It is easy to foresee that the further prolongation of the computation must afford a corresponding term in the expression for the pressure. By this means the expression for the rotatory motion will suffer some change; still it is to be seen that the order of magnitude of this is already correctly established. After the execution of the further computations just indicated, I expect then to elaborate in a similar manner the average distribution of pressure in summer and in winter in order to determine more precisely the changes of the rotatory motion with the seasons. The formula above found is only to be applied with caution to the northern hemisphere, since in this hemisphere the fundamental condition that the temperature is a function of the geographical latitude applies much less truly than in the southern hemisphere.

Reprinted from C. Abbe's translation in *Smithsonian Miscellaneous Collection*, 1891. The article originally appeared in *Sitzungsberichte der Königlichen Preussischen Akademie der Wissenschaften*, 1888.

V.

ON ATMOSPHERIC MOTIONS.*

(*FIRST PAPER.*)

By Prof. H. VON HELMHOLTZ.

I. INFLUENCE OF VISCOSITY ON THE GENERAL CIRCULATION OF THE ATMOSPHERE.

The influence of fluid friction in the interior of very extended regions that are filled with fluid and contain no vortex motion is always relatively very small. This can be proved from considerations that are based upon the principle of mechanical similarity. If we form the Eulerian hydro-dynamic equations and in them indicate by u, v, w the components of the velocity parallel to the axes of x, y, z; by ε the density, by p the pressure, by P the potential of the forces that act upon a unit of mass of the fluid; then if we consider P, ε, p, u, v, w as functions of x, y, z, t we have, as is well-known, the following partial differential equations for a fluid under the influence of friction†:

$$-\frac{\partial P}{\partial x}-\frac{1}{\varepsilon}\frac{\partial p}{\partial x}=\frac{\partial u}{\partial t}+u\frac{\partial u}{\partial x}+v\frac{\partial u}{\partial y}+w\frac{\partial u}{\partial z}-\frac{k^2}{\varepsilon}\left[\frac{\partial^2 u}{\partial x^2}+\frac{\partial^2 u}{\partial y^2}+\frac{\partial^2 u}{\partial z^2}\right] \quad . \quad . \quad . \quad . \quad (1)$$

$$-\frac{\partial \varepsilon}{\partial t}=\frac{\partial(\varepsilon u)}{\partial x}+\frac{\partial(\varepsilon v)}{\partial y}+\frac{\partial(\varepsilon w)}{\partial z} \quad . \quad . \quad . \quad . \quad . \quad . \quad . \quad (1a)$$

Two other equations symmetrical with regard to the other coördinates are to be added to the first of these equations. If now we have found any special integral whatever of these equations, which obtains for a definite region, then the equations will also hold good for a second case where all the linear dimensions x, y, z and also the time t and the friction constant k^2 are increased by a factor n, but where P, p, ε, u, v, w retain for every value of the new coördinates nx, ny, nz, nt, the same values as they had in the first case for the original coördinates x, y, z, t. Hence it follows that when in the movement of the magnified mass the friction constant can be also simultaneously and correspondingly increased, the

*From the *Sitzungsberichte* of the Royal Prussian Academy of Science at Berlin, 1888, May 31, pp. 647–663.

[†Namely viscosity as represented by Maxwell's kinematic coefficient ν or Helmholtz' $\frac{k^2}{\varepsilon}=\frac{0.0001878}{0.001293}=0.13417$]

movement takes place in an analogous manner, only slower. When this is not the case and when the friction retains its value unchanged then will the influence of the friction on the increased mass be very much less than upon the smaller mass. In consequence of this the greater mass will show the effects of its inertia as influenced much less by friction.

It is to be remarked that the potential P remains unchanged by the increase of the mass, but the force $\frac{\partial P}{\partial x}$ is reduced to $\frac{1}{n}$ of its value and that the whole process as already remarked requires for its completion n times the time.

Since the density and pressure are to remain unchanged therefore also any temperature differences that are present retain their magnitude and influence and do not disturb the relations implied in the mechanical similarity.

Unfortunately we can not imitate in small models the varying density of the atmosphere at different altitudes since we can not correspondingly change the force of gravity that is included in the expression $\frac{\partial P}{\partial x}$. Our mechanical comparisons are only able to imitate an atmosphere of constant density. Such an one must, as is well known, have an altitude of 8026 metres at 0° C. in order to produce the mean barometrical reading of 76 centimetres of mercury. If we desire in a model to represent the atmosphere by a layer of one metre in altitude, then we would need to reduce the day to 10. 8 seconds, or the year to 65. 5 minutes, and the influence of friction in movements at velocities that correspond to those of the atmosphere would in a small model be 8026 times as great as in the atmosphere. The loss of living force in the atmosphere during a year would therefore correspond to that lost in our model in $\frac{65.5}{8026}$ of a minute, which corresponds to less than a half a second.

On the other hand it is possible with the measured value of the friction constant of the air to compute for some simple cases how long a time would be required in order to reduce to one-half of its velocity any motion that is hindered only by internal friction. In this case the assumption of a constant density is for our purpose more unfavorable than the adoption of the actual variable density.

Assume that a stratum of air whose constant density is such as that of the lower stratum of the atmosphere, spreads over an unlimited plane and has a forward movement whose velocity is u in the direction of x parallel to the plane. Let z be the vertical coördinate, then the equation of motion for the interior of the mass is

$$\frac{\partial u}{\partial t} - \frac{k^2}{\varepsilon} \cdot \frac{\partial^2 u}{\partial z^2} = 0 \quad \ldots \ldots \ldots \quad (2)$$

Assume that the fluid adheres to the earth's surface where $z = 0$, therefore for this surface we have

$$u = 0_{z=0} \quad . \quad . \quad . \quad . \quad . \quad . \quad . \quad . \quad . \quad . \quad (2a$$

At the upper boundary surface where $z = h$ the fluid experiences no friction, therefore for that surface we have

$$\frac{\partial u}{\partial z} = 0_{z=h} \quad . \quad . \quad . \quad . \quad . \quad . \quad . \quad . \quad . \quad . \quad (2b)$$

Of the special integrals of the equation (2) that fulfill the boundary condition ($2a$), namely:

$$u = Ae^{-nt} sin\ (qx)$$
$$n = \frac{k^2}{\varepsilon} q^2$$

the one that also fulfills the condition (2_b) and is the most slowly diminishing is given by the value

$$q = \frac{\pi}{2h}$$

Hence follows

$$n = \frac{k^2}{\varepsilon} \cdot \frac{\pi^2}{4h^2}$$

The factor e^{-nt} becomes 1 at the time $t=0$: in order that this factor may be equal to one-half we must have

$$nt = \text{nat. log. } 2 = 0.69315.$$

According to Maxwell's determinations (Theory of Heat, London 1871, p. 279, where $\frac{k^2}{\varepsilon}$ is expressed by ν and k^2 by μ), we have

$$\frac{k^2}{\varepsilon} = 0.13417\ [1 + 0.00366\theta_c] \cdot \frac{[\text{centimetre}]^2}{\text{second}}$$

where θ_c indicates the temperature centigrade. From this there results, for the temperature 0° C.,

$$t = 42747 \text{ years.}$$

If we distribute the same mass of air throughout a thicker stratum with less density so that $\varepsilon \cdot h$, as also the k^2 which is independent of ε, retains its value unchanged, then t must increase with h. Hence it follows that in the upper thinner strata of the atmosphere the effect of viscosity propagates itself through atmospheric strata of equal mass more slowly than through the lower denser strata.

On the other hand an increase of the absolute temperature θ will cause the time t to diminish as $\frac{1}{\theta}$. The lower temperature of the upper strata of the atmosphere also diminishes the effect of the viscosity here under consideration.

This computation also shows how extremely unimportant for the upper strata of the air are those effects of viscosity that can arise on the earth's surface in the course of a year.

Only at the fixed boundaries of the space that the atmosphere fills, or at the interior surfaces of discontinuity where currents of different velocity border on each other, do the surface forces remain the same when the scale of dimensions is increased and the coefficient of friction is not simultaneously increased, and this allows us to recognize that the annulment of living force by viscosity can take place principally only at the surface of the ground and at the discontinuous surfaces that occur in vortex motions.

A similar relation obtains with regard to those temperature changes that can be effected by the true conduction of heat in the narrower sense, namely, the diffusion of moving molecules of gas between the warmer and colder strata. The coefficient $\varkappa$ of conduction for heat, when we choose as the unit of heat that which warms a unit volume of the substance by one degree in temperature (or the thermometric coefficient of conduction), is, according to Maxwell (Theory of Heat, page 302):

$$\varkappa = \frac{5}{3.\gamma} \cdot \left(\frac{k^2}{\varepsilon}\right)$$

where γ is the ratio between the two specific heats of gases.

In order to solve the corresponding problem for the conduction of heat this $\varkappa$ is to be substituted in equation (2) instead of $\frac{k^2}{\varepsilon}$, and if we put $\gamma = 1.41$ it is seen that in the above-assumed atmosphere of uniform density under a pressure of 76 centimetres of mercury and at a temperature of 0° an interval of 36164 years would be necessary in order by conduction to reduce by one-half the final difference in temperature of the upper and lower surfaces. Therefore also in the interchange of heat only its radiation and its convection by the motion of the air need be taken into consideration, except at the boundary between it and the earth's surface and at the interior surfaces of discontinuity.

On the other hand, simple computations have frequently shown that an unrestricted circulation of the air in the trade zones can not exist even up to 30° latitude.

If we imagine a rotating ring of air whose axis coincides with that of the earth and which, by the pressure of neighboring similar rings, is pushed now northward and now southward, and in which we can neglect the friction, then, according to the well-known general mechanical principle, the moment of rotation of this ring must remain constant. We will indicate this moment as computed for the unit of mass by Ω, and the angular velocity of the ring by ω, and its radius by ρ; then, as is well known,

$$\Omega = \omega \rho^2 \quad . \quad . \quad . \quad . \quad . \quad . \quad . \quad . \quad . \quad . \quad . \quad (3)$$

and therefor ω must vary inversely proportionally with ρ^2. If we indicate the mean radius of the earth by $R = 6379600$ metres, the geographical latitude by β, and the velocity of diurnal rotation of the earth by ω_0, then the corresponding relative velocity at the earth's surface for a ring of air that preserves a calm at the equator is

$$\rho(\omega - \omega_0) = \omega_0 \left[\frac{R}{\cos \beta} - R \cos \beta \right].$$

For air that is resting quietly at the equator in the zone of calms and is thence pushed up to the latitude of 10°, this expression gives the acquired wind velocity 14.18 metres per second, and similarly for air pushed up to latitude 20°, 57.63 metres, and for 30°, 133.65 metres per second.

Since 20 metres per second is the velocity of a railroad express train, therefore these numbers show without further consideration that such gales do not exist over any broad zone of the earth. We therefore ought not to make the assumption that the air which has risen at the equator reaches the earth's surface again unchecked in its motion even 20° farther northwards.

The matter is not much better if we assume the atmospheric ring resting at some intermediate latitude. In that case it would give an east wind at the equator, but a west wind at 30° latitude; but both velocities would far exceed the ordinary velocities of the observed winds.

Since now in fact observations do demonstrate a circulation of the air in the trade-wind zone, therefore the question recurs: By what means is the west-east velocity of this mass of air checked and altered? The resolution of this question is the object of the following remarks:

II. ON THE EQUILIBRIUM OF ROTATING RINGS OF AIR AT DIFFERENT TEMPERATURES.

If we introduce into equations (1) only rotatory motions about the axis, whereby ω, Ω, and ρ retain the significance just given them we then have

$$u = 0$$

$$v = -z\,\omega = -z.\frac{\Omega}{\rho^2}$$

$$w = y\,\omega = y.\frac{\Omega}{\rho^2}$$

and if we consider a steady mode of motion, in which Ω, p, P, and ε are functions of x and ρ only, then the equations (1) become

$$-\frac{\partial P}{\partial x}-\frac{1}{\varepsilon}\cdot\frac{\partial p}{\partial x}=0 \quad . \quad . \quad . \quad . \quad . \quad . \quad . \quad . \quad (3a)$$

$$-\frac{\partial P}{\partial \rho}\cdot\frac{y}{\rho}-\frac{1}{\varepsilon}\cdot\frac{\partial p}{\partial \rho}\cdot\frac{y}{\rho}=-y\cdot\frac{\Omega^2}{\rho^4}$$

$$-\frac{\partial P}{\partial \rho}\cdot\frac{z}{\rho}-\frac{1}{\varepsilon}\cdot\frac{\partial p}{\partial \rho}\cdot\frac{z}{\rho}=-z\cdot\frac{\Omega^2}{\rho^4}.$$

The two last equations combine into the one following:

$$\frac{\partial P}{\partial \rho}+\frac{1}{\varepsilon}\cdot\frac{\partial p}{\partial \rho}=\frac{\Omega^2}{\rho^3} \quad . \quad . \quad . \quad . \quad . \quad . \quad . \quad . \quad (3b)$$

Equation 1_a is satisfied by the above adopted values of u, v, w. Therefore the only equations to be satisfied are (3*a*) and (3*b*).

As concerns the value of the density ε, this depends upon the pressure p and the temperature θ. Since appreciable effective conduction of heat is excluded, therefore we must here retain the law of adiabatic variations between p and ε; therefore we have

$$\left(\frac{p}{p_0}\right)^{\frac{1}{\gamma}}=\frac{\varepsilon}{\varepsilon_0},$$

wherein γ again represents the ratio of the specific heats. If we indicate by θ the temperature that the mass of air under consideration would acquire adiabatically under the pressure p_0 (wherefore θ indicates the constant quantity of heat contained in the air while its temperature is varying with the pressure), and if we put

$$\frac{p_0}{\varepsilon_0\theta}=\mathfrak{R}$$

then we have

$$\frac{1}{\varepsilon}\cdot\frac{\partial p}{\partial \rho}=\left(\frac{p_0}{p}\right)^{\frac{1}{\gamma}}\cdot\frac{\theta\cdot\mathfrak{R}}{p_0}\cdot\frac{\partial p}{\partial \rho};$$

or if, for further abbreviation, we put

$$\frac{\gamma}{\gamma-1}\cdot\mathfrak{R}\cdot p^{\frac{1-\gamma}{\gamma}}=q \quad . \quad . \quad . \quad . \quad . \quad . \quad (3c)$$

$$p^{\frac{\gamma-1}{\gamma}}=\pi \quad . \quad . \quad . \quad . \quad . \quad . \quad . \quad . \quad (3d)$$

we shall have

$$\frac{1}{\varepsilon}\cdot\frac{\partial p}{\partial \rho}=q\cdot\theta\cdot\frac{\partial \pi}{\partial \rho},$$

wherein q indicates a constant peculiar to the gas and independent of θ and p. Similarly we also have

$$\frac{1}{\varepsilon}\cdot\frac{\partial p}{\partial x}=q\theta\frac{\partial \pi}{\partial x}$$

and therefore within a stratum of air having a constant θ and Ω we have, according to equations (3*a*) and (3*b*),

$$P+q\cdot\theta\cdot\pi=-\frac{1}{2}\cdot\frac{\Omega^2}{\rho^2} \quad . \quad . \quad . \quad . \quad . \quad . \quad . \quad (3e)$$

The very slight deviation of the earth from a spherical form allows us to simplify the computation on the one hand by regarding the earth's surface as a sphere, but on the other hand by giving the potential P an addition, the effect of which is that for the normal velocity of rotation ω_0 of the earth, its spherical surface becomes a level surface. To this end we put

$$P=-\frac{G}{r}+\frac{1}{2}\omega_0^2\rho^2,$$

[Where G=normal force of gravity: r=distance from center of gravity to point or stratum in the actual atmosphere.]

This gives the component in the direction of x, of the forces acting upon the unit of mass,

$$X=-\frac{\partial P}{\partial x}=-\frac{Gx}{r^2};$$

and, for the component in the direction of ρ,

$$P=-\frac{\partial P}{\partial \rho}=-\frac{G.\rho}{r^3}-\omega^2\rho$$

If to the latter the centrifugal force $+\omega^2.\rho$ is also added, there remains only one force on the rotating earth and which is directed normal to the spherical surface. Thus the spherical surface becomes the level surface of the combined potential force and centrifugal force, as indeed the surface of the earth really is.

Thus our equation (3*e*) becomes

$$q.\theta.\pi=-\frac{1}{2}\cdot\frac{\Omega^2}{\rho^2}+\frac{G}{r}-\frac{1}{2}\omega_0^2\rho^2+C \quad . \quad . \quad . \quad . \quad (3f)$$

The function π which is some power of the pressure p with positive exponent, increases and diminishes with p, and remains unchanged when p remains unchanged, so that we can determine the direction of the changes of the pressure easily by the changes of π.

Within a uniform stratum and with unchanged r, that is to say, for a constant elevation above the earth's surface, π has a maximum value at the station and latitude where

$$\frac{\Omega^2}{\rho^3}=\omega_0^2\rho;$$

or, if we introduce ω instead of Ω from equation (3), the maximum occurs where

$$\omega^2=\omega_0^2;$$

that is to say, where the [movement of the] ring causes a calm [on the earth's surface]. Towards this locality the pressure increases both from the pole and from the equator.

III. EQULIBRIUM BETWEEN ADJACENT STRATA HAVING DIFFERENT VALUES OF θ AND Ω.

On both sides of the surfaces separating such strata, p and therefore also $q\cdot\pi$ (see equation $3d$) must have the same value. If we distinguish the quantities on either side [of the boundary surface] by the indices 1 and 2 we obtain from equation ($3f$)

$$\left(\frac{1}{\theta_1}-\frac{1}{\theta_2}\right)\cdot\frac{G}{r}=\tfrac{1}{2}\cdot\frac{1}{\rho^2}\left[\frac{\Omega_1^2}{\theta_1}-\frac{\Omega_2^2}{\theta_2}\right]+\tfrac{1}{2}\omega_0^2\rho^2\left[\frac{1}{\theta_1}-\frac{1}{\theta_2}\right]-\frac{C_1}{\theta_1}+\frac{C_2}{\theta_2}\quad . \quad . \quad (4).$$

This should be the equation of the boundary curve, linear with respect to r and quadratic with respect to ρ^2.

In order to find the direction of the tangent to this curve we differentiate equation (4) with respect to r and ρ, whence we get

$$\frac{G}{r^2}dr=\frac{d\rho}{\rho^3}\left[\frac{\Omega_1^2\theta_2-\Omega_2^2\theta_1}{\theta_2-\theta_1}-\omega_0^2\rho^4\right]\quad . \quad . \quad . \quad . \quad . \quad (4a)$$

or, if instead of Ω we introduce the corresponding value of ω from equation (3),

$$+\frac{G}{r^2}dr=\rho.d\rho.\ \frac{(\omega_2^2-\omega_0^2)\theta_1-(\omega_1^2-\omega_0^2)\theta_2}{\theta_1-\theta_2}\quad . \quad . \quad . \quad . \quad . \quad (4b).$$

In order to decide how the two layers must lie with respect to the boundary surface if they are to have stable equilibrium, we reason as follows: The equation of the boundary surface (4) can, in accordance with the method of its deduction, be also written

$$\pi_1-\pi_2=\text{constant}\quad . \quad . \quad . \quad . \quad . \quad . \quad . \quad . \quad . \quad (4c);$$

or, if we designate by ds one of its elements of length,

$$\frac{\partial}{\partial s}[\pi_1-\pi_2]=0.$$

Now π_1 and π_2 are functions that also have a meaning when continued beyond the boundary curve, and can be so extended by continuous change [*i. e.*, without discontinuity]. The difference $(\pi_1 - \pi_2)$ will therefore in general increase on one side of the surface for increasing distance dn from this surface, but decrease, that is to say, become negative, on the other side; and thus on the side where $\frac{d(\omega_1 - \omega_2)}{dn}$ is positive we must have $\frac{\partial}{\partial h}(\pi_1 - \pi_2) > 0$ or positive for every other direction dh, in which one moves from any point of the surface towards the same side as dn.

If dh is drawn toward the other side of the surface for which $\pi_1 - \pi_2 = 0$, then will

$$\frac{\partial}{\partial h}(\pi_1 - \pi_2) < 0, \text{ or negative.}$$

If now the difference is positive on that side of the surface designated by the subscript index 1, then in case there is an infinitely small protrusion of the boundary surface toward this side, this protrusion will be pressed back by the exterior and greater π_1; similarly an infinitely small protrusion toward the negative side will also be pushed back, since there, on the other hand, π_1 diminishes more rapidly in the interior of such protrusion. Therefore in both these cases the equilibrium is stable. On the other hand, the equilibrium is unstable when the difference $(\pi_1 - \pi_2)$ on the side of π_1 is negative.

Now we need not form the differential quotients for the direction dn. It suffices to form them for dr or $d\rho$, and to merely determine whether the positive dr or $d\rho$ look toward the side whose index is 1 or that whose index is 2.

By forming these differential quotients from the equation $(3f)$ there results

$$q.\frac{\partial(\pi_1 - \pi_2)}{\partial r} = -\frac{G}{r_2}\left[\frac{1}{\theta_1} - \frac{1}{\theta_2}\right] \quad . \quad . \quad . \quad . \quad (4d).$$

The differential quotient is positive when $\theta_1 > \theta_2$. The partial differentiation with respect to r while ρ remains unchanged, indicates a progress in an ascending direction parallel to the earth's axis; that is to say, in the direction of a line pointing towards the celestial pole.

The equilibrium is stable when the strata containing the greater quantity of heat lie at higher elevations on the side towards the celestial poles.

We now form the other differential quotients

$$q.\frac{\partial}{\partial \rho}(\pi_1 - \pi_2) = \frac{1}{\rho^3}\left(\frac{\Omega_1^2}{\theta_1} - \frac{\Omega_2^2}{\theta_2}\right) - \omega_0^2\rho\left(\frac{1}{\theta_1} - \frac{1}{\theta_2}\right) \quad . \quad . \quad . \quad . \quad (4e).$$

$$= \rho\left[\frac{\omega_1^2 - \omega_0^2}{\theta_1} - \frac{\omega_2^2 - \omega_0^2}{\theta_2}\right] \quad . \quad . \quad . \quad . \quad . \quad (4f).$$

If in these equations θ_1 indicates the greater quantity of heat, then the equilibrium is stable when everywhere along the boundary surface we have

$$\rho\frac{\omega_1^2 - \omega_0^2}{\theta_1} > \rho.\frac{\omega_2^2 - \omega_0^2}{\theta_2} \quad . \quad . \quad . \quad . \quad . \quad . \quad . \quad . \quad (4g).$$

Both these values are positive where the west wind prevails; both negative where the east wind prevails.

The equation (4*e*) can also be written

$$q. \frac{\partial}{\partial \rho}(\pi_1 - \pi_2) = \frac{1}{\rho^3} \cdot \frac{\theta_1 - \theta_2}{\theta_1 \theta_2} \left[\omega_0^2 \rho^4 + \frac{\Omega_1^2 \theta_2 - \Omega_2^2 \theta_1}{\theta_1 - \theta_2} \right].$$

In order that this may be positive at all latitudes, the following inequality must be satisfied

$$\Omega_1^2 \theta_2 > \Omega_2^2 \theta_1$$

or,

$$\frac{\Omega_1^2}{\theta_1} > \frac{\Omega_2^2}{\theta_2}.$$

Ordinarily this will be the case, since in general θ increases simultaneously with ρ and from a definite value at the pole to a finite value at the equator. Similarly Ω_1^2 also increases with ρ, and from zero at the pole to $\omega_0^2 \rho^2$ at the equator, so that $\frac{\Omega^2}{\theta}$ also increases from zero at the pole to a definite positive value at the equator. We will therefore designate this case as the normal case. Exceptions can only occur under special conditions within limited zones.

In the normal case as we progress along the same level, the warmer π_1 lies on the side of the greater ρ; that is to say, on the side towards the equator, and equally on the side of the greater r if we progress toward the celestial pole; that is to say, ρ and r increase toward the same side of the boundary surface, and this surface must be so inclined that the tangent of its meridian section intersects the celestial sphere between the pole and the point of the horizon lying immediately beneath it. Near the equator, where the pole rises very little above the horizon, this gives an inclination to the boundary surface such that it makes a very small acute angle with the horizon.

In accordance with this, equation (4*a*) shows us that under those circumstances $\frac{dr}{d\rho}$ is negative along the boundary surface itself.

Therefore the normal inclination of the bounding surface is in an ascending direction toward a point situated beneath the celestial pole.

If on the other hand exceptional localities should exist at which

$$\omega_0^2 \rho^4 + \frac{\Omega_1^2 \theta_2 - \Omega_2^2 \theta_1}{\theta_1 - \theta_2} < 0 \quad . \quad . \quad . \quad . \quad . \quad (4h)$$

then in such cases according to equation (4*a*) $\frac{dr}{d\rho}$ will be positive; that is to say, the boundary line will ascend to higher levels as we depart from the earth's axis.

Since moreover equation (4*d*) shows that as we proceed in the direction of a line drawn to the pole, the warmer air must lie higher, therefore this line can not twice intersect the boundary surface between two layers, and consequently in the abnormal case this line must necessarily lie between the boundary surface and the horizontal plane located at the pole. Therefore the tangents to the meridional section of the boundary surfaces must intersect the greater arcs on the celestial sphere somewhere between the pole and the equatorial side of the horizon.

The smaller the difference of temperature is relative to the difference of the velocities of rotation so much the nearer does the tangent just referred to approach the pole.

Moreover at different points of the bounding line of the same two layers there can occur both normal and abnormal inclinations. For since in the expression (see equation $4h$) on whose positive or negative value such occurrence depends, the Ω and θ throughout the extent of each layer are constant, therefore for the same altitude above the earth this value can have a positive value near the equator but a negative value near the poles. Between these the boundary curve must attain a maximum altitude where the quantity under consideration passes from positive through zero to negative. At this place also, according to equation ($4a$), we have $\frac{dr}{d\rho} = 0$, therefore r is a limiting value and is here a maximum.

Location of the strata in the case when the velocity of rotation varies continuously with the quantity of heat contained.—The considerations hitherto set forth can also be extended to the case where Ω is a continuous function of θ, and the value of θ in the atmospheric strata is continually changing. The individual strata are in this case to be considered as indefinitely thin. Equation ($4a$) now becomes.

$$G\frac{dr}{r^2} = \frac{d\rho}{\rho_3}\left[\frac{d\left[\frac{\Omega^2}{\theta}\right]}{d\left(\frac{1}{\theta}\right)} - \omega_0^2\,\rho^4\right]$$

$$= \frac{d\rho}{\rho_3}\left[\Omega^2 - \theta\frac{d\Omega^2}{d\theta} - \omega_0^0\,\rho^4\right]$$

In order that the equilibrium may be stable the quantity of contained heat (see equation $4h$) must increase in the direction towards the celestial pole. But the layers of similar air are less inclined than the inclination of the polar axis at all places where the quantity

$$\Omega^2 - \theta.\ \frac{d\Omega^2}{d\theta} < \omega_0^2\,\rho^4;$$

but on the other hand their inclination is steeper where the left-hand side of this inequality is greater than the right.

IV. GRADUAL VARIATIONS OF THE EQUILIBRIUM BY FRICTION AND HEATING.

It is well known how very differently the propagation of changes of temperature in the air goes on according as heat is added or withdrawn below or above.

If the lower side of a stratum of air is warmed, as occurs at the surface of the earth, by action of the solar rays, then the heated stratum of air seeks to rise. This is effected very soon all over the surface in small tremulous and flickering streams such as we see over any plane surface strongly heated by the sun; but soon these smaller streams collect into larger ones when the locality affords opportunity, especially on the side of a hill. The propagation of heat goes on relatively rapidly through the whole thickness of the atmospheric layer, and when it has a uniform quantity of heat throughout its whole depth and is therefore in adiabatic equilibrium then also the newly added air seeks *de nova* to distribute itself through the entire depth.

The same process occurs with like rapidity when the upper side of a stratum of air is cooled.

On the other hand, when the upper side is warmed and the lower side cooled such convective movements do not occur. The conduction of heat operates very slowly in large dimensions, as I have already explained above. Radiation can only make itself felt to any considerable extent for those classes of rays that are strongly absorbed. On the other hand, experiments on the radiation from ice and observations of nocturnal frosts show that most rays of even such low temperatures can pass through thick layers of clear atmosphere without material absorption.

Therefore a cold stratum of air can lie for a long time on the earth, or equally a warm stratum remain at an altitude, without changing its temperature otherwise than very slowly.

Similar differences exist also in the case of the change of velocity by friction. For the normal inclination of an atmospheric stratum its upper end is nearer to the earth's axis than its lower end. If the stratum appears at the earth's surface as a west wind, then the moment of rotation of the lowest layer is delayed [by resistance of the earth's surface], its centrifugal force is diminished, and on the polar side of the stratum this lowest portion will slide outwards, approaching the axis in order to find its position of stable equilibrium at the upper end of the stratum. This movement will ordinarily take place in small tremulous streams similar to the ascent of warm air and must diminish the moment of rotation of the whole layer rather uniformly, but in the upper portions a little later than in the lower. Since, however, this latter effect distributes itself throughout the whole mass of air, it will become much less apparent on the lower side of the stratum than if it were confined to the lower stratum.

For the east wind matters are reversed. Its moment of rotation is increased by the friction on the earth's surface. The accelerated mass of air [the ground layer] already finds itself in that position of equilibrium which it has to occupy within its stratum, and can only press forward equatorially along the earth's surface into the stratum lying in front of it. If it is also simultaneously heated then the resulting ascent takes place more slowly than would occur in a stratum of air that is at rest at the bottom.

Hence it is to be concluded that in the east wind, the change due to friction is confined to the lower layer of air, and furthermore that it is relatively more effective here than in the case of a west wind of equal velocity. In general, the retarded layer of air will press forward toward the equator, in the Northern Hemisphere as northeast wind. In this motion it will continue to appear as an easterly wind since it is continually arriving at more rapidly rotating zones on the earth. The air of the stratum lying above the retarded layer will, where the region is free from obstruction, as at the outer border of the trade wind zone, fall behind and will appear as an east wind, retaining its moment of rotation unchanged and gradually pushing toward the equator will itself in its turn experience the above described influence of friction. I would here further remark that the water so abundantly evaporated in the tropical zone also enters into the trade wind, but with the greater velocity of rotation of the revolving earth and must diminish the retardation of the latter with respect to the earth.

The lower layers of the trade wind can press in under the equatorial calm zone itself only when any difference between their velocity of rotation and that of the earth's surface is entirely destroyed. They then blend with the zone of calms and increase its mass so that the latter broadens with its inclined boundary surface always higher above the layer of diminishing east wind beneath it.

Thus it is brought about that whereas below [nearer the earth's surface] mostly continuous changes are taking place in the temperature and the moment of rotation of the strata, on the other hand above, the boundaries of the broadening zones of calms (that have the great moment of rotation that pertains to the equatorial air and which at 10° latitude must appear as a strong west wind, and at 20° latitude as a westerly storm), occur in direct contact with the underlying stratum that has less velocity of rotation and lower temperature. Evidently the upper side of this latter [lower] stratum can scarcely be changed as to the quantity of its contained heat and of its moment of rotation, while after the loss of its lower layer it is being pushed sidewise and towards the equator.

As I have already shown in my communication to this Academy, April 23, 1868, on "Discontinuous Fluid Motions,"* such discontinuous motions can continue for a while, but the equilibrium at their boundary

* [See No. III of this collection of Translations.]

surfaces is unstable, and sooner or later they break up into whirls that lead to general mixture of the two strata. This statement is confirmed by the experiments with sensitive flames and by those in which by means of a cylindrical current of air blown from a tube we make a section in a flame and thus make visible the boundary of the moving and the quiet mass. If, as in our case, the lower stratum is the heavier it can be shown that the perturbations must at first be similar to the waves of water that are excited by the wind. The process is made evident by the striated cirrus clouds that are visible when fog is precipitated at the boundary of the two strata. The great billows of water that are raised by the wind show the same process which is different in degree only, by reason of the greater difference of the specific gravities. The severer storms even turn the aqueous billows to breakers, that is to say, they form caps of froth and throw drops of water from the upper crest high into the air. Up to a certain limit, this process can be mathematically deduced and analyzed, on which subject I propose a later communication. For slighter differences of specific gravity the result of this process must be a mixture of the two strata with a formation of whirls and under some circumstances with heavy rainfall. An observation of one such process under very favorable circumstances I once made accidentally upon the Rigi and have described.*

The mixed strata acquire a temperature and moment of inertia whose values lie between those of the component parts of the mixture, and its position of equilibrium will therefore be found nearer the equator than the position previously occupied by the colder stratum that enters into it. The mixed stratum will descend toward the equator and push back the strata lying on the polar side. Into the empty space thus created above, the strata from which this descending portion has been drawn stretch upwards, and thus their cross section must be diminished. Wherever the lower layers are pushed apart by descending masses of air, as is well known, there arise anti-cyclones; wherever cavities or gaps arise by reason of ascending masses of air, there arise cyclones. Anti-cyclones and the corresponding barometric maxima are shown, with very great regularity, by the meteorological charts † along the very irregularly varying limits of the northeast trade in the Atlantic Ocean—in the winter, under latitude 30°; in summer, under 40° latitude. On account of the inclined position of the strata, the rain that frequently forms by reason of the mixture of air (Dove's Subtropical Rain) falls somewhat farther northward because the water must fall down almost vertically. ‡

* See Proceedings of the Physical Society in Berlin, October 22, 1886.

† Daily Synoptic Weather Charts. Published by the Danish Meteorological Institute and the German Seewarte, Copenhagen and Hamburg.

‡ [The results stated in the above paragraph were subsequently greatly modified by Helmholtz. See Section v of his second memoir, or page 98 of these Translations.—*C. A.*]

Therefore the zone of cyclones begins there, but these become more frequent farther northward. We can certainly assume that the process of mixture is not perfected immediately at the exact border of the trade-wind zone, but that a part of the rapidly-rotating warm upper stratum remains unchanged or half mixed, which will presently bring about new mixtures farther on toward the pole.

In general, in this zone of mixture, even below at the earth's surface, the west wind must retain the upper hand because the increase of the total moment of rotation which the mass of air, through friction, experiences in the east wind of the trade zone must finally rise to such a pitch that somewhere the west wind again touches the earth and experiences sufficient friction to entirely give back the increase that it had. The masses of air resting in the equilibrium of stratification can certainly have no long-continued motion of rotation that differs essentially from that of the earth beneath them. When therefore they are mixed with the stronger west wind of the air from above, they receive a movement toward the east. Moreover the falling rain that in great part comes from the upper west winds, must transmit its motion to the lower strata through which the rain falls. Eventually all zones that are pressed polewards by intermixed masses moving equatorially and descending from them will become west winds.

Another permanent source of winds is the cooling of the earth at the poles. The cold layers endeavor to flow outwards from each other at the earth's surface and form east wind (or anti-cyclones). Above these the warmer upper strata must fill the vacancy and continue as west winds (or cyclones). Thus an equilibrium would come about, as is shown in Sect. II, if it were not that the lower cold stratum acquires, through friction, a more rapid movement of rotation, and is therefore competent for further advance. In doing this, according to the above given views this lower stratum must remain on the earth's surface. That in fact it does so is shown by frequent experiences during our northeast winter winds whose low temperatures frequently enough do not extend up to even the summit of the North German Mountains. Moreover on the front border of these east winds advancing into the warmer zone, the same circumstances are effective in order to bring about a discontinuity between the movement of the upper and lower currents, as in the advancing trade-winds, and there is therefore here a new cause for the formation of vortex motions.

The advance of the polar east wind, although recognizable in its principal features, proceeds relatively very irregularly since the cold pole does not agree with the pole of rotation of the earth, and also because low mountain ranges have a large influence. In addition to this comes the consideration that in the cold zone fog causes only a moderate cooling of the thicker stratum of air, but clear air brings about a very intense cooling of the lower layer. By such irregularities, it is brought about that the anti-cyclonic movement of the lower stratum and the great and gradually increasing cyclone of the upper stratum (that should otherwise be expected at the pole) break up into a large number of irregular, wandering cyclones and anti-cyclones, with a preponderance of the former.

From these considerations, I draw the conclusion that the principal obstacle to the circulation of our atmosphere, which prevents the development of far more violent winds than are actually experienced, is to be found not so much in the friction on the earth's surface as in the mixing of differently moving strata of air by means of whirls that originate in the unrolling of surfaces of discontinuity. In the interior of such whirls the strata of air originally separate are wound in continually more numerous, and therefore also thinner layers spirally about each other, and therefore by means of the enormously extended surfaces of contact there thus becomes possible a more rapid interchange of temperature and equalization of their movement by friction.

The present memoir is intended only to show how by means of continually effective forces, there arises in the atmosphere the formation of surfaces of discontinuity. I propose, at a future time, to present further analytical investigations as to the phenomena of such disturbances of continuity.

Reprinted from *Procès-Verbaux de l'Association de Météorologie,* UGGI (Lisbon), Part II (Mémoires), 1933.

THE FUNCTION OF CYCLONES IN THE GENERAL CIRCULATION

by HAROLD JEFFREYS.

The customary attitude of meteorologists to cyclones seems to be to regard them as disturbances superposed in some way upon a general circulation of the atmosphere, the latter being tacitly supposed capable of independent existence. I wish here to bring forward an alternative view, namely that cyclones are an essential part of the general circulation, which could not exist without them.

Let the north polar distance of any point be θ, and the east longitude φ. The velocities of the air to the south and the east respectively are u, v. The perpendicular distance of a point from the axis is ϖ, and the mean radius of the earth a. The density of the air is ρ, and the pressure p, the earth's speed of rotation Ω, and the height above sea level z. We can prove three propositions, one relating to the variation of the geostrophic wind with height, one to the existence of steady motion in the absence of friction, and one to the conservation of angular momentum for the air north of any given parallel of latitude.

1. For the first purpose we may neglect effects due to the curvature of the earth and, taking an origin of Cartesian coordinates at a given point on the surface, denote the southward and eastward distances by x, y, and the component of angular velocity about the vertical by ω. Then

$$\omega = \Omega \cos \theta. \qquad (1)$$

The geostrophic wind is then given by

$$u = -\frac{1}{2\,\omega\,\rho}\frac{dp}{dy}\,;\; v = \frac{1}{2\,\omega\,\rho}\frac{dp}{dx} \qquad (2)$$

For a given gas

$$p = R'\rho\, T \qquad (3)$$

where R' is a constant and T the absolute temperature. If the composition is not uniform, T is the virtual temperature as defined in a previous paper. Then

$$2\,\omega\frac{dv}{dz}=\frac{d}{dz}\left(\frac{R'T}{p}\frac{dp}{dx}\right)=-\frac{R'T}{p^2}\frac{dp}{dz}\frac{dp}{dx}+\frac{R'}{p}\frac{dT}{dz}\frac{dp}{dx}+\frac{R'T}{p}\frac{d^2p}{dz\,dx} \quad (4)$$

But

$$\frac{dp}{dz}=-g\rho=-\frac{gp}{R'T} \quad (5)$$

Hence

$$2\,\omega\frac{dv}{dz}=\frac{g}{p}\frac{dp}{dx}+\frac{R'}{p}\frac{dT}{dz}\frac{dp}{dx}-\frac{gT}{p}\frac{d}{dx}\left(\frac{p}{T}\right)=\frac{R'}{p}\frac{dT}{dz}\frac{dp}{dx}+\frac{g}{T}\frac{dT}{dx} \quad (6)$$

But we may eliminate R' by using (5); then

$$2\,\omega\frac{dv}{dz}=\frac{g}{T}\left(\frac{dT}{dx}\frac{dp}{dz}-\frac{dT}{dz}\frac{dp}{dx}\right)\Big/\frac{dp}{dz} \quad (7)$$

Similarly

$$2\,\omega\frac{du}{dz}=-\frac{g}{T}\left(\frac{dT}{dy}\frac{dp}{dz}-\frac{dT}{dz}\frac{dp}{dy}\right)\Big/\frac{dp}{dz} \quad (8)$$

The expressions (7) and (8) vanish if T is a function of p; hence if the surfaces of equal pressure and density coincide the geostrophic wind does not vary with height.

This theorem was proved in a different way by W. H. DINES (1).

For our purpose, since the temperature normally increases to the south, the first term in (7) corresponds to an increase with height of the component of the wind to the east (westerly in usual language). To estimate the amount of the effect, we notice that $\Omega=7.3\times10^{-5}$/sec. so that in middle latitudes ω is about 5×10^{-5}/sec. T varies by about 30° from the Arctic to the equator, or about 1 part in 10. Hence the contribution to dv/dz from the first term in (7) is about 10^{-3}/sec, or 1 metre per sec. per kilometre. The sign of dp/dx, on the other hand, is variable, so that the contribution from the second term is sometimes positive and sometimes negative. Its ratio to the first term may be estimated as follows. We have near the surface dp/dz = — 1.3 dyne/cm³; dT/dz = — 6°$\times10^{-5}$/cm.; and if a horizontal variation of tem-

(1) Nature, 99, 1917. 24. Cf, also, SHAW, J. Scott. Meteor. Soc. 16, 1913, 171; Manual of Meteorology. 4, 196.

perature of 30° is associated with one of 20 mb. ($= 2\times 10^4$ dynes/cm²) in pressure,

$$\frac{dT}{dz}\frac{dp}{dx}\bigg/\frac{dT}{dx}\frac{dp}{dz} = \frac{6\times 10^{-5}\times 2\times 10^4}{30\times 1.3} = \frac{1}{30} \tag{9}$$

roughly. It appears therefore that with ordinary limits of variation the second term is a small fraction of the first. Thus the variation of the westerly wind with height depends on the variation of temperature with latitude, and is substantially independent of anything else.

The geostrophic wind is a good approximation to the actual wind except in disturbances of small horizontal extent, such as tropical cyclones and land and sea breezes, and in the lowest kilometre of the atmosphere, where the wind is appreciably influenced by the friction of the ground. Subject to these restrictions the above rules may be applied to the actual wind.

2. With any given steady distribution of temperature the number of possible steady motions of the atmosphere is infinite in the absence of friction. For the geostrophic wind is given by

$$2\,\Omega\,u\cos\theta = -\frac{1}{\rho}\frac{dp}{a\sin\theta\,d\varphi}\,;\; 2\,\Omega\,v\cos\theta = \frac{1}{\rho}\frac{dp}{a\,d\theta} \tag{10}$$

The rate of loss of mass due to horizontal flow in an element of volume specified by $d\theta\, d\varphi\, dz$ is

$$d\theta\, d\varphi\, dz\left\{\frac{d}{d\theta}(\rho u\, a\sin\theta) + \frac{d}{d\varphi}(\rho v a)\right\} = \frac{1}{2\,\Omega}\,d\theta\, d\varphi\, dz\left\{-\frac{d}{d\theta}\left(\sec\theta\,\frac{dp}{d\varphi}\right)\right.$$

$$\left. + \frac{d}{d\varphi}\left(\sec\theta\,\frac{dp}{d\theta}\right)\right\} = -\frac{1}{2\,\Omega}\sec\theta\tan\theta\, d\theta\, d\varphi\, dz\,\frac{dp}{d\varphi} \tag{11}$$

Now if the pressure at height o is p_s, we have from (3) and (5)

$$\frac{p}{p_s} = \exp\left(-\int_0^z \frac{g\,dz}{R'T}\right) \tag{12}$$

and the rate of increase of mass per unit area is dp_s/gdt. Hence, integrating (11) with regard to z from o to infinity, we get

$$\frac{dp_s}{g\,dt} = -\frac{1}{a^2\sin\theta}\left[\frac{d}{d\theta}(\rho u\, a\sin\theta) + \frac{d}{d\varphi}(\rho v a)\right] = \frac{1}{2\Omega a^2\cos^2\theta}\frac{dP}{d\,d\varphi} \tag{13}$$

where

$$P = \int_0^\infty p dz \tag{14}$$

It follows that if P is independent of the longitude, p_s does not vary with time; and therefore with T independent of the time it follows from (12) that the pressure at every height is independent of the time. It is not necessary that p should be independent of φ; for though there would otherwise be inflow at some levels and outflow at others, this would be accommodated by vertical motion within the column, leaving the pressure at ground level unaltered. Thus P may be any function of latitude only. With any such function p_s may be found from (12) and (14), and therefore a steady *régime* exists. Thus with any steady distribution of temperature there are an infinite number of possible steady motions of the atmosphere. This is the meteorological analogue of a theorem relating to free steady motions in the ocean given by RAYLEIGH and extended by LAMB (1).

It appears further that if P increases to the east there will be accumulation of mass, and the pressure at all levels will increase with the time; thus anomalies in P will move to the west (2). If the pressure anomalies remain of the same order of magnitude up to height *h*, the rate of travel will be

$$\frac{gh \sin \theta}{2 \Omega a \cos^2 \theta} \tag{15}$$

With h = 8 km. and $\theta = 60^\circ$, this is about 3×10^4 cm/sec. This is much faster than the ordinary rate of travel of a cyclone, besides being in the wrong direction in temperate latitudes. Ordinary cyclones must therefore apparently be phenomena involving such temperature variation that the variation of P is small compared with that of hp_s, or else the travel arising from the linear terms must be balanced by a second order effect; it was found previously that the second order terms gave a rate of travel in the right direction but embarrassingly large (3)

(1) Hydrodynamics, art. 333.

(2) This was noticed by L. F. RICHARDSON, *Weather Prediction by a Numerical Process* 1922, 9. I obtained it about the same time (Q. J. R. Met. Soc. 48, 1922, 36), but there seems to be a numerical error in the estimated rate of travel.

(3) Phil. Mag. 37, 1919, 1-8.

3. The main result of the last section is that we cannot hope to determine the general circulation uniquely from frictionless theory alone, since with any assigned distribution of temperature the number of possible general circulations is infinite. The actual general circulation must therefore apparently either have been given in the beginning and persisted ever since, or else be essentially controlled by friction. Now it is easily seen that friction must have a very important influence on the general circulation. With an easterly or westerly wind the magnitude of the frictional stress is $k\rho\, v_S^2$, where k is a numerical constant equal to about 0.002. With a velocity of 400 cm/sec this is about 0.4 dyne/cm². Now the momentum of a column of air 1 cm² in cross section extending the whole height of the atmosphere and moving with velocity 400 cm/sec is 4×10^5 gm.cm./sec. It would therefore be annihilated by friction in 10^6 seconds, or about 12 days. Allowance for the variation of wind with height makes no difference; for this variation is determined by temperature distribution alone, and therefore any loss of momentum due to friction is redistributed through the column so as to leave the vertical variation of wind unaltered. The time needed to abolish the *surface* wind remains as estimated. This effect is so drastic that we may say at once that only such motions are possible as are permitted by friction. It further becomes clear that either there must be no surface wind anywhere, or the surface winds must be eastward in some places and westward in others; for in the latter case the friction will tend to accelerate rotation of the atmosphere in some places and retard it in others, and with a suitable distribution the two effects may balance. But we must go into greater detail; for not only must the angular momentum of the whole atmosphere be steady, but also that between any two given parallels must be steady. Now if the winds between any given pair of parallels are prevailingly in one direction, the friction will be in the opposite direction, and the circulation will be rapidly brought to rest unless new angular momentum is brought in. Pressure within the belt cannot do this, and ordinary viscosity is ineffective. The only possible source of the new angular momentum is interchange of air with the regions to the north and south, air that has lost its angular momentum travelling out of the zone and being replaced by other air with a new supply.

The theory of turbulence in the atmosphere implies a drift

across the isobars in the lowest kilometre, due to friction, and with a symmetrical distribution of pressure this would imply a transfer of angular momentum in the right sense. But it proves to be quantitatively inadequate. Let us consider the southward transfer across a given parallel. The rate of transfer of mass is

$$Q = \int_0^{2\pi} \int_0^{\infty} \rho \, (\varpi + z \sin \theta) \, u d\varphi \, dz = 0 \qquad (16)$$

since the total mass must not vary secularly. The angular momentum per unit mass is $(\varpi + z \sin \theta)^2 (\Omega + \dot{\varphi})$. Hence the rate of transfer of angular momentum to the south is

$$M = \int_0^{2\pi} \int_0^{\infty} \rho \, (\varpi + z \sin \theta)^3 \, (\Omega + \dot{\varphi}) \, u d\varphi \, dz \qquad (17)$$

Now ϖ and Ω are independent of φ and z; so if we multiply (16) by $\varpi^2 \Omega$ and subtract from (17) we find

$$M =$$

$$\int_0^{2\pi} \int_0^{\infty} \rho u \left[\{(\varpi + z \sin \theta)^2 - \varpi^2\} \Omega + (\varpi + z \sin \theta)^2 \dot{\varphi} \right] (\varpi + z \sin \theta) \, d\varphi dz.$$

$$\int_0^{2\pi} \int_0^{\infty} \rho u \, \varpi^2 \, (2 \, \Omega \, z \sin \theta + v) \, d\varphi dz \qquad (18)$$

nearly. Now in any case ρu is negligible when z is more than about 20 km. If then we take $z = 2 \times 10^6$ cm., $\Omega = 7.3 \times 10^{-5}$/sec., $\Omega z = 150$ cm/sec. But the velocity of prevailing winds is of order 400 cm/sec or more; hence with this hypothesis, which is unduly favourable to the first term in the integrand, the contribution from v is three times that from Ωz (1). Hence we have approximately

$$M = a^2 \sin^2 \theta \int_0^{2\pi} \int_0^{\infty} \rho u v \, d\varphi \, dz. \qquad (19)$$

This evidently has an intimate relation to REYNOLDS's eddy shear stress u'v'. The present proof is simplified from an earlier one (2); REYNOLDS's discussion cannot of course be applied directly because we have to consider the amount of the complication introduced by the earth's rotation.

---

(1) This might not hold for a planet with a deep atmosphere, such as, probably, Saturn.

(2) Q. J. R. Met. Soc. 52, 1926, 96.

Now consider the rate of change of angular momentum due to friction. We use suffix *s* to indicate surface values; the frictional stress is $-k\,\rho_s\,(u_s^2+v_s^2)^{\frac{1}{2}}\,v_s$, and the moment of the friction about the polar axis is

$$-k\int_0^{\theta}\int_0^{2\pi}\rho_s\,(u_s^2+v_s^2)^{\frac{1}{2}}\,v_s\,a^3\sin^2\theta\,d\theta\,d\varphi \qquad (20)$$

The condition for the constancy of angular momentum north of colatitude θ is therefore

$$\sin^2\theta\int_0^{2\pi}\int_0^{\infty}\rho\,uv\,d\varphi\,dz=-ka\int_0^{2\pi}\int_0^{\theta}\rho_s\,(v_s^2+u_s^2)^{\frac{1}{2}}\,v_s\sin^2\theta\,d\varphi\,d\theta. \qquad (21)$$

This should hold as an approximation for all values of θ.

4. Now consider the possibility that the pressure is independent of φ. Then the geostrophic wind is eastward or westward, and the integration with regard to φ merely gives a factor 2π on each side. The southward component u is zero except in the lowest kilometre, where it has the opposite sign from v in the northern hemisphere, reaching about $\frac{1}{4}$ v on the ground. Hence (dropping the factor 2π) we see that the left side is about $-\frac{1}{8}\rho_s\,v_s^2\sin^2\theta$ (1 km). The right side is of order $-\frac{1}{3}\,ka\,\rho_s\,v_s^2\sin^3\theta$. A balance can therefore be obtained if $\sin\theta$ is about $\frac{3}{8}\,\frac{1\text{ km}}{ka}=\frac{1}{32}$. Thus a balance of the angular momentum equation due to inflow through friction cannot hold for more than about 2° from the pole. Further, even if this held in such a restricted region, we should still need to apply the principle to the northern hemisphere as a whole. We may suppose similarity of thermal conditions between the northern and southern hemispheres, so that there is no correlation between u and v on the equator, and the left side vanishes there. Hence the contributions to the right of (21) from the ranges $0 < \theta < 2^o$ and $2^o < \theta < 90^o$ must be equal and opposite. In view of the factor $\sin^2\theta$ in the integrand this would imply such a concentration of velocity near the poles as seems entirely unplausible, if not impossible. It seems therefore that we are entitled to say that when friction is taken into account it is impossible to reconcile

a steady general circulation with the equation of angular momentum.

5. It appears therefore that the general circulation must either involve no surface winds and therefore no friction, or else be unsymmetrical. We can see that the latter condition makes it possible to satisfy (21). Consider a moderate latitude, say 45°, and suppose that north of it the order of magnitude of the velocities remains the same. Then the right of (21) is of order $-ka \times 2\pi \times 0{\cdot}14 \rho_S v^2_S$. The left is $\pi \int_0^\infty \rho\, uvdz$, a mean with regard to longitude being understood. Hence

$$\int_0^\infty \rho\, uvdz = -\ .0006\ a\ \rho_S\ v_S^2\ = -\ \rho_S v_S^2\ (4\ \text{km}).$$

It appears therefore that (21) can be satisfied if u is equal and opposite to v over a height of rather more than 4 km. (since we must allow for the reduction of density with height). To maintain an eastward circulation in high latitudes the winds at the southern boundary must be mostly north-east and south west. This agrees with observation; *mutatis mutandis*, it holds also in the southern hemisphere. But the correlation between u and v can hardly be complete, and if we allow for this it seems that the currents must persist through about the whole height of the troposphere. The same must therefore apply to the associated pressure gradients. This agrees with the work of W. H. DINES, who shows that the pressure on the ground is (coefficient = + 0.68 to 0.88) positively correlated with that at heights up to 9 km. (2). On the other hand the constitution of the cyclone as fundamentally a combination of south-west and north-east winds seems to agree better with the model of BJERKNES than with the symmetrical model of earlier writers. I think, however, that the apparent difference is one of emphasis and method of approach rather than one of fact. On the other hand the suggestions that the cyclones represent either an instability of the general circulation, or oscillations about a steady general circulation, appear to be incorrect. These sugges-

(1) It might appear that (21) could be satisfied without departure from symmetry if there were S W winds on the ground, with NE winds above them. But if this held all round a parallel of latitude we should h ve the component of velocity to the south always diminishing with height, and therefore, by (8), the temperature always decreasing to the east. Hence the temperature could not be continuous.

(2) Collected papers, 247.

tions agree in assuming that a steady symmetrical general circulation is possible; whereas it has been shown here that friction renders such a circulation impossible *ab initio*. Cyclones are then only the irregularities inevitable in any circulation when skin friction over the earth's surface is taken into account. Their fundamental function is to transport momentum, just as in the smaller eddies usually considered in turbulence; and DEFANT's notion of a horizontal Austausch including the cyclones exhibits their true nature.

6. The foregoing inferences proceed from the assumption that there is a systematic circulation involving surface winds. The result is therefore a necessary condition for the existence of such a circulation. The main problem of the circulation, however, may be stated as follows : given the supply of heat, the mean of which with regard to time is a function of latitude only, why should there be any surface winds at all? If the atmosphere was originally isothermal and at rest, and was heated up in such a way that there was no horizontal outflow, there would be no change of the mass above any point, and none of surface pressure; and therefore when the atmosphere was left to itself there would be no geostrophic wind on the ground and therefore, apparently, no surface wind. At other levels there would of course be a geostrophic wind, since the temperature is a function of latitude. But if there is no surface wind the right side of (21) vanishes, and the left side will vanish if $u = 0$, and the equation is satisfied. Our problem is, then, why is this not the correct solution? The question is serious because it appears at first sight as if such a solution would be stable. Suppose we have a symmetrical circulation; friction makes the air drift towards the regions of low pressure and therefore tends to fill them up, so that a state with no surface inequalities of pressure apparently tends to be restored. We may however proced by comparing this motion with one that is certainly stable : that where the whole atmosphere rotates like a rigid body with the earth and the temperature is a function of height only (more strictly, of the geopotential). Here there are no winds at all at any height. The motion to be considered differs from this in two respects. The temperature depends on the latitude; and the velocity depends on the height. The former condition leads to disturbances of the thermal state by

radiation and heat conduction, but there seems to be no reason to suppose that these would be unsymmetrical. The latter on the other hand implies a general shear in the atmosphere, of an amount far greater than is required to initiate turbulence according to REYNOLDS's results. Thus momentum would tend to be transferred downwards, producing surface winds, until these reached such strength that the friction balanced the downward transfer to the surface layer. But then the friction on the ground would imply a secular change of angular momentum in the column as a whole, unless this was restored by interchange of air between different latitudes. It seems therefore that the state with no surface winds would lead to a state involving cyclones. The nature of the resulting movement is not easy to see in this way, but can be seen from other considerations. The initial state considered is not one of rotation like a rigid body, and therefore, by a well-known theorem, involves dissipation of energy though viscosity. Now it contains only one source of energy, namely the variation of density over the level surfaces. On account of the higher temperature near the equator, combined with the assumed uniformity of pressure at the surface, the pressure at any height other than zero is greatest at the equator, and the mean height of the air is greatest there. Hence there is a store of potential energy corresponding to this variation of the mean height. In establishing any other motion this potential energy must be drawn upon (1). Hence the pressure near the equator must be diminished and that in higher latitudes increased. Thus the final state will involve a belt of low pressure around the equator, with a system of easterly tradewinds. But the winds elsewhere must be westerly, so that there must be westerly circulations in middle latitudes, corresponding to the usual prevailing winds there. It seems probable, however, that these would not extend to the poles. To maintain such circulations near the poles NE and SW winds would have to extend in spirals all the way to the poles, a state of affairs probably difficult to realize dynamically. It seems more plausible that a southeast wind should turn round before it reaches

(1) Dr L. F. RICHARDSON, in a letter to me, puts this point in another way. " Why are there surface winds? We see the answer most clearly by studying the conditions under which an occasional surface calm is moved by the wind in an upper layer. This commonly happens about 3 hours after sunrise." Clearly there is downward transport of momentum even when there is no surface wind initially.

the pole. If it does so, the shift would most frequently occur through the air passing around the north of a cyclone, its direction changing from SW through SE to NE, and the velocity would diminish through friction in the process. Since the transmission of angular momentum depends on the product ρuv, and the average value of ρu is zero, we shall expect the SE winds to make a somewhat larger contribution to the angular momentum near the north pole than the NE ones do. Thus the mean of ρuv would be positive and weak anticyclonic circulations would be expected near the poles. Such an effect would be complicated by the effect of unsymmetrical distribution of land near the pole, notably by Greenland, and would probably be difficult to disentangle from the observational material; on the other hand it may possibly be identified with the phenomenon of " polar air ".

7. The foregoing development is mainly qualitative or relating to orders of magnitude rather than to accurate values. This appears to be inevitable at present. The ordinary phenomena of turbulence are still only somewhat vaguely understood, and here we have the additional complications of rotation and a spherical boundary. It does however indicate some considerations that seem fundamentally important in the theory of atmospheric motions, and that will have to appear in some form or other in any more precise theory.

DISCUSSION

Dr. F. Y. W. Whipple : one of the first problems to be studied in dynamical meteorology was the cause of the Trade Winds. It is certain that the solution given by Hadley and still reproduced in texbooks of geography is inadequate. — Hadley's scheme would logically entail high pressure over the poles, low pressure over the equator and winds with easterly components in all latitudes. The real problem of the Trade Winds is to explain the belts of high pressure north and south of the tropics.

I believe that Dr. Jeffreys's analysis supports the suggestion which I put forward some years ago that the westerly surface winds of the middle latitudes are produced through turbulence by the westerly upper winds and that the westerly surface winds produce by geostrophic force the high pressure belts. The upper west winds are themselves explained by the distribution of temperature and the trade winds are explained by the fall of pressure towards the equator.

The difficulty in the chain of cause and effect is to see how the drag of the upper winds is exerted to produce the westerly surface winds. The mechanism which Dr. JEFFREYS has explained must serve the purpose but I must confess I am not yet able to picture just how this happens. The recognition that the departures from the average flow are as important as the average flow is, however, a notable advance in the subject.

Sir G. T. WALKER says that after Dr. WHIPPLE'S challenge he must express his view that if the earth's atmosphere has assumed a steady state there must be an east wind round the equator, for the air may be regarded as having in a state of steady motion all the angular momentum about the earth's axis that it will acquire; and hence the resultant of the couples about the earth axis of the friction between the air and the earth will be zero. Now near the equator the wind will be easterly, for there is no place from which a particle could arrive with a more rapid angular velocity than that of the earth at the equator. Then since the total couple is zero the friction at a distance from the equator must be in the negative direction : hence the winds there must be westerly. These results hold whether the equator is hotter or colder than the other parts of the earth.

In his reply Dr. H. JEFFREYS agrees with Dr. WHIPPLE'S remarks. He thinks that Sir G. T. WALKER, overlooks the possibility that surface air at the equator may be air that has descended from some height; then the reduced distance from the axis gives an increased absolute velocity and therefore a wind from the west. This would not arise in the actual case of high temperatures near the equator; but if the temperature distribution was reversed Dr. JEFFREYS thinks that it would, and that the final result would be a reversal of the directions of the prevailing winds everywhere.

Reprinted from *Journal of Marine Research*, Vol. 2, Jun. 21, 1939.

RELATION BETWEEN VARIATIONS IN THE INTENSITY OF THE ZONAL CIRCULATION OF THE ATMOSPHERE AND THE DISPLACEMENTS OF THE SEMI-PERMANENT CENTERS OF ACTION*

By

C.-G. ROSSBY AND COLLABORATORS

Massachusetts Institute of Technology

This paper attempts to interpret, from a single point of view, several at first sight independent phenomena brought into focus through the synoptic investigations carried on at the Massachusetts Institute of Technology during the last few years. Since this interpretation is very largely based on a consideration of the changes in vorticity which must occur in vertical air columns which are displaced from one latitude to another and since such vorticity changes play a fundamental role also in Ekman's general ocean current theory (1932), the results would appear to be of enough interest to physical oceanographers to warrant their publication in this journal. The particular phenomena brought out in the course of our studies are listed below.

1. Mean monthly isentropic charts for the month of August from the last few years show that the atmosphere over the United States at that time of the year is characterized by a well-marked anticyclonic cellular structure, each cell or eddy consisting of a dry current from the north and a moist current from the south, the total diameter of each cell being from 1500 to 2500 miles (Namias and Wexler, 1938). Eddies of this type also represent the most outstanding feature of the *daily* isentropic charts for the summer season; the fact that the mean monthly charts show the same structure proves that the individual eddies are very nearly stationary and that they frequently regenerate in certain preferred locations. A comparison of the mean charts from different years shows that in spite of marked differences from year to year, one tongue of moist air always enters the United States

* This paper contains a preliminary report on certain phases of an investigation carried on at the Massachusetts Institute of Technology in cooperation with the U. S. Department of Agriculture, the objective being the development of adequate methods for weekly weather forecasts. The synoptic phases of this project, involving the preparation of daily weather charts for the Northern Hemisphere, is under the direction of Dr. H. C. Willett with the cooperation of Messrs. J. Holmboe and J. Namias. The statistical phases are under the direction of Mr. L. Page with the co-operation of Mr. R. Allen, both of the Bureau of Agricultural Economics.

from the southeast around or to the west of El Paso in New Mexico. Another moist tongue from the south frequently appears over western Florida. This recurrence suggests that the *position* of the eddies very largely must depend upon geographic factors. Nothing is known, however, about the dynamic factors which presumably control the *size* of the eddies.

2. During the last three years we have constructed daily weather maps for the Northern Hemisphere for use in an effort to extend the time range of our synoptic forecasts. In the course of these studies seven-day, later five-day mean pressure charts were constructed weekly. Underlying the construction of these mean charts is the assumption that the averaging process, at least partially, removes perturbations in the pressure distribution associated with the rapidly moving wave cyclones. The remaining perturbations are of larger dimensions and appear to determine the path of the wave disturbances. On the winter maps there are normally at least five such perturbations to be seen, the Icelandic and the Aleutian Lows, the Azores and the Asiatic Highs and finally the Pacific High, but one or several of these centers frequently breaks up into two parts. It is well known that these perturbations at higher levels no longer appear as closed isobaric systems but merely as undulations in the prevailing zonal pressure distribution. The sea level perturbations sometimes move westward several weeks in succession, finally splitting up into several parts. No explanation of these displacements and of the ultimate breaking up of the perturbations has been offered.

3. Five-day mean isentropic charts and five-day mean pressure charts for the three kilometer level have been constructed weekly. These upper level mean pressure charts often indicate the existence, during the winter season, of a trough of low pressure over the United States. The trough may remain stationary for several weeks in succession, but hitherto no adequate explanation of its position and displacement has been offered. The significance of the trough is best seen from the isentropic charts which show that even a fairly feeble low pressure trough over the Mississippi Valley with west-southwesterly gradient wind over the eastern part of the country in isentropic representation appears as a strong moist current extending from the Gulf northeastward towards the middle Atlantic coast.

4. In an attempt to obtain simple indices to the intensity of the general zonal circulation of the Northern Hemisphere, five-day means of the mean pressure on each latitude circle were computed and plotted weekly in the form of pressure profiles from equatorial to polar regions. Such curves were first used systematically by H. H. Clayton (1923). These curves of mean pressure against latitude have on several occasions shown marked trends towards increasing or decreasing zonal circulation, persisting through several weeks.

In the attempt to understand the dynamics of the upper level trough over the United States, the author found great help in a remarkable paper by J. Bjerknes (1937) which offers a simple explanation for the displacement of perturbations superimposed upon the zonal pressure distribution which normally prevails in the upper part of the troposphere. Bjerknes studied the amount of air transported across a section perpendicular to two consecutive isobars and found that this transport depends upon the curvature

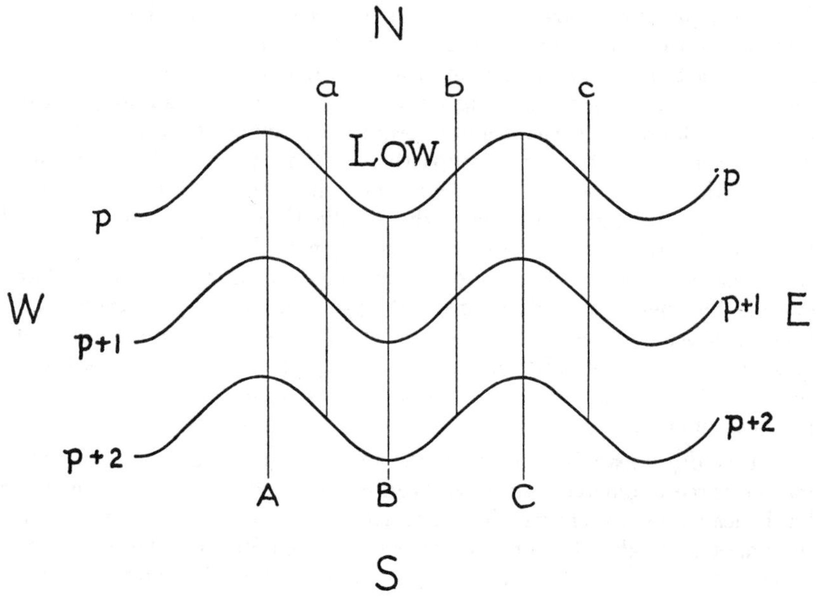

Figure 11. Sinusoidal Perturbation on Zonal Motion.

of the isobars and upon the latitude of the section. Thus, if the pressure distribution is not strictly zonal but characterized by a certain perturbation, regions of convergence and divergence and hence of rising and falling pressure are created which lead to a displacement of the perturbation. Bjerknes' reasoning may be seen from Figure 11. Disregarding at first variations in latitude, it is evident that more air is transported through the sections *A* and *C* where the curvature is anticyclonic than through section *B*, where the curvature of the isobars is cyclonic. Thus horizontal divergence is created between *B* and *C* and a drop in pressure occurs to the east of the trough at *B*, while horizontal convergence and a rise in pressure will occur between *A* and *B*. As a result the trough will move eastward.

Since the variations in the transport and thus in the magnitude of the pressure changes increase with decreasing radius of curvature of the isobars, it follows that for the same amplitude short waves must move more rapidly eastward than long waves.

Considering now solely the effect of variation in latitude, it may be seen from the gradient wind relationship that more air is transported between consecutive isobars in low latitudes than in high. Thus the transport across *B* is greater than the transport across *A* or *C* and hence there must be convergence and pressure rise between *B* and *C*, divergence and pressure fall between *A* and *B*. The variations in transport are independent of the wave length of the perturbation, but increase with its amplitude. In the absence of other factors, the latitude effect here described would lead to a westward displacement of the perturbations.

For perturbations of the dimensions actually observed in the free atmosphere the two effects are approximately of the same magnitude. It follows that long waves must travel westward and shorter waves eastward. An intermediate wave length must exist such that the corresponding perturbations remain stationary.

The stream line pattern to which the above analysis by Bjerknes applies must satisfy not only the equation of continuity but also the equations of motion. If one considers the very simplest case of an ideal (non-friction) homogeneous, incompressible atmosphere *in purely horizontal motion,* the two equations of motion may, through the elimination of pressure, be compressed into a single equation expressing the conservation of absolute vorticity. Thus, if f represents the Coriolis' parameter ($f = 2\Omega \sin \varphi$) and consequently also the vertical component of the vorticity due to the rotation of the earth, and if ζ is the vertical component of the vorticity of the motion of the air relative to the earth's surface, then each individual vertical column must satisfy the condition

$$f + \zeta = \text{constant}. \tag{1}$$

In this equation

$$\zeta = \frac{\partial v}{\partial x} - \frac{\partial u}{\partial y}. \tag{2}$$

It is assumed that the x-axis points eastward, the y-axis northward. Vorticity is counted positive for cyclonic rotation, negative for anticyclonic rotation. Thus equation (1) implies that an air column which is displaced towards higher latitudes, where the cyclonic vertical component of the earth's rotation is stronger, will experience a decreasing cyclonic, or increasing anticyclonic, rotation. A column displaced towards lower latitudes will experience an increasing cyclonic, or decreasing anticyclonic, rotation.

It follows from (1) that the relative vorticity ζ must remain constant in the absence of variations in latitude. The stream lines in Figure 11 show cyclonic vorticity between a and b, anticyclonic vorticity between b and c and hence such a pattern cannot be established through purely horizontal motion except possibly as the result of latitude variations. It is the purpose of the simple analysis below to show that the latitude variations are sufficient to bring about the required vorticity variations.

It follows from (1) that the individual variation of vorticity with time must obey the law

$$\frac{d\zeta}{dt} = -\frac{df}{dt}. \tag{3}$$

Since the Coriolis' parameter does not depend on longitude or time, it follows that

$$\frac{df}{dt} = v\frac{\partial f}{\partial y} = \beta v \left(\beta = \frac{\partial f}{\partial y}\right) \tag{4}$$

and hence

$$\frac{d\zeta}{dt} = -\beta v. \tag{5}$$

In (5) β represents the rate at which the Coriolis' parameter increases northward. It is easily seen that β may be computed from the equation

$$\beta = \frac{\partial f}{\partial y} = \frac{\partial f}{R\partial \varphi} = \frac{2\Omega \cos \varphi}{R}, \tag{6}$$

R being the mean radius of the earth. Table I gives the results of such a computation. In the subsequent analysis it is necessary to treat β as a constant and hence independent of y. This assumption is reasonably justified near the equator where β has its maximum and its rate of variation in per cent is very small, but represents a rather severe restriction in higher latitudes. Thus β decreases by about 29% from 45° N. to 60° N.

TABLE I

VARIATION OF β WITH LATITUDE

φ	$10^{13} \cdot \beta = \frac{2\Omega \cos \varphi}{R} \cdot 10^{13}$
90°	0.0 cm^{-1} sec^{-1}
75°	0.593
60°	1.145
45°	1.619
30°	1.983
15°	2.212
0°	2.290

We shall now apply (5) to the case of a zonal current of uniform constant velocity U upon which is superimposed a perturbation with the velocity components u' and v'. Thus the total velocities are

$$u = u' + U, \quad v = v'. \tag{7}$$

Since the zonal current U is independent of x and y it follows that

$$\zeta = \zeta' = \frac{\partial v'}{\partial x} - \frac{\partial u'}{\partial y}. \tag{8}$$

The vorticity equation (5) may be expanded and gives then

$$\frac{\partial \zeta}{\partial t} + u\frac{\partial \zeta}{\partial x} + v\frac{\partial \zeta}{\partial y} = -\beta v \tag{9}$$

or

$$\frac{\partial \zeta}{\partial t} + U\frac{\partial \zeta}{\partial x} + \left[u'\frac{\partial \zeta}{\partial x} + v'\frac{\partial \zeta}{\partial y}\right] = -\beta v'. \tag{10}$$

For small perturbations the terms within the bracket may be neglected as small terms of second order (ζ, u' and v' are all small terms of the first order). Thus the equation reduces to

$$\frac{\partial \zeta}{\partial t} + U\frac{\partial \zeta}{\partial x} = -\beta v'. \tag{11}$$

Now let us look for perturbations traveling without change in shape. If c is the eastward speed of such a wave, it follows that

$$\frac{\partial \zeta}{\partial t} = -c\frac{\partial \zeta}{\partial x} \tag{12}$$

and consequently (11) transforms into

$$(U - c)\frac{\partial \zeta}{\partial x} = -\beta v'. \tag{13}$$

In the case of perturbations independent of y it follows from (8) that

$$\zeta = \frac{\partial v'}{\partial x} \tag{14}$$

and thus

$$(U - c)\frac{\partial^2 v'}{\partial x^2} = -\beta v'. \tag{15}$$

In the case of a simple sinusoidal disturbance of the wave length L the perturbation must be given by an expression of the form

(16) $$v' \backsim \sin \frac{2\pi}{L}(x - ct).$$

Substitution of (16) in (15) shows that

(17) $$c = U - \frac{\beta L^2}{4\pi^2},$$

This expression gives the wave velocity in terms of the gradient wind velocity and the wave length L.

It appears that the waves become stationary when

(18) $$c = U - \frac{\beta L_s^2}{4\pi^2} = 0, \quad L_s = 2\pi\sqrt{\frac{U}{\beta}}.$$

Waves of greater length than L_s travel westward (c negative), shorter waves travel eastward. A combination of (17) and (18) gives

(19) $$c = U\left(1 - \frac{L^2}{L_s^2}\right),$$

from which the relation between wave length and speed is most readily seen. The stationary wave length is given in Table II as a function of the latitude and of the zonal circulation U.

TABLE II

STATIONARY WAVE LENGTH IN KM AS FUNCTION OF ZONAL VELOCITY (U) AND LATITUDE (φ)

φ \ U	*4 m/sec*	*8 m/sec*	*12 m/sec*	*16 m/sec*	*20 m/sec*
30°	2822 km	3990 km	4888 km	5644 km	6310 km
45°	3120	4412	5405	6241	6978
60°	3713	5252	6432	7428	8304

The total number of waves (n) around the circumference of the earth at the latitude φ is given by

(20) $$nL = 2\pi R \cos \varphi.$$

Substitution of (20) in (17) gives

(21) $$U - c = \frac{2\Omega R}{n^2} \cos^3 \varphi$$

or, for stationary waves,

(22) $$U = \frac{2\Omega R}{n_s^2} \cos^3 \varphi.$$

The velocity deficit $U - c$ obtained from (21) is given in Table III as a function of the number of perturbations and of the latitude. It is evident that if the zonal velocity distribution is known equation (22) enables one to determine the number of stationary perturbations possible in each latitude.

TABLE III

VELOCITY DEFICIT $(U-c)$ AS FUNCTION OF NUMBER OF PERTURBATIONS (n) AND LATITUDE (φ)

φ \ n	2	3	4	5	6	7
30°	150.7 m/sec	67.0	37.7	24.1	16.7	12.8
45°	82.0	36.5	20.5	13.1	9.1	6.7
60°	29.0	12.9	7.3	4.6	3.2	2.4

The preceding analysis applies to simple harmonic waves. The case of an arbitrary solitary perturbation observed at the time $t = o$ is somewhat more complicated but may be treated with the aid of Fourier integrals. Thus, in the case of a symmetric solitary pressure ridge or trough centered around $x = o$, one finds

$$v' = \int_0^\infty F(\mu) \sin \mu \left[x - Ut + \frac{\beta}{\mu^2} t \right] d\mu, \tag{23}$$

provided

$$v_o' = \int_0^\infty F(\mu) \sin \mu x \cdot d\mu \tag{24}$$

represents the velocity distribution in the initial perturbation (v_o' is antisymmetric). It follows that the harmonics corresponding to large wave lengths $\left(\mu = \frac{2\pi}{L} < \frac{2\pi}{L_s}\right)$ must travel westward, those of shorter wave length $(L < L_s)$ eastward, and thus a large initial perturbation may actually split in two centers, traveling in opposite directions.

V. Bjerknes and collaborators have computed the zonal velocity distribution from the zonal temperature distribution and from the zonal pressure distribution at the ground (V. Bjerknes and coll., 1933). The computation was made separately for the months of February and August. The aerological data used in this computation were, unfortunately, not entirely satisfactory for the purpose, since soundings from stations in widely different longitudes had to be combined (Pavia, Agra, Batavia). Bjerknes' diagram shows that the maximum velocity normally occurs just below the tropopause. The maximum velocities for the month of February have been taken from this diagram and are listed below in Table IV. Intermediate

TABLE IV

MAXIMUM ZONAL VELOCITY IN FEBRUARY ACCORDING TO BJERKNES

Lat.	*70°*	*60°*	*53°*	*45°*	*30°*	*28°*
U_{max} (mps)	10	[16]	20	[23]	[29]	30

values have been determined by interpolation and are enclosed within brackets. A study of the tabulated values indicates that this portion of the atmosphere rotates with a practically constant relative angular velocity. A comparison with Table III shows that the number of stationary perturbations must be between two and three in 60° N. and slightly above four in latitude 30° N. This result is in fair agreement with the observed dimensions both of the permanent lows and of the subtropical high pressure cells.

In applying the preceding analysis to the semipermanent centers of action, it must of course be emphasized that these centers are maintained in their normal position by permanent solenoidal fields acting alone or in cooperation with topographic factors. Thus there is no obvious reason why the character of these thermally or topographically produced "forced" perturbations should agree in detail with the stationary "free" perturbations analyzed above. To the extent that these forced perturbations are the result of solenoidal circulation they are controlled primarily by the distribution of solenoids in a vertical surface following a latitude circle around the earth. In such a surface the solenoids will be found to have their maximum concentration wherever the latitude circle crosses the boundary between continent and ocean. (Bjerknes, V. and coll., 1933, pp. 686–693). During the warm season and in lower latitudes the concentration of solenoids is particularly marked along the west coasts of North America and of Europe-Africa, during the cold season and in lower latitudes along the Pacific coast of Asia and over the eastern coast of North America. During either season the two principal regions of solenoidal activity are much further apart than the "free" stationary wave length determined above. Each one of these solenoidal zones will create a practically stationary perturbation in the zonal circulation and in the trail of this perturbation a series of stationary waves must develop in somewhat the same fashion as the standing waves which are sometimes observed in the clouds on the lee side of a mountain ridge. Mathematically the problem may be expressed by saying that if, through solenoidal or topographic influences, a perturbation of the zonal circulation is maintained at the line $x = o$, such that the perturbation velocity and vorticity there have arbitrarily prescribed values,

$$v'_{x=o} = v_o', \; \zeta'_{x=o} = \left(\frac{\partial v'}{\partial x}\right)_{x=0} = \zeta_o', \tag{25}$$

then it follows from (15) that

$$v' = v_o' \cos \frac{2\pi x}{L_s} + \frac{\zeta_o' L_s}{2\pi} \sin \frac{2\pi x}{L_s}, \tag{26}$$

for all values of $x > o$. This solution corresponds to a series of stationary perturbations of the wave length L_s. It is the author's opinion that this reasoning may help to explain the fact that the Pacific high pressure belt during the winter season generally splits into two separate cells. It is probable that upper level troughs formed in this fashion readily develop into frontogenetic zones near sea level.

TABLE V

COMPONENT FROM THE WEST (IN M.P.S.) OF VECTORIAL MEAN WIND

Va Winter

Station	*Lat. N.*	*6 km.*	*8 km.*	*10 km.*	*12 km.*	*14 km.*
Ellendale	46.0	11.2	10.3	10.7	—	—
Omaha	41.2	10.7	8.8	8.6	—	—
Broken Arrow	36.0	14.3	12.6	13.7	20.3	—
Groesbeck	31.5	13.9	12.8	14.2	17.8	—

Vb Summer

Station	*Lat. N.*	*6 km.*	*8 km.*	*10 km.*	*12 km.*	*14 km.*
Ellendale	46.0	10.2	11.9	11.2	11.1	—
Omaha	41.2	6.3	7.4	6.1	9.6	11.5
Broken Arrow	36.0	2.8	3.1	3.3	4.0	3.8
Groesbeck	31.5	0	−0.5	−0.5	0.9	0.5

Bjerknes' summer section is, unfortunately, very much disturbed by the Indian monsoon, and must therefore be used with a great deal of caution. It shows a velocity maximum of about 30 mps. in latitude 40° N. and would thus correspond to about four stationary high pressure cells in this latitude. However, the observed zonal velocity distribution over the United States differs rather markedly from the one computed by Bjerknes. In Tables Va and Vb are given the components from the west of the vectorial mean wind velocity at different heights above four stations in the vicinity of the meridian of Omaha, Nebraska, for winter and summer. They were determined graphically from vectorial mean winds published by the U. S. Weather Bureau (Stevens, L. A., 1937). These velocities are considerably less than those computed from the zonal temperature distribution. The tables show that during the winter season the west wind velocity is around 12 mps. up to about 12 km., whence it increases rapidly upward. In summer time the wind distribution is characterized by a strong anticyclonic shear in the north and by weak velocities over the greater part of the country. Assigning a value of 16 mps. to the zonal circulation during the winter season one finds, from Table III, that the number of permanent perturbations would be about 6 at 30° N., and between 4 and 5 at 45° N. Unfortunately there are no pilot balloon data available concerning the wind distribution at higher latitudes in the same meridian. If Bjerknes' computed value of the zonal circulation at latitude 60° N. is combined with the observed wind data at lower latitudes, the resulting zonal circulation is compatible with the number of perturbations observed in the polar regions. The slightly larger number, i. e. slightly smaller dimensions, of the subtropical cells is not incompatible with the actual dimensions of the anticyclones of lower latitudes.

Table Vb indicates that the summer season is characterized by a very weak zonal circulation over the United States with strong anticyclonic shear zone near the Canadian border. If a value of 4 mps. is assigned to the zonal wind, one obtains from Table II a stationary wave length of about 3000 km., in good agreement with the dimensions of the anticyclonic cells observed on our mean isentropic charts for the summer season.

The barotropic perturbations analyzed above are not associated with any available energy supply and are therefore stable and incapable of changing into real vortices. However, it is well known that a shear zone such as the one observed in the northern part of the country during the summer season is dynamically unstable and must break up into vortices which convert the energy of the zonal current into vortical kinetic energy. In this case, the equation for the conservation of vorticity should be modified to include the vorticity of the zonal current. Thus if the vorticity of the zonal current is designated by Z it follows that equation (13) changes into

$$(U - c)\frac{\partial \zeta'}{\partial x} + v'\frac{\partial Z}{\partial y} = -\beta v' \tag{27}$$

or, since

$$Z = -\frac{\partial U}{\partial y}, \tag{28}$$

$$(U - c)\frac{\partial \zeta'}{\partial x} = -\left(\beta - \frac{\partial^2 U}{\partial y^2}\right)v'. \tag{29}$$

An inspection of Table Vb shows that $\frac{\partial^2 U}{\partial y^2}$ at the most is about 25% of β. Since $\frac{\partial^2 U}{\partial y^2}$ is positive, the stationary wave length is thus increased by a maximum of about 13%. It should be remembered, however, that the original solution no longer strictly holds, since the zonal velocity (U) is a function of y and the perturbation thus also must depend on that coordinate.

The solenoidal field along the western coast of North America in combination with the steep mountain ranges creates a permanent perturbation (trough) near the coast and the permanent perturbation thus maintained will set up a series of standing perturbations in the zonal pressure distribution further down stream. The shearing zone along the northern border of the United States must necessarily break up into eddies which take care of the dissipation of the kinetic energy generated further to the north. It seems likely that the maximum size to which the frictionally driven eddies can grow is determined by the grid provided by these semi-permanent perturbations.

This grid would seem to explain the appearance of a moist tongue over western Florida in the isentropic mean charts for August and suggests an explanation for the occasional occurrence of a third moist tongue in the vicinity of Bermuda.

The large semi-permanent Bermuda high pressure cell observed on the seasonal mean sea level pressure charts, on the north side of which this grid of smaller perturbations is superimposed, is not explained by the preceding analysis, but appears to require a permanent and widespread field of solenoids for its maintenance. It is also possible that the larger dimensions of this system are associated with the higher zonal wind velocities prevailing near the base of the stratosphere.

The simple analysis carried out above does not include the effect of changes in depth of the moving fluid column. A single layer atmosphere, moving with a constant zonal velocity U must have a depth D_o which decreases northward. This slope gives rise to a pressure gradient which balances the Coriolis' force associated with the zonal motion. Thus

$$U = -\frac{g}{f}\frac{\partial D_o}{\partial y}. \tag{30}$$

It follows that fluid columns moving north or south are going to change their depth and as a result their vorticity will change. In addition, the traveling perturbations themselves cause deformations of the free surface which in turn produce changes in vorticity. To analyze the problem completely we must return to the general equations of motion. For a homogeneous incompressible atmosphere of thickness D they may be compressed into the following system:

$$\frac{d\zeta}{dt} = -\frac{df}{dt} - (f + \zeta)\left(\frac{\partial u}{\partial x} + \frac{\partial v}{\partial y}\right) \tag{31}$$

$$\tfrac{1}{2}\frac{dq^2}{dt} = -g\left(\frac{dD}{dt} - \frac{\partial D}{\partial t}\right) \tag{32}$$

$$\frac{1}{D}\frac{dD}{dt} = -\left(\frac{\partial u}{\partial x} + \frac{\partial v}{\partial y}\right). \tag{33}$$

The first of these equations expresses the conservation of vortices, the second the conservation of energy, and the third the conservation of mass. In these equations q^2 is the kinetic energy per unit mass and g the acceleration of gravity.

In our particular case

$$u = U + u',\ v = v',\ q^2 = U^2 + 2u'U + (u'^2 + v'^2) \tag{34}$$

and

$$D = D_o + \delta \tag{35}$$

D_o being the depth (decreasing northward) of the undisturbed atmosphere in zonal motion and δ the deformation due to the travelling perturbations. Neglecting squares and products of u' and v' one finds

$$\tfrac{1}{2}\frac{dq^2}{dt} = U\frac{du'}{dt} = U\left(\frac{\partial u'}{\partial t} + U\frac{\partial u'}{\partial x}\right) \tag{36}$$

and

$$\frac{dD}{dt} = \frac{\partial \delta}{\partial t} + U\frac{\partial \delta}{\partial y} + v'\frac{\partial D_o}{\partial y} \tag{37}$$

or, because of (30),

$$\frac{dD}{dt} = \frac{\partial \delta}{\partial t} + U\frac{\partial \delta}{\partial x} - \frac{fU}{g}v'. \tag{38}$$

If we replace $f + \zeta$ on the right hand side of (31) with a constant f_o* and introduce a constant mean value D_{oo} for the undifferentiated D in equation (33), equations (31) to (33) are readily solved. For perturbations which are independent of the y-coordinate, one obtains finally an equation for the wave speed which may be written

$$(U - c)\frac{4\pi^2}{L^2} = \beta + \frac{cf_o^2}{gD_{oo} - (U - c)^2}. \tag{39}$$

It is interesting to note that for $U = 0$, $\beta = 0$, this equation gives the wave velocity obtained by Sverdrup (1926) in his study of tidal waves on the North Siberian shelf. For $U = 0$, $\beta = 0$, $f_o = 0$ it reduces to the well known formula for long gravitational waves

* This substitution is justified in view of the small contribution of the divergence term in (31) to the individual change in vorticity in a single-layer barotropic atmosphere.

(40) $$c = \pm \sqrt{gD_{oo}}.$$

For standing perturbations ($c = 0$) it reduces to the relation obtained earlier in this paper by elementary methods,

(41) $$L_s = 2\pi \sqrt{\frac{U}{\beta}}.$$

For a homogeneous atmosphere the product gD_{oo} has a value of about $8 \cdot 10^8 \cdot cm^2 \cdot sec^{-2}$. For the perturbations in which we are interested $(U - c)^2$ is of the order of magnitude $10^7 \cdot cm^2 \cdot sec^{-2}$ or less. Thus it is a permissible approximation to write

(42) $$(U - c)\frac{4\pi^2}{L^2} = \beta + \frac{cf_o^2}{gD_{oo}},$$

or, after solving for c,

(43) $$c = \frac{U - \dfrac{\beta L^2}{4\pi^2}}{1 + \dfrac{L^2}{4\pi^2\lambda^2}},$$

in which expression the length λ, defined by

(44) $$\lambda = \frac{1}{f_o}\sqrt{gD_{oo}},$$

has a value of about 2800 km. for a homogeneous atmosphere. Even for wave lengths double the value of λ the wave velocity determined by (43) is only 10% less than the one obtained from the approximate formula (17).

This formula has an important forecasting implication. If a series of permanent perturbations exists at the time $t = 0$ and a study of consecutive pressure profiles suggests that the zonal circulation is slowing down, it follows that the perturbations will be displaced westward, but the rate of this displacement must be less than the reduction in the zonal circulation velocity.* It is likewise evident that an acceleration of the zonal circulation speed will bring about an eastward displacement of the perturbations, but again at a slower rate than the change in the zonal velocity.

* A preliminary analysis of perturbations in the upper, moving portion of a double-layer atmosphere with a bottom layer at rest indicates that the denominator in (43) then may reach values of 4 or 5; thus the rate of displacement of non-stationary perturbations is greatly reduced. However, the final answer to this question cannot be given until a satisfactory theoretical analysis has been carried out. The same preliminary result applies to a double-layer atmosphere in which the motion occurs in the lower layer.

It was stated earlier than an arbitrary perturbation, once created, will be displaced in such a fashion that harmonics of greater wave length will move westward, those of shorter wave length eastward, and that this process may lead to a splitting up of the perturbation. It is now evident that such displacements may be produced also by changes in the zonal circulation. It is evident that once the centers of action have been displaced from their normal positions, the fairly stationary solenoidal fields responsible for their generation and maintenance may lead to a regeneration of the centers in their normal position. In this way double centers will again be produced. An inspection of our northern hemisphere charts appears to indicate that this is particularly likely to happen when the Asiatic High, as a result of a

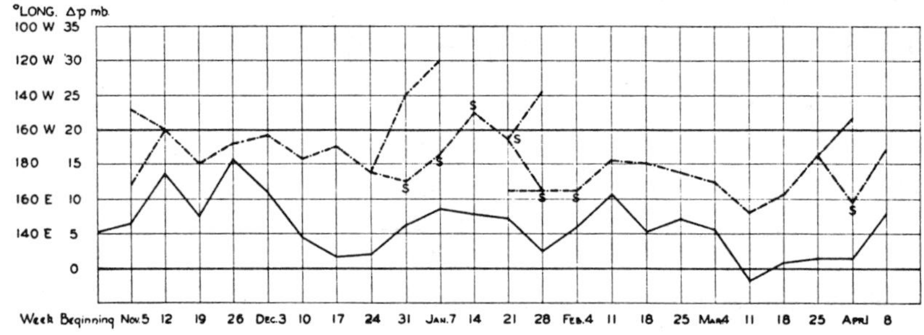

Figure 12. Relation between position of Aleutian Low and Zonal Circulation Intensity. Broken Line Indicates Longitude of Aleutian Low, as Determined from our Weekly Five Day Mean Pressure Charts and Full Line gives Zonal Circulation Intensity as Indicated by Mean Pressure Difference on the same Charts between 35° N. and 55° N.

slowing down of the general zonal circulation, has been displaced far to the west (towards Europe) of its normal position.

Two practical examples to illustrate the preceding theoretical analysis are presented below. Figure 12 contains a comparison for the winter 1938–1939 between the longitude of the Aleutian Low, as determined by my colleague Dr. H. C. Willett from the five day mean pressure charts prepared weekly under his direction at the Massachusetts Institute of Technology, and the intensity of the zonal circulation as measured by the pressure difference between latitudes 35° N. and 55° N., obtained by averaging this pressure difference all around the globe on the same charts. There are a few cases of splitting of the center and in these cases double points have been entered. If in each case the stronger of the two centers (marked *s*) is selected, it is readily seen that a good correlation is obtained between the two curves. There is also some evidence of a few days lag of the longitude curve relative to the circulation index. The correlation coefficient between the two curves is 0.665. A later and more accurate determination of the zonal circulation index resulted in a correlation coefficient of 0.695. Finally, to prove that the variations in the intensity of the zonal circulation index are not merely the result of the longitude variations of the Aleutian Low, a revised zonal circulation index was computed which excluded a section of 120 degrees of longitude over the Pacific. Even then a correlation of 0.542 with the longitude of the Aleutian Low was obtained.

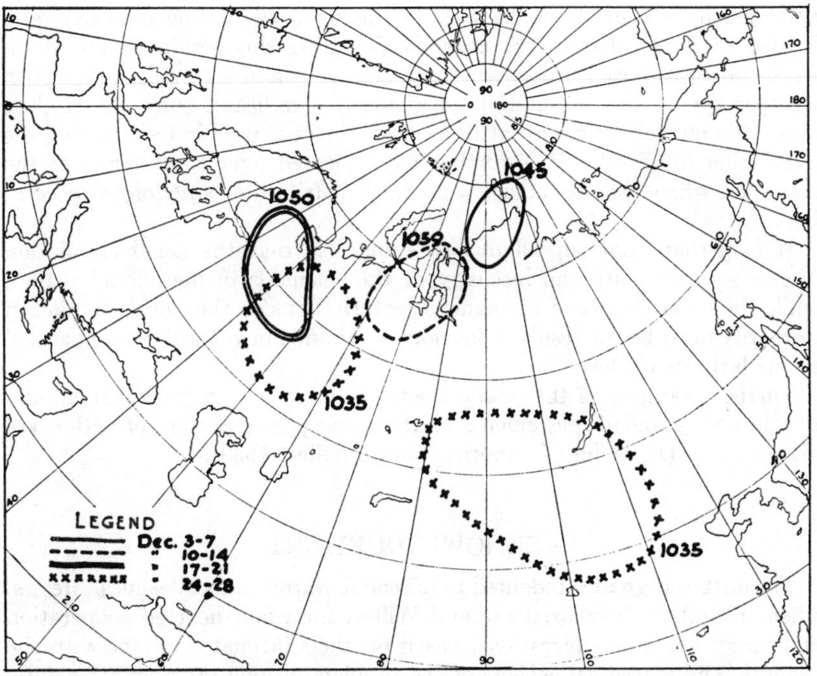

Figure 13. Successive positions of last closed isobar in Asiatic High during December 1938. These isobars were obtained from our weekly five day mean pressure charts.

It may at first sight appear unreasonable to compare the displacement of the Aleutian Low with the zonal circulation intensity in a much lower latitude. It must be remembered, however, that the positions and displacements of the semipermanent centers of action depend upon the intensity of the zonal motion in the free atmosphere well above the seat of the advective phenomena. The author has tried to demonstrate, in a previous paper (Rossby, 1938), that at least during the summer season, the westerlies south of the polar front are to a large extent maintained by isentropic stresses which transmit the motion of the polar vortex to the surface layers in somewhat lower latitudes. On the basis of this analysis, it appears reasonable to measure the intensity of the polar vortex in the free atmosphere by the sea level pressure gradient to the south of the polar front.

Figure 13 shows the successive positions of the innermost closed isobar of the Siberian High during a few weeks in December, 1938, as determined from the weekly five day mean pressure charts for this period. An inspection of the circulation index in Figure 12 shows that this period was characterized by a continuous decrease in the zonal circulation intensity, and Figure 13 shows that the Siberian High during this period advanced towards northwestern Europe, where its arrival caused a complete change in weather type. This example is particularly significant, since the High is located in entirely different latitudes from the ones used in determining the circulation intensity. It is further more located over the interior of the continent where the normal zonal pressure distribution is no longer discernible.

It is perhaps not superfluous to emphasize that the zonal circulation intensity varies with the intensity of the solenoids in meridional planes, while the maintenance of permanent perturbations on this zonal circulation primarily must be the result of solenoids contained in vertical planes parallel to the latitude circles.

Further examples of the relation between variations in the zonal circulation intensity and displacements of the atmospheric centers of action are discussed by Dr. Willett in another place (Willett 1939).

ACKNOWLEDGEMENT

The author is greatly indebted to his collaborators and colleagues, Messrs. Allen, Holmboe, Namias, Page and Willett for whole-hearted cooperation and many valuable suggestions, based on their intimate contact with the synoptic and statistical aspects of the problem of long range weather forecasting.

REFERENCES

BJERKNES, J.

1937. Die Theorie der aussertropischen Zyklonenbildung, *Meteorologische Zeitschrift*, Vol. 54, pp. 460–466.

BJERKNES, V. AND COLLABORATORS.

1933. *Physikalische Hydrodynamik*, Julius Springer, pp. 648–653.

CLAYTON, H. H.

1923. World Weather, The MacMillan Co., New York.

EKMAN, V. W.

1932. Studien zur Dynamik der Meeresströmungen, *Gerlands Beiträge zur Geophysik*, Bd. 36, pp. 385–438.

NAMIAS, J. AND WEXLER, H.

1938. Mean Monthly Isentropic Charts and their Relation to Departures of Summer Rainfall, *Transactions of the American Geophysical Union*, Nineteenth Annual Meeting.

ROSSBY, C.-G.

1938. On the Maintenance of the Westerlies South of the Polar Front, in *Papers in Physical Oceanography and Meteorology*, Vol. VII, No. 1.

SVERDRUP, H. U.

1926. Dynamics of Tides on the North Siberian Shelf, *Geofysiske Publikasjoner*, Vol. IV, No. 5.

STEVENS, L. A.

1937. Winds in the Upper Troposphere and Lower Stratosphere over the United States, *Monthly Weather Review*, Supplement 36.

WILLETT, H. C.

1939. Certain Statistical Relationships Bearing on the Preparation of Five-Day Weather Forecasting in the United States, presented at the April 1939 meeting of the American Meteorological Society in Washington, D. C., and to be published later on.

Reprinted (with corrections) from *Journal of Meteorology*, Vol. 4, No. 5, Oct., 1947, published by the American Meteorological Society.

THE DYNAMICS OF LONG WAVES IN A BAROCLINIC WESTERLY CURRENT

By J. G. Charney

University of California at Los Angeles[1]

(Manuscript received 9 December 1946)

ABSTRACT

Previous studies of the long-wave perturbations of the free atmosphere have been based on mathematical models which either fail to take properly into account the continuous vertical shear in the zonal current or else neglect the variations of the vertical component of the earth's angular velocity. The present treatment attempts to supply both these elements and thereby to lead to a solution more nearly in accord with the observed behavior of the atmosphere.

By eliminating from consideration at the outset the meteorologically unimportant acoustic and shearing-gravitational oscillations, the perturbation equations are reduced to a system whose solution is readily obtained.

Exact stability criteria are deduced, and it is shown that the instability increases with shear, lapse rate, and latitude, and decreases with wave length. Application of the criteria to the seasonal averages of zonal wind suggests that the westerlies of middle latitudes are a seat of constant dynamic instability.

The unstable waves are similar in many respects to the observed perturbations: The speed of propagation is generally toward the east and is approximately equal to the speed of the surface zonal current. The waves exhibit thermal asymmetry and a westward tilt of the wave pattern with height. In the lower troposphere the maximum positive vertical velocities occur between the trough and the nodal line to the east in the pressure field.

The distribution of the horizontal mass divergence is calculated, and it is shown that the notion of a fixed level of nondivergence must be replaced by that of a sloping surface of nondivergence.

The Rossby formula for the speed of propagation of the barotropic wave is generalized to a baroclinic atmosphere. It is shown that the barotropic formula holds if the constant value used for the zonal wind is that observed in the neighborhood of 600 mb.

CONTENTS

[1] U.C.L.A. Department of Meteorology, Papers in Meteorology, No. 4.
At present the author is National Research Fellow at the Institute for Theoretical Astrophysics, University of Oslo.

1. Introduction

The large-scale weather phenomena in the extratropical zones of the earth are associated with great migratory vortices (cyclones) traveling in the belt of prevailing westerly winds. One of the fundamental problems in theoretical meteorology has been the explanation of the origin and development of these cyclones. The first significant step toward a solution was taken in 1916 by V. Bjerknes [8, p. 785], who advanced the theory, based upon general hydrodynamic considerations, that cyclones originate as dynamically unstable wavelike disturbances in the westerly current. The subsequent discovery of the polar front by J. Bjerknes [2] made possible an empirical confirmation of the theory, for, following this discovery, the synoptic studies of J. Bjerknes and

H. Solberg [3, 4] revealed that cyclones actually develop from wavelike perturbations on the polar front.

These important discoveries initiated several attempts to construct a mathematical theory of the frontal wave, the most successful of which was the theory presented by Solberg [15, 16]. Assuming a model consisting of two isothermal layers in parallel motion, he demonstrated that unstable waves, similar to young cyclones with respect to wave length and velocity of propagation, can exist in the sloping surface of separation between the two layers.

In 1937 J. Bjerknes [6] studied cyclogenesis from a new approach based on the concept of the upper-air wave as an independent entity. Starting from the principle embodied in the tendency equation that the surface pressure changes are due to the integrated effect of the horizontal mass divergence, he found that the deepening of cyclones can be attributed to the relative horizontal displacement of the upper-air wave with respect to the surface cyclone. This displacement in turn is a consequence of the baroclinicity of the atmosphere in middle latitudes which necessitates a vertical shear of the westerly winds. Accordingly, the responsibility for the intensification of pressure systems is transferred from the shear at the frontal surface to a general shearing motion throughout the troposphere.

The early investigators of the cyclone problem were, however, hindered by the sparsity of observations and consequently were forced to rely primarily upon indirect information. The gradual establishment of more dense observational networks made available additional information concerning the nature of the atmospheric flow patterns. The observations failed to reveal a one-to-one correspondence between the surface frontal perturbations and the major perturbations of the upper atmosphere. It was found instead that the number of surface frontal perturbations greatly exceeds the relatively small number of major waves and vortices at upper levels. Apparently there exists a fundamental difference between the long (3000–6000 km) waves and the frontal waves of length 1000–2000 km studied by Solberg, and, while there is undoubtedly a connection between the two types, it is natural, because of the difference in scale, to attempt to explain the motion of the long waves in terms of the properties of the general westerly flow without reference to frontal surfaces.

In line with this trend of ideas, in 1939 Rossby [14] gave a theoretical treatment of the motion of long waves for the special case of constant zonal motion of a homogeneous incompressible atmosphere. His theory led to the result that the speed of propagation of the waves depends on (a) the strength of the westerlies and (b) the wave length. It was found that the speed of propagation toward the east decreases with increasing wave length up to the critical wave length at which the waves become stationary and beyond which they become retrograde. The theory was extended in 1940 by Haurwitz [10, 11], who took into account the curvature of the earth and the finite lateral extent of the wave. Finally, in 1944, Holmboe [12] derived a formula analogous to that of Rossby for the more general barotropic atmosphere. The results of these investigations were in agreement with the qualitative conclusions of J. Bjerknes's theory.

The studies of incompressible and barotropic atmospheres with no shear, however, cannot solve the problem of instability. Neither model contains a source of potential energy that can automatically convert itself into the energy of wave motion. It can be shown that waves in an atmosphere without shear are necessarily stable. This serious limitation can be overcome only by the adoption of a baroclinic model.

In 1944 J. Bjerknes and Holmboe [7] presented a theory of wave motion in a baroclinic atmosphere. Their solution is derived from the following principle [7, p. 10]:

> The wave will travel with such a speed that the pressure tendencies arising from the displacement of the pressure pattern are in accordance with the field of horizontal divergence.

The field of horizontal divergence is evaluated from the pressure pattern by means of gradient-wind relationships, and on this basis the following relation is established: If $\bar{u}(z)$ denotes the speed of the westerly current at any height z, u_c an increasing function of wave length, and c the wave-velocity, then

$$c = \bar{u}(h) - u_c$$

where h is the height at which the mass divergence in the horizontal velocity field is zero; the wave is unstable provided that h is sufficiently small.

This work presents a clear physical explanation of instability in the westerlies and establishes necessary criteria, such as the relation above, that any exact mathematical treatment of baroclinic waves must satisfy. However, fundamental problems concerning the dynamics of the waves and their three-dimensional structure cannot be solved by a method of analysis based on semiempirical considerations of the gradient wind.

It is the purpose of the present investigation to present a theoretical solution of these remaining problems. A complete solution to the problem of baroclinic waves can be obtained only by integrating the fundamental equations of motion. Integration of the tendency equation alone could lead to a solution for barotropic waves, in which the motion is independent of height, but it cannot lead to a solution for the more general case of baroclinic waves because the wave patterns must first be ascertained. It will be demonstrated that integration of the fundamental equations of motion leads to the solution of the following basic problems:

(a) The determination of the speed of propagation of the wave.

(b) The establishment of exact stability criteria.

(c) The determination of the three-dimensional structure of the wave, i.e., particle velocities, pressure pattern, temperature pattern, etc.

2. Discussion of results

A description unencumbered by mathematical detail will now be given of the main contents of the investigation in order to set forth more clearly the physical basis of the procedure followed and the results obtained.

Section 3 concerns the construction of a model that corresponds to the observed state of the atmosphere and yet permits a not too cumbersome mathematical treatment. The troposphere is characterized by nearly constant values of vertical lapse rate and horizontal gradient of temperature, and a consequent increase of the zonal wind at a constant rate with height; the stratosphere is assumed to be isothermal with a zonal wind independent of height (see fig. 1).

In sections 4 and 5 the equations of motion and the boundary conditions are formulated for a compressible atmosphere in which the individual changes of pressure and density are adiabatic. It is shown in section 6 that these equations are satisfied by the mean flow prescribed in the model.

The actual flow is considered to be a small perturbation superimposed on the mean flow. The linearized equations of motion for this perturbation are then derived. They admit of a solution in the form of a sinusoidal wave traveling in the west–east direction with constant speed and with an amplitude depending on elevation. The problem is reduced to that of determining the amplitude as a function of height, and the speed of propagation as a function of the wave length and the parameters characterizing the mean state of the atmosphere, namely, the vertical shear of the zonal wind, the surface zonal wind, the vertical lapse rate of temperature, and the mean latitude of the wave. The possibility that both velocity and amplitude of the wave may be complex is not precluded, so that, for certain values of the parameters, the wave may become unstable and the phase of the wave may alter with height. These phenomena are regularly observed on weather maps but are not explainable in terms of a barotropic atmosphere. They may, therefore, be attributed to the vertical shear of the zonal wind, i.e., to the baroclinicity of the atmosphere.

As an application of the general theory, the equations are integrated for the special case of the barotropic atmosphere, and the wave-velocity formula of Rossby and Holmboe is rederived. Since the mode of excitation is not specified, the solution includes both the gravitational wave components, which are propagated by the action of gravity, and the long waves, in which the wave propagating force is predominantly inertial. The two wave types are distinguished by the fact that the wave velocity in the former greatly exceeds that of the latter. As pure gravitational waves have no appreciable influence on large-scale weather phenomena, it is shown, by means of a certain inequality, how these waves might have been eliminated from the outset. Although nothing is gained by this procedure in the study of the barotropic wave, the process of elimination becomes of great value for the more general baroclinic wave, since here, were one to attempt to carry through the general solution embracing all wave types, severe analytic difficulties would supervene. Accordingly, in the discussion of the general problem of baroclinic motion, the elimination of inconsequential wave types is carried out and a set of equations obtained which are integrable by known methods. An interesting by-product of the calculation is that the meridional velocity component of the wave perturbation is nearly geostrophic. Indeed, had this been assumed *ab initio*, the simplified equations of motion would have been obtained directly.

Before the integration is carried through, however, a generalization of the Rossby formula is derived. It is shown that the simple formula for the speed of a barotropic wave will apply to the baroclinic wave if the constant value of the zonal wind in the formula is the mean zonal wind averaged with respect to pressure from the top to the bottom of the baroclinic atmosphere. It turns out that this value is the zonal wind in the vicinity of 600 mb, a fact which appears to be in good agreement with experience. A further result is the fact that the magnitude or direction of the zonal wind at very high levels in the stratosphere, say above 20 km, is of little consequence in the determination of the wave velocity. It is hoped that this result will help to clarify the rather vexing question regarding the influence of motions at high levels upon low-level weather phenomena.

It has been pointed out by Holmboe that the formula for the barotropic wave speed is strictly true only at the level of nondivergence in the atmosphere. It follows, therefore, that this level is in the vicinity of 600 mb.

It is of some interest to consider the case of a baroclinic atmosphere in which the zonal wind is constant. This atmosphere differs from the barotropic only by having statical stability. It is shown that this stability alone has no perceptible influence on the motion of the wave, so that the speed is virtually the same as that given by the formula for the barotropic wave.

The integration of the equations of motion for the general case is accomplished by their reduction to a single second-order linear differential equation of the confluent hypergeometric type. The boundary conditions reduce to a single transcendental equation relating the wave speed to the wave length and physical parameters. In order to solve this equation it is necessary to simplify the model further by supposing that the zonal wind continues to increase with height above the tropopause; it is shown, however, that this expediency leads to no significant change in the stability criteria. This may be seen by comparing the dashed curve in fig. 7 with the solid curve beneath.

For a given wave length, the waves are found to be neutral if the shear of the zonal wind lies below a certain critical value which increases with wave length. Beyond this value the waves are unstable, and the instability becomes more pronounced with increasing shear. The stability of the wave is almost independent of the value of the surface zonal speed (see fig. 7).

For a given value of the surface zonal speed, the speed of the neutral wave increases with the shear of the zonal wind, and, in the vicinity of the critical shear, the wave speed is nearly equal to the surface zonal speed (see fig. 9). This conclusion is in qualitative agreement with the results of Solberg and Godske [5], who find that the incipient cyclone wave's propagation speed, which must be intermediate between the translational speed of the warm layer and that of the cold layer of the model described in the introduction, is much nearer to the translational speed of the warm layer. In the present case, of course, no surface of discontinuity exists, but, if the shallow cold layer is ignored and the theory is applied to the thick overlying warm layer and if the surface zonal wind is taken to be that of the lower part of the warm layer, the results may be interpreted to mean that the incipient cyclone wave moves with approximately the speed of the surface wind in the warm air. However, it should again be emphasized that the waves considered by Solberg and Godske are of a different order of magnitude, and it may not be permissible to force a comparison between the two theories.

A discussion of the properties of the damped or stable baroclinic wave is not attempted, for presumably such components are extinguished as soon as they are formed.

The structure of the neutral baroclinic wave is similar to that of the barotropic wave. The two differ only in that the perturbation fields of velocity in the baroclinic case diminish with increasing height and eventually approach zero, whereas in the barotropic case these fields remain constant. In both cases the wave in the meridional-velocity field lags 90° behind the wave in the pressure field and the wave in the density field is in phase with the pressure wave. Furthermore, the wave in the latitudinal-velocity field is 180° out of phase with the pressure wave, and the vertical-velocity wave lags 90° behind the pressure wave, and in neither case is there a change of phase with height. (Some of these relationships are shown in fig. 10.)

With the appearance of instability, a thermal asymmetry develops in the baroclinic wave, so that the colder air is found behind the trough in the isobars. This asymmetry results in a tilt of the axes of low and high pressure toward the west, the tilt being most pronounced at low levels and diminishing to zero as height increases. Like the neutral wave, the meridional-velocity wave lags 90° behind the pressure wave. (These relationships are represented in fig. 11.) The waves in the remaining two velocity components show a more complicated relationship to the pressure wave. Vertical cross sections of the fields of vertical velocity, vertical momentum, and horizontal mass divergence are given in figs. 12 and 13. These diagrams show that, at low levels, the maximum vertical component of velocity occurs some distance behind the inflection point in the pressure profile, whereas at high levels it is found to be slightly in advance of the point of inflection.

The existing data on the three-dimensional distribution of the vertical velocity component appear to support these conclusions. Where it can be ascertained, the maximum vertical velocity component at, say, 700 mb is found closer to the trough than to the preceding wedge in the pressure field, while at high levels, although no conclusive data are available, one may cite as evidence that upper clouds are frequently observed to form with west to northwest wind. The maximum absolute magnitude is found at levels above the tropopause. This result is questionable and probably is due to the assumption of a continued increase of the zonal wind above the tropopause. It should be expected that, were the model to provide for a decrease in the zonal wind above the tropopause, the position of the maximum would be brought much lower, so that the change from ascending to descending motion which is often observed to take place near the tropopause would be verified.

Fig. 13 shows that the maximum horizontal mass divergence takes place between the trough and preceding wedge in the pressure pattern at low levels and is replaced by convergence at higher levels. It is also seen that with instability there no longer exists a constant level at which the divergence vanishes; rather the divergence vanishes along an inclined surface. However, with slight instability, the major part of the surface of nondivergence is nearly horizontal and is found to be between 350 mb and 400 mb. It is proved in section 11 by means of the generalization of the Rossby-Holmboe formula that, when observed zonal winds are used in place of the assumed winds, this level is in the vicinity of 600 mb. The discrepancy here can also be attributed to the lack of correspondence between the model and the observed state of the atmosphere at high levels.

The field of vertical momentum shown in fig. 13 has a maximum along any vertical at the altitude where the horizontal divergence vanishes. This result would have been obtained had the local time rate of change of density as well as the horizontal density advection been ignored in comparison with the remaining terms in the equation of continuity. One may therefore infer that these quantities, at least in the case of the baroclinic wave of small amplitude, can properly be ignored. This conclusion has been verified by those who have calculated vertical velocities by means of the equation of continuity.

It is seen from the preceding discussion that the baroclinic wave model exhibits many of the characteristics of the waves observed on the daily weather maps, both with respect to speed of propagation and internal structure. The theory, moreover, predicts that waves of length less than 6000 km will be unstable when the vertical shear of the zonal wind is greater than about 1.0 m $sec^{-1}km^{-1}$ (see fig. 7). Since this value is usually exceeded in middle latitudes, particularly in the winter months, one may infer that the westerlies are a seat of constant instability. This conclusion is verified by the observed storminess in these regions and also by the fact that the observed wave patterns almost invariably exhibit the tilt with height which, according to the theory, is characteristic of instability.

It should here be remarked that the investigation does not tell what relationship exists, in the generation of cyclones, between the frontal perturbation and the long atmospheric wave. J. Bjerknes and Holmboe [7] adopt the point of view that the initial impulse for wave formation in the free atmosphere is supplied by the frontal perturbation and that, thereafter, the induced upper wave propagates and develops according to its own law of motion, independently, so to speak, of the frontal wave. The two, however, develop and move along together, the upper waves lagging a little behind in phase. There is here a suggestion both of independence and of dependence in the motions of the frontal and upper-air waves. On one hand, it is true that by far the majority of deepening upper-air waves in middle latitudes are associated with frontal perturbations. On the other, it seems equally clear that waves which form on a surface of shearing discontinuity possess essentially different characteristics from the long upper-air waves—the waves differ in length and also frequently in direction of motion. Waves of short period, having periods of the order of 24 hours and lengths of the order of 1000 km, are often found on the frontal surface, but they are certainly not the same as the long upper-air waves. Nevertheless the two types of wave cannot be treated as independent phenomena, as, for example, the gravitational waves and the long waves in the atmosphere, for, whereas there is no appreciable linkage between the latter pair (see the discussion in section 7), there must be a linkage between the frontal and long wave.

The author wishes to make a final remark concerning the application of the present theory to the problem of wave motion in the tropical easterlies. In this case, the mathematical formulation of the problem is similar to that for the westerlies. Although the solution has not yet been brought to completion, a preliminary analysis indicates that, where the shear of the zonal current is positive, the stability criteria are qualitatively the same as for the westerlies, but, where the normal meridional temperature gradient is reversed so that the shear is negative, the flow is unstable.

3. The atmospheric model

We shall adopt, as an approximation to the atmosphere in middle latitudes, a model whose undisturbed state is characterized as follows: (a) the motion is zonal; the speed is constant in each horizontal level, is a linear function of height in the troposphere, and is independent of height in the stratosphere; (b) the lapse rate of temperature is constant in the troposphere and zero in the stratosphere. A comparison, in meridional cross section, of the theoretical model with the observed mean state of the atmosphere is shown in fig. 1. It will be seen that the model corresponds closely with the mean atmosphere in low levels. The deviations are most pronounced at high levels, where they become relatively unimportant because of the exponential decrease of density with height. Thus, in February, only 10 per cent of the atmosphere in middle latitudes lies above 16 km.

4. The fundamental equations

We assume for purposes of mathematical simplicity that the curvature of the earth can be neglected. This simplification is permissible when the length of the wave is small compared with the circumference of the zonal circle along which the wave moves. The mean motion can therefore be considered planar, and a rectangular system of coordinates x, y, and z can conveniently be introduced with x increasing eastward, y northward, and z vertically upward. If the corresponding velocity components are denoted by u, v, and w, density by ρ, pressure by p, angular velocity of the earth by Ω, and geographical latitude by

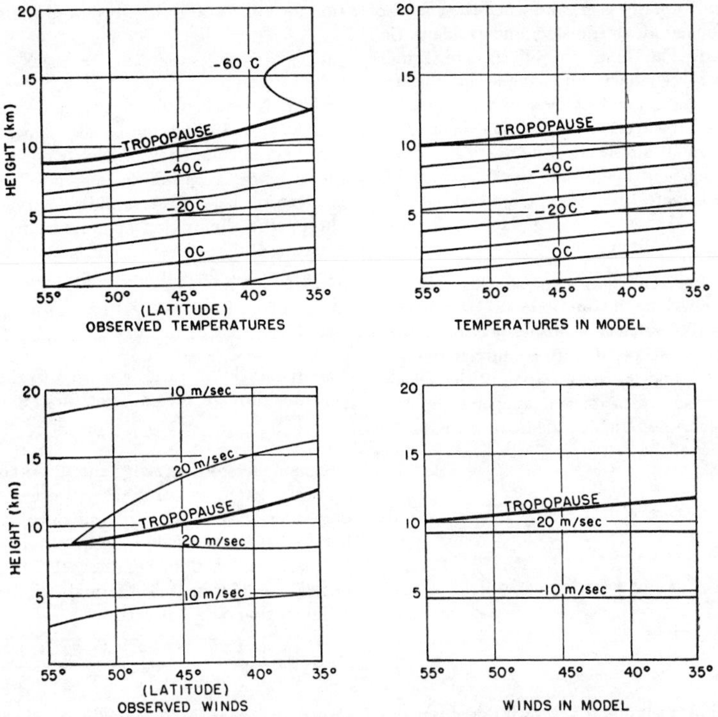

FIG. 1. Comparison of the theoretical model (right) with the mean state of the atmosphere (left) for the month of February. (After V. Bjerknes *et al.* [8, pp. 628, 649].)

φ, the Eulerian equations of motion become

$$\frac{du}{dt} = -\frac{1}{\rho}\frac{\partial p}{\partial x} + 2\Omega v \sin\varphi - 2\Omega w \cos\varphi \qquad (1)$$

$$\frac{dv}{dt} = -\frac{1}{\rho}\frac{\partial p}{\partial y} - 2\Omega u \sin\varphi \qquad (2)$$

$$\frac{dw}{dt} = -\frac{1}{\rho}\frac{\partial p}{\partial z} + 2\Omega u \cos\varphi - g. \qquad (3)$$

In dealing with the large-scale quasi-horizontal motions of the atmosphere it is customary to omit the vertical components of acceleration and Coriolis force as well as the horizontal component of the Coriolis force involving w, for these quantities may be shown both empirically and theoretically to be negligible in comparison with the forces of pressure and gravity. We may therefore replace the first equation of motion by

$$\frac{du}{dt} = -\frac{1}{\rho}\frac{\partial p}{\partial x} + 2\Omega v \sin\varphi \qquad (1')$$

and the third by the hydrostatic equation,

$$0 = -\frac{1}{\rho}\frac{\partial p}{\partial z} - g. \qquad (3')$$

A fourth equation is obtained from the law of conservation of mass,

$$\frac{\partial \rho}{\partial t} = -\frac{\partial}{\partial x}(\rho u) - \frac{\partial}{\partial y}(\rho v) - \frac{\partial}{\partial z}(\rho w), \qquad (4)$$

and a fifth equation from the condition that the motion be adiabatic. This condition is expressed by means of the differential relationship

$$\frac{dp}{dt} = \sigma^2 \frac{d\rho}{dt}, \qquad (5)$$

where σ is the Laplacian velocity of sound. If ϵ is the ratio of the specific heat of air at constant pressure to that at constant volume, R the gas constant referred to unit mass of dry air, and T the absolute temperature, σ is given by the equation

$$\sigma^2 = \epsilon R T.$$

The adiabatic hypothesis is valid when the effects of radiation, turbulent heat transfer, and condensation can be ignored. The first two effects are usually regarded as of secondary importance in the free atmosphere, whereas condensation can produce appreciable errors. However, as long as one is concerned with waves of small amplitude, the vertical motions will not be of sufficient magnitude to cause condensation, so that this factor may also be ignored.

5. The boundary conditions

The boundary conditions express the following physical properties of the motion: (a) the normal component of the velocity vanishes at the surface of the earth, (b) the energy density is finite at the limit of the atmosphere, and (c) the variation of the velocity components, pressure, density, and temperature across the tropopause must be zero, i.e., the tropopause is a discontinuity surface of the first order. Condition (a) gives

$$w(x, y, 0, t) = 0. \tag{6}$$

Condition (b) gives

$$\lim_{z\to\infty} \rho u^2 = \lim_{z\to\infty} \rho v^2 = \lim_{z\to\infty} \rho w^2 = 0, \tag{7}$$

and condition (c) gives

$$\Delta u = \Delta v = \Delta w = \Delta p = \Delta \rho = \Delta T = 0, \tag{8}$$

where the symbol Δ stands for a variation from one side to the other of the tropopause.

6. The steady state

The fundamental equations (1′–5) together with the boundary conditions (6–8) impose the necessary restrictions on the theoretical model. It will be shown that the specifications already given are consistent with these restrictions and are sufficient to determine completely the mean state of the atmosphere.

We adopt the convention of denoting a steady-state quantity by a bar placed over the symbol representing the same quantity in the perturbed state. The condition for zonal flow is then given by the equations

$$\bar u = \bar u(y, z), \qquad \bar v = 0, \qquad \bar w = 0.$$

Since $\bar v = \bar w = d\bar u/dt = \partial\bar\rho/\partial t = 0$, (1′) and (4) state that $\bar\rho$ and $\bar p$ are functions of y and z only. Equation (2) states that the undisturbed flow must satisfy the condition of geostrophic equilibrium,

$$0 = -\frac{1}{\bar\rho}\frac{\partial \bar p}{\partial y} - f\bar u, \tag{9}$$

where the symbol f is used to denote the Coriolis parameter $2\Omega \sin\varphi$. Equation (3′) expresses the condition for hydrostatic equilibrium in the mean state

$$0 = -\frac{1}{\bar\rho}\frac{\partial \bar p}{\partial z} - g, \tag{10}$$

and (5) is satisfied identically, since $d\bar\rho/dt$ and $d\bar p/dt$ both vanish. Integration of (10) shows that the pressure field is completely specified by the mass field if the pressure vanishes at $z = \infty$. The relationship between the fields of mass and velocity is then brought out by the elimination of pressure from (9). Differentiating with respect to z, and substituting $\partial\bar p/\partial z$ from the hydrostatic equation, we obtain

$$\frac{1}{\bar\rho}\frac{\partial\bar\rho}{\partial y} = \frac{f\bar u}{g}\left(\frac{1}{\bar\rho}\frac{\partial\bar\rho}{\partial z} + \frac{1}{\bar u}\frac{\partial \bar u}{\partial z}\right). \tag{11}$$

The mass field, in turn, is related to the field of temperature through the equation of state

$$\bar p = \bar\rho R\bar T. \tag{12}$$

We may therefore regard $\bar u$ and $\bar T$ as the fundamental variables by means of which all other quantities are determined. The necessary and sufficient relationship between these two fields can be obtained by elimination of $\bar\rho$ and $\bar p$ from equations (9, 10, 12). By this means we obtain the thermal wind equation for zonal motion on a flat earth,

$$-\frac{1}{\bar T}\frac{\partial\bar T}{\partial y} = \frac{f\bar u}{g}\left(-\frac{1}{\bar T}\frac{\partial\bar T}{\partial z} + \frac{1}{\bar u}\frac{\partial\bar u}{\partial z}\right). \tag{13}$$

Any distribution of $\bar u$ and $\bar T$ that satisfies (13) and the boundary conditions (6–8) will therefore automatically satisfy the fundamental equations. We shall now show that this is the case for the distribution prescribed in section 3. This distribution is expressed by the equations

$$\bar u(z) = \bar u_0 + \Lambda z \qquad (\bar u_0,\ \Lambda = \text{const}), \tag{14a}$$

$$\bar T(y, z) = \bar T(y, 0) - \gamma z \qquad (\gamma = \text{const}) \tag{14b}$$

in the troposphere, and

$$\partial\bar u/\partial z = 0, \tag{15a}$$

$$\bar T = \bar T_S \qquad (\bar T_S = \text{const}) \tag{15b}$$

in the stratosphere. Inserting the tropospheric values of $\bar u$ and $\partial\bar T/\partial z$ into (13) we obtain the equation

$$\frac{\partial\bar T}{\partial y} + \frac{f\Lambda}{g}\bar T = -\frac{f\bar u\gamma}{g}, \tag{16}$$

whose solution, subject to the condition (14b), is given by

$$\begin{aligned}\bar T(y, z) &= [\bar T(0, 0) + \bar u_0\gamma/\Lambda]e^{-f\Lambda y/g} - \bar u_0\gamma/\Lambda - \gamma z \\ &= \bar T(y, 0) - \gamma z\end{aligned} \tag{17}$$

and holds throughout the troposphere. Equations (14a) and (14b), therefore, suffice to determine $\bar u$ and

$\bar{T}$ everywhere in the troposphere. Since the stratospheric values of $\bar{u}$ and $\bar{T}$ prescribed by (15a) and (15b) satisfy (13) identically, it remains only to show that the boundary conditions are satisfied. The requirement of continuity for $\bar{T}$ in (8) will be fulfilled if the tropopause is isothermal and has a temperature equal to that of the stratosphere. The equation of the tropopause is obtained therefore by setting $\bar{T}(y, z)$ in (17) equal to $\bar{T}_S$. Differentiation of the resulting equation with respect to y then gives the slope of the tropopause the value

$$\frac{dz}{dy} = -\frac{f\Lambda}{\gamma g}\bar{T}_S - \frac{f\bar{u}}{g} \approx -\frac{f\Lambda}{\gamma g}\bar{T}_S, \tag{18}$$

and the variation of $\bar{u}$ on the tropospheric side of the tropopause is obtained from the equation

$$\frac{d\bar{u}}{dy} = \frac{d\bar{u}}{dz}\frac{dz}{dy} \approx -\frac{f\Lambda^2}{\gamma g}\bar{T}_S, \tag{19}$$

which by the condition of continuity in $\bar{u}$ in (8) also determines the corresponding variation of $\bar{u}$ with y on the stratospheric side of the tropopause. This condition coupled with the requirement (15a) completely determines $\bar{u}$ in the stratosphere. The boundary condition (6) is satisfied since $\bar{w} = 0$, and (7) is satisfied since $\bar{p} \to 0$, and therefore also $\bar{\rho}\bar{u}^2 \to 0$, as $z \to \infty$. Hence the model prescribed in equations (14a–15b, 17, 19) is consistent with the fundamental equations (1′–5) and satisfies the boundary conditions (6–8).

The theoretical cross section shown in fig. 1 is constructed in accordance with these equations by using $\bar{u}_0 = 0$ m sec^{-1}, $\Lambda = 2.2$ m sec^{-1}km^{-1}, $\bar{T}(0, 0) = 288$C, $\bar{T}_S = 213$C, and $\gamma = 6.5$ C km^{-1}.

7. The perturbation equations

The motion may be regarded as a small perturbation with velocity components u', v', and w' superimposed on the steady zonal current $\bar{u} = \bar{u}(z)$. Thus

$$\left.\begin{aligned} u &= u'(x, y, z, t) + \bar{u}(z) \\ v &= v'(x, y, z, t) \\ w &= w'(x, y, z, t). \end{aligned}\right\} \tag{20}$$

Similar expressions obtain for the density and pressure in the disturbed state, thus

$$\left.\begin{aligned} \rho &= \rho'(x, y, z, t) + \bar{\rho}(y, z), \\ p &= p'(x, y, z, t) + \bar{p}(y, z). \end{aligned}\right\} \tag{21}$$

We assume that the velocity perturbation is independent of the meridional coordinate. This assumption, introduced by Rossby, reduces the differential equations in the final formulation of the problem from the partial to the ordinary variety and leads to a considerable simplification.

Substituting the perturbed velocity, pressure, and mass fields into the fundamental equations (1′–5), and simplifying by means of the steady-state relations (9–11), we obtain the system

$$\left.\begin{aligned} L(u') - fv' + \Lambda w' + \frac{1}{\bar{\rho}}p'_x &= 0 \\ fu' + L(v') + \frac{f\bar{u}}{\bar{\rho}}\rho' + \frac{1}{\bar{\rho}}p'_y &= 0 \\ g\rho' + p'_z &= 0 \\ u'_x + \frac{f}{g}(s\bar{u} + \Lambda)v' + \frac{1}{\bar{\rho}}(\bar{\rho}w')_z + \frac{1}{\bar{\rho}}L(\rho') &= 0 \\ f\left(k\bar{u} + \frac{\bar{\sigma}^2\Lambda}{g}\right)v' + gkw' - \frac{1}{\bar{\rho}}L(p') + \frac{\bar{\sigma}^2}{\bar{\rho}}L(\rho') &= 0 \end{aligned}\right\} \tag{22}$$

where the abridged notation

$$\left.\begin{aligned} s &= \partial \ln \bar{\rho}/\partial z \\ k &= 1 + \bar{\sigma}^2 s/g \\ L &= \partial/\partial t + \bar{u}\,\partial/\partial x \end{aligned}\right\} \tag{23}$$

has been adopted, and the subscripts x, y, and z denote partial differentiation with respect to x, y, z respectively. From the definition of k it follows that

$$k = -\epsilon R(\gamma_d - \gamma)/g, \tag{24}$$

where γ_d is the adiabatic lapse rate. Elimination of ρ' and p' from (22) gives

$$\left.\begin{aligned} &gu'_{xx} + s\,L^2(u') + \Lambda\,L(u'_x) + L^2(u'_z) \\ &\quad + f(s\bar{u} + \Lambda)v'_x - sf\,L(v') - f\,L(v'_z) \\ &\quad + \frac{g}{\bar{\rho}}(\bar{\rho}w')_{xz} + \frac{\Lambda}{\bar{\rho}}L[(\bar{\rho}w')_z] = 0 \\ &k\,L^2(u') + \frac{\bar{\sigma}^2\Lambda}{g}L(u'_x) + \frac{\bar{\sigma}^2}{g}L^2(u'_z) \\ &\quad - kf\,L(v') + f\left(k\bar{u} + \frac{\bar{\sigma}^2\Lambda}{g}\right)v'_x - \frac{\bar{\sigma}^2 f}{g}L(v'_z) \\ &\quad + \frac{\bar{\sigma}^2\Lambda}{g\bar{\rho}}L[(\bar{\rho}w')_z] + \frac{gk}{\bar{\rho}}(\bar{\rho}w')_x + \frac{\Lambda}{\bar{\rho}}L(\bar{\rho}w') = 0 \\ &\left(1 + \frac{\Lambda\bar{u}}{g}\right)u'_x - \frac{\Lambda}{g}L(u') + \frac{\bar{u}}{g}L(u'_z) \\ &\quad + f\left(\frac{f_y}{f^2} + \frac{\Lambda}{g}\right)v' - \frac{f\bar{u}}{g}v'_z + \frac{1}{f}L(v'_x) \\ &\quad + \frac{\Lambda\bar{u}}{g\bar{\rho}}(\bar{\rho}w')_z - \frac{\Lambda}{g\bar{\rho}}(s\bar{u} + \Lambda)\bar{\rho}w' = 0. \end{aligned}\right\} \tag{25}$$

The details of the elimination will be found in appendix A.

The assumption that u', v', and w' are independent of y is inconsistent with the fact that some of the coefficients in (25) involve y. We may overcome this difficulty by a mathematical expedient: following Rossby [14], we replace f, wherever it occurs in *undifferentiated* form, and f_y by their values at the mean latitude of the disturbance. Thus, if we are concerned with waves in the zone between 35° and 55°, we replace f by the constant value $2\Omega \sin 45°$, and we replace f_y, which may be written

$$f_y = \frac{d}{dy}(2\Omega \sin \varphi) = \frac{d}{d\varphi}(2\Omega \sin \varphi)\frac{d\varphi}{dy} = \frac{2\Omega \cos \varphi}{\mathcal{R}},$$

where $\mathcal{R}$ is the radius of the earth, by $(2\Omega \cos 45°)/\mathcal{R}$. The quantities $\bar{u}$ and $\bar{T}$, which are also involved in the coefficients, are treated in a similar manner. Since $\bar{u}$ is independent of y in the troposphere, we need only be concerned with its variation in the stratosphere, and this usually is small. For example, if $\gamma = 6.5$ C km^{-1}, $\Lambda = 2$ m sec^{-1}km^{-1}, and $\bar{T} = 220$C, equation (19) gives $\partial\bar{u}/\partial y = 3.0$ m sec^{-1}(20° lat.)$^{-1}$; and, taking the mean value of $\bar{u}$ at the tropopause to be 25 m sec^{-1}, we find that the largest proportional deviation from this value in the zone 35°–55° is only 6 per cent. We may therefore with fair approximation replace $\bar{u}$ in the stratosphere by its mean value. Finally we assume that, in the troposphere, $\bar{T}$ may be regarded as a constant, independent of y and z, whenever it occurs in *undifferentiated* form. This approximation is similar to that made in the study of motion in an incompressible homogeneous atmosphere moving zonally with constant speed. In this case the condition of geostrophic balance requires the height of the atmosphere to increase on the right of the current, but this height may be assumed with good approximation to be constant as long as it does not appear in differentiated form (Rossby [14]).

8. Form of the perturbation and definition of stability

The most general expression for the velocity components of a simple harmonic perturbation of infinite lateral extent and wave length L, traveling in the x-direction with constant velocity, is

$$\left.\begin{aligned} u' &= U(z)\, e^{i\mu(x-ct)} \\ v' &= V(z)\, e^{i\mu(x-ct)} \\ w' &= W(z)\, e^{i\mu(x-ct)}, \end{aligned}\right\} \quad (26)$$

where $\mu = 2\pi/L$. While μ is always real and positive, c may be complex, i.e.,

$$c = c_r + ic_i$$

and the functions U, V, and W may also be complex. If c is complex, the exponential factor in (26) becomes

$$\exp\,[i\mu(x - c_r t)]\,\exp\,[\mu c_i t].$$

The first factor represents a sinusoidal wave of constant amplitude traveling with the velocity c_r. The second factor either increases indefinitely or decreases to zero, according as c_i is positive or negative. In the first instance the wave is said to be unstable, in the second it is said to be stable, and, if $c_i = 0$, the wave is said to be neutral.

9. The barotropic wave

As an introduction to the general problem, the solution for the barotropic wave is derived here. From the condition of barotropy

$$\rho = \rho(p),$$

together with equations (5, 9, 10), we obtain

$$k = \Lambda = 0.$$

Simplifying the perturbation equation (25) by means of these relations and introducing the expressions (26) for u', v', and w', we obtain

$$\left.\begin{aligned} &i\mu g[1 + (s/g)(\bar{u} - c)^2]U + sfcV \\ &\quad + i\mu(\bar{u} - c)^2 U_z - f(\bar{u} - c)V_z = -(g/\rho)(\bar{\rho}W)_z \\ &i\mu(\bar{u} - c)^2 U_z - f(u - c)V_z = 0 \\ &i\mu U + (1/f)[f_y - \mu^2(\bar{u} - c)]V \\ &\qquad + (i\mu\bar{u}/g)(\bar{u} - c)U_z - (f\bar{u}/g)V_z = 0. \end{aligned}\right\} \quad (27)$$

The last two equations show that U and V are constant, and elimination of U between the first and third equations gives

$$\left\{ \frac{\partial\bar{\rho}}{\partial z}\left[c + \frac{\mu^2}{f^2}(\bar{u} - c - u_c)(\bar{u} - c)^2 \right] + \frac{\mu^2}{f^2} g\bar{\rho}(\bar{u} - c - u_c) \right\} V = -\frac{g}{f}(\bar{\rho}W)_z, \quad (28)$$

where the quantity u_c is defined by

$$u_c = \frac{f_y}{\mu^2} = \frac{\Omega L^2 \cos \varphi}{2\pi^2 \mathcal{R}} \quad (29)$$

and is called the 'critical speed' by Bjerknes and Holmboe [7]. Integrating (28) from 0 to z, and utilizing the condition $W(0) = 0$, we obtain

$$\left\{ (\bar{\rho} - \bar{\rho}_0)\left[c + \frac{\mu^2}{f^2}(\bar{u} - c - u_c)(\bar{u} - c)^2 \right] - \frac{\mu^2}{f^2}(\bar{p} - \bar{p}_0)(\bar{u} - c - u_c) \right\} V \doteq -\frac{g\bar{\rho}}{f} W, \quad (30)$$

where $\bar{\rho}_0$ and $\bar{p}_0$ are the mean surface density and pressure. Evaluating the terms at $z = \infty$, we derive the following equation for the wave velocity:

$$\bar{u} - c - u_c = \frac{f^2}{\mu^2} \frac{c}{gH_0 - (\bar{u} - c)^2}, \quad (31)$$

where $H_0 = R\bar{T}_0/g$ is the height of a homogeneous

atmosphere whose surface temperature $\bar{T}_0$ is equal to the mean surface temperature of the barotropic atmosphere. This equation was derived by Rossby [14] for an incompressible atmosphere and by Holmboe [12] for a barotropic atmosphere.

Introduction of $\bar{u} - c - u_c$, from (31), into (30) gives

$$W = -\frac{fc}{g}\left[1 - \frac{gH - (\bar{u} - c)^2}{gH_0 - (\bar{u} - c)^2}\right]V, \qquad (32)$$

where $H = R\bar{T}/g$. It can be shown that the equations of the present section hold not only for an adiabatic barotropic atmosphere but also for an arbitrary barotropic atmosphere. In particular, we may set $H = H_0$ in (32) and deduce the interesting conclusion that $W \equiv 0$ in an isothermal barotropic atmosphere.

Since (31) is of the third degree in c, it has three roots. Two of the roots can be shown to be nearly equal to the solutions of

$$(\bar{u} - c)^2 - gH_0 = 0, \qquad (33)$$

which is Lagrange's equation for gravitational waves in a moving fluid. Writing

$$gH_0 = R\bar{T}_0 = \bar{\sigma}_0^2/\epsilon,$$

we see that the gravitational wave speed is of the order of magnitude of σ, the speed of sound. As we are here concerned only with long waves whose speeds are very small compared with that of sound, we may ignore $(\bar{u} - c)^2$ in comparison with gH_0 in (31) and so obtain the equation

$$\bar{u} - c - u_c = \frac{f^2 c}{\mu^2 g H_0}, \qquad (34)$$

whose solution can be shown to be nearly equal to the third root of equation (31).

The preceding considerations suggest the following principle which will be adopted in the sequel: whenever $\bar{u}$ or c occurs in conjunction with σ in a mathematical expression, the expression can always be simplified by means of any of the inequalities

$$1 \gg \frac{\bar{u}^2}{\bar{\sigma}^2}, \quad \frac{\bar{u}(\bar{u} - c)}{\bar{\sigma}^2}, \quad \frac{c(\bar{u} - c)}{\bar{\sigma}^2}, \quad \frac{c^2}{\bar{\sigma}^2}. \qquad (35)$$

By means of this principle we can separate out the gravitational and acoustic wave components from our solution and leave only the long wave component.[2]

It will now be shown that v', the meridional component of the perturbation velocity, is approximately geostrophic. From (22) and (26) we derive

$$v' - v'_{gs} = v' - \frac{1}{\bar{\rho} f} p'_x = \frac{1}{f} L(u') = \frac{i\mu}{f}(\bar{u} - c)\, U e^{i\mu(x-ct)},$$

and substituting for U in terms of V from the third of equations (27), we obtain

$$v' - v'_{gs} = \eta V e^{i\mu(x-ct)} = \eta v', \qquad (36)$$

where

$$\eta = (\mu^2/f^2)(\bar{u} - c)(\bar{u} - c - u_c). \qquad (37)$$

We now replace $(\bar{u} - c - u_c)$ by its value from (34) and obtain

$$\eta = \frac{c(\bar{u} - c)}{gH_0} = \frac{\epsilon c(\bar{u} - c)}{\bar{\sigma}_0^2}, \qquad (38)$$

which by (35) is much less than 1. Hence from (36)

$$v' \approx v'_{gs}.$$

10. Reduction of the perturbation equations

Returning to the problem of the baroclinic wave, we substitute the wave expressions (26) into the perturbations (25) and obtain

$$-(g/\bar{p})(\bar{p}W)_z = i\mu g U + f(\Lambda + sc)V + i\mu(\bar{u} - c)^2 U_z - f(\bar{u} - c)V_z \qquad (39)$$

$$\frac{\bar{\sigma}^2\Lambda}{g\bar{p}}(\bar{u} - c)(\bar{p}W)_z + \frac{gk}{\bar{p}}(\bar{p}W) = -i\mu\left[k(\bar{u} - c)^2 + \frac{\bar{\sigma}^2\Lambda}{g}(\bar{u} - c)\right]U - f\left(kc + \frac{\bar{\sigma}^2\Lambda}{g}\right)V - \frac{i\mu\bar{\sigma}^2}{g}(\bar{u} - c)^2 U_z + \frac{\bar{\sigma}^2 f}{g}(\bar{u} - c)V_z \qquad (40)$$

$$-\frac{\Lambda\bar{u}}{g\bar{p}}(\bar{p}W)_z + \frac{\Lambda}{g\bar{p}}(su + \Lambda)\bar{p}W = i\mu U - f\left(\chi - \frac{\Lambda}{g}\right)V + \frac{i\mu}{g}\bar{u}(\bar{u} - c)U_z - \frac{f\bar{u}}{g}V_z, \qquad (41)$$

[2] Strictly speaking, sound waves, whose vertical accelerations are of the same order of magnitude as the vertical pressure forces per unit mass, are excluded by the requirement of quasi-hydrostatic equilibrium. An important exception occurs when the wave fronts are planes perpendicular to the ground. In this case, since sound waves are longitudinal, the vertical acceleration vanishes identically; the force of gravity is exactly balanced by the vertical pressure force, and the sound waves are consequently indistinguishable from long gravitational waves. In order for such waves to exist the atmosphere must be *isothermal:* if the wave fronts are to remain perpendicular to the ground, the relative wave speed $(dp/d\rho)^{\frac{1}{2}}$ must be constant; therefore it follows from (12) that T must be constant and $(dp/d\rho)^{\frac{1}{2}}$ equal to $(RT)^{\frac{1}{2}}$, the Newtonian velocity of sound. Since the relative speed of long gravitational waves in an *arbitrary* barotropic atmosphere depends only on the mean surface temperature (33), we have an explanation for the fact that this speed is always equal to the Newtonian velocity of sound. Furthermore, since (33) applies in the limiting case of constant density if H_0 is interpreted as the actual height, we see why RT/g must be the height of the homogeneous atmosphere.

where

$$\chi = (\mu^2/f^2)(\bar{u} - c - u_c)$$

and the following inequalities are assumed to hold:

$$1 \gg \left\{ \left|\frac{(\bar{u}-c)^2}{\bar{\sigma}^2}\right|, \left|\frac{u(\bar{u}-c)}{\bar{\sigma}^2}\right|, \left|\frac{c(\bar{u}-c)}{\bar{\sigma}^2}\right|, \left|\frac{\bar{u}^2}{\bar{\sigma}^2}\right| \right\} \sim 10^{-2}\text{–}10^{-3} \quad (42)$$

$$1 \gg \left\{ \left|\frac{s(\bar{u}-c)^2}{g}\right|, \left|\frac{s\bar{u}(\bar{u}-c)}{g}\right|, \left|\frac{sc(\bar{u}-c)}{g}\right|, \left|\frac{s\bar{u}^2}{g}\right| \right\} \sim 10^{-2}\text{–}10^{-3} \quad (43)$$

$$1 \gg \left\{ \left|\frac{\Lambda(\bar{u}-c)}{g}\right|, \left|\frac{\Lambda\bar{u}}{g}\right| \right\} \sim 10^{-2}\text{–}10^{-3}. \quad (44)$$

The justification of the first set follows directly from (35) or may be verified by the substitution of observed values of c, $\bar{u}$, and $\bar{\sigma}$. The orders of magnitude obtained by the latter method are shown at the right. The second set receives a similar justification since s/g is of the order of magnitude of $1/\bar{\sigma}^2$. To show this we write

$$-\frac{s}{g} = -\frac{1}{g\bar{\rho}}\frac{\partial\bar{\rho}}{\partial z} = -\frac{1}{g\bar{p}}\frac{\partial\bar{p}}{\partial z} + \frac{1}{g\bar{T}}\frac{\partial\bar{T}}{\partial z}$$
$$= \frac{1-\gamma R/g}{R\bar{T}} \sim \frac{1}{R\bar{T}} = \frac{\epsilon}{\bar{\sigma}^2}. \quad (45)$$

The last set of inequalities (44) can be demonstrated by exhibiting them in a form similar to that of the first two. For instance, the second inequality in (44) may be written

$$1 \gg \frac{\Lambda\bar{u}}{g} = \frac{\Lambda z\bar{u}}{gz} = \frac{(\bar{u}-\bar{u}_0)\bar{u}}{gz}.$$

Since the expression on the extreme right is an increasing function of z, it has its maximum value at the tropopause. Hence, if the height of the tropopause is z_T, we must show that

$$1 \gg \frac{[\bar{u}(z_T) - \bar{u}_0]\bar{u}(z_T)}{gz_T}.$$

But gz_T is of the same order of magnitude as the dynamic height, $R\bar{T}_0$, of a homogeneous atmosphere, so that the last inequality is equivalent to

$$1 \gg \frac{[\bar{u}(z_T) - \bar{u}_0]\bar{u}(z_T)}{R\bar{T}_0} < \frac{\bar{u}^2(z_T)}{R\bar{T}_0} = \frac{\epsilon\,\bar{u}^2(z_T)}{\bar{\sigma}^2},$$

which was established in (42). Finally, the first of the inequalities (44) can be demonstrated by similar reasoning.

By linear combination of equations (39–41) and the use of the inequalities (42–44), we obtain (see appendix B)

$$(g\bar{u}/\bar{\rho})(\bar{\rho}W)_z = -i\mu gcU - f(\Lambda c + s\bar{u}c + g\eta)V, \quad (46)$$

$$(gk\bar{u}/\bar{\rho})(\bar{\rho}W) = i\mu\bar{\sigma}^2(\bar{u}-c)U - f(k\bar{u}c + \bar{\sigma}^2\Lambda c/g + \bar{\sigma}^2\eta)V, \quad (47)$$

$$0 = -i\mu U + f\left(\chi - \frac{\Lambda}{g}\right)V - \frac{i\mu}{g}\bar{u}(\bar{u}-c)U_z + \frac{f\bar{u}}{g}V_z, \quad (48)$$

and eliminating $\bar{\rho}W$ between (46) and (47) we get

$$i\mu[(g\bar{u} + \epsilon R\gamma\bar{u} + \bar{\sigma}^2\Lambda)c - \epsilon g\bar{u}^2]U + f[(\bar{u} + \epsilon R\gamma\bar{u}/g + \bar{\sigma}^2\Lambda/g)\Lambda c + g\eta\bar{u} - \bar{u}^2(\bar{\sigma}^2\eta/\bar{u})_z]V + i\mu\bar{\sigma}^2\bar{u}(\bar{u}-c)U_z - f(kc\bar{u}^2 + \bar{\sigma}^2\Lambda\bar{u}c/g + \bar{\sigma}^2\eta\bar{u})V_z = 0. \quad (49)$$

By linear combination of equations (46–49) and use of inequalities (42–44), we at last arrive at the system,

$$i\mu U = f(\chi - \Lambda/g)V + (1-\eta)(f\bar{u}/g)V_z, \quad (50)$$

$$g^2kW = -f(gkc + \bar{\sigma}^2\Lambda)V + (1-\eta)f\bar{\sigma}^2(\bar{u}-c)V_z, \quad (51)$$

$$-(g/\bar{\rho})(\bar{\rho}W)_z = f(cs + g\chi)V + (1-\eta)fcV_z, \quad (52)$$

where U, V, W, and $(\bar{\rho}W)_z$ are now expressed in terms of V and V_z.

The quantity η appearing in (50–52) and defined by (37) was shown to be entirely negligible in the case of the barotropic wave. The following argument will serve to demonstrate that η is always small. Referring to (37) we observe that η is of the same order of magnitude as the quantity μ^2c^2/f^2, which may be written

$$\left(\frac{2\pi}{f}\right)^2 \bigg/ \frac{L^2}{c^2} = \frac{P_i^2}{P_l^2},$$

where P_i is the period of an inertial oscillation at the latitude of the long wave, and P_l is the period of the long wave. The inertial period is one half of a pendulum day, or approximately 17 hours at 45°. On the other hand, the period of oscillation of the long waves in the atmosphere is of the order of three to four days. The ratio P_i^2/P_l^2 is therefore of the order of 0.05 and may be neglected in comparison with 1.

The approximation $\eta \ll 1$ has an interpretation similar to that given for the barotropic wave; when taken together with the inequalities (42–44), it is equivalent to the assumption that v' is nearly geostrophic; for if v' is assumed to be geostrophic, then without further assumption a system identical to (50–52), without the η-term, will result; and, conversely, if we begin with the system (50–52) without the η-term, it can be shown by retracing the steps that v' will be geostrophic.

Equations (50–52) can now be replaced by the

system

$$i\mu U = f(\chi - \Lambda/g)V + (f\bar{u}/g)V_z, \quad (53)$$

$$g^2kW = -f(gkc + \bar{\sigma}^2\Lambda)V + f\bar{\sigma}^2(\bar{u} - c)V_z, \quad (54)$$

$$-(g/\bar{p})(\bar{p}W)_z = f(cs + g\chi)V + fcV_z, \quad (55)$$

which will be taken as the starting point for all future deductions.

We have in effect obtained the system of equations above by ignoring acoustic and shearing-gravitational wave components, both of which are contained in the original equations of motion. We have shown that this procedure is equivalent to assuming v' to be geostrophic. It would be desirable to have a general principle whereby this assumption could have been introduced a priori. Such a principle would be useful for eliminating what may be called the 'meteorological noises' from the problems of motion and would thereby lead to a considerable simplification of the analysis of these problems.

11. Generalization of the Rossby formula

Recalling the definitions of s and χ (in sections 7 and 10 respectively), we may write for (55)

$$-(g/f)(\bar{p}W)_z = g\bar{p}(\mu/f)^2(\bar{u} - c - u_c)V + c(\bar{p}_zV + \bar{p}V_z), \quad (55')$$

and integrating from 0 to ∞ we obtain, with the aid of condition (7),

$$g\frac{\mu^2}{f^2}\int_0^\infty (\bar{u} - c - u_c)V\bar{p}\,dz = -c\int_0^\infty (\bar{p}V)_z\,dz, \quad (56)$$

or

$$\int_{\bar{p}_0}^0 (\bar{u} - c - u_c)V\,d\bar{p} = -\frac{f^2c}{\mu^2}\bar{p}_0V_0, \quad (56')$$

where V_0 is the surface value of V. The last equation may be regarded as a generalization of the formula of Rossby [14] and Holmboe [12], since it reduces to (34) in the special case of a barotropic atmosphere. To show this we substitute the barotropic conditions $V = V_0$ and $\bar{u}$ = const and obtain

$$\bar{u} - c - u_c = \frac{f^2c\bar{p}_0V_0}{\mu^2\bar{p}_0V_0} = \frac{f^2c}{\mu^2gH_0},$$

which is identical with (34).

Equation (56′), although not the final solution for the wave velocity c since it contains the unknown amplitude factor V, is well adapted to computation from observed data. Both V and $\bar{u}$ may be determined empirically as functions of the mean pressure, and c obtained by a numerical integration. If this is done, the right-hand term is found small in comparison with the individual left-hand terms, never amounting to more than 10 per cent of the latter, and may therefore be ignored.

While, strictly, (56′) is derived for a constantly increasing zonal wind, this assumption need not have been made, and by a slight modification of the proof the equation can be shown to hold for any zonal-wind profile whose curvature is not excessive.

Let us denote the function V by

$$V = |V|e^{i\psi(z)},$$

where ψ is the phase angle between the wave at the level z and the surface wave. If the displacement of the trough between the upper wave and the surface wave is denoted by l, ψ becomes

$$\psi = 2\pi l/L,$$

and substitution into equation (56′) gives

$$c = \frac{\int_{\bar{p}_0}^0 \bar{u}|V|(\cos\psi + i\sin\psi)d\bar{p}}{\int_{\bar{p}_0}^0 |V|(\cos\psi + i\sin\psi)d\bar{p}} - u_c,$$

from which both the real and imaginary parts of c can be calculated. Ordinarily it will be found that the imaginary part is small in comparison with the real part and that the amplitude remains nearly constant. Under these circumstances we may set $\sin\psi = 0$, $\cos\psi = 1$, $|V|$ = const, and obtain the simplified expression,

$$c_r = -\frac{1}{\bar{p}_0}\int_{\bar{p}_0}^0 \bar{u}(\bar{p})\,d\bar{p} - u_c = \bar{u}^* - u_c, \quad (56'')$$

where $\bar{u}^*$ is the mean value of the zonal speed averaged with respect to pressure from the bottom to the top of the atmosphere. Let h be the level at which $\bar{u}^*$ is equal to $\bar{u}$ so that

$$c_r = \bar{u}(h) - u_c.$$

In this form the formula for the wave speed is closely analogous to (34) without the small right-hand term. It implies that the correct value for the wave speed is obtained from (34) if the actual atmosphere is replaced by a barotropic atmosphere whose zonal wind is given by $\bar{u}(h)$.

Because of the practical use which has been made of (34) at the University of Chicago and in the 5-day forecasting project of the U. S. Weather Bureau, it is of interest to indicate the proper level h at which (34) applies. It has been pointed out by Holmboe that this equation is strictly true only at the level of non-divergence in the atmosphere. A determination of h by means of (56″) will therefore also fix this level.

The quantity $\bar{u}^*$ is evaluated by calculating the area bounded by the curve $\bar{u} = \bar{u}(\bar{p})$, the lines $\bar{p} = \bar{p}_0$, $\bar{p} = 0$, and the $\bar{p}$-axis from $\bar{p}_0$ to 0, and dividing this area by $\bar{p}_0$. In fig. 2, curves of $\bar{u}(\bar{p})$ are drawn for the following distributions of zonal speed: (A) That

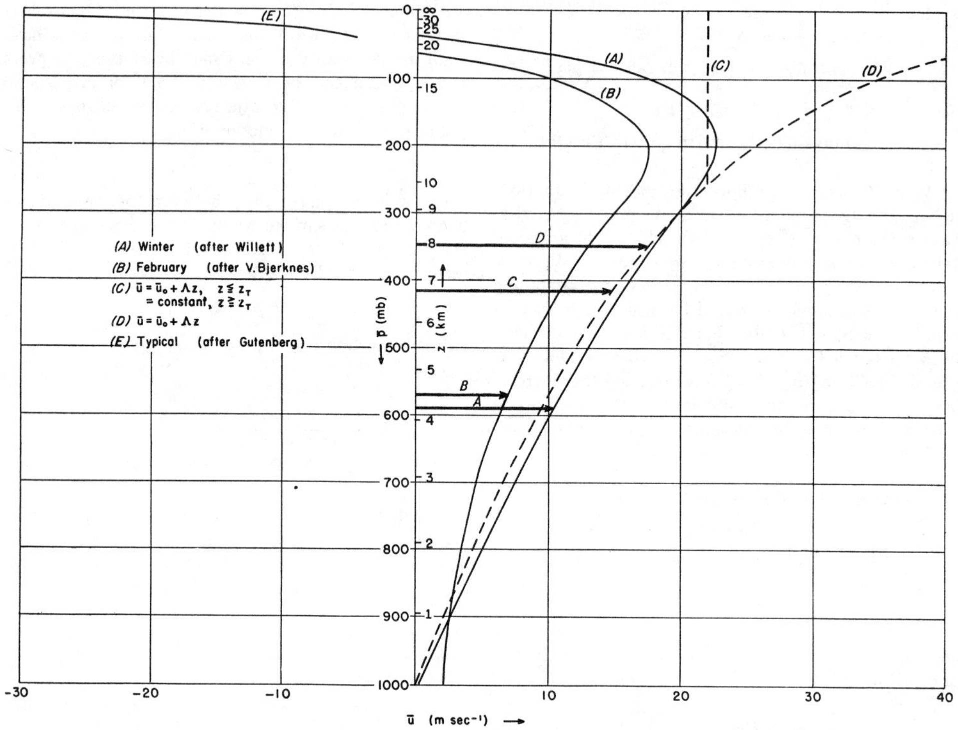

FIG. 2. Illustration of the method of calculation of $\bar{u}^* = \bar{u}(h)$ for observed and theoretical distributions of zonal velocity.

between 35°N and 55°N compiled from mean data for the month of February by V. Bjerknes [8, p. 649]. (B) That for the same zone compiled by Willett [18] from more extensive North American winter data. (C) The distribution prescribed for the model. (D) The distribution corresponding to a constant increase of wind to the top of the atmosphere. (E) The distribution above 20 km compiled by Gutenberg [9] from mean data.

By piecing together curves (A) and (E) and (B) and (E), two curves representing somewhat different versions of the variation of zonal wind in the atmosphere are obtained. The values of $\bar{u}^*$ are calculated for each of these curves and also for the theoretical distributions (C) and (D). These values are represented by the horizontal arrows A, B, C, and D.

Both Bjerknes's and Willett's data indicate that the zonal wind should be evaluated at a level between 4.0 km and 4.5 km, or 610 mb and 570 mb. This result agrees well with the experience at the University of Chicago, where it is found that the level at which (34) holds best is in the vicinity of 600 mb. The levels at which $\bar{u}^*$ is evaluated for the curves (C) and (D) are found to be too high. This is to be expected since neither of these distributions provides for a decrease of zonal velocity above the tropopause.

From the character of curve (E), which represents the variation of the zonal wind above 20 km, it can be seen that, although the velocities become very large, their contribution to the total area is very small. It may therefore be stated that the motion in the stratospheric regions above 20 km has no appreciable influence on motions in the lower troposphere.

12. The normal equation for V

Elimination of W from (54) and (55) gives

$$\frac{\bar{\sigma}^2}{g}(\bar{u}-c)V_{zz} - \epsilon(\bar{u}-c)V_z + (\epsilon\Lambda + gk\chi)V = 0. \quad (57)$$

This becomes, if the explicit values of $\bar{\sigma}^2$, k, and χ are substituted,

$$V_{zz} - \frac{1}{H}V_z - a^2\frac{\bar{u}-c-\bar{u}_c}{\bar{u}-c}V = 0, \quad (58)$$

where

$$a^2 = \mu^2 R(\gamma_d - \gamma)/(f^2 H), \quad (59)$$

and

$$\bar{u}_c = u_c + \Lambda/(a^2 H), \quad (60)$$

and Λ and γ are both understood to be replaced by zero in the stratosphere.

13. The boundary condition for V

The solution of (58) is subject to the boundary conditions (6–8). Condition (6) states that W must vanish at the ground. If W is set equal to zero in (54), the condition to be satisfied by V at the ground becomes

$$\left(\frac{V_z}{V}\right)_{z=0} = \frac{gkc + \bar{\sigma}^2\Lambda}{\bar{\sigma}^2(\bar{u} - c)}. \tag{61}$$

Condition (8) implies that V and W are continuous at the tropopause. Applying this condition to V and W in equation (54) we obtain

$$V\Delta(k^{-1}\bar{\sigma}^2\Lambda) = (\bar{u}-c)\Delta(k^{-1}\bar{\sigma}^2 V_z)$$

V must therefore satisfy the relations

$$\left.\begin{aligned} \Delta V &= 0 \\ \frac{1}{V}\Delta\left(\frac{\bar{\sigma}^2 V_z}{k}\right) &= \frac{1}{\bar{u} - c}\Delta\left(\frac{\bar{\sigma}^2\Lambda}{k}\right) \end{aligned}\right\} \tag{62}$$

at the tropopause. Condition (7) requires that

$$\lim_{z\to\infty} \bar{\rho} V^2 = 0 \tag{63}$$

at the top of the atmosphere. Since $\bar{\rho}$ is proportional to $\exp\left[-gz/R\bar{T}_S\right]$ in an isothermal atmosphere whose temperature $\bar{T}_S$ is equal to that of the stratosphere, this condition may be written

$$\lim_{z\to\infty} V^2 \exp\left(-z/H_S\right) = 0 \tag{63'}$$

where $H_S = R\bar{T}_S/g$.

14. Solution of the normal equation

Case I, $\Lambda = 0$

We shall first investigate the simplest case, where $\Lambda = 0$ throughout the atmosphere. In this case, the coefficients in (58) depend only on $\bar{T}$, and, while it is possible to perform the integration of (58) keeping $\bar{T}$ a linear function of z in the troposphere, no appreciable error is introduced if $\bar{T}$ is replaced by a suitable mean value. With this simplification the coefficients become constant, and the integral can immediately be written down as follows:

$$V = Ae^{mz} + Be^{nz}, \tag{64}$$

where m and n have the values

$$\left.\begin{aligned} m &= \frac{1}{2H} - \left(\frac{1}{4H^2} + a^2\frac{\bar{u} - c - u_c}{\bar{u} - c}\right)^{\frac{1}{2}} \\ n &= \frac{1}{2H} + \left(\frac{1}{4H^2} + a^2\frac{\bar{u} - c - u_c}{\bar{u} - c}\right)^{\frac{1}{2}} \end{aligned}\right\} \tag{65}$$

The constants involved in the expressions for m and n, as well as the constants of integration A and B, will, in general, have different values in the troposphere and stratosphere. If we denote tropospheric quantities by the subscript T and stratospheric quantities by the subscript S, conditions (61) and (62) become

$$A_T m_T + B_T n_T = gkc[\bar{\sigma}^2(\bar{u} - c)]^{-1}(A_T + B_T), \tag{66}$$

$$\begin{aligned} A_T \exp(m_T z_T) &+ B_T \exp(n_T z_T) \\ &= A_S \exp(m_S z_T) + B_S \exp(n_S z_T), \end{aligned} \tag{67}$$

$$\begin{aligned} m_T A_T \exp(m_T z_T) &+ n_T B_T \exp(n_T z_T) \\ &= m_S A_S \exp(m_S z_T) + n_S B_S \exp(n_S z_T). \end{aligned} \tag{68}$$

Suppose now that $a^2(\bar{u} - c - u_c)/(\bar{u} - c) + 1/4H^2$ is positive;[3] then it follows from (65) that $n_S > 1/H_S$, and condition (63′) gives $B_S = 0$. With substitution of $B_S = 0$, equations (66–68) become linear and homogeneous in A_T, B_T, and A_S. A necessary and sufficient condition for their consistency is the vanishing of the determinant of the coefficients. Thus we obtain the following determinantal equation for the wave speed c:

$$\begin{vmatrix} m_T - \delta & n_T - \delta & 0 \\ \exp(m_T z_T) & \exp(n_T z_T) & \exp(m_S z_T) \\ m_T \exp(m_T z_T) & n_T \exp(n_T z_T) & m_S \exp(m_S z_T) \end{vmatrix} = 0 \tag{69}$$

where $\delta = gkc/[\bar{\sigma}^2(\bar{u} - c)]$. Expansion and rearrangement of terms gives

$$m_T - \delta = (n_T - \delta)\frac{m_S - m_T}{m_S - n_T}\exp\left[(m_T - n_T)z_T\right]. \tag{70}$$

Substitution of typical values of $\bar{T}$, L, f, γ, $\bar{u}$, and c into the right-hand term of the last equation shows that it is small in comparison with m_T and δ. Hence, approximately,

$$m_T - \delta = 0$$

or

$$\frac{1}{2H_T} - \left(\frac{1}{4H_T^2} + a_T^2\frac{\bar{u} - c - u_c}{\bar{u} - c}\right)^{\frac{1}{2}} = \frac{gkc}{\bar{\sigma}^2(\bar{u} - c)}.$$

Transposing, squaring, and rearranging, we obtain

$$\bar{u} - c - u_c - \frac{f^2 c}{\mu^2 g H_T}\left(1 - \frac{k}{\epsilon}\frac{c}{\bar{u} - c}\right) = 0 \tag{71}$$

since, by (24) and (59),

$$a^2 = -g^2\mu^2 k/(f^2\bar{\sigma}^2).$$

The nondimensional factor $-k/\epsilon = R(\gamma_d - \gamma)/g$ appearing in (71) measures the extent of the baroclinicity of the atmosphere. It varies from 0.0 in a barotropic

[3] This assumption is required for determinacy of the solution under the condition that $\bar{\rho}V^2$ shall approach zero with increasing height. Professor Rossby has called my attention to the fact that negative values of $a^2(\bar{u} - c - u_c)/(\bar{u} - c) + 1/4H^2$ correspond to long internal waves having nodal surfaces at finite levels.

atmosphere to 0.289 in an isothermal atmosphere. One root of (71) is extraneous and the other can be shown to be very close to the solution of the equation

$$\bar{u} - c - u_c - \frac{f^2 c}{\mu^2 g H_T}\left(1 - \frac{k}{\epsilon}\frac{\bar{u} - u_c}{u_c}\right) = 0,$$

which, except for the occurrence of

$$\frac{1}{H_T}\left(1 - \frac{k}{\epsilon}\frac{\bar{u} - u_c}{u_c}\right)$$

instead of $1/H_0$ in the small term $f^2c/(\mu^2 g H_0)$, is identical to (34). Hence there is no significant difference, with respect to the motion of long waves, between a barotropic atmosphere and a baroclinic atmosphere with a constant zonal wind. One may conclude that here, at least, the statical stability of the atmosphere plays no important role.

Case II, $\Lambda \neq 0$

We now consider the problem of wave motion in the baroclinic model specified in section 3. We shall solve this problem by determining $V(z)$, the amplitude factor of the meridional component of wave velocity. All other quantities can easily be found in terms of V.

The equations governing V are (58–60). For the sake of mathematical simplicity, the following approximations are made: $\bar{T}$ is replaced by its mean value, $\bar{T}_T$, in the troposphere and z_T, the height of the tropopause, is replaced by its value at a mean latitude. The quantities H, a, and $\bar{u}_c$ then become constant, and the boundary conditions (62) apply at the constant level z_T. The mathematical problem is now strictly determined; we must find the solution to (58) that satisfies the boundary conditions (61–63′) at $z = 0$, z_T, and ∞.

In the troposphere $\Lambda \neq 0$, and (58) can be reduced to a standard form by the following change of dependent and independent variables:

$$\left.\begin{aligned}\psi &= V \exp\left[(\bar{a} - \tfrac{1}{2}H_T^{-1})z\right]\\ \xi &= (2\bar{a}/\Lambda)(\bar{u} - c) = 2\bar{a}z + (2\bar{a}/\Lambda)(\bar{u}_0 - c),\end{aligned}\right\} \quad (72)$$

where

$$\bar{a}^2 = a^2 + 1/(4H_T^2). \quad (73)$$

With this change of variables (58) becomes

$$\xi\frac{d^2\psi}{d\xi^2} - \xi\frac{d\psi}{d\xi} + r\psi = 0, \quad (74)$$

where

$$r = \frac{\bar{a}}{2\Lambda}\left(\frac{a^2}{\bar{a}^2}u_c + \frac{\Lambda}{\bar{a}^2 H_T}\right) = \frac{a^2\bar{u}_c}{2\bar{a}\Lambda}. \quad (75)$$

Equation (74) is a special case of the confluent hypergeometric equation

$$\xi\frac{d^2\psi}{d\xi^2} + (b - \xi)\frac{d\psi}{d\xi} - a\psi = 0, \quad (76)$$

which is satisfied by the functions

$$\psi = M(a, b, \xi) = 1 + \frac{a}{1\cdot b}\xi + \frac{a(a+1)}{2!\,b(b+1)}\xi^2 + \cdots \quad (77)$$

and

$$\psi = \xi^{1-b} M(a - b + 1, 2 - b, \xi). \quad (78)$$

In the present case only the latter integral is a solution of equation (74), since $M(a, b, \xi)$ is undefined for $b = 0$. Another solution is obtained by contour integration in the complex domain; it is shown in appendix C that the following function satisfies (74):

$$\psi = \frac{\sin \pi a}{\pi}\left\{ a\xi\, M(a + 1, 2, \xi) \times\left[\ln \xi + \frac{\Gamma'(a)}{\Gamma(a)} - 2\frac{\Gamma'(1)}{\Gamma(1)}\right] + 1 + \sum_{n=1}^{\infty} B_n \frac{a(a+1)\cdots(a+n-1)}{(n-1)!\,n!}\xi^n\right\}, \quad (79)$$

where $a = -r$, and

$$B_n = \sum_{\nu=0}^{n-1}\left(\frac{1}{a+\nu} - \frac{2}{1+\nu}\right) + \frac{1}{n}.$$

The tabulated values of the two functions (78) and (79) will be found in appendix D. Denoting (79) by ψ_1 and (78) by ψ_2, we may take, as the general solution of (74), the linear combination

$$\psi = A\psi_1 + B\psi_2. \quad (80)$$

The solution for the stratosphere has already been determined in the investigation of the case $\Lambda = 0$. Recalling equation (64) we may write, since $B_S = 0$,

$$V = A_S \exp(m_S z), \quad (81)$$

where m_S is defined by (65).

15. Determination of the wave velocity

The arbitrary constants in the solutions (80) and (81) must be chosen in such a way that they satisfy the boundary conditions (61–63′). We see from the manner in which the solution for the stratosphere was determined that it automatically satisfies the condition (63′). For the purpose of satisfying condition (62) we change to the new variables ψ and ξ defined by (72), and obtain

$$\frac{1}{V}\frac{dV}{dz} = -\left(\bar{a} - \frac{1}{2H_T}\right) + \frac{1}{\psi}\frac{d\psi}{d\xi}\frac{d\xi}{dz} = -\bar{a} + \frac{1}{2H_T} + \frac{2\bar{a}}{\psi}\frac{d\psi}{d\xi} \quad (82)$$

in the troposphere and

$$(1/V)dV/dz = m_S \quad (83)$$

in the stratosphere. If these values of V_z/V are substituted into (62), we obtain

$$\frac{\psi'}{\psi} = \frac{1}{2} - \frac{1}{4\bar{a}_T H_T} + \frac{a_T^2}{a_S^2}\frac{m_S}{2\bar{a}_T} + \frac{\Lambda}{2\bar{a}_T[\bar{u}(z_T) - c]}, \tag{84}$$

where $\psi' = d\psi/d\xi$. Let us denote the right-hand side of this equation by λ and the value of ξ at the tropopause by ξ_1; then, if we substitute for ψ the expression in (80), we derive

$$\frac{A\,\psi_1'(\xi_1) + B\,\psi_2'(\xi_1)}{A\,\psi_1(\xi_1) + B\,\psi_2(\xi_1)} = \lambda. \tag{85}$$

We satisfy condition (61) by a similar procedure and obtain

$$\frac{A\,\psi_1'(\xi_0) + B\,\psi_2'(\xi_0)}{A\,\psi_1(\xi_0) + B\,\psi_2(\xi_0)} = \alpha + \frac{\beta}{\xi_0}, \tag{86}$$

where ξ_0 is the value of ξ at $z = 0$ and α and β are defined by the equations

$$\alpha = \tfrac{1}{2} - gk/(2\bar{a}\bar{\sigma}^2) - 1/(4\bar{a}H_T), \tag{87}$$

$$\beta = 1 + gk\bar{u}_0/(\Lambda\bar{\sigma}^2). \tag{88}$$

Equations (85) and (86) are linear and homogeneous in A and B. The determinant of the coefficients of A and B must therefore vanish. This gives the following equation for the determination of c:

$$\frac{\Delta_{11} - \lambda\Delta_{10}}{\Delta_{01} - \lambda\Delta_{00}} = \alpha + \frac{\beta}{\xi_0}, \tag{89}$$

where

$$\Delta_{ij} = \begin{vmatrix} \psi_1^{(i)}(\xi_0) & \psi_2^{(j)}(\xi_0) \\ \psi_1^{(i)}(\xi_1) & \psi_2^{(j)}(\xi_1) \end{vmatrix}$$

and $\psi_1^{(0)} = \psi_1$, $\psi_2^{(0)} = \psi_2$, $\psi_1^{(1)} = \psi_1'$, $\psi_2^{(1)} = \psi_2'$.

Equation (89) is of the form

$$F(\xi_0, \xi_1, r, \lambda, \alpha, \beta) = 0. \tag{90}$$

Since α, β, and r are functions of Λ, $\bar{u}_0$, and L, while ξ_0, ξ_1, and λ involve these quantities as well as c, we may write instead

$$F(\Lambda, \bar{u}_0, L, c) = 0. \tag{90'}$$

This equation expresses the dependency of the wave speed c on both the wave length and the physical parameters characterizing the mean flow of the atmosphere. As we are not primarily concerned with the variation of the parameters γ, φ, $\bar{T}_0$, $\bar{T}_T$, and $\bar{z}_T$, they are given appropriate constant values. We shall, however, be able to say something about the influence of φ and γ on stability.

Equation (89) is solved by a graphical method. The left- and right-hand sides of the equation are plotted separately as functions of ξ_0. The graphs consist of two triply infinite families of curves depending on the parameters Λ, $\bar{u}_0$, and L. The points of intersection of members corresponding to the same values of L, Λ, and $\bar{u}_0$ give the roots ξ_0. Since ξ_0 is a function of c, the value of c is determined. The points of tangency give the critical values of the parameters at which c becomes complex. Since (89) has analytic functions of ξ_0 on each side, except at $\xi_0 = 0$, the roots of this equation will occur in conjugate complex pairs. According to the definition of stability in section 8, a value of c with a positive imaginary part corresponds to an amplified wave, and a value of c with a negative imaginary part corresponds to a damped wave. Thus, if complex roots exist at all, there must be both stable and unstable wave components. Presumably the stable component is damped out as soon as it is formed, so that we may limit our considerations to neutral and unstable waves.

Fig. 3 shows the critical curve for $\bar{u}_0 = 0$ calculated from (89). Values of Λ and L at points above the curve

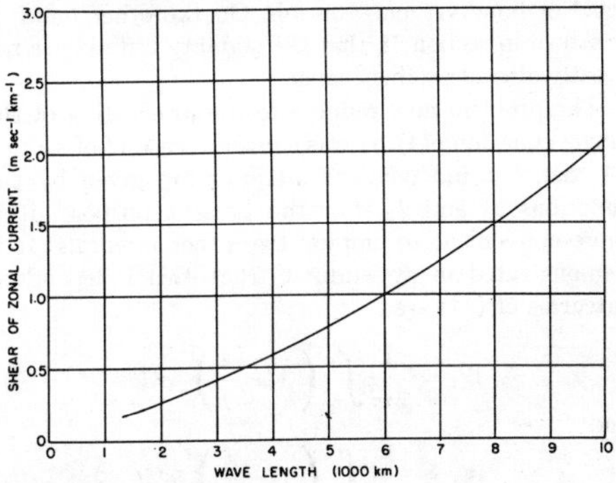

FIG. 3. The critical stability curve for $\bar{u}_0 = 0$.

correspond to instability and values at points below correspond to stability. The curve shows that instability increases with shear and diminishes with wave length. Although calculated for a particular value of $\bar{u}_0$, the curve represents approximately the stability criteria for a wide range of $\bar{u}_0$. A proof of this assertion will be given in section 16. Here, to make the assertion plausible, the explanation may be offered that increases in $\bar{u}_0$ unaccompanied by variations in Λ merely impart to the atmosphere a slightly greater absolute rate of rotation without changing the relative motion of its parts. Such a change should not be expected to affect the stability beyond increasing slightly the gyroscopic stability that a rotating body has by virtue of the conservation of angular momentum.

In order to avoid the extremely laborious computations involved in a further analysis of (89), we shall assume that the zonal wind in the atmospheric model is defined in the stratosphere as well as in the tropo-

[4] It may be shown that there exist neutral as well as unstable waves at points above the critical curve.

sphere by the function $\bar{u}_0 + \Lambda z$. This assumption eliminates the necessity of piecing together separate solutions for the two atmospheric layers, but is of course subject to the criticism that the zonal winds in the statosphere will here depart considerably from the observed values. However, the influence of this discrepancy upon the wave motion cannot be great, for the exponential decrease of density with height reduces the zonal momentum to a negligible value and nullifies the influence of the increasingly large zonal winds. Thus it is shown in section 11 that the rapid increase of the magnitude of the zonal wind above 20 km has no perceptible influence on the wave speed in the troposphere. The effects produced at lower stratospheric levels by deviations of the postulated from the observed winds are indicated in fig. 2, where it will be seen that the change from a constant to an increasing zonal-wind distribution lifts the mean level of nondivergence 68 mb. On the other hand, it is shown in section 16 that the stability criteria are not greatly altered by this change.

The problem now reduces to the integration of the single equation (74). It was shown in case II of section 14 that two independent integrals are given by the functions ψ_1 and ψ_2. For the present purpose, it is more convenient to employ two other integrals. It is demonstrated in appendix C that two independent integrals of (74) are

$$W_1 = \frac{1}{2\pi i}\int_{\gamma_1}\left(1 - \frac{\xi}{t}\right)^r e^t dt \qquad (91)$$

and

$$W_2 = \frac{1}{2\pi i}\int_{\gamma_2}\left(1 - \frac{\xi}{t}\right)^r e^t dt, \qquad (92)$$

where the paths of integration γ_1 and γ_2 are shown in fig. 4. The asymptotic expansions of W_1 and W_2 are given by

$$W_1 \sim [(-\xi)^r/\Gamma(r)]G(-r, 1-r; -\xi), \qquad (93)$$

$$W_2 \sim [\xi^{-r}e^{\xi}/\Gamma(-r)]G(1+r, r; \xi), \qquad (94)$$

where

$$G(\mu, \nu; \xi) = 1 + \frac{\mu\nu}{1!\,\xi} + \frac{\mu(\mu+1)\nu(\nu+1)}{2!\,\xi^2} + \cdots. \qquad (95)$$

The general solution of (74) may be written

$$\psi = A_1W_1 + A_2W_2. \qquad (96)$$

This function must satisfy the boundary condition (63′)

$$\lim_{z\to\infty} V \exp\left(-\frac{z}{H_S}\right) = 0.$$

The behavior of the functions W_1 and W_2 at infinity is determined by the asymptotic expansions (93) and (94). Transferring back to the variables V and z, we find that

$$V_1 = W_1(\xi)\exp[-(\bar{a} - \tfrac{1}{2}H_T^{-1})z] \sim K_1z^r \exp[-(\bar{a} - \tfrac{1}{2}H_T^{-1})z], \qquad (93')$$

and

$$V_2 = W_2(\xi)\exp[-(\bar{a} - \tfrac{1}{2}H_T^{-1})z] \sim K_2z^{-r}\exp[(\bar{a} + \tfrac{1}{2}H_T^{-1})z], \qquad (94')$$

where V_1 and V_2 are particular solutions of (58) corresponding to W_1 and W_2, and K_1 and K_2 are constants. Since

$$\bar{a} = \left(a^2 + \frac{1}{4H_T^2}\right)^{\frac{1}{2}} > \frac{1}{2H_T} \approx \frac{1}{2H_S},$$

the first of the expansions above shows that

$$V_1 \exp(-z/H_S) \to 0,$$

whereas the second shows that

$$V_2 \exp(-z/H_S) \to \infty.$$

Consequently, (96) can satisfy the boundary condition at infinity only if $A_2 = 0$, i.e., if $\psi = A_1W_1$. Now it can be shown that the function ψ_1, defined by (79), is equal to $(-1)^{-r}W_1$ (see appendix C). Hence the appropriate solution of (74) is given by a constant multiple of ψ_1.

An equation similar to (86) is obtained from the requirement that ψ satisfy the surface boundary condition (61). In the present case, instead of two functions

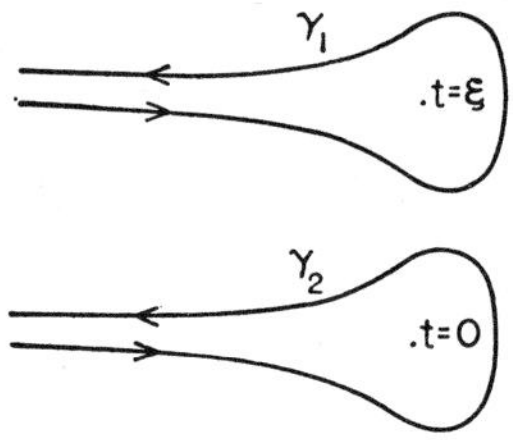

FIG. 4. Paths of integration for the integrals W_1 and W_2.

ψ_1 and ψ_2, only the single function ψ_1 is involved, and the resulting equation becomes

$$\frac{\psi_1'(\xi_0, r)}{\psi_1(\xi_0, r)} = \alpha + \frac{\beta}{\xi_0}, \qquad (97)$$

where, as before,

$$\alpha = \tfrac{1}{2} - gk/(2\bar{a}\bar{\sigma}^2) - 1/(4\bar{a}H_T) = \tfrac{1}{2} + \Delta\alpha,$$

$$\beta = 1 + gk\bar{u}_0/(\Lambda\bar{\sigma}^2) = 1 + \Delta\beta,$$

$$r = \frac{\bar{a}}{2\Lambda}\left(\frac{a^2u_c}{\bar{a}^2} + \frac{\Lambda}{\bar{a}^2H_T}\right).$$

For convenience in following the ensuing discussion the definitions of the quantities involved in ξ_0, r, α, and β are here reproduced:

Ω = angular velocity of earth,
φ = latitude,
γ = lapse rate in troposphere,
γ_d = adiabatic lapse rate,
R = gas constant,
$\mathcal{R}$ = radius of earth,
$\bar{T}_T$ = mean temperature in troposphere,
L = wave length,
$\bar{u}_0$ = mean surface zonal speed,
Λ = shear of mean zonal speed,
$f = 2\Omega \sin \varphi$, $\mu = 2\pi/L$, $\bar{u} = \bar{u}_0 + \Lambda z$,
$\bar{\sigma}^2 = \epsilon R \bar{T}_T$, $H_T = R\bar{T}_T/g$, $k = -(\epsilon R/g)(\gamma_d - \gamma)$,

$$u_c = \frac{\Omega L^2 \cos \varphi}{2\pi^2 \mathcal{R}}, \quad a^2 = \frac{\mu^2 R}{f^2 H_T}(\gamma_d - \gamma), \quad \bar{a}^2 = a^2 + \frac{1}{4H_T{}^2}$$

In order to solve (97) for c, suitable numerical values must be assigned to the constant parameters φ, γ, and $\bar{T}_T$. The following values are selected:

$$\varphi = 45°,$$
$$\gamma = 6.5 \text{ C km}^{-1},$$
$$\bar{T}_T = 260\text{C}.$$

With the assignment of these quantities, we may derive numerical expressions for the parameters ξ_0, r, α, and β in terms of the fundamental parameters L, Λ, and $\bar{u}_0$. Thus,

$$\bar{a} = (0.48/L^2 + 4.0 \times 10^{-9})^{\frac{1}{2}},$$
$$\xi_0 = 2\bar{a}(\bar{u}_0 - c) \times 10^3/\Lambda,$$
$$\Delta\alpha = \alpha - \tfrac{1}{2} = -2.50 \times 10^{-5}/\bar{a},$$
$$\Delta\beta = \beta - 1 = -\bar{u}_0/(78\Lambda),$$
$$r = -\Delta\alpha(2.52 + 3.90/\Lambda),$$

where L is measured in km, $\bar{u}_0$ and c in m sec^{-1}, and Λ in m sec^{-1}km^{-1}.

Equation (97) is solved for ξ_0, and hence c, by graphing the quantities ψ_1'/ψ_1 and $\alpha + \beta/\xi_0$ as functions of ξ_0. (The values of ψ_1 and ψ_1' are given in tables 1 and 2 of the appendix, and the graphs of ψ_1'/ψ_1 are shown in fig. 5.) The intersections of the graphs of ψ_1'/ψ_1 and $\alpha + \beta/\xi_0$ determine the roots. The critical values of ξ_0 separating real from complex solutions are determined by the points of tangency. The roots are most conveniently represented graphically by plotting ξ_0 as a function of r for constant values of α and β. The graphs obtained in this way are shown in fig. 6. The parameters φ, γ, and $\bar{T}$ need not have been specified in this type of representation, so that the effect on the wave velocity of varying these parameters can be studied.

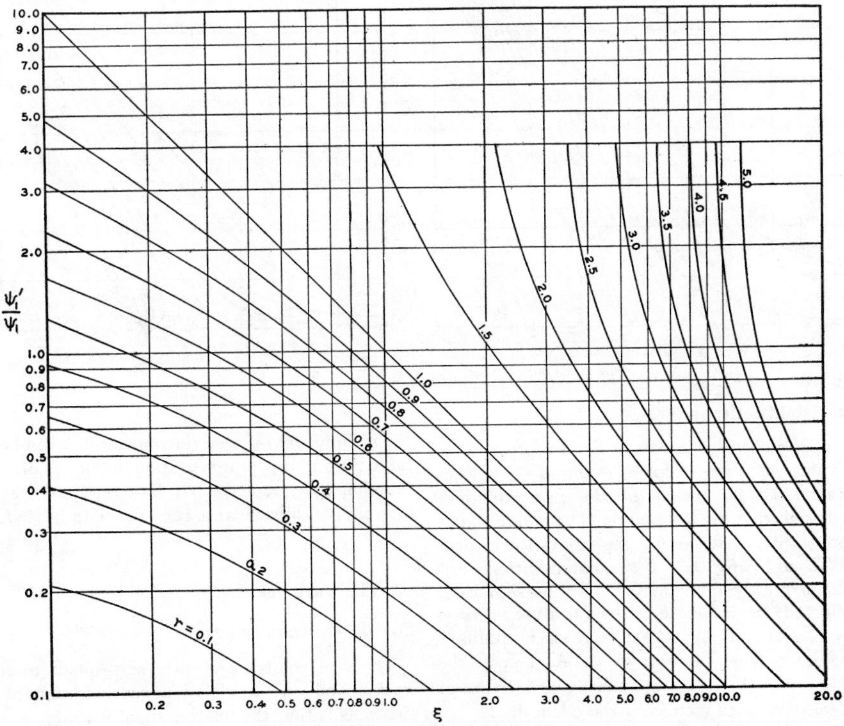

FIG. 5. Graph of the function $\psi_1'(\xi, r)/\psi_1(\xi, r)$.

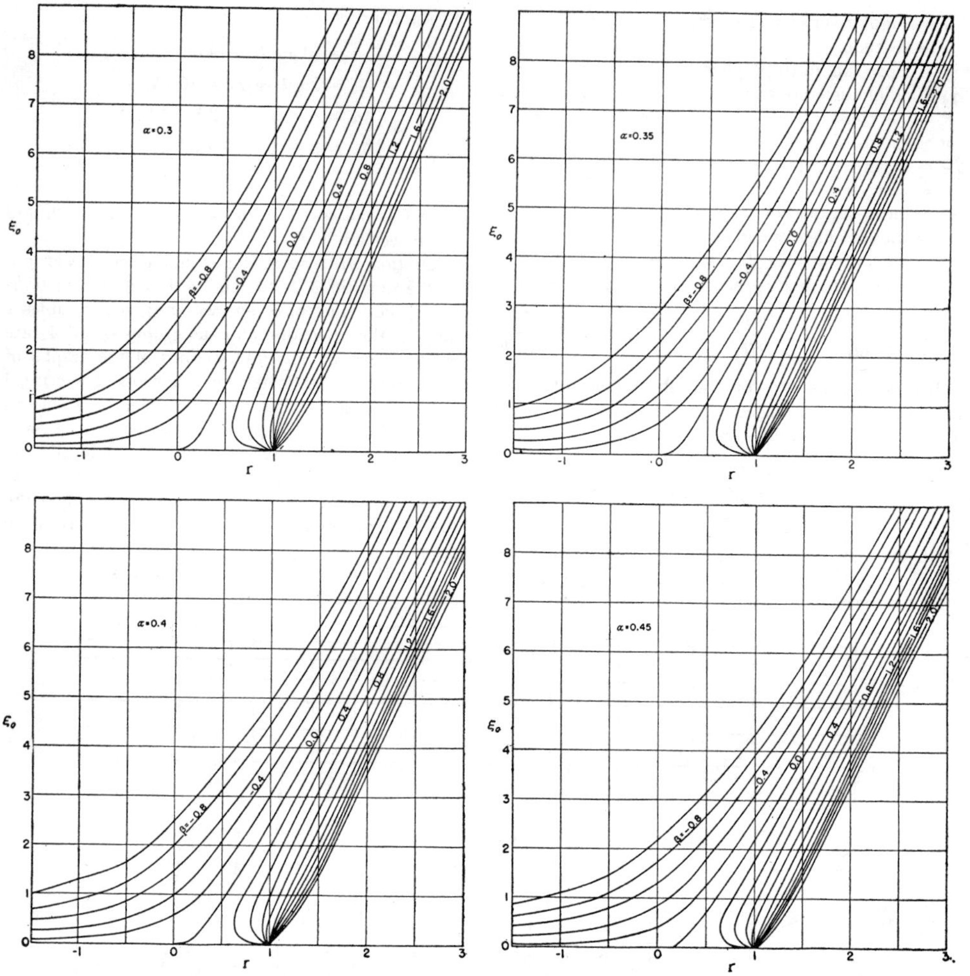

FIG. 6. Representation of ξ_0 as a function of r, α, and β.

16. The stability criteria

The upper and lower curves in fig. 7 represent the critical values of L and Λ for $\bar{u}_0 = 0$ and $\bar{u}_0 = 20$ m sec^{-1}, calculated by means of the approximative process described in the last section. The middle curve is a reproduction of fig. 3 and represents the critical values of L and Λ for $\bar{u}_0 = 0$ calculated without approximation directly from (89). It will be seen that, as anticipated, the influence of the variation in $\bar{u}_0$ on stability is small; a very slight increase in stability accompanies a large increase in $\bar{u}_0$. As before, the curves show a slightly greater than linear increase of the critical shear with increasing wave length.

The influence of lapse rate on stability can be ascertained from the representation in fig. 6 of ξ_0 as a function of r, α, and β. It is found that instability increases both with lapse rate and with latitude.

17. The wave velocity

Case I, the neutral wave

The real solutions of (97) correspond to neutral waves, and one result of a consideration of these solutions is that the relative zonal velocity, $u_0 - c$, is

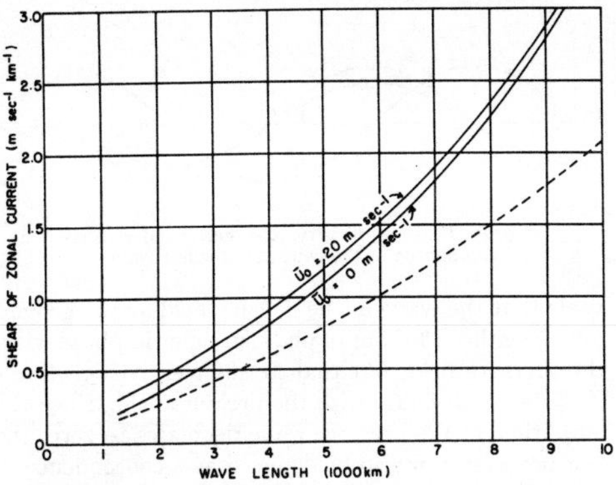

FIG. 7. Approximate critical stability curves for $\bar{u}_0 = 0$ and $\bar{u}_0 = 20$ m sec^{-1}. The dashed curve is a duplicate of the exact curve in fig. 3.

always positive. This is a consequence of the fact that $\ln \xi_0$ appears in the expression for both $\psi_1(\xi_0)$ and $\psi_1'(\xi_0)$. If ξ_0 were real and negative, $\ln \xi_0$ would be complex, and the left-hand side of (97) then would also be complex; but this is an impossibility because the right-hand side is always real for real values of ξ_0. Since $\xi_0 = 2\bar{a}(\bar{u}_0 - c)/\Lambda$, we conclude that $\bar{u}_0 - c$ is always positive.

The speed of the neutral wave is a function of the parameters L, Λ, and $\bar{u}_0$. The dependency on L and Λ when $\bar{u}_0 = 0$ is illustrated in fig. 8. Changes in $\bar{u}_0$ have a small effect upon the character of the curves. The exact nature of this effect is illustrated in fig. 9, where $\bar{u}_0 - c$ is plotted as a function of Λ for different values of $\bar{u}_0$ and for $L = 4150$ km. Referring to fig. 8 we note that the limiting curve corresponding to $\Lambda = 0$ virtually coincides with the graph of

$$\bar{u} - c - u_c = f^2 c/(\mu^2 g H_0).$$

This result was anticipated when it was shown in section 14, case I, that waves in a baroclinic atmosphere with zero shear have virtually the same velocity as waves in the corresponding barotropic atmosphere.

The curves in fig. 8 show that the wave velocity, at constant wave length and constant surface zonal speed, increases rapidly with increasing shear; and that for $\Lambda > 0$ we always have

$$0 < \bar{u}_0 - c < u_c.$$

Case II, the unstable wave

In order to calculate the speed of the unstable wave it would be necessary to evaluate the complex roots of (97), and this is an extremely difficult process. However, one may make several inferences concerning this speed from the real solutions already obtained.

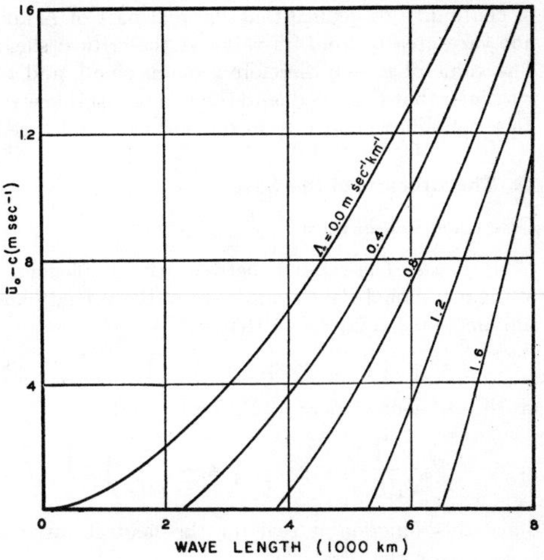

FIG. 8. The speed of the neutral wave as a function of Λ and of wave length L.

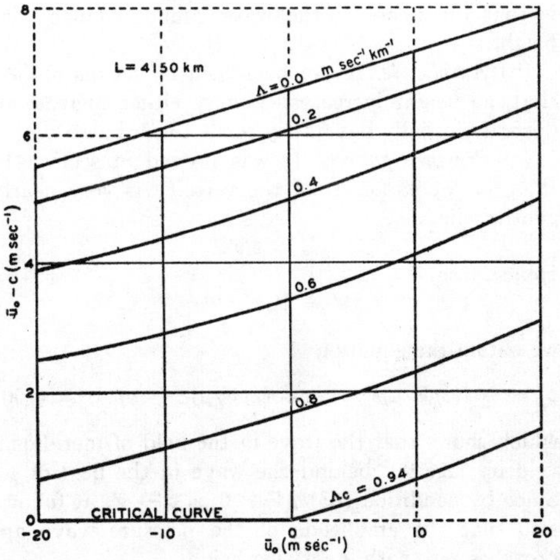

FIG. 9. The speed of the neutral wave as a function of Λ and $\bar{u}_0$.

Let us consider what happens to the speed of a neutral wave when the shear is gradually increased while L and $\bar{u}_0$ remain constant. An inspection of fig. 9 shows that $\bar{u}_0 - c$ decreases from its value in a barotropic atmosphere to its value at the point where Λ is equal to Λ_c, the critical shear corresponding to the given values of L and $\bar{u}_0$. It can be seen that for $\bar{u}_0 > 0$ the value of $\bar{u}_0 - c$ at $\Lambda = \Lambda_c$ is slightly greater than zero, whereas for $\bar{u}_0 \leqq 0$ it is equal to zero. In either case $\bar{u}_0 - c$ is small. In the case of incipient instability, where the shear is only slightly greater than its critical value, we may employ the argument of continuity to deduce that the real part of ξ_0 does not vary greatly from its value at the critical shear. The value of $\bar{u}_0 - c$ therefore remains small, and we may infer that the speed of the incipient unstable wave does not differ greatly from the surface zonal speed.

18. The structure of the wave

Case I, the neutral wave

(a) *Phase.* The relation between the amplitude V of the meridional wave component of the velocity and the function ψ_1 may be written

$$V(z) = A\,\psi_1(\xi, r)\exp\left[-(\bar{a} - \tfrac{1}{2}H_T^{-1})z\right], \quad (98)$$

or, if we define $V_0 = V(0)$,

$$V(z) = V_0\frac{\psi_1(\xi, r)}{\psi_1(\xi_0, r)}\exp\left[-\left(\bar{a} - \frac{1}{2H_T}\right)z\right]. \quad (99)$$

Since this function is real for the neutral wave, a consequence of the relation

$$v' = Ve^{i\mu(x-ct)}$$

is that the phase of the wave cannot change with height.

(b) *Amplitude.* It can be shown by means of (99) that, as height increases, V may either increase or decrease initially but finally tends toward zero.

(c) *Pressure pattern.* It was proved in section 10 that the y-component of the velocity is very nearly geostrophic, i.e.,

$$p'_x \approx \bar{\rho}fv'.$$

Hence, from

$$v' = Ve^{i\mu(x-ct)}$$

we obtain the equation

$$p' = -i(\bar{\rho}fV/\mu)e^{i\mu(x-ct)} = (\bar{\rho}fV/\mu)e^{i\mu(x-ct)-\frac{1}{2}i\pi}, \quad (100)$$

which shows that the wave in the field of meridional velocity lags 90° behind the wave in the field of p'. Since by condition (63) $\bar{\rho}V \to 0$ as $z \to \infty$, it follows also that the amplitude of the pressure wave approaches zero with increasing height.

(d) *Density pattern.* The density perturbation is obtained from the pressure perturbation by means of the third of equations (22). Substituting the expression for p' in (100), we obtain

$$\rho' = i\frac{f\bar{\rho}V}{\mu}\left(s + \frac{V_z}{V}\right)e^{i\mu(x-ct)}, \quad (101)$$

and, introducing the value of V_z/V given by (82), we obtain

$$\rho' = i\frac{f\bar{\rho}V}{\mu}\left(s - \bar{a} + \frac{1}{2H_T} + 2\bar{a}\frac{\psi_1'}{\psi_1}\right)e^{i\mu(x-ct)}. \quad (102)$$

Examination of the coefficient of $e^{i\mu(x-ct)}$ in (102) reveals that the wave in the density field at the ground may be either 180° out of phase with, or in phase with, the pressure field, but that at sufficiently high levels it is always in phase with the pressure field. Since the amplitude of the pressure wave decreases to zero, the last property can also be deduced as a consequence of the rule derived from the hydrostatic equation that cold highs and warm lows decrease in intensity with height. The upper-level density field together with the fields of pressure and velocity are shown in fig. 10.

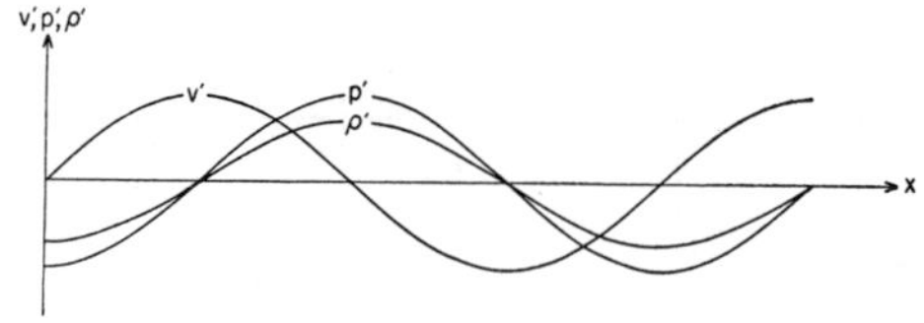

FIG. 10. Pressure, density, and meridional velocity component in the neutral baroclinic wave.

(e) *Pattern of vertical velocity component.* The amplitude W of the w'-perturbation is expressed in terms of V by (54), thus

$$\frac{g^2k}{f\bar{\sigma}^2}W = -\left(\frac{gkc}{\bar{\sigma}^2} + \Lambda\right)V + (\bar{u} - c)V_z$$

$$= (\bar{u} - c)V\left(\frac{V_z}{V} - \frac{gkc/\bar{\sigma}^2 + \Lambda}{\bar{u} - c}\right)$$

$$= 2\bar{a}(\bar{u} - c)V\left(\frac{\psi_1'}{\psi_1} - \alpha - \frac{\beta}{\xi}\right). \quad (103)$$

By (97) the last parenthesized quantity equals zero when $z = 0$, and, since, as can be shown, ψ_1'/ψ_1 decreases faster than $\alpha + \beta/\xi$, the parenthesized expression is negative. From this, together with the fact that k is negative and $\bar{u} - c$ positive, it follows that W has the same sign as V, and the w'-perturbation is always in phase with the v'-perturbation.

(f) *The horizontal divergence.* The horizontal mass divergence D is defined by

$$D = (\rho u)_x + (\rho v)_y. \quad (104)$$

In terms of the perturbations u' and v', D may be written, with the aid of (11),

$$D = \bar{\rho}u'_x + (\bar{\rho}f/g)(su + \Lambda)v'$$
$$= \bar{\rho}[i\mu U + (f/g)(s\bar{u} + \Lambda)V]e^{i\mu(x-ct)}, \quad (104')$$

whence by (53) we obtain

$$D = \bar{\rho}f\left[\left(\chi + \frac{s\bar{u}}{g}\right)V + \frac{\bar{u}}{g}V_z\right]e^{i\mu(x-ct)}$$

$$= \bar{\rho}fV\frac{\mu^2}{f^2}\left(\bar{u} - c - u_c + \frac{f^2s\bar{u}}{\mu^2g} + \frac{f^2\bar{u}}{\mu^2g}\frac{V_z}{V}\right)e^{i\mu(x-ct)}. \quad (104'')$$

An evaluation of the orders of magnitude of

$$\frac{f^2 s\bar{u}}{\mu^2 g} \quad \text{and} \quad \frac{f^2\bar{u}}{\mu^2 g}\frac{V_z}{V}$$

in this equation shows that these terms are negligible in comparison with the remaining parenthetical terms. Therefore, we may write

$$D \approx (\bar{\rho} V\mu^2/f)(\bar{u} - c - u_c)e^{i\mu(x-ct)}. \quad (105)$$

The level where $D = 0$ is called the level of nondivergence. If the height of this level is denoted by h, we derive from the preceding equation the result that

$$\bar{u}(h) - c - u_c \approx 0. \quad (106)$$

Since at the ground $\bar{u} - c$ is less than u_c, the result follows from (105) that the field of D is 180° out of phase with the field of v' at low levels; but, at levels above the level of nondivergence, D is in phase with the field of v'.

Case II, the unstable wave

The velocities of the unstable waves correspond to complex roots of (97), whose evaluation presents great difficulties. However, a qualitative description of the structure of the unstable wave can be given without such an evaluation. For this purpose, we approximate ξ_0 in the vicinity of its critical values by means of an expansion in Taylor's series in the following manner: Consider the variation in ξ_0 produced by a small increase of r from its critical value r_c. We may study this variation in one of the diagrams of fig. 6 by noting the intersections of the vertical line for constant r with the curve for constant β. If we confine our attention to the case $\bar{u}_0 > 0$, $\Delta\beta$ is less than zero, and we need only consider the curves for $\beta < 1$. Denote the critical values of r, α, and β by r_c, α_c, and β_c; then the line corresponding to $r = r_c$ is tangent to the curve corresponding to $\beta = \beta_c$ in the diagram for $\alpha = \alpha_c$. At the point of tangency, $\partial r/\partial\xi_0 = 0$ and $\partial^2 r/\partial\xi_0^2 > 0$. The relationship between ξ_0, r, α, and β is expressed by

$$F = \frac{\psi_1'(\xi_0, r)}{\psi_1(\xi_0, r)} - \alpha - \frac{\beta}{\xi_0} = 0. \quad (97)$$

If F is analytic, this equation defines r as an analytic function of ξ_0 in the vicinity of its critical value. An inspection of the expression for ξ_1 in (79) shows that F is analytic whenever ξ_0 is greater than zero. As this condition is assured by the provision that $\bar{u}_0$ be greater than zero, r may be expanded in Taylor's series about ξ_0; thus,

$$r = r_c + \left(\frac{\partial r}{\partial \xi_0}\right)_c (\xi_0 - \xi_{0c}) + \frac{1}{2!}\left(\frac{\partial^2 r}{\partial \xi_0^2}\right)_c (\xi_0 - \xi_{0c})^2 + \cdots, \quad (107)$$

where ξ_{0c}, $(\partial r/\partial\xi_0)_c$, and $(\partial^2 r/\partial\xi_0^2)_c$ denote critical values. Recalling that $(\partial r/\partial\xi_0)_c = 0$ and $(\partial^2 r/\partial\xi_0^2)_c > 0$, we obtain

$$\xi_0 - \xi_{0c} \approx \pm\left(2\frac{r - r_c}{(\partial^2 r/\partial\xi_0^2)_c}\right)^{\frac{1}{2}}, \quad (108)$$

if terms of third and higher orders are neglected. Since $r - r_c$ is negative when $\Lambda - \Lambda_c$ is positive, we may write

$$\xi_0 = \xi_{0c} + i\xi_i, \quad (109)$$

where

$$\xi_i = -\left(-2\frac{r - r_c}{(\partial^2 r/\partial\xi_0^2)_c}\right)^{\frac{1}{2}},$$

the minus sign in (108) being selected since c_i is greater than zero and therefore ξ_i is less than zero in the unstable wave.

Equation (109) gives the surface value of ξ. The corresponding value of ξ at any height z is

$$\xi = (2\bar{a}/\Lambda)(\bar{u}_0 - c) + 2\bar{a}z = \xi_0 + 2\bar{a}z = \xi_{0c} + 2\bar{a}z + i\xi_i,$$

and, if the quantity $\xi_{0c} + 2\bar{a}z$ is denoted by ξ_c, we have

$$\xi = \xi_c + i\xi_i. \quad (110)$$

Expanding the function ψ_1 about ξ_c we obtain

$$\psi_1(\xi) = \psi_1(\xi_c) + i\xi_i\psi_1'(\xi_c) \quad (111)$$

if terms of second and higher orders are neglected; or, in polar coordinates,

$$\psi_1(\xi) = |\psi_1(\xi)|e^{i\mu\Phi(z)} = \{\psi_1^2(\xi_c) + \xi_i^2[\psi_1'(\xi_c)]^2\}^{\frac{1}{2}}e^{i\mu\Phi(z)}, \quad (111')$$

where

$$\Phi(z) = \frac{1}{\mu}\tan^{-1}\left[\xi_i\frac{\psi_1'(\xi_c)}{\psi_1(\xi_c)}\right], \quad (112)$$

and, if this expression is substituted into equation (99), we obtain

$$V = \left\{V_0 \exp\left[-\left(\bar{a} - \frac{1}{2H_T}\right)z\right]\right\} \times \left|\frac{\psi_1(\xi)}{\psi_1(\xi_0)}\right| e^{i\mu[\Phi(z) - \Phi(0)]}. \quad (98')$$

Since $v' = Ve^{i\mu(x-ct)}$, we may infer that the phase of the unstable wave changes with height and that the equation of the trough line at the time $t = 0$ is given by

$$x + \Phi(z) - \Phi(0) = 0. \quad (113)$$

Since ξ_i is negative and $\psi_1'(\xi_c)/\psi_1(\xi_c)$ is a positive, monotonically decreasing function of ξ_c, the trough line slopes toward the west at first rapidly and then less rapidly with height and eventually approaches the vertical. (See fig. 12.)

The expressions (98–105) for the fields of pressure,

density, vertical velocity component, and horizontal divergence derived for the neutral wave hold as well for the unstable wave. The real parts of the functions involving ξ_0 and ξ are sensibly unaltered by the change from ξ_{0c} and ξ_c, since ξ_i is assumed to be small compared with ξ_0, but we have now to consider the imaginary parts.

(a) *The pressure pattern.* Since ξ is not involved explicitly in the equation between p' and v', the phase relationship between these two fields remains the same as for the neutral wave.

(b) *The density pattern.* The nature of the density perturbation may be deduced from (102). If we define the function $Q(\xi)$ by

$$Q(\xi) = \frac{\psi_1'(\xi)}{\psi_1(\xi)} - \frac{1}{2} + \frac{s}{2\bar{a}} + \frac{1}{4\bar{a}H_T}$$

and recall the relation (100) between p' and v', we may write for equation (102)

$$\rho' = -\,2\bar{a}\,Q(\xi)\,p'. \qquad (102')$$

Approximating Q by a terminating Taylor's series about $\xi = \xi_c$ we obtain

$$Q(\xi) = Q(\xi_c + i\xi_i) \approx Q(\xi_c) + i\xi_i\,Q'(\xi_c),$$

or in polar coordinates

$$Q(\xi) \approx [Q^2(\xi_c) + \xi_i^2\,Q'^2(\xi_c)]^{\frac{1}{2}} \times \exp\{i\tan^{-1}[\xi_i\,Q'(\xi_c)/Q(\xi_c)]\}$$
$$\approx Q(\xi_c)\exp\{i\tan^{-1}[\xi_i\,Q'(\xi_c)/Q(\xi_c)]\}.$$

It can be shown that, depending on the values of Λ, L, and $\bar{u}_0$, (a′) Q may be positive or negative at the ground and (b′) Q decreases monotonically with height and approaches a negative value. These properties imply that the wave in the density field precedes the pressure wave by a phase angle $|\tan^{-1}(\xi_i Q'/Q)|$, which increases with increasing $|\xi_i|$ and therefore with increasing instability. Thus, with the appearance of instability, the density wave develops, with respect to the pressure wave, an asymmetry of such a nature that the coldest air is in advance of the wedge in the isobars. It is this asymmetry which accounts for the previously noted tilt in the pressure and meridional velocity waves. The phase relationship between the waves ρ', p', and v' is illustrated in fig. 11.

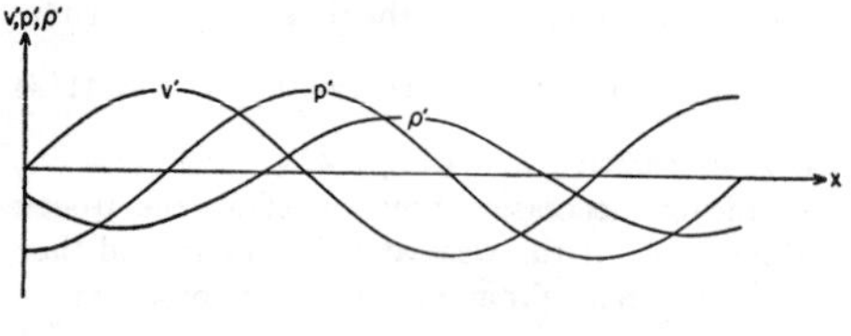

FIG. 11. Pressure, density, and meridional velocity component in the unstable baroclinic wave.

(c) *The pattern of the vertical velocity component.* The nature of the field of vertical velocity may be deduced from (103). If we replace $2\bar{a}(\bar{u} - c)$ by $\Lambda\xi$ and multiply through by $e^{i\mu(x-ct)}$, this equation becomes

$$w' = -\,[f\bar{\sigma}^2\Lambda/(g^2k)]\,M(\xi)\,v',$$

where

$$M(\xi) = -\,\xi\left[\frac{\psi_1'(\xi)}{\psi_1(\xi)} - \alpha - \frac{\beta}{\xi}\right].$$

It is not possible to approximate M at the ground by the first terms of a Taylor's series because M vanishes there. However, for large values of ξ, the approximation is valid and we may write

$$M(\xi) \approx M(\xi_c) + i\xi_i\,M'(\xi_c)$$
$$\approx M(\xi_c)\exp\{i\tan^{-1}[\xi_i\,M'(\xi_c)/M(\xi_c)]\}, \qquad (103')$$

from which it can be shown that (a′) $|M|$ increases continuously with height and is asymptotic to $\alpha\xi_c$, and (b′) the argument of M is negative and approaches zero with increasing height. Since, by (93′), $\xi_c V \to 0$ as $z \to \infty$, it follows from (103′) and (a′) that w' finally approaches zero with increasing height. The conclusion (b′) together with (103′) leads to the result that the w'-wave precedes the v'-wave by the angle $|\tan^{-1}(\xi_i\,M'/M)|$ at high levels.

Near the ground w' is evaluated indirectly by numerical integration of (55) with the result that the amplitude of the w'-wave increases with height and the wave lags, in low levels, behind the v'-wave. Since the v'-wave lags 90° behind the wave in the pressure field, we may summarize the statements above by saying that in low levels the maximum vertical velocities occur between the point of inflection and the trough to the west in the pressure profile whereas at high levels the maximum vertical velocities occur between the point of inflection and the wedge to the east.

Fig. 12 contains a schematic representation of the field of vertical velocity in the unstable wave. The corresponding horizontal patterns of pressure and vertical velocity at a constant level are also indicated in the lower part of the diagram.

(d) *The horizontal divergence.* If the real and imaginary parts of the wave velocity are denoted by c_r and c_i respectively, (105) becomes

$$D \approx (\bar{\rho}\mu^2/f)(\bar{u} - c_r - u_c)\,Ve^{i\mu(x-ct)} - i(\bar{\rho}\mu^2/f)c_i\,Ve^{i\mu(x-ct)}, \qquad (114)$$

and it follows that the field of horizontal divergence consists of two wave components: the first in phase with, or 180° out of phase with, the v'-wave according as $\bar{u} - c_r - u_c \gtrless 0$; the second preceding the v'-wave by 90° since c_i is positive.

No definition of a level of nondivergence can be given, for there is no constant level at which both wave components vanish simultaneously. If, however, the

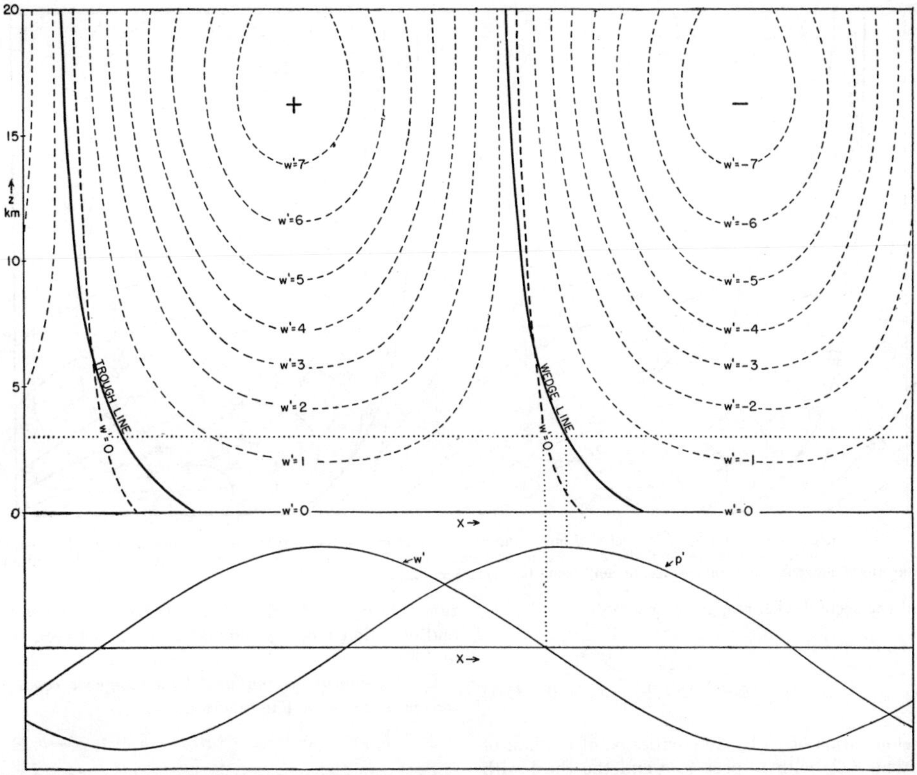

FIG. 12. Schematic representation of the field of vertical velocity component in the unstable baroclinic wave in vertical cross section (upper diagram). The dashed lines in the upper diagram are isopleths of vertical velocity component, the unit being cm sec^{-1}, and the solid lines indicate the positions of the trough and wedge in the pressure field. The position of the vertical-velocity wave relative to the pressure wave at the level indicated by the dotted line is shown in the lower diagram.

wave is only slightly unstable, c_i will be small in comparison with c_r, and the second component will be negligible. In this case the level of nondivergence is approximately determined by $u - c_r - u_c = 0$. In general, it is possible to define a *surface* of nondivergence by setting the magnitude of D in (114) equal to zero. For this purpose let $V = |V| e^{i\mu\,\Phi(z)}$, $\Phi(z)$ being defined by (112), and obtain

$$D \approx (\bar{\rho}\mu^2/f)(\bar{u} - c_r - u_c)\,|V|\,e^{i\mu(x-ct+\Phi)} + (\bar{\rho}\mu^2/f)c_i\,|V|\,e^{i\mu(x-ct+\Phi)-i\pi/2}, \quad (114')$$

and, when $|D| = 0$,

$$(\bar{u} - c_r - u_c)\sin[\mu(x - c_r t + \Phi)] - c_i \cos[\mu(x - c_r t + \Phi)] = 0, \quad (115)$$

or

$$x - c_r t = -\Phi + \frac{1}{\mu}\tan^{-1}\frac{c_i}{\bar{u} - c_r - u_c}. \quad (116)$$

(We note that the same result could have been obtained by a polar representation of (114).) A vertical cross section showing the field of divergence, calculated from (114′), and the field of vertical momentum, calculated from the vertical velocities of fig. 12, is given in fig. 13. The numerical values used in figs. 12 and 13 are correct only in order of magnitude and do not necessarily correspond to an actual situation.

Acknowledgment. The author wishes to express his gratitude to Professor J. Holmboe for his many helpful suggestions during the preparation of the manuscript, to Professor C.-G. Rossby for his help in clarifying the questions of the scale of atmospheric disturbances discussed in sections 1 and 2, and to his wife Elinor Charney for her unfailing help and encouragement throughout the work.

APPENDIX

A. *Elimination of density and pressure from the perturbation equations.* Elimination of p'_y by differentiation of the first of equations (22) with respect to

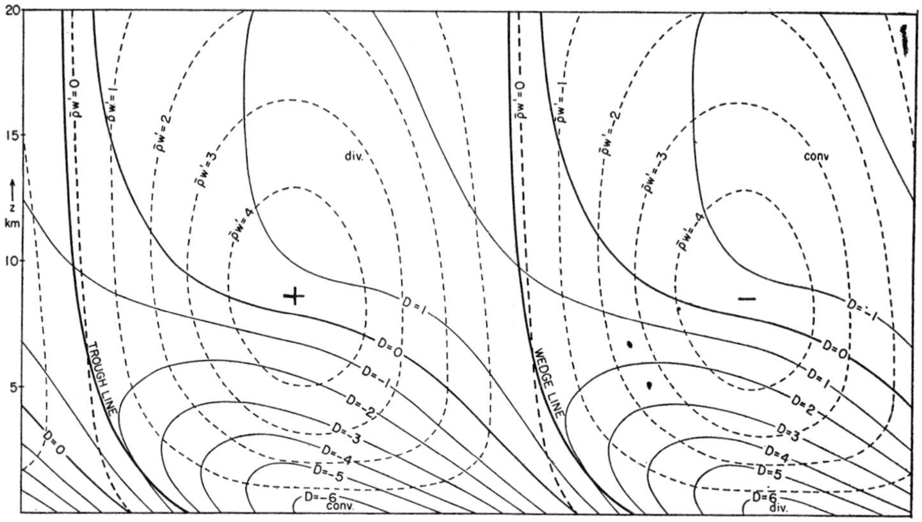

FIG. 13. Schematic representation of the fields of horizontal mass divergence and vertical momentum component in the unstable baroclinic wave. The dashed lines are isopleths of vertical momentum component, the unit being 10^{-3} g cm^{-2} sec^{-1}. The light solid lines are isopleths of horizontal mass divergence, the unit being 10^{-8} g cm^{-3} sec^{-1}.

y and the second with respect to x gives

$$fu'_x + f_y v' + L(v'_x) + \frac{f}{g\bar{\rho}}(s\bar{u} + \Lambda)p'_x + \frac{f\bar{u}}{\bar{\rho}}\rho'_x = 0, \quad (1A)$$

and elimination of p'_z by differentiation of the first of equations (22) with respect to z and the third with respect to x gives

$$\Lambda u'_z + sL(u') - sfv' + L(u'_z) - fv'_z + \frac{\Lambda}{\bar{\rho}}(\bar{\rho}w')_z - \frac{g}{\bar{\rho}}\rho'_x = 0. \quad (2A)$$

The last two equations together with the first, fourth, and fifth of (22) constitute a system equivalent to (22).

The first of equations (25) is now obtained by elimination of ρ' from (2A) and the fourth of (22), the second by elimination of ρ' and p' from (2A) and the first and fifth of (22), and the last by elimination of ρ' and p' from (1A), (2A), and the first of (22).

B. *Reduction of the perturbation equations.* Equation (48) is obtained by elimination of $\bar{\rho}W$ and $(\bar{\rho}W)_z$ between (39), (40), and (41); equation (47) is obtained by elimination of U_z, V_z, and $(\bar{\rho}W)_z$ between (39), (40), and (48); and equation (46) is obtained by elimination of U_z, V_z, and $\bar{\rho}W$ between (39) and (48), when, after each elimination, the resulting expressions are simplified by means of the inequalities (42–44).

Applying the same inequalities, we obtain equation (50) by elimination of U_z between (48) and (49), equation (51) by elimination of U between (47) and (50), and equation (56) by elimination of U between (46) and (50).

C. *Solution of the confluent hypergeometric equation for the case* $b = 0$. The functions

$$M(a, b, \xi) \quad \text{and} \quad \xi^{1-b}M(a - b + 1, 2 - b, \xi)$$

fail to yield two independent integrals of (76) when b is an integer, for $M(a, b, \xi)$ is then undefined. Two different independent integrals may be derived by the method of Laplace: thus Mott and Massey [13] prove that the integrals

$$W_1 = \frac{1}{2\pi i}\int_{\gamma_1}\left(1 - \frac{\xi}{t}\right)^{-a} e^t dt,$$

$$W_2 = \frac{1}{2\pi i}\int_{\gamma}\left(1 - \frac{\xi}{t}\right)^{-a} e^t dt$$

satisfy (76) when $b = 0$. The paths of integration γ_1 and γ_2 are shown in fig. 4. The first integral may be expanded in an infinite series as follows: if we express $\psi_1 = (-1)^a W_1$ as a contour integral of the Mellin-Barnes type, it can be shown, by a method employed by Archibald [1], that

$$\psi_1 = \frac{\xi^{-a}}{2\pi i\,\Gamma(-a)} \times \int_{-\infty i}^{\infty i}\frac{\Gamma(s)\,\Gamma(-s + a)\,\Gamma(-s + a + 1)}{\Gamma(a)\,\Gamma(a + 1)}\xi^s ds,$$

where the contour has loops if necessary so that the poles of $\Gamma(s)$ and those of $\Gamma(-s + a)\,\Gamma(-s + a + 1)$

TABLE 1. Values of the function $-(\pi/\sin \pi r)\psi_1(\xi, r)$

$$-\frac{\pi}{\sin \pi r}\psi_1(\xi, r) = \left\{ a\xi\, M(a+1, 2, \xi)\left[\ln \xi + \frac{\Gamma'(a)}{\Gamma(a)} - 2\frac{\Gamma'(1)}{\Gamma(1)}\right] + 1 + \sum_{n=1}^{\infty} B_n \frac{a(a+1)\cdots(a+n-1)}{(n-1)!\,n!}\xi^n \right\};^*$$

$$B_n = \sum_{\nu=0}^{n-1}\left(\frac{1}{a+\nu} - \frac{2}{1+\nu}\right) + \frac{1}{n};\ a = -r.$$

The function ψ_1 satisfies the confluent hypergeometric differential equation $\xi\psi'' - \xi\psi' + r\psi = 0$.

ξ \ r	0.1	0.2	0.3	0.4	0.5	0.6	0.7	0.8
0	1	1	1	1	1	1	1	1
0.1	1.031	1.065	1.105	1.152	1.210	1.287	1.400	1.598
0.2	1.049	1.106	1.173	1.254	1.357	1.497	1.708	2.090
0.4	1.077	1.167	1.277	1.414	1.595	1.847	2.239	2.972
0.6	1.098	1.215	1.360	1.545	1.793	2.147	2.709	3.780
0.8	1.115	1.255	1.431	1.659	1.969	2.418	3.142	4.542
1.0	1.130	1.290	1.494	1.760	2.128	2.667	3.548	5.271
2.0	1.184	1.421	1.735	2.164	2.781	3.726	5.334	8.604
3.0	1.222	1.515	1.914	2.474	3.302	4.606	6.884	11.63
4.0	1.251	1.590	2.059	2.734	3.750	5.384	8.293	14.46
5.0	1.275	1.652	2.184	2.960	4.149	6.092	9.604	17.16
6.0	1.296	1.706	2.294	3.163	4.513	6.748	10.84	19.75
7.0	1.314	1.754	2.392	3.348	4.849	7.364	12.02	22.27
8.0	1.331	1.798	2.482	3.518	5.164	7.948	13.16	24.71
9.0	1.348	1.839	2.564	3.677	5.460	8.504	14.25	27.09
10.0	1.369	1.878	2.641	3.826	5.740	9.036	15.30	29.41
ξ \ r	0.9	1.5	2.5	3.5	4.5	5.5	−0.5	−1.5
0	1	1	1	1	1	1	1	1
0.1	2.133	1.296	1.295	1.242	1.154	1.039	0.8820	0.7304
0.2	3.145	1.351	1.164	0.883	0.553	0.198	0.8202	0.6114
0.4	5.048	1.175	0.442	− 0.361	− 1.124	− 1.786	0.7390	0.4742
0.6	6.863	0.753	− 0.588	− 1.788	− 2.681	− 3.216	0.6815	0.3878
0.8	8.622	0.149	− 1.750	− 3.089	− 3.722	− 3.693	0.6381	0.3290
1.0	10.34	− 0.603	− 2.932	− 4.088	− 4.076	− 3.158	0.6035	0.2865
2.0	18.53	− 6.053	− 6.816	− 2.126	3.779	8.004	0.4882	0.1468
3.0	26.33	− 13.64	− 3.302	10.99	15.86	10.15	0.4270	0.1138
4.0	33.87	− 22.88	11.51	27.48	12.04	− 14.10	0.3840	0.0890
5.0	41.22	− 33.55	40.54	33.56	− 21.36	− 52.55	0.3600	0.1700
6.0	48.42	− 45.46	86.41	10.90	− 83.30	− 66.43	0.3300	0.1070
7.0	55.52	− 58.50	151.15	− 62.42	−151.20	− 4.78	0.3080	0.0770
8.0	62.52	− 72.58	236.76	−211.53	−176.32	171.95	0.2940	0.1280
9.0	69.42	− 87.63	345.06	−464.46	− 79.65	464.46	0.2740	0.0190
10.0	76.25	−103.59	477.68	−851.77	252.41	795.68	0.2900	0.6400

* See table 3 for definition of M.

are on opposite sides of it. The integrand has a simple pole at $s = a$ and double poles at $s = a + n$, where $n = 1, 2, 3, \cdots$. Therefore (see Whittaker and Watson [17])

$$\psi_1 = -\frac{\xi^{-a}}{\Gamma(-a)\,\Gamma(a)\,\Gamma(a+1)}\left(R_0 + \sum_{n=1}^{\infty} R_n\right),$$

where R_0 denotes the residue of

$$f(s) = \Gamma(s)\,\Gamma(-s+a)\,\Gamma(-s+a+1)\xi^s$$

at the simple pole $s = a$, and R_n the residue at the double pole $s = a + n$. Since

$$\Gamma(z) = \Psi(z) + \frac{1}{0!\,z} - \frac{1}{1!\,(z+1)} + \frac{1}{2!\,(z+2)} - \cdots,$$

where Ψ is an integral function, the residue of $\Gamma(-s+a)$ at $s = a$ is -1. Therefore

$$R_0 = -\Gamma(a)\,\xi^a.$$

To evaluate R_n we proceed as follows: By means of the relation

$$\Gamma(\chi)\,\Gamma(1-\chi) = \pi/(\sin \pi\chi)$$

we may express $f(s)$ as

$$f(s) = -\pi^2\{\sin^2[\pi(s-a)]\}^{-1}\varphi(s),$$

where

$$\varphi(s) = \frac{\Gamma(s)\,\xi^s}{\Gamma(1-a+s)\,\Gamma(-a+s)}.$$

Now, utilizing the relation

$$\frac{\pi^2}{\sin^2[\pi(s-a)]} = \sum_{-\infty}^{\infty}\frac{1}{(s-a+n)^2}$$

and the Taylor expansion of $\varphi(s)$ about $s = a + n$, we find that the residue of $f(s)$ at the pole $a + n$ is $-\varphi'(a+n)$. But

$$\varphi'(a+n) = \frac{d}{d\sigma}\left[\frac{\Gamma(\sigma+a)\,\xi^{\sigma+a}}{\Gamma(\sigma+1)\,\Gamma(\sigma)}\right]_{\sigma=n}$$

$$= \frac{\Gamma(n+a)\,\xi^{n+a}}{\Gamma(n+1)\,\Gamma(n)}\left[\frac{\Gamma'(n+a)}{\Gamma(n+a)} - \frac{\Gamma'(n+1)}{\Gamma(n+1)} - \frac{\Gamma'(n)}{\Gamma(n)} + \ln \xi\right],$$

TABLE 2. Values of the function $-(\pi/\sin \pi r)\, \psi_1'(\xi, r)$

ξ \ r	0.1	0.2	0.3	0.4	0.5	0.6	0.7	0.8
0								
0.1	0.217	0.471	0.775	1.152	1.637	2.306	3.329	5.206
0.2	0.163	0.362	0.607	0.921	1.341	1.940	2.889	4.689
0.4	0.117	0.266	0.457	0.713	1.080	1.638	2.474	4.191
0.6	0.094	0.217	0.380	0.604	0.926	1.417	2.245	3.912
0.8	0.080	0.186	0.331	0.534	0.832	1.295	2.090	3.719
1.0	0.069	0.164	0.295	0.483	0.762	1.204	1.974	3.574
2.0	0.044	0.108	0.202	0.346	0.572	0.950	1.643	3.147
3.0	0.033	0.083	0.159	0.281	0.479	0.821	1.470	2.916
4.0	0.026	0.068	0.134	0.241	0.421	0.740	1.355	2.759
5.0	0.022	0.058	0.116	0.213	0.380	0.680	1.272	2.643
6.0	0.019	0.051	0.104	0.193	0.349	0.635	1.207	2.551
7.0	0.017	0.046	0.094	0.177	0.325	0.599	1.154	2.476
8.0	0.017	0.042	0.086	0.164	0.305	0.569	1.111	2.412
9.0	0.018	0.040	0.079	0.154	0.288	0.544	1.074	2.357
10.0	0.023	0.040	0.078	0.145	0.274	0.522	1.042	2.308
ξ \ r	0.9	1.5	2.5	3.5	4.5	5.5	0.5	1.5
0								
0.1	10.45	1.27					−0.691	−1.460
0.2	9.847	− 0.04					−0.459	−0.849
0.4	9.257	− 1.57					−0.314	−0.472
0.6	8.918	− 2.60					−0.242	−0.329
0.8	8.682	− 3.411					−0.194	−0.255
1.0	8.502	− 4.093					−0.163	−0.207
2.0	7.954	− 6.625					−0.081	−0.082
3.0	7.650	− 8.472					−0.048	−0.009
4.0	7.439	− 9.986	21.49				−0.040	
5.0	7.277	−11.31	37.07				−0.027	
6.0	7.146	−12.49	54.94				−0.021	
7.0	7.039	−13.57	74.86	−106.77			−0.016	
8.0	6.948	−14.58	96.68	−196.14			−0.012	
9.0	6.866	−15.51	120.17	−314.78				
10.0	6.796	−16.40	145.32	−465.31	496.88			

and

$$\frac{\Gamma'(n+a)}{\Gamma(n+a)} = \sum_{\nu=0}^{n-1} \frac{1}{a+\nu} + \frac{\Gamma'(a)}{\Gamma(a)},$$

$$\frac{\Gamma'(n+1)}{\Gamma(n+1)} = \sum_{\nu=0}^{n-1} \frac{1}{1+\nu} + \frac{\Gamma'(1)}{\Gamma(1)},$$

$$\frac{\Gamma'(n)}{\Gamma(n)} = \sum_{\nu=0}^{n-2} \frac{1}{1+\nu} + \frac{\Gamma'(1)}{\Gamma(1)}.$$

Combining these results we obtain

$$\psi_1 = \frac{\xi^{-a}}{\Gamma(-a)\,\Gamma(a)\,\Gamma(a+1)} \Bigg\{ \Gamma(a)\,\xi^a + \ln \xi \sum_{n=1}^{\infty} \frac{\Gamma(n+a)}{\Gamma(n+1)\,\Gamma(n)} \xi^{n+a} + \sum_{n=1}^{\infty} B_n \frac{\Gamma(n+a)}{\Gamma(n+1)\,\Gamma(n)} \xi^{n+a} + \left[\frac{\Gamma'(a)}{\Gamma(a)} - 2\frac{\Gamma'(1)}{\Gamma(1)} \right] \sum_{n=1}^{\infty} \frac{\Gamma(n+a)}{\Gamma(n+1)\,\Gamma(n)} \xi^{n+a} \Bigg\},$$

where

$$B_n = \sum_{\nu=0}^{n-1} \left(\frac{1}{a+\nu} - \frac{2}{1+\nu} \right) + \frac{1}{n}.$$

From the definition of M in (77) it follows that

$$\sum_{n=1}^{\infty} \frac{\Gamma(n+a)}{\Gamma(n+1)\,\Gamma(n)} \xi^n = a\,\Gamma(a)\,\xi\, M(a+1, 2, \xi),$$

whence we obtain for ψ_1 the expression

$$\psi_1 = \frac{\sin \pi a}{\pi} \Bigg\{ a\xi\, M(a+1, 2, \xi) \times \left[\ln \xi + \frac{\Gamma'(a)}{\Gamma(a)} - 2\frac{\Gamma'(1)}{\Gamma(1)} \right] + 1 + \sum_{n=1}^{\infty} B_n \frac{a(a+1)\cdots(a+n-1)}{(n-1)!\,n!} \xi^n \Bigg\}.$$

The asymptotic expansions of W_1 and W_2 given in (93) and (94) are demonstrated by Mott and Massey [13, p. 39].

D. *Tables of ψ_1 and ψ_2.* The function $\psi_1(\xi, r)$ was evaluated for $\xi \leqq 4$ by means of the infinite series expansion (79), and for $\xi \geqq 4$ by means of the asymptotic expansion (93). Some of the calculations were facilitated by use of the recursion formula

$$r\,\psi_1(\xi, r-1) + r\,\psi_1(\xi, r+1) = -(\xi - 2r)\,\psi_1(\xi, r).$$

The tabulations are given in table 1. The derivatives of ψ_1, evaluated graphically, are tabulated in table 2.

The function $\psi_2(\xi, r)$, defined by

$$\psi_2 = \xi\, M(a+1, 2, \xi) = \xi \left[1 + \frac{a+1}{1!\,2!}\xi + \frac{(a+1)(a+2)}{2!\,3!}\xi^2 + \cdots \right], \qquad a = -r,$$

was evaluated directly from the infinite series, and its derivatives were calculated graphically. The tabulated values are given in tables 3 and 4.

TABLE 3. Values of the function $a\psi_2(\xi, r) = a\xi\, M(a+1, 2, \xi)$, where $a = -r$ and

$$M(a, b, \xi) = 1 + \frac{a}{1!\,b}\xi + \frac{a(a+1)}{2!\,b(b+1)}\xi^2 + \cdots.$$

The function ψ_2 satisfies the confluent hypergeometric differential equation $\xi\psi'' - \xi\psi' + r\psi = 0$.

ξ \ r	0.1	0.2	0.3	0.4	0.5	0.6	0.7	0.8
0	0.00000	0.00000	0.00000	0.00000	0.00000	0.00000	0.00000	0.00000
0.1	−0.01046	−0.02082	−0.03108	−0.04123	−0.05128	−0.06123	−0.07107	−0.08082
0.2	−0.02192	−0.04340	−0.06445	−0.08507	−0.10526	−0.12503	−0.14439	−0.16334
0.4	−0.04821	−0.09450	−0.13889	−0.18144	−0.22218	−0.26114	−0.29838	−0.33390
0.6	−0.07978	−0.15480	−0.22520	−0.29112	−0.35269	−0.41005	−0.46334	−0.51267
0.8	−0.11776	−0.22618	−0.32564	−0.41649	−0.49909	−0.57378	−0.64090	−0.70077
1.0	−0.16349	−0.31086	−0.44291	−0.56040	−0.66410	−0.75474	−0.83293	−0.89944
2.0	−0.58020	−1.05048	−1.42153	−1.70335	−1.90526	−2.03598	−2.10350	−2.11552
3.0	−1.66374	−2.88290	−3.72026	−4.23255	−4.47087	−4.48115	−4.30451	−3.97768
4.0	−4.515	−7.538	−9.338	−10.151	−10.181	−9.607	−8.581	−7.233

TABLE 3.—*Continued.*

ξ \ r	0.9	1.5	2.5
0	0.00000	0.00000	0.00000
0.1	−0.09046	−0.14622	−0.23141
0.2	−0.18187	−0.28474	−0.42626
0.4	−0.36777	−0.53789	−0.71017
0.6	−0.55819	−0.75770	−0.85963
0.8	−0.75370	−0.94222	−0.88284
1.0	−0.945499	−1.08929	−0.78828
2.0	−2.07882	−1.16727	1.12710
3.0	−3.53321	0.21402	4.47087
4.0	−5.6754	3.89355	7.58565
5.0	−9.320	11.53170	8.17913
6.0	−16.37	26.51661	2.85015
7.0	−31.36	56.14203	−13.82990
8.0	−65.26	116.4045	−51.15560

TABLE 4. Values of the function $a\psi_2'$

ξ \ r	0.7	0.8	0.9
0	−0.700	−0.800	−0.900
0.1	−0.722	−0.817	−0.909
0.2	−0.745	−0.834	−0.919
0.4	−0.796	−0.872	−0.940
0.6	−0.855	−0.916	−0.964
0.8	−0.922	−0.966	−0.991
1.0	−1.000	−1.022	−1.011
2.0	−1.618	−1.461	−1.251
3.0	−2.961	−2.380	−1.713
4.0	−6.01	−4.401	−2.697

TABLE 5. Values of the function

$$X = \xi\left[\ln\xi + \sum_{n=1}^{\infty}\frac{\xi^n}{(n+1)!\,n}\right] - 1$$

and of its derivative.

ξ	X	$dX/d\xi$
0.0	−1.000	−∞
0.1	−1.225	−1.20
0.2	−1.301	−0.40
0.4	−1.280	0.53
0.6	−1.106	1.19
0.8	−0.809	1.77
1.0	−0.400	2.32
2.0	3.362	5.38
3.0	10.98	10.36
4.0	25.62	20.06
5.0	54.60	40.60
6.0	114.7	86.36
7.0	248	192.1

When r is a positive integer, both ψ_1 and ψ_2 are undefined. In this case it is necessary to derive the solutions of (74) anew. In particular, when $r = 1$, we have

$$\xi\psi'' - \xi\psi' + \psi = 0.$$

Two solutions of this equation are found to be ξ and

$$X = \xi\left[\ln\xi + \sum_{n=1}^{\infty}\frac{\xi^n}{(n+1)!\,n}\right] - 1.$$

The function X and its derivative are tabulated in table 5.

REFERENCES

1. Archibald, W. J., 1938: The complete solution of the differential equation for the confluent hypergeometric function. *Phil. Mag.*, 7 ser., **26**, 415–419.
2. Bjerknes, J., 1919: On the structure of moving cyclones. *Geofys. Publ.*, **1**, no. 2, 8 pp.
3. —— and Solberg, H., 1921: Meteorological conditions for the formation of rain. *Ibid.*, **2**, no. 3, 61 pp.
4. ——, ——, 1922: Life cycle of cyclones and the polar front theory of atmospheric circulation. *Ibid.*, **3**, no. 1, 18 pp.
5. —— and Godske, C. L., 1936: On the theory of cyclone formation at extra-tropical fronts. *Astrophys. norv.*, **1**, 199–235.
6. ——, 1937: Theorie der aussertropischen Zyklonenbildung. *Meteor. Z.*, **54**, 462–466.
7. —— and Holmboe, J., 1944: On the theory of cyclones. *J. Meteor.*, **1**, 1–22.
8. Bjerknes, V., Bjerknes, J., Solberg, H., Bergeron, T., 1933: *Physikalische Hydrodynamik.* Berlin, J. Springer, 797 pp.
9. Gutenberg, B., 1946: Physical properties of the atmosphere up to 100 km. *J. Meteor.*, **3**, 27–30.
10. Haurwitz, B., 1940: The motion of atmospheric disturbances. *J. marine Res.*, **3**, 35–50.
11. ——, 1940: The motion of atmospheric disturbances on the spherical earth. *Ibid.*, pp. 254–267.
12. Holmboe, J., Forsythe, G. E., Gustin, W., 1945: *Dynamic meteorology.* New York, John Wiley and Sons, 378 pp. (see ch. 12).
13. Mott, N. F., and Massey, H. S. W., 1933: *Theory of atomic collisions.* Oxford University Press, 283 pp. (see p. 36).
14. Rossby, C.-G., and collaborators, 1939: Relation between variations in the intensity of the zonal circulation of the atmosphere and the displacements of the semi-permanent centers of action. *J. marine Res.*, **2**, 38–55.
15. Solberg, H., 1928: Integrationen des atmosphärischen Störungsgleichungen. *Geofys. Publ.*, **5**, no. 9, 120 pp.
16. ——, 1931: Das Zyklonenproblem. *Proc. 3rd int. Congr. appl. Mech.*, Stockholm, **1**, 121–131.
17. Whittaker, E. T., and Watson, G. N., 1927: *A course of modern analysis*, 4th ed. Cambridge University Press, 606 pp. (see p. 343). (Reprinted in 1943, New York. Macmillan Company.)
18. Willett, H. C., 1944: *Descriptive meteorology.* New York, Academic Press, 310 pp. (see p. 132).

Reprinted (with corrections) from *Tellus*, Vol. 1, No. 3, Aug., 1949.

Long Waves and Cyclone Waves

By E. T. EADY, Imperial College of Science, London

(Manuscript received 28 Febr. 1949)

Abstract

By obtaining complete solutions, satisfying all the relevant simultaneous differential equations and boundary conditions, representing small disturbances of simple states of steady baroclinic large-scale atmospheric motion it is shown that these simple states of motion are almost invariably unstable. An arbitrary disturbance (corresponding to some inhomogeneity of an actual system) may be regarded as analysed into "components" of a certain simple type, some of which grow exponentially with time. In all the cases examined there exists one particular component which grows faster than any other. It is shown how, by a process analogous to "natural selection", this component becomes dominant in that almost any disturbance tends eventually to a definite size, structure and growth-rate (and to a characteristic life-history after the disturbance has ceased to be "small"), which depends only on the broad characteristics of the initial (unperturbed) system. The characteristic disturbances (forms of breakdown) of certain types of initial system (approximating to those observed in practice) are identified as the ideal forms of the observed cyclone waves and long waves of middle and high latitudes. The implications regarding the ultimate limitations of weather forecasting are discussed.

The present paper aims at developing from first principles a quantitative theory of the initial stages of development of wave-cyclones and long waves. For reasons of space and readability both the argument and the mathematics have been rather heavily compressed. A fuller and extended treatment of several of the points raised will be given in subsequent papers.

I. The Equations of Motion

Owing to the complexity (and non-linearity) of the simultaneous partial differential equations governing atmospheric motion it is desirable to simplify these by the omission of all those terms which do not make a major contribution *to the particular type and scale of motion envisaged.* This procedure is made possible by the fact that we know, from observation, roughly what the answers must look like. Its utility is justified by the fact that, having once obtained a crude model of the motion, we may then by successive approximation take into account any or all of the terms originally omitted. In the present instance we are concerned with relatively rapid development, by comparison with which radiative processes (or rather their differential effects) are slow. For a first approximation therefore we consider the motion as adiabatic. Also we are concerned with the motion of deep layers and for a first approximation we neglect the effects of internal friction ("turbulence") and skin friction. A rough calculation shows that the energy dissipated in the surface friction layer is usually much less than the energy supply to the growing disturbance and this is probably, in most cases, the major source of energy loss. The present paper is concerned only with systems which are initially (and also after a small perturbation) convectively stable, i.e., with those systems which would appear to be least favourable with regard to instability. Hence we use a system of equations appropriate to laminar frictionless adiabatic motion of a rotating baroclinic fluid. Restriction to convective stability makes possible a further slight simplification in that in almost all[1] such cases (except very close to the border-line) we may neglect vertical accelerations and use the hydrostatic equation — the disturbances are "quasi-static". Briefly, the explanation is that in such cases the energy associated with horizontal perturbations greatly exceeds that associated with vertical motion.

The atmosphere is a compressible fluid and in estimating the significance of this fact it is convenient to consider separately the static effect, manifested by the decrease of density with height, and the dynamic effect, manifested by elastic forces in the equations of motion. The static effect has two consequences. In the first place, the static stability, a measure of the force tending to restore a displaced particle to its equilibrium position, is measured not by the vertical density gradient but by the gradient of potential density (or by the difference between actual and adiabatic lapse-rate). As compared with incompressible flow this involves only the modification of a parameter. In the second place, a given mass of air occupies, at higher levels, a greater height range. The result is that atmospheric flow can never be quite equivalent to incompressible flow but (as may be inferred from the detailed treatment) the difference is to be regarded as a distortion rather than any difference in kind. For systems which are not too deep there is an equivalent incompressible system whose behaviour closely parallels that of the atmospheric one. The nature of the "correction" for very deep systems is discussed below. The significance of the elastic forces depends on the type of solution in which we are interested. In the theory of atmospheric tides and the diurnal variation of pressure, where the wave-velocities are comparable with the speed of sound, these forces play an essential part. But in all waves associated with "weather" the wave-velocities are, by observation, small compared with the speed of sound and this is true, as we shall see, of both the real and imaginary parts of the wave-velocities of the theoretical solutions. We are therefore justified in treating the motion, from the dynamic point of view, as incompressible. The net result is that we can construct an equivalent "incompressible flow" problem and then use as our continuity equation:[1]

$$\mathrm{div}_H \mathbf{v} + \frac{\partial}{\partial z} V_z = 0 \qquad (1)$$

For systems which are not too large we may use the ordinary cartesian co-ordinates fixed in the earth in which we imagine a small spherical cap to be "flattened" on to the tangent plane so that gravity acts along parallel lines. This involves a certain amount of geometrical distortion (and consequently a distortion of our solutions). A more serious error results from the assumption of a constant Coriolis parameter and we may obtain a first approximation to this error by using the same co-ordinate system but regarding the Coriolis parameter as a function of y (the N—S co-ordinate). A more precise treatment of long waves requires the use of a polar (or equivalent) co-ordinate system and crude solutions, using numerical methods, have been obtained in this case. The broad resemblance of these solutions to those obtained by analytical methods in the cartesian system justifies the use of the latter as a first rough approximation.

If we define, for unsaturated air:

$$\Phi = \frac{1}{\gamma} \log p - \log \varrho \qquad (2)$$

so that Φ is proportional to the entropy, we have for adiabatic motion:

$$\frac{d}{dt} \Phi = 0 \qquad (3)$$

We shall *define* the static stability as $\frac{\partial}{\partial z} \Phi$. To study the motion of saturated air in contact with cloud we have only to alter the effective value of the static stability (our norm is now the wet adiabatic). Usually the reduction is

[1] The exception is the case of strong anticyclonic horizontal shear approaching in magnitude the Coriolis parameter—see below.

[1] When not otherwise stated, the symbols employed are those normally used in theoretical meteorological literature.

very significant, the forces opposing vertical motion being much less inside than outside a cloud, a fact having, as we shall see, important consequences. Moreover we obtain a direct translation from atmospheric motion to incompressible flow by the substitution:

$$\Phi \rightarrow -\log \varrho \qquad (4)$$

Alternatively, we may regard γ as having, for saturated air, a value slowly varying from considerably less than 1.4 at high temperatures but asymptotically approaching the dry adiabatic value at low temperatures. For an incompressible fluid γ is effectively infinite.

With the approximations mentioned above we have the dynamic equations (where K[1] is the Coriolis parameter):

$$-\frac{1}{\varrho}\frac{\partial p}{\partial x} = \frac{d}{dt} V_x - KV_y$$

$$-\frac{1}{\varrho}\frac{\partial p}{\partial y} = \frac{d}{dt} V_y + KV_x$$

$$-\frac{1}{\varrho}\frac{\partial p}{\partial z} = g \qquad (5)$$

These equations, together with equations (I. 1)—(I. 3), form a complete set. Further simplification is however possible. (For the present we take K to be constant.) By partial differentiation with respect to z of the first two of equations (I. 5), using equation (I. 2) and the last of equations (I. 5):

$$\left(\frac{\partial}{\partial z} - \frac{\partial \Phi}{\partial z}\right)\left(\frac{d}{dt} V_x - KV_y\right) = -g\frac{\partial \Phi}{\partial x},$$

$$\left(\frac{\partial}{\partial z} - \frac{\partial \Phi}{\partial z}\right)\left(\frac{d}{dt} V_y + KV_x\right) = -g\frac{\partial \Phi}{\partial y}, \qquad (6)$$

where the first brackets are regarded as operators. We shall see that the solutions with which we are concerned "oscillate" in the direction of z (it is immaterial that the "oscillation" is not sinusoidal) and if this "oscillation" is sufficiently rapid (if the disturbances are not too deep) the effect of the operator $\frac{\partial}{\partial z}$ swamps that of the multiplier $\frac{\partial \Phi}{\partial z}$. By numerical substitution in the final answers we can verify that this is the case for the solutions in which we are interested. Then for a first approximation we may use in place of (I. 6):

$$\frac{\partial}{\partial z}\left(\frac{d}{dt} V_x - KV_y\right) = -g\frac{\partial \Phi}{\partial x},$$

$$\frac{\partial}{\partial z}\left(\frac{d}{dt} V_y + KV_x\right) = -g\frac{\partial \Phi}{\partial y}. \qquad (7)$$

Equations (I. 7) together with (I. 1) and (I. 3) form a complete set involving only the dependent variables V_x, V_y, V_z, Φ (note that the operator $\frac{d}{dt}$ involves V_x, V_y, V_z: the equations are non-linear). However in the elimination process we have lost a function of integration. If we differentiate the first two of equations (I. 5) with respect to y and x respectively and subtract we obtain, using (I. 2):

$$\left(\frac{\partial}{\partial y} - \frac{\partial \Phi}{\partial y}\right)\left(\frac{d}{dt} V_x - KV_y\right) - \left(\frac{\partial}{\partial x} - \frac{\partial \Phi}{\partial x}\right)\left(\frac{d}{dt} V_y + KV_x\right) = 0 \qquad (8)$$

Numerical substitution then shows that in the cases in which we are interested the effects of the operators $\frac{\partial}{\partial x}, \frac{\partial}{\partial y}$ swamp those of the multipliers $\frac{\partial \Phi}{\partial x}, \frac{\partial \Phi}{\partial y}$ and to a sufficiently close approximation:

$$\frac{\partial}{\partial y}\left(\frac{d}{dt} V_x - KV_y\right) - \frac{\partial}{\partial x}\left(\frac{d}{dt} V_y + KV_x\right) = 0 \qquad (9)$$

Elimination of Φ from equations (I. 7) gives simply $\frac{\partial}{\partial z}$ of equation (I. 9) — the approximations in the two cases are consistent. On rearrangement of terms (I. 9) becomes:

$$\mathrm{div}_H \mathbf{v} \cdot (K + \mathrm{curl}_H \mathbf{v}) + \frac{d}{dt}\mathrm{curl}_H \mathbf{v} + \left(\frac{\partial V_z}{\partial x}\cdot\frac{\partial V_y}{\partial z} - \frac{\partial V_z}{\partial y}\cdot\frac{\partial V_x}{\partial z}\right) = 0 \qquad (10)$$

[1] Now usually represented by f.

To obtain a fourth equation symmetrical in V_x and V_y we differentiate equations (I. 7) with respect to x and y respectively and add. Then on re-arrangement:

$$\frac{\partial}{\partial z}\Big[K\,\mathrm{curl}_H\mathbf{v}-\frac{d}{dt}\,\mathrm{div}_H\mathbf{v}-\Big\{\Big(\frac{\partial V_x}{\partial x}\Big)^2+$$

$$+2\,\frac{\partial V_x}{\partial y}\cdot\frac{\partial V_y}{\partial x}+\Big(\frac{\partial V_y}{\partial y}\Big)^2\Big\}-\Big(\frac{\partial V_z}{\partial x}\cdot\frac{\partial V_x}{\partial z}+$$

$$+\frac{\partial V_z}{\partial y}\cdot\frac{\partial V_y}{\partial z}\Big)\Big]=g\cdot\nabla_H^2\Phi \qquad (11)$$

where the suffix H in all cases indicates differentiation with respect to x, y only. We shall use equations (I. 1), (I. 3), (I. 10) and (I. 11) as our fundamental set. When other dependent variables are required (e.g., pressure, which may appear in boundary conditions) they are easily computed in terms of our fundamental set.

An important feature of this set of equations is that transformation to a co-ordinate system in uniform horizontal relative motion is almost as simple as in the Newtonian case. V_x and V_y transform as in the latter case by vectorial addition of the relative velocity, V_z and Φ being unchanged. The only difference is that we must add a pressure field (at all levels) whose gradient corresponds to the relative velocity regarded as a geostrophic wind. This is consistent with the assumption that the so-called "tendency equation" is not to be interpreted as an expression of accumulation of mass but rather that the terms associated with this process are usually negligibly small compared with those associated with change of flow — as in classical (subsonic) aerodynamics.

The approximations made could be more convincingly justified by a detailed analysis, but a rigorous proof is possible only *after* obtaining the complete solutions of the approximate equations, when we can check on the precise effect of the omitted terms. A simpler but nevertheless fairly convincing check is the "lifelike" behaviour of the solutions, both qualitatively and quantitatively.

II. Disturbances of Steady Baroclinic Flow

We shall consider first a state of steady baroclinic flow in which the motion is uniform at each level and for simplicity we shall suppose both the "thermal wind" and the static stability constant, i.e., Φ is a linear function of x, y, z. In view of the transformation theorem referred to above there is no loss of generality in supposing:

$$V_x = U(z):\quad V_y = V_z = 0:\quad \Phi = Ay + Bz: \qquad (1)$$

So long as we ignore the variability of K the equations of motion are horizontally isotropic — the orientation of the y-axis is irrelevant. Equations (II. 1) are consistent with steady motion if:

$$\frac{dU}{dz} = -\frac{gA}{K} \qquad (2)$$

by reason of (I. 6). The approximation is good except when the thermal wind is very small (or the pressure gradient abnormally large). Since we are interested in the behaviour of strongly baroclinic systems no serious errors are introduced.

We now introduce a small perturbation and write:

$$V_x = U + v_x:\quad V_y = v_y:\quad V_z = v_z:\quad \Phi = Ay + Bz + \varphi: \qquad (3)$$

where v_x, v_y, v_z, φ are infinitesimal functions of x, y, z, t. Substituting in our fundamental set of equations we obtain the perturbation equations (which are of course linear)

$$\mathrm{div}_H\mathbf{v} + \frac{\partial}{\partial z}v_z = 0:$$

$$K^2(av_y + bv_z) + \frac{d}{dt}(g\varphi) = 0:$$

$$K\,\mathrm{div}_H\mathbf{v} + \frac{d}{dt}\mathrm{curl}_H\mathbf{v} + Ka\frac{\partial}{\partial y}v_z = 0:$$

$$\frac{\partial}{\partial z}\Big[K\,\mathrm{curl}_H\mathbf{v} - \frac{d}{dt}\,\mathrm{div}_H\mathbf{v} + Ka\frac{\partial v_z}{\partial x}\Big] = \nabla_H^2(g\varphi), \qquad (4)$$

where:

$$a \equiv \frac{gA}{K^2}\,;\; b \equiv \frac{gB}{K^2}\,;\; \frac{d}{dt} = U\frac{\partial}{\partial x} + \frac{\partial}{\partial t}\,; \quad (5)$$

By using the identities:

$$\left(\frac{\partial}{\partial z}\frac{d}{dt} - \frac{d}{dt}\frac{\partial}{\partial z}\right) \equiv -Ka\frac{\partial}{\partial x}:$$

$$\nabla_H^2 v_y \equiv \frac{\partial}{\partial y}\operatorname{div}_H \mathbf{v} + \frac{\partial}{\partial x}\operatorname{curl}_H \mathbf{v}: \quad (6)$$

we may eliminate successively φ, $\operatorname{curl}_H \mathbf{v}$, $\operatorname{div}_H \mathbf{v}$ from equations (II. 4). Finally we obtain a single partial differential equation involving v_z as the only dependent variable:

$$\frac{d}{dt}\left(K^2 + \frac{d^2}{dt^2}\right)\frac{\partial^2 v_z}{\partial z^2} + 2K^2 a\left(K\frac{\partial}{\partial x} - \right.$$
$$\left. - \frac{d}{dt}\frac{\partial}{\partial y}\right)\frac{\partial v_z}{\partial z} + K^2\left[b\frac{d}{dt}\left(\frac{\partial^2}{\partial x^2} + \frac{\partial^2}{\partial y^2}\right) - \right.$$
$$\left. - 2Ka^2\frac{\partial^2}{\partial x \partial y}\right] v_z = 0: \quad (7)$$

We cannot hope to solve this equation (technically of the fifth order) in complete generality but we may seek certain simple types of solution. Fortunately the simplest solutions are those of greatest practical importance. Since, apart from constants and differential operators (II. 7) involves only functions of z $\left(\text{the function } U(z) \text{ appearing in } \frac{d}{dt}\right)$ it clearly possesses solutions of the form:

$$v_z = N(z)\cdot\Psi : \Psi \equiv e^{i(\lambda x + \mu y + \vartheta t)}\,; \quad (8)$$

where λ, μ, ϑ are constants and N is a function of z only. In fact we may replace the operators:

$$\frac{\partial}{\partial x} = i\lambda\,;\; \frac{\partial}{\partial y} = i\mu\,;\; \frac{d}{dt} = i(U\lambda + \vartheta)\,; \quad (9)$$

and if at the same time we change our vertical co-ordinate by writing:

$$X \equiv X(z) = \frac{U\lambda + \vartheta}{K}\,;\; \frac{dX}{dz} = -a\lambda\,; \quad (10)$$

we obtain on substitution the ordinary second order differential equation to determine N:

$$X(X^2 - 1)\frac{d^2N}{dX^2} + 2(1 - i\sigma X)\frac{dN}{dX} +$$
$$+ [h^2(1 + \sigma^2)X + 2i\sigma]N = 0 \quad (11)$$

where we have written:

$$h^2 \equiv \frac{b}{a^2} = \frac{gB}{\left(\frac{dU}{dz}\right)^2}:$$

$$\sigma \equiv \frac{\mu}{\lambda}: \quad (12)$$

The parameter h^2, which involves both the horizontal and vertical entropy gradients, sums up (apart from matters of scale and boundary conditions) the characteristic properties of the flow. From (I. 4) it is clear that h^2 is simply the Richardson number of the unperturbed flow.

If we can solve (II. 11) with appropriate boundary conditions all the associated perturbation functions are readily determined by means of equations (II. 4). In fact a consistent set of solutions may be obtained in which:

$$v_x = L(z)\cdot\Psi:$$
$$v_y = M(z)\cdot\Psi:$$
$$\varphi = F(z)\cdot\Psi:$$
$$p = G(z)\cdot\Psi, \quad (13)$$

where the pressure perturbation p is determined by:

$$-\frac{1}{\varrho_0}\frac{\partial p}{\partial x} = \frac{d}{dt}v_x - Kv_y - Kav_z \quad (14)$$

or the corresponding equation for $\frac{\partial p}{\partial y}$. Here ϱ_0 is quite uncritical and we may take $\varrho_0 = \varrho_0(z)$ as the mean distribution of density with height in the system with which we are concerned.

For solutions of the form (II. 8) and (II. 13) we obtain the relations:

$$\frac{(1+\sigma^2)}{a}\cdot M=\frac{1}{X}\frac{dN}{dX}+i\sigma\left(\frac{N}{X}-\frac{dN}{dX}\right);$$

$$\frac{(1+\sigma^2)}{a}\cdot L=-\frac{\sigma}{X}\frac{dN}{dX}-i\left(\sigma^2\frac{N}{X}+\frac{dN}{dX}\right);$$

$$\frac{(1+\sigma^2)}{a}\cdot\frac{g}{Ka}\cdot F=\frac{i}{X}\left[\left\{\frac{1}{X}\frac{dN}{dX}+h^2(1+\sigma^2)N\right\}+\right.$$

$$\left.+i\sigma\left\{\frac{N}{X}-\frac{dN}{dX}\right\}\right];$$

$$\frac{(1+\sigma^2)}{a}\cdot\frac{i\lambda}{K\varrho_0}\cdot G=$$

$$=\left(\frac{1}{X}\frac{dN}{dX}+i\sigma\frac{N}{X}\right)+\left(N-X\frac{dN}{dX}\right)\quad(15)$$

With the substitution:

$$N=\left(\frac{1-X}{1+X}\right)^{\frac{i\sigma}{2}}\cdot R\qquad(16)$$

equation (II. 11) becomes

$$X(X^2-1)\frac{d^2R}{dX^2}+2\frac{dR}{dX}+X\left[h^2(1+\sigma^2)+\right.$$

$$\left.+\frac{\sigma^2}{(X^2-1)}\right]R=0\qquad(17)$$

which is in some ways more convenient.

We will suppose for the moment that λ, μ are real. If at the same time ϑ is real the solution (II. 8) will correspond to a system of stable waves. For the unstable waves we are seeking, ϑ must have a non-vanishing imaginary part and we shall write:

$$\vartheta=\vartheta_0-i\,\vartheta_1\qquad(18)$$

For such solutions (if any) X defined by (II. 10) becomes a complex variable (with a constant imaginary part) and it is convenient to regard R, determined by (II. 17), as a function of this complex variable. Thus in general L, M, N etc. as well as Ψ are complex numbers. This in no way affects the physical interpretation of v_x, v_y, v_z etc., as the real parts (for example) of the expressions (II. 8) and (II. 13). All it means is that the phase of the wave corresponding to each element (velocity-component, pressure etc.) as well as the amplitude varies with height.

Numerical substitution shows that in normal, convectively stable conditions (we are concerned with mean values over considerable depths) we have:

$$h^2\gg 1\qquad(19)$$

We shall for the present confine our attention to this, the most interesting case. It can be shown by energy considerations (see below) that in this case we should have:

$$|X^2|\ll 1\qquad(20)$$

over the range for which the perturbations have significant amplitudes. Alternatively we may assume this result and show that our final solutions are consistent with this assumption. Then (II. 17) becomes approximately:

$$\frac{d^2R}{dX^2}-\frac{2}{X}\frac{dR}{dX}-h^2(1+\sigma^2)R=0\qquad(21)$$

and with the substitutions:

$$H^2=h^2(1+\sigma^2);\ Q=HX;\qquad(22)$$

we obtain:

$$\frac{d^2R}{dQ^2}-\frac{2}{Q}\frac{dR}{dQ}-R=0\qquad(23)$$

the general solution of which is:

$$R=a_1R_1+a_2R_2$$
$$R_1\equiv e^{Q}(1-Q)$$
$$R_2\equiv e^{-Q}(1+Q):\qquad(24)$$

where a_1, a_2 are arbitrary constants.

Consider first a hypothetical (but physically possible) system in which motion takes place between two horizontal rigid plane boundaries which, without loss of generality, we may suppose to be at $z=\pm\frac{z_0}{2}$ corresponding to X_1, Q_1, and X_2, Q_2 respectively. We shall suppose the fluid unbounded in any horizontal direction. Then for the functions to be finite at infinity we must take λ, μ real. At $z = \pm \frac{z_0}{2}$ the normal velocity v_z must vanish which will be the case if:

$$R = 0;\ Q = Q_1,\ Q_2 \tag{25}$$

Then we have:

$$-\frac{a_2}{a_1} = e^{2Q_1}\left(\frac{1 - Q_1}{1 + Q_1}\right) = e^{2Q_2}\left(\frac{1 - Q_2}{1 + Q_2}\right): \tag{26}$$

and if we write:

$$(Q_2 - Q_1) = 2\,\alpha:$$
$$(Q_2 + Q_1) = -2\,i\beta, \tag{27}$$

we have:

$$\beta^2 = 2\,\alpha \coth 2\,\alpha - 1 - \alpha^2 \equiv$$
$$\equiv (\alpha - \tanh \alpha)(\coth \alpha - \alpha) \tag{28}$$

as the condition to be satisfied if solutions are to exist. On substitution for Q_1, Q_2 in (II. 27) we have:

$$2\,\alpha = \frac{H}{K} \cdot \frac{dU}{dz} \lambda z_0:$$
$$-2\,i\beta = \frac{H}{K}\left[\lambda (U_1 + U_2) + 2\,\vartheta_0\right]$$
$$-2\,i\vartheta_1 \cdot \frac{H}{K} \tag{29}$$

so that α is necessarily real. It follows from (II. 28) that β is either purely real or purely imaginary. Only when β is real, i.e. when

$$|\alpha| < \alpha_0 = 1.1997\,[\alpha_0 = \coth \alpha_0] \tag{30}$$

do unstable solutions exist. Then by (II. 29):

$$\vartheta_1 = \beta \cdot \frac{K}{H}: -\frac{\vartheta_0}{\lambda} = \frac{(U_1 + U_2)}{2} \tag{31}$$

where U_1, U_2 are the unperturbed velocities at levels $z = \pm \frac{z_0}{2}$ respectively. The second of these equations shows that the waves travel with the mean unperturbed current (we may

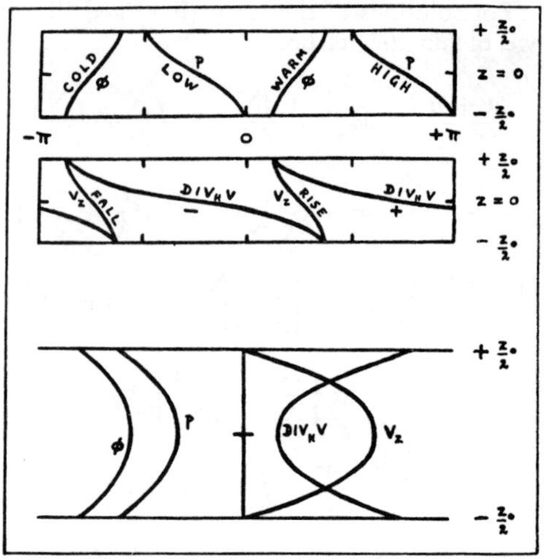

a

b

Fig. 1 a. Phase Variations: Above p, φ; Below v_z, $\text{div}_H \mathbf{v}$;
Fig. 1 b. Amplitude Variations: Left p, φ; Right v_z, $\text{div}_H \mathbf{v}$.

call the level $z = 0$ the "steering level"). The first equation determines the growth-rate. It is easily shown that $|\beta|$ defined by (II. 28) has a maximum for a particular value of α. Then:

$$|\beta| = 0.3098$$
$$|\alpha| = 0.8031 \tag{32}$$

For these values, with the additional condition $\sigma = 0$, the growth-rate is a maximum. At the same time (II. 29) determines the wavelength $\frac{2\pi}{\lambda}$ in terms of the parameters of the unperturbed system. The disturbances are easily seen to be, at each level, a series of (growing) ridges and troughs with their axes at right angles to the unperturbed thermal wind. Since the structure of these disturbances is very similar to that of the disturbances of more realistic systems it is of interest to examine them in detail. This structure is most conveniently described by graphs showing the variation with height of the phase and amplitude of the waves representing various salient features such as the pressure perturbation, vertical velocity, etc. The graphs for p, φ, v_z, $\text{div}_H \mathbf{v}$ are shown in Fig. 1. The distribution for v_y may be inferred directly from the pressure field since it is easily shown that for these disturbances [and in fact for the disturbances of all systems satisfying (II. 19)] the winds are to a first approximation geostrophic. Ageostrophic winds (including in the present instance v_x) are of order $\frac{1}{h}$.

It will be observed that the pressure trough slopes upwards and backwards in the atmosphere while the warm tongue (entropy maximum) slopes upwards and forwards. At low levels the warm tongue is slightly ahead of the pressure trough but at high levels the warm tongue is slightly to the rear of the upper pressure ridge. Upward motion (and hence, potentially, rainfall) is a maximum at middle levels $^1/_8$ wavelength ahead of the surface pressure trough. We may note that at middle levels v_y and v_z are in phase, the combined motion being upwards towards cold, downwards towards warm air. We may note also that at the same level v_z and φ are in phase with rising warm and descending cold air, corresponding to a decrease in potential energy. In fact on integration over a whole wavelength we find that there is a positive correlation between v_z and φ and a net decrease in the potential energy of the system as a result of the disturbance. It is of course this release of potential energy which feeds the kinetic energy of the growing disturbance. Our analysis shows that such a process (similar to that conceived by Margules) is consistent with all the equations and constraints of motion and in fact that such processes must occur from time to time.

It is easily verified by substituting typical values of the parameters that if z_0 is taken as the height of the tropopause the wavelength of the disturbance of maximum growth-rate is of approximately the same size as observed long waves. For smaller values of the static stability (as in large cloud masses) and smaller vertical extents we obtain "dominant" wavelengths of the order of magnitude of observed extratropical wave-cyclones. Thus we are certainly concerned with disturbances of the right order of magnitude. Our systems are not yet however sufficiently realistic for positive identification. As a first step towards realism we remove the artificial boundary at $z = +\frac{z_0}{2}$ and consider a system in which the atmosphere extends upwards indefinitely but at some definite level the static stability increases abruptly. For mathematical simplicity we take the "thermal wind" to be the same in both the lower and upper "regimes". This system is unsymmetrical so we shall put $z = 0$ at the earth's surface (rigid boundary) and $z = z_0$ at the boundary between the two regimes. Thus $z = z_0$ might correspond to an inversion or stabilisation of lapse-rate — were it not for the observed thermal wind change z_0 might be the height of the tropopause. Alternatively, the lower regime might be a (baroclinic) cloud mass of low base (small effective static stability) surmounted by unsaturated air. In all these cases the Richardson number (h_1^2) in the lower "regime" is less than that (h_2^2) in the upper regime. We can write down, as before, the general solution of (II. 21) appropriate to each regime. Clearly for continuity at the boundary we must have λ, μ, ϑ (and therefore X but not Q) the same in each regime. We still have two more arbitrary constants than before, but we have two additional "internal" boundary conditions since both the phase and amplitude (one complex number) of p and v_z (normal velocity) must be continuous at $z = z_0$. Our upper boundary condition is now $v_z \to 0$ as $z \to \infty$ for it is clear from (II. 24) that one of R_1, R_2 increases and the other decreases exponentially with height. (The boundary condition ensures that *all* the perturbation functions decrease exponentially.) Finally, we obtain, as before, a relation between λ and $\dot{\vartheta}$. If we write:

$$2\,\alpha = h_1 \sqrt{1 + \sigma^2}\,\frac{\lambda}{K}\,\frac{dU}{dz}\,z_0,$$

$$\beta = h_1 \sqrt{1 + \sigma^2} \cdot \frac{\vartheta_1}{K},$$

$$k_1 = \frac{h_1}{h_2}, \tag{33}$$

then

$$\beta^2 = \frac{(1 - k_1^2)\,(2\,\alpha - \tanh 2\,\alpha)}{(k_1 + \tanh 2\,\alpha)} - \left(\alpha - \frac{k_1}{2}\right)^2 \tag{34}$$

replaces (II.28) while for the "steering level" as defined above:

$$z_\omega = \frac{z_0}{2}\left(1 + \frac{k_1}{2\alpha}\right) \qquad (35)$$

If we put $h_2 = \infty$ (infinite static stability) equations (II.34) and (II.35) reduce to formulae appropriate to the "two rigid boundary" system and the disturbance is confined to the lower regime. As k_1 increases from zero the disturbance gradually extends into the upper regime but as there is always exponential decrease with height in the upper regime, provided $k_1 < 1$, then, except near this limit, the actual conditions much above $z = z_0$ are quite uncritical. In many practical cases k_1 is nearer zero than unity and then the disturbance in the lower regime does not differ greatly from that of our original system (the limiting case). For a given value of k_1 we find as before that β is real only for sufficiently long waves (α sufficiently small) and for one particular wavelength β (and therefore growth-rate) is a maximum. As k_1 increases from zero β decreases slowly at first from its limiting value but vanishes when $k_1 = 1$. For $k_1 > 1$ there are no unstable solutions. (It would appear to be a general result that for instability of this type the Richardson number must have a minimum value within a certain finite region; the resulting disturbances then have their maximum amplitude in this region with exponential decrease in the surrounding regions. These conditions are satisfied in practice as a general rule.)

Similar calculations may be made for systems of three (or more) horizontally stratified regimes. An easily investigated system, representing the opposite extreme to the two-regime system discussed above, is that in which the static stability is relatively small within a layer which we take to be between levels $z = \pm \frac{z_0}{2}$ and relatively large both above and below. The outer regimes we take (for simplicity) to be of indefinite extent. This system corresponds, for example, to a baroclinic cloud mass of very high base. For simplicity we take $h = h_2$ in each of the outer regimes, $h = h_1$ in the inner regime. Then with the same notation as before:

$$\beta^2 = \frac{(1-k_1^2)\{2\alpha(\coth 2\alpha + k_1) - (1-k_1^2)\}}{(1 + k_1^2 + 2k_1 \coth 2\alpha)} - \alpha^2 \qquad (36)$$

The general behaviour is similar to that of the two-regime system except that now the disturbance decreases exponentially in both directions away from the inner regime. (For small values of k_1 it is almost as if the conditions at the boundaries of the inner regime were independent.) Thus disturbances developing on a high level cloud sheet, for example, would be unnoticed at ground level in their early stages.

Table 1 gives values of α, β corresponding to the "dominant" disturbance of maximum growth-rate calculated for $k_1^2 = 1/_6$, typical of the change from cloud to unsaturated air, for the three systems discussed above. Note the relatively small decrease in β due to "losses" at "imperfectly rigid" boundaries.

Table 1

System	I	II	III
α	0.8031	0.6190	0.4445
β	0.3098	0.2988	0.2885

The structure of the disturbances of the more complex systems may be studied in the same way as before. Figs. 2 and 3, to be interpreted as Fig. 1, correspond to the two-regime and three-regime systems respectively.

An interesting feature of the two-regime system appears when we compute the displacement of the internal boundary (the base of the change in lapse-rate) at $z = z_0$ due to the growing disturbance. This boundary (which might correspond roughly to the tropopause) is sucked down in the vicinity of the upper (i.e., at $z = z_0$) pressure minimum and pushed up in the vicinity of the upper pressure maximum (the phase coincidence becomes exact as $k_1 \to 0$, otherwise it is a close approximation). This result (opposite to that to be expected if cyclonic vorticity were generated by a simple vertical "stretching" — but note that behaviour in the upper regime, e.g., the stratosphere, *is* consistent with this view) is in good agreement with observed behaviour.

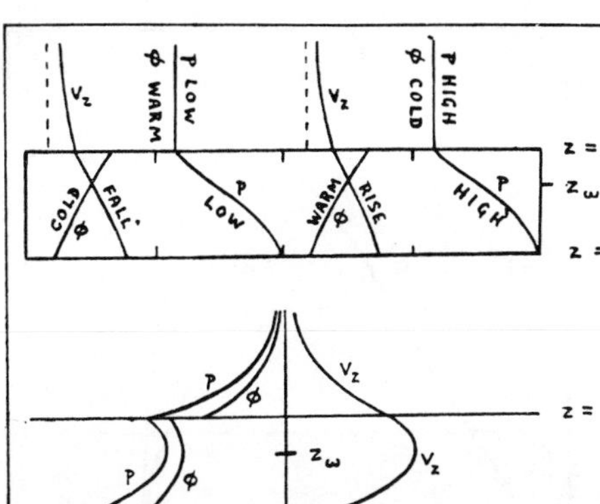

Fig. 2. Above: Phases. Below: Amplitudes.

In the above we have considered only the case of uniform thermal wind, the changes in Richardson number being due to changes in static stability. The general case, when both thermal wind and static stability change, is much less simple mathematically though it could probably be tackled by numerical methods. But from energy considerations there seems little doubt that the general behaviour of any system depends primarily on the distribution of Richardson number and much less on the way in which it is compounded.

We have still only considered systems which are horizontally of infinite extent and although strongly baroclinic regimes are often of considerable longitudinal extent (in the direction of the thermal wind), they are seldom very broad. As a further step towards realism we consider a three-regime system in which the regimes are now side by side. For simplicity we commence with the case of motion between horizontal rigid boundaries which we found previously to be a useful first approximation. We suppose the inner regime to occupy $-\frac{y_0}{2} < y < \frac{y_0}{2}$ and the outer regimes to be of indefinite extent. All three regimes occupy $-\frac{z_0}{2} < z < \frac{z_0}{2}$. Once again we suppose differences in Richardson number to be due solely to differences in static stability (consistent with a continuous temperature distribution if the stability reduction is due to cloud). We take $h = h_1$ in the inner regime, $h = h_2$ in each outer regime with $|h_1| < |h_2|$ so that the inner regime corresponds, for example, to a baroclinic cloud mass. In previous cases we found the only restriction on σ was that it must be real, though the most interesting case (maximum growth-rate) was $\sigma = 0$. In the present instance we find simple solutions only if:

$$h_1^2 (1 + \sigma_1^2) = h_2^2 (1 + \sigma_2^2) \equiv H^2 \qquad (37)$$

and then $Q = HX$ has the same interpretation everywhere. The boundary conditions at $z = \pm \frac{z_0}{2}$ are satisfied as in our first problem and then they are satisfied in all regimes simultaneously. The internal boundary conditions require continuity of p and v_y (normal velocity) at $y = \pm \frac{y_0}{2}$. (Since the winds are roughly geostrophic these conditions are nearly equivalent — hence the "fit" must be

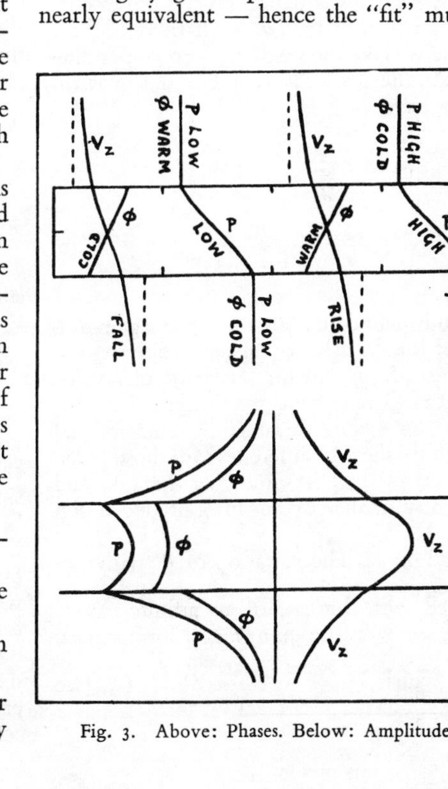

Fig. 3. Above: Phases. Below: Amplitudes.

correct to a higher order in $\frac{1}{h}\Big)$. We shall suppose (and our solutions require) that σ_1 is real, σ_2 purely imaginary, consistent with our assumption that $k_2 \equiv \frac{h_1}{h_2} < 1$. Then the boundary conditions at $y = \pm \infty$ are satisfied (all perturbations decreasing exponentially) with appropriate (opposite) choice of roots $\pm \sigma_2$ in the two outer regimes. In the inner regime we take a linear combination of the solutions corresponding to $\pm \sigma_1$ respectively and then have sufficient arbitrary constants to satisfy all the boundary conditions if, at the same time:

$$\frac{i\,\sigma_2}{\sigma_1} = \tan\left(\frac{\lambda\sigma_1}{2}\,y_0\right) \qquad (38)$$

or, by (II. 37)

$$\sigma_1^2\left[k_2^2 + \tan^2\left(\frac{\lambda y_0}{2}\sigma_1\right)\right] = 1 - k_2^2 \quad (39)$$

Since $k_2^2 < 1$ this equation always possesses at least one real root for $|\sigma_1|$. (If there is more than one we take the smallest — corresponding to maximum growth-rate.) For the growth-rate we have:

$$\vartheta_1 = \beta'\,\frac{K}{h_2}:$$

$$\beta' \equiv \frac{1}{k_2}\cdot\frac{\beta}{\sqrt{1+\sigma_1^2}}, \qquad (40)$$

where β is defined by (II. 28). Once again β' is real, and the disturbance unstable, only within the range (II. 30) and for one particular value of α growth-rate is a maximum. Since σ_1 depends on λ the "dominant" values of $|\alpha|$ and $|\beta|$ are slightly different from those given by (II. 32) — $|\alpha|$ is somewhat greater and $|\beta|$ slightly smaller by an amount depending on $\frac{y_0}{z_0}$ and on k_2. The variation of β' with α as compared with the case of an infinite cloud-sheet ($y_0 = \infty$) is shown in Fig. 4 for a typical case in which $k_2^2 = \frac{1}{10}$; $\frac{1}{\sqrt{b_2}}\frac{y_0}{z_0} = \frac{1}{4}$; (see II. 5).

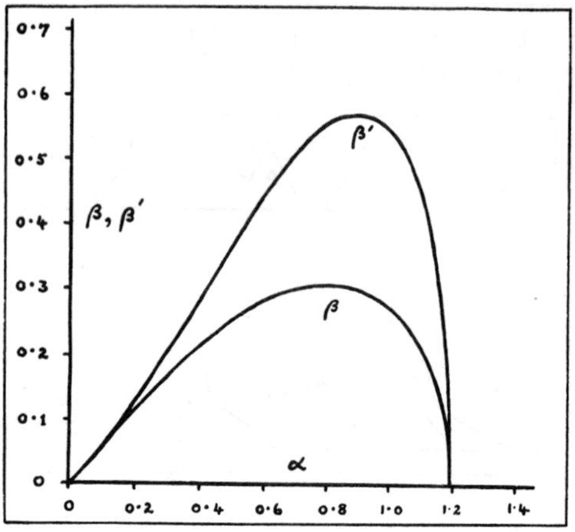

Fig. 4. Selection Curves.

It will be observed that the "selectivity" (i.e. the sharpness of the maximum) is increased. As a numerical example we may compute the characteristic features of the dominant wave of the system to which Fig. 4 applies, assuming in addition $K = 0.4$ hr^{-1} (lat. 50° approximately) : $\sqrt{b_2} = 115$ (typical for unsaturated air) : $z_0 = 5$ km : $y_0 = 150$ km (height and width of cloud mass) : $\frac{dU}{dz} = 10$ hr^{-1}. Then we derive:

$$h_2^2 = 21;\ \alpha = 0.893;\ \beta' = 0.575;\ \sigma_1 = 1.333; \qquad (41)$$

and then:

$$\frac{1}{\vartheta_1} = 19.9 \text{ hr};\ \mathbf{L} \equiv \frac{2\pi}{\lambda} = 1{,}070 \text{ Km}, \qquad (42)$$

so that the disturbance doubles its size in approximately 14 hours. The growth-rate is slightly less than that sometimes observed since in practice the effective Richardson number may be smaller than that assumed (and then our approximations are not so good — but see below). But both growth-rate and wavelength are of the right order of magnitude for cyclone waves. On the other hand when z_0 is the height of the tropopause and the Richardson number is not much less than that appropriate to unsaturated air (only cloud masses comparable in size with the disturbance pro-

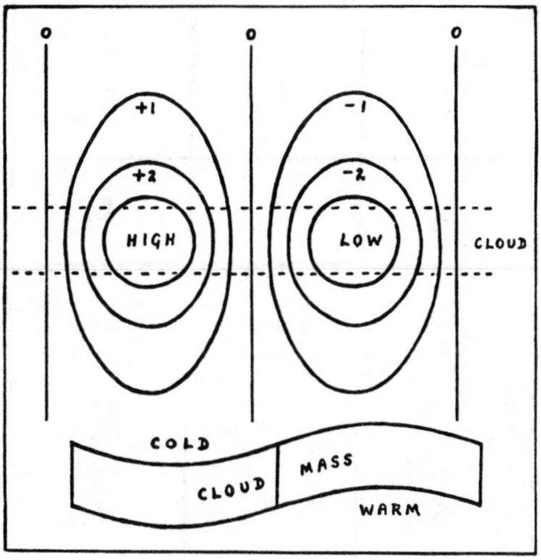

Fig. 5. Pressure-field and Cloud-mass Perturbation.

duce a large reduction in effective Richardson number) we find that **L** is more than doubled (in a typical case we find **L** is of the order of 4,000 Km) while ϑ_1 is considerably reduced $\left(\text{in a typical case } \frac{1}{\vartheta_1} = 60 \text{ hr}\right)$. These values are in good agreement with observed values in long waves. In general we find that growth-rate is intermediate between the values appropriate to infinite sheets of Richardson number h_1 and h_2 respectively, approaching the former for very broad, the latter for very narrow "cloud belts".

The structure of the "dominant" disturbance has many interesting features which will be discussed only briefly. The vertical distribution of phase and amplitude of the perturbation functions is exactly as in Fig. 1, but the horizontal structure is of course more complex. The approximate pressure-perturbation pattern $\left(\text{correct to zero order in } \frac{1}{h}\right)$ is shown in Fig. 5.

Apart from the changes of phase and amplitude indicated in Fig. 1, the pattern is the same at all levels. For comparison with observation we must superpose the unperturbed pressure field. We then find that (except when $U = 0$) closed centres are absent until the disturbance has attained a definite size (different at different levels and perhaps never attained, especially at high levels, — but this question cannot be discussed on a theory of small perturbations, which applies only to the early stages of development). Since the winds are roughly geostrophic $\left(\text{correct to zero order in } \frac{1}{h}\right)$ we may infer the approximate horizontal wind field from Fig. 5. But note that the trajectories are not even approximately along the isobars except at the steering level $z = 0$. Relative to the disturbance the air is blowing through from, say, the east at low levels and the west at high levels. The combined relative motion is associated with a deformation of the cloud mass. This deformation is shown below Fig. 5 (since it is "infinitesimal"), in correct phase for the level $z = -\frac{z_0}{2}$ (corresponding to the earth's surface). The phase varies with height and is the same as that of the entropy perturbation (warm tongue) at levels $z = 0$, $\pm \frac{z_0}{2}$, the phase-difference elsewhere being very small. Clearly the cloud-mass corresponds to the frontal region of the growing cyclone and its displacement towards cold air to the boundary of the "warm sector". It should be emphasised that we are concerned here only with the *broad* features of disturbances. Errors of detail are inevitable since actual initial systems are usually more complicated in structure than we have assumed. From this point of view it does not seem to matter very much whether or not the velocity field contains discontinuities (except when these are unusually large *and* extensive) provided the smoothed fields are the same. Moreover sharp discontinuities observed in practice are often the result of rather than the prerequisite for development. When the theoretical fields are more accurately computed (correct to the first order in $\frac{1}{h}$, the maximum attainable with present approximations) we find discontinuities of wind, pressure gradient, entropy developing along each surface of the cloud mass. This behaviour may be regarded as the realisation of a latent discontinuity — in effective static stability — between saturated and unsaturated air. These discontinuities are more complex in structure (and in some ways in better agreement with observation) than those at the plane surfaces ascribed to theoretical "fronts". Moreover the genesis of discontinuity by development is consistent with the observed "sharpening" of fronts during cyclogenesis. But a satisfactory theory of frontogenesis cannot be based on considerations of small disturbances and we must leave this aspect (from our point of view a matter of detailed structure) for the present.

It is easy to combine the virtues (from the point of view of realism) of the horizontally and vertically "stratified" systems by considering the systems shown in cross-section in Fig. 6. The only difference as compared with the system last considered, is that in place of Fig. 1, we use Figs. 2 and 3 respectively for the vertical variations of phase and amplitude provided that the conditions:

$$\frac{h_2^2}{h_1^2} = \frac{h_4^2}{h_3^2} \qquad (43)$$

are satisfied. We then find that all the boundary conditions can be satisfied simultaneously. The condition (II. 43) is necessary for solutions of simple mathematical form but it has little physical significance since very little perturbation-energy is associated with the "corner" regimes. In fact when h_1^2 is considerably smaller than the value of h^2 outside it is this alone (together with the dimensions of the cloud mass) which is the main determining factor of the features of the disturbance.

Several refinements and extensions of the theory will not be discussed in detail here. Thus the solutions of (II. 17) correct to order $\frac{1}{h^3}$ are easily determined. Applied to the first system considered they yield more precise formulae for growth-rate etc. It appears that serious errors do not result until h^2 approaches fairly close to unity. For $h^2 < 1$ a second type of instability (corresponding to "vertical overturning" — see below) becomes possible. This type of instability is associated with development on a smaller scale (motion in the vicinity of cold fronts, tropical cyclones etc.) and will be discussed elsewhere. Another extension is the calculation of second-order

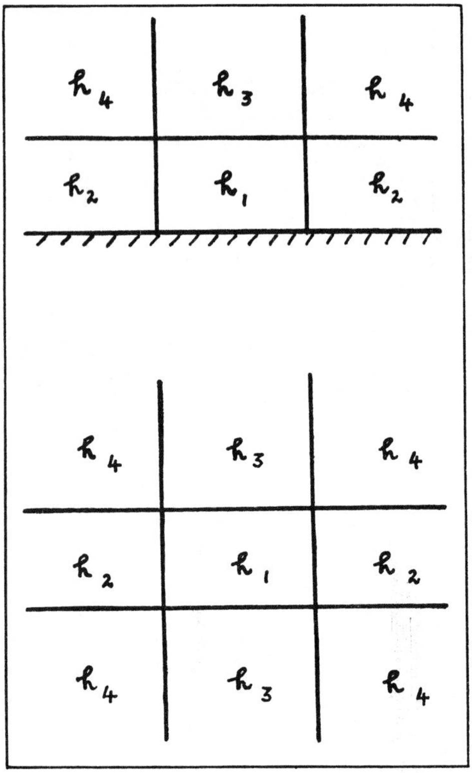

Fig. 6. 6- and 9-regime Systems (Vertical Section).

perturbations i.e. correct to the second order of small quantities. We then obtain terms involving Ψ^2 i.e., second harmonic terms. Calculations are simple for the first system, corresponding to Fig. 1. We find that the complete perturbation is no longer symmetrical as between "high" and "low". At all levels the pressure troughs are accentuated and the ridges flattened, in good agreement with observed behaviour. In fact, correct to zero order in $\frac{1}{h}$, the phase-lines of the first and second order perturbations of pressure coincide (for troughs) at all levels. We also obtain terms independent of Ψ, corresponding to "transport" phenomena. Thus for example the disturbances transport heat *upwards* and their final effect must be to *increase* the static stability of the system. (In this case of course the same result is obtained from the integrated correlation of v_z and φ.) An important corollary is that since large-scale disturbances are always transporting heat upwards we must, for statistical balance, have net cooling of the upper troposphere by radiation. Independent calculations of radiation flux have led to the same conclusion.

III. Long Wave Modifications

In the previous analysis, in which we have neglected the variability of the Coriolis parameter, we found that the disturbances move with the unperturbed current at the "steering level" which, in the case of symmetrical systems (Figs. 1 and 3) is the middle level of the system. In the system to which Fig. 2 applies the steering level is somewhat elevated, corresponding to a limited extension of the disturbance into the upper layer. If we apply the superposition (of uniform wind and corresponding geostrophic pressure gradient) theorem referred to in the first section we obtain the law of "contour steering" (*not*, as is often stated "thermal steering") at the steering level. So far at least as direction of travel is concerned this is in good agreement with observation (though we have proved the result only for nascent disturbances). But this law applies only to disturbances on not too large a scale. As we shall see, the most important new feature arising when we take into account the variation of K with latitude is a modification in the steering law.

For dealing with the more complicated problems in which we take into account the variability of the Coriolis parameter, or use a polar co-ordinate system, or are dealing with complicated boundary conditions, etc., it is convenient to reformulate the perturbation equations. This involves further approximations so that the solutions are valid only to zero order in $\frac{1}{h}$ (on the other hand in long wave problems h^2 is much larger than in cyclone problems) and the calculations are not so easily extended to the second order of small quantities but the differential equations are of a simpler form, are better adapted to numerical work and the solutions still retain the essential features we are seeking to determine. We commence with a "standard" distribution $\varrho_0(z)$, which may be the actual distribution in some central part of the region in which we are interested, and we shall suppose $p_0(z)$ the corresponding pressure distribution. Let p', ϱ' be the differences at any point from the "standard" values at the same level. Then $\frac{1}{\gamma} \cdot \frac{p'}{p_0}$, $\frac{\varrho'}{\varrho_0}$ are both small compared with unity and normally in regions of strong thermal wind the former is much smaller than the latter. Hence approximately:

$$\varphi = \frac{1}{g\varrho_0} \cdot \frac{\partial p}{\partial z} = \frac{1}{g} \frac{\partial}{\partial z} \left(\frac{p}{\varrho_0}\right) \tag{1}$$

for perturbations of sufficiently shallow systems, in which $\left|\frac{\partial}{\partial z} \log p\right| \gg \left|\frac{d}{dz} \log \varrho_0\right|$. If in the initial system the static stability and thermal wind are uniform we have for adiabatic motion (cf. II. 4):

$$a v_y + b v_z + \frac{1}{K^2} \cdot \frac{d}{dt} \frac{\partial}{\partial z} \left(\frac{p}{\varrho_0}\right) = 0 \tag{2}$$

We have noted that the perturbation winds are, to zero order in $\frac{1}{h}$, geostrophic. Then replacing v_y by $\frac{1}{K\varrho_0} \cdot \frac{\partial p}{\partial x}$ and differentiating:

$$b \frac{\partial v_z}{\partial z} + \frac{1}{K^2} \left(\frac{\partial}{\partial z} \frac{d}{dt} + Ka \frac{\partial}{\partial x}\right) \frac{\partial}{\partial z} \left(\frac{p}{\varrho_0}\right) = 0 \tag{3}$$

neglecting once again the variation of $\log \varrho_0$. Hence by the first of equations (II. 4) and (II. 6):

$$b \cdot \operatorname{div}_H \mathbf{v} = \frac{1}{K^2} \cdot \frac{d}{dt} \frac{\partial^2}{\partial z^2} \left(\frac{p}{\varrho_0}\right) \tag{4}$$

When h^2 is large the third of equations (II. 4) approximates to:

$$-\operatorname{div}_H \mathbf{v} = \frac{1}{K} \cdot \frac{d}{dt} \operatorname{curl}_H \mathbf{v} = \frac{1}{K^2} \cdot \frac{d}{dt} \nabla_H^2 \left(\frac{p}{\varrho_0}\right) \tag{5}$$

on substitution of the geostrophic winds. Combining (III. 4) and (III. 5)

$$\frac{d}{dt}\left[\frac{\partial^2 p}{\partial x^2}+\frac{\partial^2 p}{\partial y^2}+\frac{1}{b}\frac{\partial^2 p}{\partial z^2}\right]=0 \qquad (6)$$

and this condition is certainly satisfied if:

$$\frac{\partial^2 p}{\partial x^2}+\frac{\partial^2 p}{\partial y^2}+\frac{\partial^2 p}{\partial(\sqrt{b}\cdot z)^2}=0 \qquad (7)$$

All the other perturbation functions are readily expressible in terms of p and using (III. 7) in place of (II. 7) we can obtain, correct only to zero order in $\frac{1}{h}$, the results of section II. Our present approximations are therefore consistent with, albeit more drastic than those made earlier. Now if we take into account the variability of K we have, in place of (III. 5):

$$-\operatorname{div}_H \mathbf{v}=\frac{1}{K}\frac{d}{dt}(K+\operatorname{curl}_H \mathbf{v})=$$

$$=\frac{1}{K^2}\left[\frac{d}{dt}\nabla^2_H\left(\frac{p}{\varrho_0}\right)+\frac{dK}{dy}\cdot\frac{\partial}{\partial x}\left(\frac{p}{\varrho_0}\right)\right] \qquad (8)$$

and then, in place of (II. 6)

$$\frac{d}{dt}\left\{\nabla^2_H p+\frac{1}{b}\frac{\partial^2 p}{\partial z^2}\right\}+\frac{dK}{dy}:\frac{\partial p}{\partial x}=0 \qquad (9)$$

For solutions of the type (II. 8 and II. 13) studied in the previous section (III. 9) leads to the ordinary differential equation:

$$\frac{d^2G}{dP^2}=\left(\frac{1}{C^2}-\frac{1}{P}\right)G \qquad (10)$$

where

$$C^2\equiv\frac{h^2}{(\lambda^2+\mu^2)}\cdot\left(\frac{1}{K}\frac{dK}{dy}\right)^2$$

$$P\equiv CQ=Ch\sqrt{1+\sigma^2}\cdot X. \qquad (11)$$

From (III. 2) and (III. 10) we obtain the relation:

$$N=-P^2\frac{d}{dP}\left(\frac{G}{P}\right) \qquad (12)$$

and in place of (III. 10) we may use:

$$Q(Q-C)\frac{d^2N}{dQ^2}-(2Q-C)\frac{dN}{dQ}-$$
$$-(Q-C)^2 N=0 \qquad (13)$$

which of course reduces to (II. 23) when C = 0. (To our present approximation N and R are equivalent.) The general solutions of (III. 10) and (III. 13) are expressible in terms of Whittaker functions but since we are interested in functions of a complex variable evaluation of the solutions and determination of the dominant solution is in general a laborious process. If however, in order to discover the initial effect of the term involving $\frac{dK}{dy}$ when the "correction" is not too large, i.e. for waves which are not too long, we assume $|C|\ll 1$ then (III. 13) approximates to:

$$Q\frac{d^2N}{dQ^2}-2\frac{dN}{dQ}-QN=$$

$$=C\left[\frac{d^2N_0}{dQ^2}-\frac{1}{Q}\frac{dN_0}{dQ}-2N_0\right] \qquad (14)$$

(where N_0 corresponds to $C=0$), which is easily solved by variation of parameters (the L. H. S. is the same as in II. 23), the solutions involving exponential integrals. If we consider now the first initial system (two rigid boundaries) and compare our solutions for C small but non-vanishing with our original solutions for $C=0$ we find that the dominant wavelength and the corresponding value of ϑ_1 are unaltered, but that we obtain an additional term in the real part of the wave-velocity, corresponding to a lowering of the steering-level, given by:

$$-\delta U_\omega=0.726\cdot\frac{1}{(\lambda^2+\mu^2)}\cdot\frac{dK}{dy} \qquad (15)$$

a formula differing only by a numerical factor from that applicable to (hypothetical) barotropic waves. The formula appears to be in reasonably good agreement with observation in middle-high latitudes (poleward of 45° lat.) where the dominant wavelength is typically about 4,000 Km (though we have proved the result only for *growing* waves).

The steering-level corresponds roughly with minimum amplitude of the pressure perturbation (cf. Fig. 2) and the present lowering of the steering-level is associated with an increase of perturbation amplitude at high levels (i.e., towards the tropopause) and a decrease at low levels. That long waves are more intense at high as compared with low levels is of course well known.

We have observed that the decrease of mean density with height involves a "distortion" which is most serious in the case of deep waves such as long waves. An approximation to the modifications involved is obtained by replacing the first of equations (II. 4) by:

$$\mathrm{div}_H \mathbf{v} + \frac{\partial v_z}{\partial z} - \frac{1}{z_c} \cdot v_z = 0 \qquad (16)$$

where

$$\frac{1}{z_c} = -\frac{d}{dz} \log \varrho_0 = \frac{g}{\gamma RT} \qquad (17)$$

Then in place of (II. 23) we obtain finally:

$$\left[Q \frac{d^2R}{dQ^2} - 2 \frac{dR}{dQ} - QR\right] + + m \left[Q \frac{dR}{dQ} - 2 R\right] = 0 \qquad (18)$$

where

$$m \equiv \frac{1}{Ha\lambda z_c} = -\frac{1}{2\alpha} \cdot \frac{z_0}{z_c} \qquad (19)$$

(cf. II. 29, II. 5 and II. 2). Once again we shall consider the initial form of the "correction" when it is small, i.e. when z_0 is appreciably less than 1.6 z_c. Making the substitution:

$$R = e^{-\frac{m}{2} Q} \cdot R' \qquad (20)$$

and neglecting m^2 we get in place of (III. 18):

$$Q \frac{d^2R'}{dQ^2} - 2 \frac{dR'}{dQ} - (Q + m) R' = 0 \qquad (21)$$

Using once again the method of variation of parameters we obtain the general solution of (III. 21) and can study the modifications resulting from small but non-vanishing m as compared with our original solutions when $m = 0$. As above, when we were concerned with the effect of $\frac{dK}{dy}$, we find that the formulae for dominant wavelength and growth-rate are unaffected but there is an additional term in the real part of the wave-velocity. Expressed in terms of the steering-level we find that the latter is depressed by an amount $-\delta z$ where:

$$-\frac{\delta z}{z_0} = 0.0875 \left(\frac{z_0}{z_c}\right) \qquad (22)$$

Even when, as is the case in practice, $\frac{z_0}{z_c}$ is comparable with unity, and the correction is rather rough, this depression of the steering-level due to decrease of density with height is much smaller, for long waves, than that due to variation of the Coriolis parameter. To our present approximations these effects are of course additive. We may note that the factor $e^{-\frac{m}{2} Q}$ in (III. 20) is simply $\frac{1}{\sqrt{\varrho_0}}$ multiplied by a (complex) constant. Thus apart from the difference in behaviour of the amplitudes of perturbations which are functions of R' as compared with those of the R of (II. 23), a relatively minor difference, we find that perturbation amplitudes are multiplied by $\frac{1}{\sqrt{\varrho_0}}$, corresponding to increase in relative amplitude with height (and, to this extent, constancy of wave-energy density) and further accentuating the feature, already noted above, that long wave amplitude increases (on the whole) with height. Of course the corrections (III. 15) and (III. 22) apply to cyclone waves as well as long waves. But since both corrections are proportional to the square of the wavelength they can usually be neglected for practical purposes in the former case.

For practical application we have identified z_0 for long waves as the height of the tropopause since the mean value of h^2 over a considerable depth of the stratosphere is normally considerably larger, in significant regions, than in the troposphere. For a closer approximation we may study a system, similar to that to which Fig. 2 applies, in which the disturbance extends (but with exponential decrease with height) into the stratosphere. We cannot immediately apply our previous results since the sign of $\frac{dU}{dz}$ in the upper regime is reversed and the internal boundary (i.e., the tropopause) is no longer horizontal so that a precise mathematical formulation leads to a more complicated problem. Nevertheless it is easy to see that the two cases are not very different (and incidentally provide confirmatory evidence that the essential characteristics of a system depend on the Richardson number rather than its component elements). For the solutions R_1, R_2 (equation II. 24) are simply interchanged (h replaced by $-h$) when $\frac{dU}{dz}$ is reversed. In order to satisfy the boundary conditions at $z = \infty$ we have to choose the same solution (i.e., that which decreases with height) as before. We shall suppose the change in h^2 at the tropopause large (k_1 small) so that decrease in the stratosphere is rapid and most of the wave-energy in this regime concentrated just above the tropopause. The distribution of $\text{curl}_H \mathbf{v}$ in the lower regime, and in particular at the tropopause, cannot differ much from the limiting case (Fig. 1 — cf. Fig. 2). Since there are no discontinuities of velocity in our initial system we find that $\text{curl}_H \mathbf{v}$ must be continuous (at least to zero order in $\frac{1}{h}$, the winds being roughly geostrophic) at the tropopause. Hence $\text{curl}_H \mathbf{v}$ in the lower stratosphere is not much altered when $\frac{dU}{dz}$ is reversed. And just above the tropopause U is only slightly reduced by this reversal. Hence $\frac{\partial v_z}{\partial z}$, which is determined to this order of accuracy, by $\left(U\frac{\partial}{\partial x} + \frac{\partial}{\partial t}\right)$ $\text{curl}_H \mathbf{v}$ is not much altered and this is consistent with our choice of R_1 or R_2 corresponding to v_z decreasing. In Fig. 2 both v_y and v_z are continuous at the internal boundary, the resultant velocity having a slope smaller than that of the isentropic surfaces in the lower regime but greater than that in the upper regime and producing the 180° phase change in φ. When $\frac{dU}{dz}$ in the stratosphere is reversed the slope of the isentropic surfaces there is reversed but there is no qualitative (and only a relatively small quantitative) change in the above description. In fact in the significant region (i.e., just above the tropopause) we can reverse the sign of $\frac{dU}{dz}$ and our original solution (Fig. 2) is still a rough approximation to the required solution. Alternatively we may imagine the stratospheric value of $\frac{dU}{dz}$ changing gradually through zero. The general form of the solution in the stratosphere does not change appreciably, only the scale, which depends on h^2, *not* on the sign of $\frac{dU}{dz}$. We may therefore still use Fig. 2 as an approximate description in the more realistic case. In particular we find that the effect of this refinement is a raising of the steering-level. It is a convenient accident that in the case of typical long waves this correction very roughly cancels the correction for variation of ϱ_0 (depression of steering-level) so that we may obtain quite accurate steering velocities by omitting both corrections.

When discussing the system to which Fig. 2 applies we noted the sucking down of the internal boundary in the vicinity of the upper trough (or low pressure centre) and its pushing up in the vicinity of the upper ridge. We may now apply this result directly to the tropopause when there is long wave development. Apart from the agreement with observation so far as the tropopause itself is concerned we may note that we have here a mechanism ("advection" plus "stretching") to account quantitatively for observed changes in ozone measurements by purely dynamical considerations.

IV. Energy Analysis

The above account is based on obtaining complete solutions of the perturbation equations for certain simple initial systems thereby proving the systems unstable and determining the manner of breakdown. It is instructive to consider an alternative analysis in which we merely show the *possibility* of instability.

Nevertheless this more limited analysis makes clear the general nature of the process and makes possible an estimate of maximum growth rate for disturbances (strictly it determines an absolute upper limit to growth-rate) of a wider range of initial systems.

We commence with a system (such as one of those with which we have been concerned) initially in equilibrium and imagine displacements δx, δy, δz at each point, in general functions of x, y, z, t. For simplicity we consider the "incompressible" case (or analogue). The loss in potential energy is computed correct to the second order of small quantities and equated to the gain in kinetic energy, i.e., the kinetic energy associated with a growing disturbance. If we confine our attention to disturbances of "constant shape" in which all the displacements contain the factor $e^{\vartheta_1 t}$ then the kinetic energy involves terms such as $\vartheta_1^2 \cdot \delta y^2$ etc. In this way we obtain ϑ_1^2 as a function of the displacements and, making use of the constraints implied by the continuity equation and one of the momentum equations, we determine an upper limit to ϑ_1^2. If this upper limit is positive we infer that the system is unstable "potentially", i.e., subject to compatibility with other constraints not considered. (In all the cases examined we are able to find physically possible boundary conditions such that this upper limiting growth-rate is actually attained within an arbitrarily small amount. Other boundary conditions yield smaller, but in general comparable, maximum growth-rates. It appears to be a general rule that "potentially" unstable systems are actually so, a feature which may be associated with the infinitude of degrees of freedom of fluid motion.) Apart from the change in sign of ϑ_1^2 the method is essentially the same as that used by RAYLEIGH to determine minimum frequencies of oscillation.

Applied to a barotropic system with uniform velocity this analysis gives an upper limit to the initial rate of growth of a Bénard cell:

$$\vartheta_1^2 \leq -gB \tag{1}$$

Growth-rate is a maximum when δz is everywhere large compared with δx, δy and there is instability only when $B < 0$.

Now consider a baroclinic system. Potential energy is released by a process of "overturning" (we consider the initial stage of this process). It will be convenient to consider separately "vertical overturning" in a plane at right angles to the thermal wind and "quasi-horizontal overturning" in a sloping plane parallel to the thermal wind. The latter case corresponds to the disturbances with which we have hitherto been concerned and it will be convenient to take this case first. Assuming that the disturbances are periodic in the direction of the thermal wind we obtain finally the result:

$$\vartheta_1^2 \leq -g_s \frac{\partial \Phi}{\partial s} \tag{2}$$

if overturning takes place in the xs plane (the s axis being in the yz plane) and g_s is the component of gravity along the s-axis. By hypothesis the isentropic surfaces are not horizontal and if α is their angle of slope (acute angle) we find that ϑ_1^2 is positive if the s-axis slopes at a smaller angle. If α is small we find that growth-rate is a maximum when the s-axis has a slope $\frac{\alpha}{2}$ and then:

$$\vartheta_1^2 \leq \frac{1}{4} g \frac{A^2}{B} \tag{3}$$

and from the definition (II. 12) this is the same as:

$$|\vartheta_1| \leq \frac{1}{2} \cdot \frac{K}{h} \tag{4}$$

Our complete solution (II. 31) therefore corresponds to about 62 % efficiency. The reduction is of course due to the constraints of the rigid boundaries which prevent all the fluid particles being displaced in the optimum direction. (But it is easily verified that in the central region, near $z = 0$, the displacements are nearly in the optimum direction, i.e., along the bisector of the angle between the isentropic surfaces and the horizontal.)

The analogy between (IV. 2) and (IV. 1) is evident — we are here concerned with a kind of "convection" on a large scale, the main displacements being not vertical but in the direction of the s-axis. (Isentropic charts sometimes suggest this kind of picture.)

In the above we have supposed U independent of y as in the systems for which we have obtained complete solutions. We may attempt to generalise the above analysis by considering a system in which initially $V_x = U(z) + W(y)$ but for solutions periodic in the x-direction we have to abandon the assumption of "constant shape". (We are confronted with difficulties similar to those arising in a study of the stability of Couette flow). On the other hand it is easy to study the effect of vertical overturning (in the yz plane) in such a system. We obtain finally:

$$2\,\vartheta_1^2 \leq -\left[gB + K\left(K - \frac{dW}{dy}\right)\right] + \sqrt{\left[gB+K\left(K-\frac{dW}{dy}\right)\right]^2 + 4\left[(gA)^2 - gB\cdot KK - \left(\frac{dW}{dy}\right)\right]} \qquad (5)$$

and if we suppose (as is usually the case):

$$B > 0 : \frac{dW}{dy} < K ; \qquad (6)$$

the condition for "potential" instability is:

$$(gA)^2 > gB \cdot K\left(K - \frac{dW}{dy}\right) \qquad (7)$$

which is the same as:

$$\frac{1}{h^2} > \left(1 - \frac{1}{K}\frac{dW}{dy}\right) \qquad (8)$$

There is instability for any Richardson number if $\frac{dW}{dy} > K$, i.e., for an anticyclonic wind shear greater than K, a well-known result but probably not one of very great importance from a practical point of view. On the other hand when $\frac{dW}{dy} \ll K$, (IV. 8) becomes approximately $h^2 < 1$. Thus whereas the atmosphere is normally unstable from the point of view of "quasi-horizontal overturning" it is only so in special circumstances from the point of view of "vertical overturning". We should therefore expect the former process to be dominant in atmospheric development and observation appears to confirm this result at least in middle and high latitudes. (In low latitudes any kind of development is slow unless the static stability is small or negative.) Now the overturning process is an irreversible one and "quasi-horizontal overturning" leads to interchange between warm air at low levels and cold air at high levels. As noted earlier heat is transported *upwards*, statistically balancing radiative cooling at high levels. At the same time heat is normally transported polewards (the main transport is probably associated with long waves) to balance statistically net radiative cooling in high latitudes.

V. The Ultimate Limitations of Weather Forecasting

We may infer from the above analysis (in so far as the atmosphere is always, on a large scale, baroclinic) that atmospheric motion is normally unstable. The fact that practical systems are usually more complicated than those studied does not affect the generality of this result. In fact we have in practice what may legitimately be described as "fully developed turbulence" of a particular kind, the turbulent motion being maintained against frictional dissipation by the growth, from time to time, of disturbances of the kind we have been studying. (The only essential difference between this large-scale turbulence and that occurring on a smaller scale is the manner in which energy is supplied to the turbulent disturbances). Assuming sufficient analytical skill, what are the possibilities of forecasting for such a system? Suppose we attempt to formulate the problem as one of determining a final (forecast) state from a given initial one. The initial state is in practice "given" only within a certain margin of error. For concreteness let us consider pressure at a given point, known within a margin δp. Let ϑ_1 be the maximum growth-rate of unstable disturbances of the system. Then in the final (forecast) state we can guarantee pressure correct only within a margin $\delta p \cdot e^{\vartheta_1 t}$ since disturbances below the margin of error initially (and therefore completely unknown) will have attained this size. It is clear that "guaranteed" forecasts are possible (even in theory) only for intervals less than t_1 where t_1 is of the order of $\frac{1}{\vartheta_1}$, for beyond this time the margin of uncertainty is so large as to make such "guaranteed" information valueless. Reduction of initial error-margin makes possible only a very limited extension of time interval. For larger time intervals we must reformulate our problem.

Although we cannot, with complete certainty, say anything about long-term develop ments $\left(t \gg \frac{1}{\vartheta_1}\right)$ it does not follow that all possible developments are equally probable. On the contrary we may infer that probabilities are very unequally distributed (and therefore that information of this kind may be, from a practical point of view, almost as good as "guaranteed" information). As an example consider a set of unstable disturbances of various growth-rates. So long as the determining (perturbation) equations are substantially linear it is clear that the relative importance of the disturbance of maximum growth-rate increases with time i.e., any disturbance composed of components of varying growth-rates will tend towards the size, structure and growth-rate of the "dominant" wave by a process of "natural selection". We may generalise this result by including stable components in the initial perturbation and there can be little doubt that the result is true of *almost* any arbitrary disturbance. Of course in practice conditions are more complicated, the concept of an initial system is less clear-cut and the dominant disturbance is a relatively slowly varying function of the time, quite apart from the modifications which ensue when the disturbance becomes "finite" and the governing equations non-linear. (Moreover we may *choose* to regard certain initial irregularities as "finite" perturbations of a larger system.) Nevertheless the reality of the selection process is made clear every day when we see recognisable, well-known patterns developing "as if from nowhere" which more or less closely resemble in size, structure and behaviour the ideal disturbances we have discussed theoretically.

The above is no more than a prelude to the rather formidable task facing theoretical meteorology — that of discovering the nature of and determining quantitavely all the forecastable regularities of a "permanently unstable" (i.e., permanently turbulent) system. We can be certain that these regularities are necessarily statistical and to this extent our technique must resemble statistical mechanics. But we do not yet know enough about the "atoms" (the life-histories of disturbances) nor are we concerned with "atoms" with a clear-cut individuality. Clearly there are difficulties from the point of view of formulation and it is by no means clear what kind of problem we ought to attempt to solve. But these difficulties are inherent in the study of any kind of turbulent motion and perhaps in the study of irreversible processes (other than isolated ones) in general.

Much of the above formed the subject of a series of colloquia given, at the kind invitation of Profs. J. BJERKNES and C. L. GODSKE, at the Geofysisk Institutt, Bergen in April, 1947. A more detailed treatment of cyclone theory was given in a doctoral thesis (unpublished: London, 1948). The literature on cyclone and long wave theory is extensive and the writer would like to be excused the compilation of a list of references. He would however like to refer to an independent analysis by J. G. CHARNEY (Journal of Meteorology, Vol. 4, No. 5, Oct., 1947) which in many (but not all) respects is consistent with his own.

Reprinted (with corrections) from *Journal of Meteorology*, Vol. 6, No. 2, Apr., 1949, published by the American Meteorological Society.

DYNAMIC INSTABILITY OF TWO-DIMENSIONAL NONDIVERGENT FLOW IN A BAROTROPIC ATMOSPHERE

By Hsiao-lan Kuo

University of Chicago

(Manuscript received 10 May 1948)

ABSTRACT

In discussing wave motions along a strong jet of westerlies, we can no longer neglect the variation of west wind with latitude, and therefore must consider the possibility of having a phase velocity whose value is between the maximum and minimum west-wind velocities. The study of wave motions is thus extended from the very long and slowly moving or retrograding waves into the realm of ordinary waves and cyclone waves and it is found that, for nondivergent barotropic motion, the condition for the presence of neutral and amplified waves with a phase velocity whose value is between the maximum and minimum wind velocity in the belt is the existence of *critical* points where the absolute vorticity has an extreme value. If no such point exists, then all perturbations must be damped.

When this condition is satisfied, both amplified (unstable) and neutral waves can be expected. The wave moving with a velocity equal to the current velocity at the critical point is neutral while those with a velocity less than this value but greater than the minimum wind velocity will be amplified. The amplification will be greatest when the phase velocity is intermediate between the latter two values; therefore, both fast and slowly moving waves will have little amplification. The degree of instability will also depend upon the sharpness of the velocity profile.

When the wave is unstable, the trough line will be directed from southeast toward northwest to the south of the point of minimum absolute vorticity and from southwest toward northeast to the north of the point of maximum vorticity.

CONTENTS

1. Introduction

In the last ten years the concept of conservation of absolute vorticity has been advanced in theoretical meteorology by many authors and also has been applied in synoptic meteorology. By introducing β, the variation of the Coriolis parameter $f = 2\omega \sin \phi$ with latitude, into the vorticity equation, Rossby (1939) discovered the law governing the motion of long waves in the upper atmosphere. Since all these studies are restricted to uniform westerlies, the waves are definitely neutral.

The study of dynamic instability may be dated back to Helmholtz and Reynolds (see Lamb, 1932) and since then has attracted the attention of many workers in hydrodynamics and meteorology. Helmholtz investigated wave motions along a surface of discontinuity with an abrupt change in wind and density along the vertical, and showed that the common surface is unstable for sufficiently short wave disturbances. It was also shown that any finite wind discontinuity will have the effect of destabilization. Later on Rayleigh (1913) investigated the stability of horizontal parallel flows and tried to approximate the actual current profile by combining a number of belts, each with linear velocity distribution, and showed that the stability of the current will depend upon the shape of the profile. Heisenberg (1924) questioned the validity of this method; later on, most advancement of the study of instability of an inviscid fluid was made by Lin (1945; 1946), who also gave a physical interpretation in terms of conservation of vorticity.

Since all these studies are restricted to nonrotating systems, while in meteorology the earth's rotation plays a very important role in the dynamics of the atmosphere, the results of these investigations can hardly be applied in the field of meteorology except for some special phenomena occuring on a rather small scale, such as the formation of billow clouds. Parallel to this study of stability of wave disturbances was the consideration of the acceleration attained by a particle displaced from its original position, based largely on the assumption of conservation of momentum of the particle, which implies that there will be no change in the pressure field. This consideration was extended into meteorology by Solberg (1936), and later on by Kleinschmidt (1941) and Van Miegham (1944), by considering the balance of energy. The criterion thus obtained is that for instability to occur in two-dimensional horizontal motion or motion along isentropic surfaces, the wind shear along isentropic surfaces must be anticyclonic and with a value greater than the Coriolis parameter f; all velocity profiles with cyclonic shear must be absolutely stable and the disturbances set in will be damped out, according to this theory. This instability can occur only to the south of a strong jet of westerlies. To the north, where we actually find our series of cyclones in the mean seasonal situation, the atmosphere is inertially stable. Perhaps we should distinguish the inertial instability discussed by Solberg from the instability we are considering, which for the case of wave disturbances, would depend upon the wave length. Furthermore, in view of the emphasis generally given to the theory of momentum transfer in turbulent motion, it seems very desirable to consider the problem from the point of view of vorticity transfer. Besides, most writers in dealing with the problem of instability of wave motion, were satisfied by showing that the wave velocity will become complex under certain conditions; very little attention has been given to the order of magnitude of the amplifying factor, owing to mathematical difficulties. But since we can rarely identify any atmospheric system in a time interval longer than one week, very small amplifying factors will be of no practical significance in meteorology.

The purpose of this investigation is to give a detailed study of the character of nondivergent horizontal wave motion in a barotropic atmosphere, without neglecting the change in the pressure field or the horizontal shear. A rather general distribution of the zonal wind will be assumed and a small perturbation superposed upon this basic flow, so that we can study the eventual changes of these small disturbances; this is essentially the problem of dynamic instability.

As for practical applications of this study, one would think that vertical motion and solenoidal fields as well as divergence and convergence will have deciding influence upon the development of the cyclones and anticyclones, so that it seems hardly justifiable to neglect these factors, and attribute all the instability to the distribution of zonal wind. Actually this is not the case. Although our discussions are mainly for two-dimensional nondivergent flows, similar results would be obtained for the very general case with vertical motion, solenoids, and divergence and convergence, if certain approximations are made in reducing the partial differential equation for a certain dependent variable to an ordinary differential equation. This equation is very similar to the vorticity equation of two-dimensional flow, except that the coefficients of the equation involve quantities such as the vertical stratification, vertical wind shear, and the velocity of sound. Thus the only difference in the stability criterion will be a slight shift of the position of the critical point in the velocity profile and a slight difference of the degree of stability.

It should be pointed out that no attempt has been made to explain all the growth and decay of a very complicated system merely by dynamic instability. The dynamic stability or instability can only give some indication of the possibility for the development of some disturbances, while the actual mechanism of the disturbance itself must be studied from other considerations. Furthermore, since in some cases the general character of the basic current changes so rapidly that the disturbances can hardly be considered as small, and the system is receiving energy from outside, the dynamic stability will not give us the clue for these changes. But for many cases we actually find the main pattern of the flow remaining nearly the same for a long period of time without much change and with a series of waves, long or short, moving along it. It is to these cases that our results should apply; and if we can show that the order of magnitude of the amplifying factor is the same as in the actual cases, at least we can say that dynamic instability must be one of the main factors that are operating.

2. The perturbation equations

Since the large-scale atmospheric motions are mainly horizontal and the influence of compressibility negligible, we shall restrict ourselves to the study of purely horizontal and nondivergent motions. The atmosphere is assumed to be barotropic. Then the vorticity equation may be written in the following form:

$$\left(\frac{\partial}{\partial t} + U\frac{\partial}{\partial x}\right)\nabla^2\psi + (\beta - U'')\frac{\partial\psi}{\partial x} = 0, \qquad (1)$$

where ψ is the perturbation stream function and $U = U(y)$ is the basic zonal velocity. If we put $\psi(x, y, t) = \Psi(y)e^{i\alpha(x-ct)}$, then

$$(U - c)(\Psi'' - \alpha^2\Psi) + (\beta - U'')\Psi = 0, \qquad (2)$$

where α is the wave number (a real quantity) and c, the phase velocity, may be complex; that is,

$$c = c_r + ic_i. \qquad (3)$$

In (2), the primes denote differentiation with respect to y. If, in (3), $c_i \neq 0$, then the amplitude will be an exponential function of time t; for $c_i > 0$, the amplitude will increase exponentially with time and the wave is said to be *amplified*; if, on the other hand, $c_i < 0$ then the amplitude will decrease with time and the wave will be *damped*. If $c_i = 0$, the amplitude will remain constant and the waves are said to be *neutral*.

Equation (2) is of second order and is to be solved under certain boundary conditions at $y = y_1$ and $y = y_2$. Since $U = U(y)$, we have a differential equation with variable coefficients. In the atmosphere, the velocity profiles of the westerlies generally have some symmetry with respect to some latitude; for simplicity, we shall discuss symmetric profiles only. In general, we may have two different kinds of profiles and therefore two different kinds of disturbances. The first is that for a limited belt: the disturbances disappear along its two boundaries $y = y_1$ and $y = y_2$, the velocity profile is symmetric with respect to the midpoint of the belt, as is shown in fig. 1. The second kind

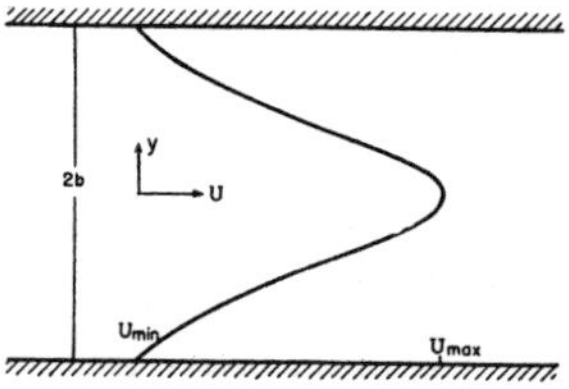

FIG. 1. The first type of symmetric velocity profile: limited belt of width $2b$.

is that for a belt extending to infinity in both directions. We shall assume in this case that there is a symmetric wind distribution in the central part and a constant wind outside this region, as is shown in fig. 2.

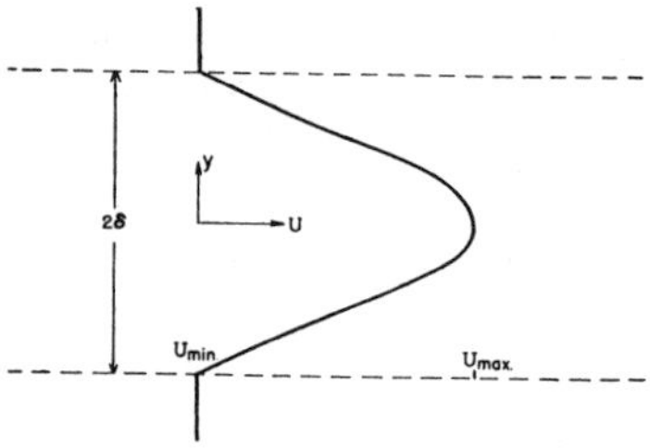

FIG. 2. The second type of symmetric velocity profile: uniform current velocity outside a belt of width 2δ.

Since only symmetric profiles and symmetric boundary conditions are considered, we should expect either symmetry or antisymmetry for the amplitude Ψ of the perturbation stream function. Therefore, only half of the belt need be considered. For the first kind of profile the conditions to be satisfied along the boundaries at $y = y_1$ and $y = y_2$ may be expressed as $\Psi = 0$. At the midpoint ($y = b$) of the region, we have $U' = 0$. Since it is very unlikely to have $v = 0$ along the line of maximum wind, we shall deal only with symmetric disturbances; for this type of disturbance $\Psi'(b) = 0$, since v has a maximum at $y = b$. Thus for the first type of profile the conditions to be satisfied are

$$\Psi(0) = 0, \quad \text{and} \quad \Psi'(b) = 0. \tag{4}$$

For the second type of profile, the same condition will be used for the midpoint, but a different condition must be applied at the two points where the central portion of the distribution joins the outer portions of uniform wind. Since (2) admits an exponential solution $\Psi \propto e^{\pm ry}$ for the region with constant wind, we should have $\Psi' \pm r\Psi = 0$ along the line where the profile changes to a constant wind profile. Thus if we take the origin of y along this line and the width of the belt 2δ, the conditions to be satisfied for the second type of profile are

$$\Psi'(0) - r\Psi(0) = 0, \quad \text{and} \quad \Psi'(\delta) = 0, \tag{5}$$

where $r^2 = \alpha^2 + \beta/(c - U_0)$. Our problem is now to solve equation (2) under the boundary conditions (4) or (5) and to find the necessary and sufficient conditions for having a complex c. This is a nonlinear characteristic-value problem with the parameter c.

Now the point $U = c$, where the wind velocity is equal to the phase velocity of the wave, is a singular point of (2). At this point, only one of the two fundamental solutions will remain regular while the other will have a logarithmically infinite derivative, corresponding to an infinite perturbation velocity u. Besides this, we shall have a sudden change of the imaginary part of u in crossing the singular point, which will give a sudden change of phase of u. In avoiding these difficulties, meteorologists have always made the assumption that c is always less than U; but by so doing, we have already restricted ourselves to the special type of slowly moving or retrograding long waves, as will be seen later. Thus in order to remove the infinity of u and the sudden change of phase, we have to take the effect of lateral mixing into consideration. By introducing the frictional terms $\nu\nabla^2\bar{u}$ and $\nu\nabla^2\bar{v}$ into the equations of motion, the vorticity equation becomes

$$d\zeta/dt + \beta v = \nu \nabla^2\zeta, \tag{6}$$

and after introducing the harmonic wave solution, it reduces to the following form

$$(U - c)(\Psi'' - \alpha^2\Psi) + (\beta - U'')\Psi = -i\nu\alpha^{-1}(\Psi^{iv} - 2\alpha^2\Psi'' + \alpha^4\Psi). \tag{7}$$

In the free atmosphere, friction may be conceived in terms of lateral mixing, and the equation to be considered should be (7) instead of (2). When $U - c$ is not too small, the right-hand side of (7) can be neglected, so that we have the vorticity equation (2). But when U is nearly equal to c, this will no longer be the case and we must consider (7) instead of (2). Since $U - c = 0$ denotes only a point in the velocity profile and $U - c$ is very small only in the immediate vicinity of this singular point, the consideration of (7) is only necessary in a very thin belt around this point. At a small but finite distance from this singular point, the right-hand side of (7) becomes very small as compared with the left, so that the solution must agree with that for (2). In this way (7) can be simplified enormously, and we get a correction for the solution of (2), so that the infinity of u can be removed and the value of the change of the imaginary part of Ψ and u determined. This method is called the method of *cross-substitution*.

3. Analytic properties of the stream function

Since (9) is of second order and the indicial equation is $r(r-1) = 0$, we see that only one of the two fundamental solutions remains regular at the singular point $y = y_s$. This solution is of the form

$$\Psi_1 = y + a_2 y^2 + a_3 y^3 + \cdots + a_n y^n + \cdots, \quad (8)$$

if we take the singular point as origin. The other linearly independent fundamental solution is of the form

$$\Psi_2 = b_0 + b_1 y + b_2 y^2 + \cdots + G_s \Psi_1 \ln y. \quad (9)$$

In (8) and (9), all the coefficients a_n, b_n, and G_s depend upon the velocity distribution $U(y)$, the wave number α and the phase velocity c. Our final aim is to find the values of α and the corresponding c that will make the general solution Ψ of (2) satisfy the given boundary conditions. Thus we see that our problem is really a problem of finding the characteristic values of α or c. This is done by substituting the general solution of (2), given by

$$\Psi = A\Psi_1 + B\Psi_2, \quad (10)$$

into the boundary conditions, and then eliminating the two arbitrary constants A and B. For the first type of profile and boundary conditions (4), the frequency equation will be of the form

$$F(\alpha, c) = \begin{vmatrix} \Psi_1(y_1;\alpha,c) & \Psi_2(y_1;\alpha,c) \\ \Psi_1'(y_2;\alpha,c) & \Psi_2'(y_2;\alpha,c) \end{vmatrix}, \quad (11)$$

where $y = y_1$ is the boundary and y_2 the midpoint. If we solve for c in terms of α and the other given parameters, we can find c_r and c_i. In general it is extremely difficult to find complex values of c satisfying (11). Frequency equations of the type (11) are generally solved by graphical methods for the real roots of c; it is then inferred that we have complex c for values of α differing slightly from the critical value corresponding to real c. Thus we are actually looking for the critical values of α and the other parameters that will give a real c. But for many cases there is actually no real value for c and therefore this method will fail, for then we will not know whether c_i is positive or negative. Further, this method provides no information as to the magnitude of c_i. Therefore we shall employ another method to find all the possible real values for c, without actually solving (11), and then investigate c_i by a continuation.

Since the coefficients in Ψ_1 and Ψ_2 depend upon the velocity distribution $U(y)$, they cannot be given explicitly unless $U(y)$ is given. But what we really wish to know is only the general nature of the functions Ψ_1 and Ψ_2 (and of $\Psi = A\Psi_1 + B\Psi_2$) and their change of value in crossing the singular point y_s where $U = c$. For the latter purpose, a Taylor expansion of $U(y)$ around this point up to the third power of y will be sufficient. Thus if we take the origin at the singular point and take the positive direction toward the region where $U > c$, we shall have $U_s' > 0$ at the singular point, the subscript $_s$ signifying that the quantity is evaluated at the singular point. The coefficients in Ψ_1 and Ψ_2 can be determined by substituting $U(y)$ and the functions Ψ_1, Ψ_2 given by (8) and (9) respectively into (2). For Ψ_2, the constant terms reduce to $U_s'G_s + (\beta - U_s'') = 0$; therefore

$$G_s = (U_s'' - \beta)/U_s'.$$

We see that Ψ_1 remains regular for all finite values of y and the derivative of Ψ_2 becomes logarithmically infinite at $y = 0$, so that u becomes infinite at this point. The point $y = 0$ is a singular point for u and is also a branch point, where a sudden change of the imaginary part will occur.

Of course, u can never become infinite and there can never be a sudden change of phase in the real atmosphere. This can be explained by the presence of viscosity. Thus in the immediate vicinity of the singular point $y = 0$, we must take the action of viscosity into consideration by using (7) instead of (2) *i.e.*, using the method of cross-substitution. By this consideration, the infinity of u can be removed and the change of its phase made gradual. But since we are not particularly interested in the details within this very thin belt, we shall not discuss this method but only take the results that may be obtained from it, and consider that the solutions (8) and (9) are corrected such that they will not give an infinite u and a sudden change of phase for u in crossing the singular point.

For a real c, the change in the imaginary part of Ψ' in going from the positive to the negative side of $y = 0$ is determined by the method of cross-substitution and is given by $-G_s\pi i$.

When c is complex ($c = c_r + ic_i$), the coefficients of (2) become complex and there will be no singular point along the real axis of y. In this case we must consider the differential equation in the complex plane; U may also be considered as complex by an analytic continuation from the real axis. Then we shall have a singular point in the complex plane of y where we have $U = c$ and the two fundamental solutions of (2) are also given by (8) and (9) with the same coefficients, y being complex. If c_i is small, this singular point is at a distance c_i/U_s' from the real axis of y, above this axis for $c_i > 0$ and below it for $c_i < 0$, if we take U_s' as positive, where U_s' is the wind shear at the point $y = y_s$ corresponding to $U = c_r$ (fig. 3). For sufficiently

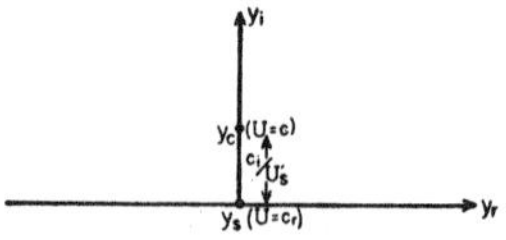

FIG. 3. The singular point y_c in the complex plane (where $U = c$) in relation to the point y_s along the real y-axis where the phase velocity c_r is equal to the current velocity U.

small values of c_i such that $|y| \gg |c_i/U_s'|$, there will also be a change of the imaginary part of Ψ' in passing from a positive real y to a negative real y, the main part of which is equal to $-G_s\pi i$, due to the logarithmic singularity.

4. Neutral waves

For the symmetric profiles we are considering on the rotating earth, the neutral waves can only have a phase velocity less than the maximum wind velocity. On the other hand the neutral waves may have a phase velocity less than the minimum wind velocity of the belt under consideration, which is impossible in a nonrotating system (Rayleigh, 1913). To show this, let us consider the solution of the differential equation (2), which may be written

$$\Psi'' = \left(\alpha^2 + \frac{\beta}{c-U} + \frac{U''}{U-c}\right)\Psi \equiv G\Psi,$$

as compared with the differential equation

$$F'' = \frac{U''}{U-c} F \equiv G_2 F. \qquad (12)$$

Take the origin $y = 0$ at the boundary so that $\Psi(0) = 0$ and $F(0) = 0$, but $\Psi'(0) \neq 0$, $F'(0) \neq 0$. Then for $c > U_{max}$, we have $G > G_2$; therefore, according to Sturm's comparison theorem, Ψ oscillates more slowly than F (Ince, 1944). But F has the solution

$$F = (c - U)\int_0^y \frac{dy}{(c-U)^2}, \qquad (13)$$

which is always positive except at $y = 0$, where it is zero. Therefore Ψ can have no zeros for $y > 0$ and can not be zero at $y = 2b$, the other boundary; that is to say, the other boundary condition can never be satisfied by any value of c greater than the maximum wind velocity.

If, on the other hand, we assume $c < U_{min}$, then G may be less than G_2 and there might be some values of c which makes Ψ equal to zero at $y = 2b$, so that Ψ is then the characteristic function which satisfies both of the two boundary conditions.

Now let us discuss the values of c. To do this, let us multiply (2) by F and (12) by Ψ, subtract and integrate from $y = 0$ to $y = b$; we get

$$[\Psi' F - F'\Psi]_0^b = \int_0^b \left(\alpha^2 - \frac{\beta}{U-c}\right) F\Psi\, dy. \qquad (14)$$

For Ψ, we have the conditions $\Psi(0) = 0$, $\Psi'(b) = 0$, $\Psi(b) > 0$, and $\Psi'(0) > 0$. If we take the solution of (12) to be

$$F = U - c, \qquad (15)$$

which satisfies $F'(b) = 0$, (14) gives

$$c = \frac{\Psi'(0)U_{min}}{\Psi'(0) + \alpha^2\gamma} + \frac{\bar{U} - \beta/\alpha^2}{1 + \Psi'(0)/\alpha^2\gamma}, \qquad (16)$$

where $\gamma \equiv \int_0^b \Psi\, dy$ and $\bar{U}$ is the mean velocity defined by

$$\bar{U} = \gamma^{-1}\int_0^b U\Psi\, dy. \qquad (17)$$

When $U =$ constant and Ψ is independent of y, then (16) gives

$$c = U - \beta/\alpha^2, \qquad (18)$$

which is Rossby's equation.

When $U =$ constant and $\Psi = A \sin(\pi y/2b)$, then from (16) we have

$$c = U - \frac{\beta}{\alpha^2 + \pi^2/4b^2}, \qquad (19)$$

which is Haurwitz' (1940) formula. Thus we see that Rossby's and Haurwitz' waves are the slowly progressive or retrograding long waves with a velocity less than the minimum wind velocity in the belt. This group of long and slowly moving waves does not give rise to any singularity to the vorticity equation (2). Thus the wave with a velocity c equal to the minimum wind velocity U_{min} is the demarcation between those waves which give a singularity to the vorticity equation and those which do not. We shall determine the wave length L_0 corresponding to this demarcation so that we can have some idea about the region of applicability of the results obtained from the assumption that $U_{min} > c$. This demarcation will give the lower limit of the wave length for the waves studied by Rossby. By taking $U_{min} = c$, (14) and (15) give

$$\beta\int_0^b \Psi\, dy = \alpha_0^2\int_0^b (U - U_{min})\Psi\, dy. \qquad (20)$$

Therefore the corresponding shortest wave length is given by

$$L_0 = 2\pi\beta^{-\frac{1}{2}}(\bar{U} - U_{min})^{\frac{1}{2}}, \qquad (21)$$

where $\bar{U}$ is defined as in (17). Take $\bar{U} - U_{min} = 10$ m sec^{-1}, which could not be too large as compared with the actual cases when the variation of U is great; then we find that L_0 is about 5200 km. Thus we see that the results obtained under the assumption of $U_{min} > c$

can not be applied to the shorter waves such as the ordinary waves and cyclones that are associated with a strong jet of westerlies. Therefore, in continuing the long slowly moving waves to the ordinary and cyclone waves, we must consider the cases with $U_{min} < c < U_{max}$. It is in this region of phase velocity that we find the most prominent unstable waves, while the long and slowly moving waves are essentially neutral and can only have very small amplifications, because the most important contribution to the imaginary part of c comes from the change of value of Ψ in crossing the singular point (see appendix B). Thus the waves with a length larger than L_0, given by (21), are essentially neutral.

Now let us consider the condition for the existence of neutral waves with $U_{min} < c < U_{max}$. We have seen in section 3 that in crossing the singular point where $U = c$, there is a change of phase for Ψ_2 equal to $-G_s\Psi_1\pi i$, where $G_s = (U_s'' - \beta)/U_s'$, both for a real and complex c. Now we shall show that it is impossible for neutral waves (c real) to have such a change of phase.

Let us consider the general solution (10) of (2), given by

$$\Psi = A\Psi_1 + B\Psi_2,$$

where Ψ_1 and Ψ_2 are the solutions given in (8) and (9). If we separate the real and imaginary parts, we may write Ψ in the following form:

$$\Psi = \Psi_r + i\Psi_i, \tag{22}$$

with

$$\Psi_i'(0+) = \Psi_i'(0-) + G_s\pi B. \tag{23}$$

In case of a real c, all the coefficients of (2) are real, so that both Ψ_r and Ψ_i must satisfy the differential equation and the boundary conditions separately, and therefore the Wronskian

$$\Delta = \Psi_i\Psi_r' - \Psi_i'\Psi_r$$

must be constant. But since both Ψ_r and Ψ_i must be zero on the boundaries and their derivatives must vanish at the midpoint of the belt, the Wronskian is equal to zero at all points except the singular point. At this point there is a sudden change of the Wronskian, given by

$$\Delta_+ - \Delta_- = \Psi_s^2[\Psi_i'(0+) - \Psi_i'(0-)] = \Psi_s^2 G_s\pi,$$

which is impossible unless this quantity vanishes, since the Wronskian is equal to zero on both sides of the singular point. Thus for the neutral waves, this expression must be zero. From this we conclude that either $U_s'' = \beta$, *i.e.*, the singular point coincides with the point where the variation of the absolute vorticity with latitude is zero, or $\Psi_s = 0$. But the latter alternative is an impossibility unless $c = 0$ (or $c = U_{min}$), *i.e.*, unless the singular point is at the boundary of the belt, which belongs to the limiting case of the very slowly moving or retrograding waves. To show this, let us compare the solutions Ψ and F of (2) and (12); both are supposed to vanish at the singular point. Take the origin at the singular point and the nearer boundary at $y = y_0$. In this belt we have $G > G_2$, since $c - U > 0$; therefore Ψ will oscillate more slowly than F, according to Sturm's comparison theorem (Ince, 1944). Take $F = c - U$; then F will be positive from the singular point to the boundary (Ψ is also assumed to be positive near the singular point, *i.e.*, for y small). But since F is always positive except at the singular point, Ψ can not be zero at the boundary since it oscillates more slowly. Thus the only possibility of satisfying the boundary condition is that the singular point coincides with the boundary. The same argument can be applied to the other type of profile if we move the boundary to infinity.

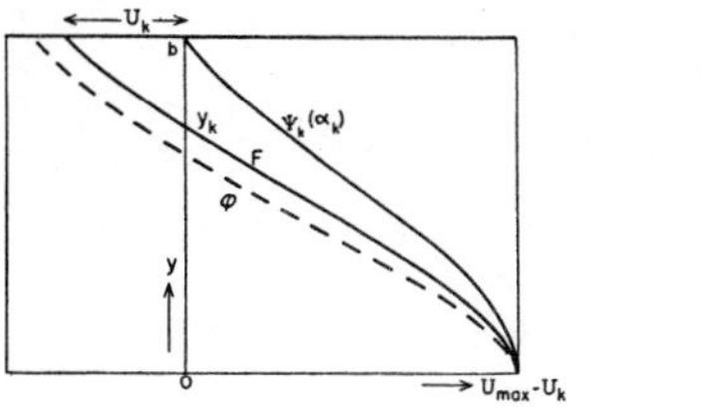

FIG. 4. The stream function Ψ_κ for the first velocity profile when there is a critical point y_κ.

Thus we have seen that the condition for having a neutral wave when $U_{min} < c < U_{max}$ is the existence of a critical point y_κ where $dZ/dy \equiv \beta - U'' = 0$. Now the question is: when this requirement is satisfied, can we actually have neutral waves, that is to say, can the given boundary conditions be satisfied by some real values of c? It can be shown that if $dZ/dy \equiv \beta - U'' = 0$ at some point y_κ, then we actually have the characteristic values $c = U_\kappa$ (or $\alpha = \alpha_\kappa$) and that it is the only one for the problem. To prove this let us consider the Sturm–Liouville system

$$\Psi'' = \left(\alpha^2 + \frac{U'' - \beta}{U - U_\kappa}\right)\Psi; \quad \Psi'(0) = 0, \tag{24}$$

where the midpoint of the velocity profile has been taken as the origin. Let us suppose that our profile is such that the critical point is a point where the absolute vorticity has its extreme value, *i.e.*, $U'' - \beta$ changes its sign there; then $(U'' - \beta)/(U - U_\kappa)$ will be negative in the whole region $(0, b)$.

If we take $\alpha = 0$ and let Ψ take the value $U(0) - U_\kappa > 0$ at the midpoint, then it will have a zero at a point $y < y_\kappa$, for the solution $F = U - U_\kappa$ of the system

$$F'' = \frac{U''}{U - U_\kappa}F; \quad F'(0) = 0, \tag{25}$$

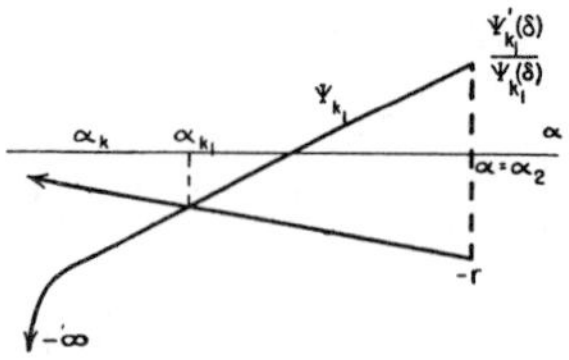

FIG. 5. The stream function Ψ_κ and the wave number α_κ for the second velocity profile.

has a zero at $y = y_\kappa$ and $(U'' - \beta)/(U - U_\kappa) < U''/(U - U_\kappa)$ in the interval $(0, y_\kappa)$; therefore, Ψ oscillates more rapidly than F and the first zero of Ψ will be nearer to the origin than the first zero of F, since both functions start from the same value at $y = 0$ (fig. 4). Thus Ψ will be negative at $y = b$. If we let α increase from zero, this zero point of Ψ will move toward the boundary $y = b$, and finally, when $\alpha = \alpha_\kappa$, we shall have the zero point of Ψ exactly at $y = b$, *i.e.*, the other boundary condition is satisfied by this particular value α_κ, the characteristic number, and Ψ_κ is then the characteristic function.

For the second profile, the zero point of Ψ is shifted to infinity, but it is easily shown that the characteristic value $\alpha_{\kappa 1}$ remains finite, for if we take $\alpha = \alpha_2$ greater than the upper limit of $(U'' - \beta)/(U - U_\kappa)$, so that the lower bound of $G_2 \equiv \alpha_2^2 + (U'' - \beta)/(U - U_\kappa)$ is k^2, which is positive, then the system

$$\varphi'' = k^2\varphi; \quad \varphi'(0) = 0 \tag{26}$$

has the non-oscillatory solution $\varphi = A \cosh ky$. When α decreases from α_2 to α_κ, the characteristic value for the first profile, a zero of Ψ will appear at $y = \delta$. Thus there must be a value $\alpha = \alpha_{\kappa 1}$ in the interval $\alpha_2 > \alpha_{\kappa 1} > \alpha_\kappa$, which will make Ψ equal to zero at infinity but not at any finite distance; this is the characteristic value for the second profile. This can also be proved by applying Sturm's oscillation theorem to (24) and (26), and finding the characteristic value $\alpha = \alpha_{\kappa 1}$ that makes Ψ, the characteristic function, satisfy the other condition

$$\Psi'(\delta) + r\Psi(\delta) = 0,$$

where $r = [\alpha^2 + \beta/(c - U_0)]^{\frac{1}{2}} > 0$. We have seen that, when $\alpha = \alpha_2$, $\Psi'/\Psi = \varphi'/\varphi > 0$, while as $\alpha \to \alpha_\kappa$, $\Psi(\delta)$ approaches zero from above, *i.e.*, $\Psi'(\delta) < 0$ and $\Psi'(\delta)/\Psi(\delta) \to -\infty$. Since $-r$ increases from $-[\alpha_2^2 + \beta/(c - U_0)]^{\frac{1}{2}}$ to $-[\alpha_\kappa^2 + \beta/(c - U_0)]^{\frac{1}{2}}$ as α decreases from α_2 to α_κ, while $\Psi'(\delta)/\Psi(\delta)$ decreases from a positive value to $-\infty$, there must be a value of $\alpha = \alpha_{\kappa 1}$, for which we have $\Psi'(\delta)/\Psi(\delta) = -r$; therefore $\alpha_{\kappa 1}$ is the characteristic value of the problem, and its value is greater than α_κ (see fig. 5).

Thus, *if there is only one critical point in the profile, we shall have one and only one neutral wave, with $c = U_\kappa$ and $L = L_\kappa$; all other waves with a phase velocity differing from U_κ will be either amplified (unstable) or damped,* aside from the group of slowly moving or retrograding long waves with $c < U_{\min}$. Therefore we must conclude that all the waves propagating with a velocity less than U_κ but greater than $U_{\min}$ will be either unstable or damped, and it will be shown later that they are actually unstable waves.[1]

If the condition $dZ/dy \equiv \beta - U'' = 0$ is satisfied for all y in the belt, which means that the profile is made up of constant-vorticity profiles, then the waves may move with any current velocity in the belt and are all neutral. This is obvious since then (2) reduces to $(U - c)\nabla^2\Psi = 0$, so that $U = c$ is always possible. In this case, there is a linear relationship between c and L.

5. The necessary condition for occurrence of unstable waves

Having now found all the neutral waves, let us consider the solutions with complex c. Equation (2) is to be solved under the condition that $\Psi = 0$ at the two boundaries $y = y_1$ and $y = y_2$. Then we have the following Sturm–Liouville system

$$\frac{d^2\Psi}{dy^2} - \left(\alpha^2 + \frac{U'' - \beta}{U - c}\right)\Psi = 0, \qquad \Psi(y_1) = 0, \quad \Psi(y_2) = 0. \tag{27}$$

We shall investigate the conditions under which we may have a complex $c = c_r + ic_i$. Suppose c complex and write $(U - c)^{-1}$ in the form $g_1 + ig_2$, with

$$g_1 = \frac{U - c_r}{(U - c_r)^2 + c_i^2}, \quad g_2 = \frac{c_i}{(U - c_r)^2 + c_i^2}. \tag{28}$$

In this case the coefficient of Ψ in (27) becomes complex and we must take Ψ to be complex, such that $\Psi = \Psi_r + i\Psi_i$. The system (27) then becomes, after separating the real and imaginary parts

$$\Psi_r'' - [\alpha^2 + (U'' - \beta)g_1]\Psi_r + (U'' - \beta)g_2\Psi_i = 0,$$
$$\Psi_i'' - [\alpha^2 + (U'' - \beta)g_1]\Psi_i - (U'' - \beta)g_2\Psi_r = 0,$$

with the conditions $\Psi_r(y_1) = \Psi_r(y_2) = 0$, $\Psi_i(y_1) = \Psi_i(y_2) = 0$. If we multiply the first equation by Ψ_i

[1] It may be mentioned that Thompson's (1948) solution is actually the one discrete neutral solution we are considering in the range of velocity $U_{\min} < c < U_{\max}$ or the one slowly moving wave with $c < U_{\min}$. His equation (4) is an equation defining the zonal current (for finite-amplitude motions we may take the values along a trough where $v = 0$) as a sine-curve profile with the parameter c. If we differentiate it with respect to y, we get the condition

$$Z' \equiv \beta - U'' = -k^2\Psi' = k^2(U - c),$$

where $Z \equiv f + \nabla^2\Psi$ is the absolute vorticity. Thus c can not take the value U unless $dZ/dy = 0$ at that point (which is the critical point). If no such point exists in the profile, c must be different from all values of U in the belt. Thus, his equation (15) must not be interpreted as a continuous relation between c and L in this range of velocity, but only expresses c_κ in terms of L_κ, which is determined from the critical point.

and the second by Ψ_r and subtract, we get

$$\frac{d}{dy}\left(\Psi_i \frac{d\Psi_r}{dy} - \Psi_r \frac{d\Psi_i}{dy}\right) = -(U'' - \beta)g_2(\Psi_r^2 + \Psi_i^2).$$

Now let us integrate this from y_1 to y_2, and make use of the boundary conditions; thus,

$$\int_{y_1}^{y_2'} (\beta - U'')g_2(\Psi_r^2 + \Psi_i^2)\, dy = 0. \quad (29)$$

But since g_2 is either always positive or always negative, according to the sign of c_i, and $\Psi_r^2 + \Psi_i^2$ always positive, we can have the integral equal to zero only if $dZ/dy \equiv \beta - U''$ is identically zero or if $\beta - U''$ somewhere changes its sign within the region, *i.e.*, it must be zero somewhere in the region.

Thus the necessary condition for having a complex c is that

$$U'' - \beta = 0 \quad (30)$$

at some point $y = y_\kappa$ in the region, and changes its sign there. This condition is both necessary and sufficient for c_i to be different from zero. It is necessary as the proof stands. By sufficient we mean that, whenever $U'' - \beta = 0$ at some point in the region, and changes its sign there, then we must have a complex c with $c_i \neq 0$. This is rather obvious since we have only a single isolated stable solution with $c = U_\kappa$, $L = L_\kappa$, while the frequency equation (11) will give c as a function of α or L for every value of L; therefore, for L different from L_κ, we must have $c_i \neq 0$.

The sufficiency of this condition for the existence of amplified waves will be proved in the next section by a more direct and rigorous method by demonstrating (*1*) the existence of characteristic values of c and α in the vicinity of the neutral wave (c_κ, L_κ) such that $c_i \neq 0$, and (*2*) that the sign of c_i is positive for $L > L_\kappa$. It must be pointed out that the condition (30) is only necessary for neutral and amplified waves but not for damped waves since the solution is not valid all along the real axis when $c_i < 0$ (see Lin, 1945).

The same criterion can also be applied to motions over the spherical earth. In this case, the vorticity equation can be written in the form

$$(\dot{\lambda} - \mu)\left(\frac{d^2\Psi}{dy^2} - n^2\Psi\right) + \frac{dZ}{dy}\Psi = 0, \quad (31)$$

where $y = \ln(\sec\phi + \tan\phi)$, $\dot{\lambda}$ is the relative angular velocity of the current, μ the angular velocity of the disturbance, and $\psi = \Psi(y)e^{in(\lambda - \mu t)}$ the stream function for the perturbation, defined by

$$\dot{\phi}\cos\phi = \partial\psi/\partial\lambda, \quad \dot{\lambda}\cos\phi = -\partial\psi/\partial\phi.$$

Since equation (31) is of the same form as (2) and the boundary conditions may be taken as $\Psi = 0$ at $y = 0$ (the equator) and $y = \infty$ (the pole), the same conclusion will be obtained as before, *i.e.*, the absolute vorticity must have some maximum or minimum in the region. Thus the curvature of the earth does not have much effect on the nature and stability of the disturdances.

The physical explanation of this condition for amplified waves may be sought from the meaning of the condition $dZ/dy \equiv \beta - U'' = 0$, which represents the points with an extreme value of absolute vorticity. If we take the zonal distribution of wind as a distribution of vortex filaments, and calculate the acceleration attained by a vortex element displaced from its original position in such a field, we shall find that the transversal acceleration will be given by (Lin, 1945)

$$\bar{a}_y = \Gamma^{-1}\iint v^2 \frac{dZ}{dy}\, dxdy,$$

where $\Gamma \equiv \int\int \zeta\, dxdy$ = circulation of the element, and y will be replaced by the expression $\ln(\sec\phi + \tan\phi)$ in case of motion over the spherical earth. Thus $\bar{a}_y$ is proportional to $dZ/dy \equiv \beta - U''$, and is always directed toward the original position if $\beta - U''$ is of the same sign in the entire region. Only when there are some points where $\beta - U''$ changes sign, could the elements gain an acceleration in the direction away from their original positions, and only those elements that actually have crossed these points will be thus accelerated.[2] It should be mentioned that the fulfilment of the condition $U'' = \beta$ only gives the *possibility* for instability to occur, unlike the criterion obtained from the assumption of conservation of absolute momentum which asserts that the situation will be definitely unstable for all moving elements in the region where we have $U' > f$, regardless of the character or size of the disturbance. The selective character of the new criterion is in agreement with results obtained from the study of stability of wave motions, which shows that the condition of stability will depend upon the wave length of the disturbance.

If, on the other hand, we have a vortex superimposed in the current of basic flow, it will also be subject to a force $\bar{a}_y$ per unit mass. Thus, if in some locality and at some instant, the motion deviates from purely horizontal nondivergent barotropic conditions, and a concentration of cyclonic or anticyclonic vorticity is produced through any process in the atmosphere, such as convergence or divergence, vertical motion or the action of a solenoidal field, while the motion of the surrounding atmosphere still retains its

[2] This selective nature of the stability criterion may be explained by the nature of the field of force. In the case of vertical stratification or horizontal distribution of centrifugal force, the force is directed in one direction only, while in our case, the point where $U'' = \beta$ may be considered as the center of a repelling or attracting force, acting in opposite directions on its two sides. Thus for small displacements, the element will be acted on by a restoring force, driving it back to its original position; but if the displacement is great enough such that the element reaches the other side of this center of force, an acceleration away from its original position will result.

horizontal and nondivergent character, then this vortex will be moving under a force $\bar{a}_y$ in the north–south direction. In the ordinary case of a strong jet of westerlies the absolute vorticity has a maximum to the north of the latitude of maximum wind and a minimum to the south. Thus if a cyclonic vortex is produced to the north of the point of maximum absolute vorticity, the force will be directed toward the south. The effect of the motion between the latitudes where Z has its extreme values gives a force in the opposite direction. It is the resultant of these two opposing forces that determines the motion of the vortex. The southward motion and the cutting-off of the lows may thus be explained by the interaction between the distribution of absolute vorticity in the basic flow and the velocity field due to the superimposed vortex.

The concentration of vorticity may be expected to occur in the troughs and ridges of the upper waves, especially when the wave length corresponds to the maximum unstable condition.

6. Amplified waves

We have proved in the preceding sections that when we have one critical point $y = y_\kappa$ where $dZ/dy \equiv \beta - U'' = 0$, we have one and only one neutral wave with a real phase velocity and that the value of this phase velocity is $c = U_\kappa$; for all other velocities such that $c_r \neq U_\kappa$, we shall have $c_i \neq 0$.

This statement is proved by considering the solution $\Psi = \Psi_\kappa + (d\Psi/d\lambda)_\kappa \Delta\lambda$ corresponding to $c = c_\kappa + (dc/d\lambda)_\kappa \Delta\lambda$, slightly different from the neutral solution Ψ_κ corresponding to $c = c_\kappa = U_\kappa$, $\lambda = \lambda_\kappa \equiv \alpha_\kappa^2$. If we write $\Delta c = \Delta c_r + ic_i$, it will be found that c_i and Δc_r are given by

$$c_i = -D\pi E^{-1}\Delta c_r, \tag{32}$$

$$(1 + D^2\pi^2E^{-2})\Delta c_r = -\frac{\Delta\lambda}{E}\int_0^b \Psi_\kappa^2 dy, \tag{33}$$

where

$$E \equiv \lim_{\epsilon\to 0}\left(\int_0^{y_\kappa-\epsilon} + \int_{y_\kappa+\epsilon}^b\right)\frac{U'' - \beta}{(U - c_\kappa)^2}\Psi_\kappa^2 dy; \tag{34}$$

and $D \equiv (U_\kappa''' - \beta')/U'^2$. Since in general we have $U'' > \beta$ from 0 to y_κ (origin at the boundary) and $U'' < \beta$ from y_κ to b, we have $D < 0$. Thus if Δc_r and E have the same sign, we shall have $c_i > 0$, while if they have opposite signs, we shall have $c_i < 0$. Since β is positive, the absolute value of $U'' - \beta$ is larger when U'' is negative than when U'' is positive; and since Ψ_κ has its maximum value at $y = b$, we should expect E to be negative by an inspection of (34); this is also shown to be the case in the examples discussed in section 7. Thus in order to have $c_i > 0$, we must have $\Delta c_r < 0$ and (33) shows that we must have $\Delta\lambda \equiv \alpha^2 - \alpha_\kappa^2 < 0$, *i.e.*, the waves longer than the neutral wave with $c = U_\kappa$ and $L = L_\kappa$ are unstable. If $E \to 0$, then $\Delta c_r/E$ will be given by $-\Delta\lambda \int_0^b \Psi_\kappa^2 dy$, which is positive for $\Delta\lambda < 0$, that is to say, c_i is also positive for $\Delta\lambda < 0$. If E is positive, a positive c_i will also require $\Delta\lambda < 0$. Thus we see that unstable waves in the neighborhood of the neutral wave with $c = U_\kappa$ always have longer wave length than L_κ. The detailed procedure in obtaining (32) and (33) is given in appendix A.

These results, with slight modification, are valid also for the second profile, as indicated in appendix A.

In the neighborhood of the stationary (or $c = U_{min}$) neutral solution, it is demonstrated in appendix B that, for $\Delta c_r > 0$ (*i.e.*, for $c_r > U_{min}$), c_r and c_i are given by the approximate equations

$$c_r\left(U'(0) + \alpha_0^2\int_0^b U\,dy\right) = \Delta(\alpha^2)\int_0^b U^2 dy, \tag{35}$$

$$c_i\left(U'(0) + \alpha_0^2\int_0^b U\,dy\right) = G_s\pi c_r^2, \tag{36}$$

which show that c_i is always positive since $U_0'' - \beta > 0$ and $U_0' > 0$.

From the preceding discussions we see that all the waves with $U_{min} < c_r < U_\kappa$ are amplified and those with $c_r > U_\kappa$ are damped. Thus, if we draw an L, c-diagram, we shall have three regions separated from each other by the values $L = L_0$ and $L = L_\kappa$ corresponding to the phase velocities $c = U_{min}$ and $c = U_\kappa$. To the right of $L = L_0$, the waves are essentially neutral; in the region $L_0 > L > L_\kappa$ ($U_{min} < c_r < U_\kappa$) we have $c_i > 0$ and the waves are amplified. The degree of instability will be greatest somewhere in the central part of this region. To the left, with $L < L_\kappa$ and $c_r > U_\kappa$, the waves will be damped (see fig. 6).

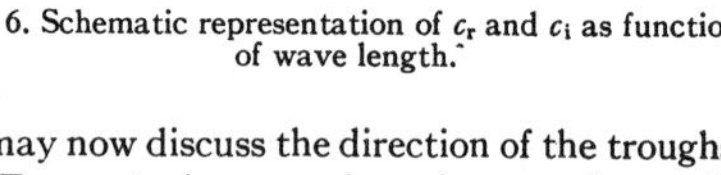

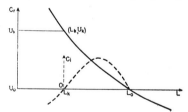

FIG. 6. Schematic representation of c_r and c_i as functions of wave length.

We may now discuss the direction of the troughs and ridges. For neutral waves, since there can be no change of phase, the troughs and ridges must be in the direction from south to north. For unstable waves, with $U'' \neq \beta$ at the point where $U = c_r$, the trough lines will be tilted, in the direction from southeast toward northwest to the south of the point of minimum absolute vorticity, and from southwest toward northeast to the north of the point maximum absolute vorticity. This can be proved by the following considerations.

Along the trough, we have $v = 0$, where v is the real part of $\partial\psi/\partial x$. Since $\psi = \Psi e^{ik(x-ct)}$, where $\Psi = \Psi_r + i\Psi_i$ and $c = c_r + ic_i$, we find that

$$v = -k(\Psi_r \sin k\xi + \Psi_i \cos k\xi)e^{c_i tk}, \tag{37}$$

in which $\xi = x - c_r t$. The trough lines are therefore to be determined from

$$\tan k\xi = -\Psi_i/\Psi_r.$$

Since the direction of the trough lines is determined by the sign of ξ', we differentiate the above equation with respect to y:

$$k\xi' \sec^2 k\xi = (\Psi_r'\Psi_i - \Psi_i'\Psi_r)/\Psi_r^2. \tag{38}$$

If we take y to be directed from the region where $U < c_r$ to the region where $U > c_r$, then for slightly amplified waves, the quantity on the right of (38) is negative, according to Tollmien (1929). Thus the troughs and ridges are directed from southeast toward northwest to the south of the point of minimum Z, and from southwest toward northeast to the north of the point of maximum Z.

This conclusion is in agreement with the consideration of the change of the kinetic energy of the eddying motion with time. Thus, the average value over a wave length of the correlation between the perturbation velocities u and v is given by

$$\overline{uv} = \tfrac{1}{2}k(\Psi_r'\Psi_i - \Psi_i'\Psi_r)e^{2k c_i t}$$

which, as already noted, is negative in the region where $U' \equiv \partial U/\partial y > 0$. Hence $U'\overline{uv}$ is negative, and the kinetic energy of the perturbation increases, while that of the basic flow decreases (see Lamb, 1932, pp. 676–677). For damped waves, the direction of the trough lines will be in the opposite sense and the correlation between u and v will be positive, corresponding to a decrease of the kinetic energy of the eddying motion and an increase of the kinetic energy of the basic flow.

7. Examples with sine-curve velocity profile

Let us apply the foregoing discussions to the sine-curve velocity profiles. For this kind of periodic profile, the stream function Ψ_κ for the neutral wave with $c = U_\kappa$ can be obtained explicitly in a simple form. Since we can fit a sine curve to most of the observed wind distributions by varying the parameters such as the maximum wind velocity $U_{\max}$, the width of the belt $2b$, and the position of the critical point $y = y_\kappa$, we shall discuss this profile in some detail.

A. Limited belt.—For the first profile, we may write

$$U = U_\kappa + \frac{\sin k(y - y_t)}{1 + \sin ky_t} U_{\max} + \frac{\beta}{k^2}, \tag{39}$$

which satisfies the conditions that $U = 0$ at $y = 0$ and $U'' = \beta$ at $y = y_\kappa$. In (39), we have $k = \frac{1}{2}\pi/(b - y_t)$; y_t is the inflection point of the profile (where $U'' = 0$), U_t is the current velocity at this point, and the midpoint of the profile is at $y = b$, where the wind velocity is equal to $U_{\max}$.

If we substitute (39) into (2) and put $c = U_\kappa$, we get the equation for Ψ_κ:

$$\Psi_\kappa'' = (\alpha_\kappa^2 - k^2)\Psi_\kappa, \tag{40}$$

which admits the solution $\Psi_\kappa = B \sin py$, where

$$p^2 = k^2 - \alpha_\kappa^2. \tag{41}$$

The boundary conditions $\Psi_\kappa(0) = 0$, $\Psi'(b) = 0$ are satisfied by $p = (2n + 1)\pi/2b$, where n is any integer. But since $0 \leq y_t < b/2$, the only possible value of p is $\pi/2b$.[3] Therefore we get

$$\Psi_\kappa = \frac{\sin(\pi y/2b)}{\sin(\pi y_\kappa/2b)}, \tag{42}$$

the constant factor being chosen to make $\Psi_\kappa = 1$ at the critical point.

The wave number α_κ is given by

$$\alpha_\kappa^2 = \frac{\pi^2}{4b^2}\left[\left(1 - \frac{y_t}{b}\right)^{-2} - 1\right]. \tag{43}$$

Thus the stable wave with $c_\kappa = U_\kappa$ is completely determined by the value of y_κ, which depends upon y_t and $U_{\max}$ and the stream function is given by (42) while the wave length $L_\kappa = 2\pi/\alpha_\kappa$ is determined by (43).

For $y_t = 0.333b$, we have $y_\kappa = 0.245b$ and

$$\alpha_\kappa b = 0.559\pi, \quad c_\kappa = U_\kappa = 0.414\,U_{\max} - 0.181b^2\beta. \tag{44}$$

For $y_t = 0.25b$, we have $y_\kappa = 0.139b$ and

$$\alpha_\kappa b = 0.440\pi, \quad c_\kappa = U_\kappa = 0.333\,U_{\max} - 0.226b^2\beta. \tag{45}$$

Thus we see that the greater the value of c_κ, the shorter will be the wave length L_κ corresponding to a larger α_κ. Since α_κ is inversely proportional the width of the belt $2b$, L_κ is directly proportional to b. For $y_t = b/3$ and $2b = 20$ degrees latitude, we get $L_\kappa = 36$ degrees latitude.

The amplifying oscillations in the neighborhood of the stable solution Ψ_κ are calculated by using (32) and (33), and the values in the vicinity of $c = 0$ (or $c = U_{\min}$) are calculated by using (35) and (36). Since we have only considered the first term in the Taylor expansion of c, the formulas thus obtained will hold

---

[3] If we eliminate the terms involving y from (39) and its second derivative and then integrate from 0 to $2b$, we get, by using (41):

$$c_\kappa = U_\kappa = \bar{U} + (\overline{U''} - \beta)\left(\frac{\pi^2}{4b^2} + \frac{4\pi^2}{L_\kappa^2}\right)^{-1}$$

which relates the phase velocity c_κ to the average value of the current $\bar{U}$; $\overline{U''}$ is the difference of the shear at the two boundaries divided by $2b$, the wave length is L_κ, and the breadth of the belt $2b$. This equation looks like a generalized Rossby's equation, but it holds only for the neutral wave with c_κ and L_κ, and must not be interpreted as a continuous relation between c and L.

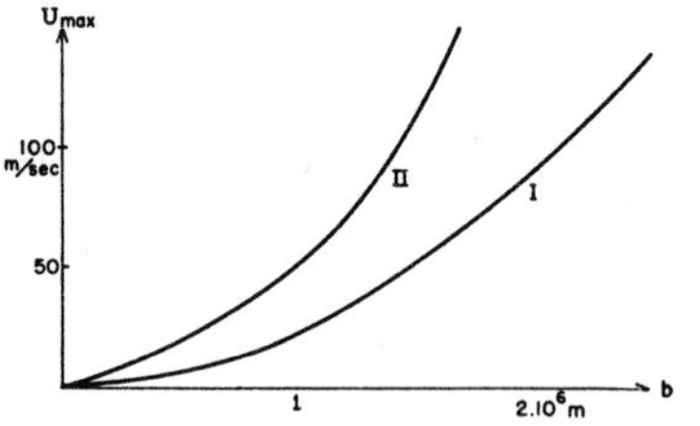

FIG. 7. The sharpness of the velocity profiles expressed as a relation between the maximum current velocity $U_{\max}$ and the width of the belt, b.

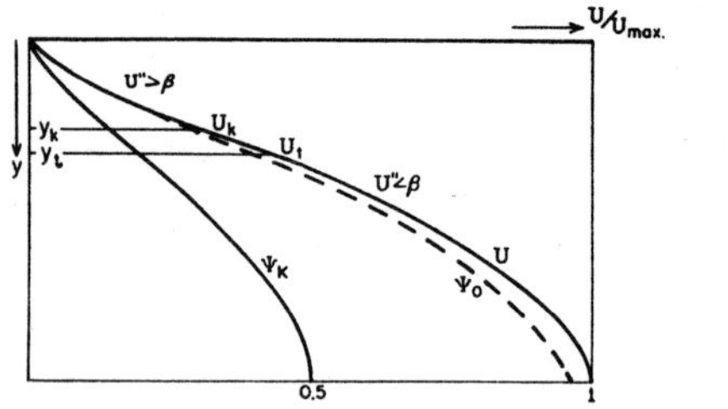

FIG. 8. $\Psi_\kappa(y)$ and $\Psi_0(y)$ for the first velocity profile in comparison with $U(y)$ as functions of y. Note that $\Psi_0(y)$ is nearly equal to $U(y)$.

only for small values of $\Delta\lambda = \Delta(\alpha^2)$. The values for the intermediate regions between $\alpha^2 = \alpha_0^2$ and $\alpha^2 = \alpha_\kappa^2$ are obtained by interpolation. If more accurate values are desired, we must calculate the second and higher derivatives; but since we are concerned only with orders of magnitude, no attempt has been made in this direction. Now let us consider the different cases separately.

Case I. Weak jet. Let $U_{\max} = 2.2 \times 10^{-11}b^2$ m sec^{-1} (fig. 7, curve I). With $y_t = b/3$, $y_\kappa = 0.2447b$, the values of c_κ and α_κ are given by (44), which, in this case, reduce to

$$c_\kappa = 0.293U_{\max}, \quad \alpha_\kappa b = 0.559\pi. \tag{46}$$

In the vicinity of $c = c_\kappa$, $\alpha = \alpha_\kappa$, we have, from (33) and (32),

$$c_r/U_{\max} = 0.099 + 0.0634\alpha^2 b, \tag{47}$$

$$c_i/U_{\max} = 0.044 - 0.0144\alpha^2 b. \tag{48}$$

From (47) and (48) we see that for $\alpha < \alpha_\kappa$, we have $c_r < c_\kappa$ and $c_i > 0$; and for $\alpha > \alpha_\kappa$, we have $c_r > c_\kappa$, $c_i < 0$. Thus waves longer than the neutral wave $c = U_\kappa$ are unstable and slower while the shorter waves are faster and damped. In the vicinity of $c = 0$ (or $= U_{\min}$), the corresponding values of c_r and c_i are obtained by using (35) and (36). Here we have $\alpha_0 b = 0.94$ and

$$c_{r0}/U_{\max} = 0.312\alpha^2 b^2 - 0.275, \tag{49}$$

$$c_{i0}/U_{\max} = 3.62\,(c_r/U_{\max})^2. \tag{50}$$

The stream function Ψ_0 is shown in fig. 8 together with U and Ψ_κ, for comparison. The values of c_r and c_i, given by (47), (48), (49), and (50) are plotted in fig. 9(A) for $y_t = b/3$. The central parts are obtained by interpolation.

For the case with $y_t = b/4$, we have $y_\kappa = 0.1388b$ and

$$c_\kappa = 0.179U_{\max}, \quad \alpha_\kappa b = 0.442\pi, \quad \alpha_0 b = 0.910; \tag{51}$$

the computed values of c_r and c_i are plotted in fig. 9(B). We see that the values of c_κ and c_i have been diminished enormously as compared with the case for $y_t = b/3$. Although the condition that $Z \equiv f - U'$ has an extreme value at some points is sufficient for the existence of some $c_i > 0$, the value of c_i depends upon the position of the critical point y_κ, which determines the factor $D \equiv U_\kappa'''/U_\kappa'^2$. The above examples show this clearly. With the point y_κ shifted toward the boundary $y = 0$, where the disturbance is supposed to be zero, very few particles can actually get across this point and the disturbance is therefore comparatively stable.

Case II. Strong jet. Let $U_{\max} = 5 \times 10^{-11}b^2$ m sec^{-1} (fig. 7, curve II). With $y_t = b/3$, we have $y_\kappa = 0.294b$ and

$$c_\kappa = 0.360U_{\max}, \quad \alpha_\kappa b = 0.559\pi, \quad \alpha_0 b = 0.626. \tag{52}$$

The profile is represented by the same curve in fig. 7, but now the ratio $b^2/U_{\max}$ has decreased so that the profile is sharper than that for case I. The value of U_κ has increased from $0.293U_{\max}$ to $0.360U_{\max}$, and y_κ is now nearer to y_t. The values of c_r and c_i for this case are represented in fig. 9(C).

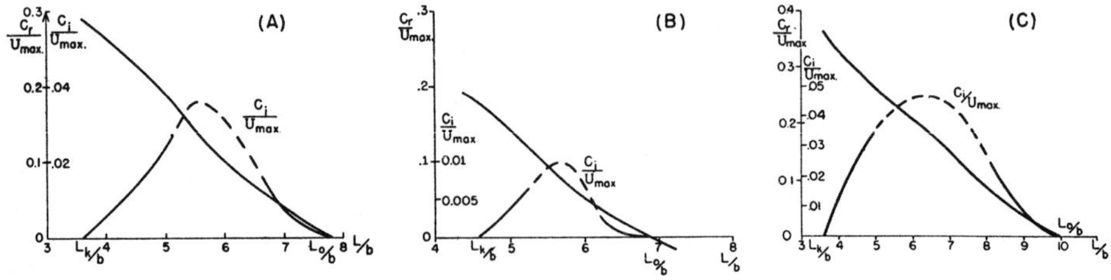

FIG. 9. c_r and c_i for the first sine-curve velocity profiles. A: for the weaker jet (I in fig. 7) with $y_t = b/3$; B: for the weaker profile (I in fig. 7) with $y_t = b/4$; C: for the stronger jet (II in fig. 7) with $y_t = b/3$.

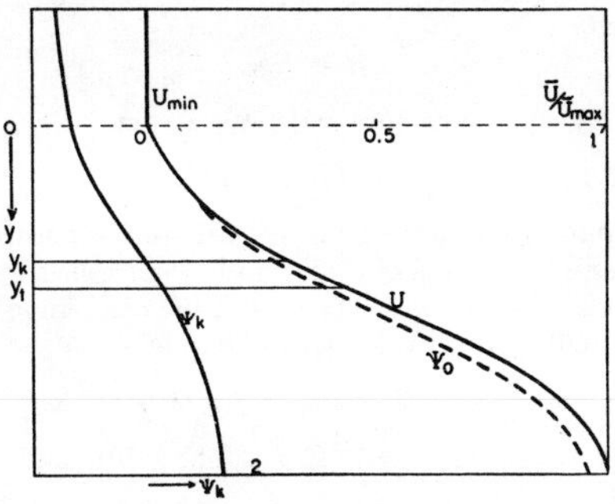

FIG. 10. Ψ_κ and Ψ_0 for the second velocity profile. Note that Ψ_0 is nearly equal to $U(y)$.

From these examples we see that the effect of sharpening the profile is to increase the values of c_κ, c_r, and c_i, *i.e.*, increase the instability.

B. Belt extending to infinity.—For the second type of profile, equations (32) and (33) are to be used for the values near $c = U_\kappa$, $\alpha = \alpha_\kappa$, with the modification mentioned at the end of section 7, while the values in the vicinity of $c = U_{\min} = U_0$ are given by the same expressions as in the preceding example for a limited belt. For this case, the conditions to be satisfied are $U = U_0$ for $y = 0$, and $U'' = \beta$ at $y = y_\kappa$. These give the following expression for U:

$$U = U_\kappa + \frac{\sin k(y - y_t)}{1 + \sin k y_t}\,\bar{U}_{\max} + \frac{\beta}{k^2}, \qquad (53)$$

the same as (39) except with $\bar{U}_{\max} = U_{\max} - U_0$, $k = \frac{1}{2}\pi/(\delta - y_t)$ (the midpoint is $y = \delta$, where $U = U_{\max}$). Let us use $\bar{c}_\kappa \equiv c_\kappa - U_0 = U_\kappa - U_0$; then the equation for $\Psi_{\kappa 1}$ reduces to (40), as in the preceding example, but now the conditions to be satisfied are

$$\Psi_{\kappa 1}'(0) = r\Psi_{\kappa 1}(0); \quad r^2 = \alpha_\kappa^2 + \frac{\beta}{U_\kappa - U_0}; \qquad \Psi_{\kappa 1}'(\delta) = 0. \qquad (54)$$

The solution which satisfies the second condition is, when normalized

$$\Psi_{\kappa 1} = \cos p(y - \delta)/\cos p(y_\kappa - \delta),$$

so the first condition requires the relation

$$r = p \tan p\delta. \qquad (55)$$

Thus we get

$$\frac{p}{\cos p\delta} = \left(k^2 + \frac{\beta}{U_\kappa - U_0}\right)^{\frac{1}{2}} = (r^2 + p^2)^{\frac{1}{2}}, \qquad (56)$$

with $0 \leq y_t < \delta/2$.

Case I. Weak jet. Let $y_t = \delta/3$, $y_\kappa = 0.245\delta$. Then

$$p\delta = 0.364\pi, \quad \alpha_\kappa\delta = 2.055, \quad r\delta = 2.56$$
$$\bar{c}_\kappa = U_\kappa - U_0 = 0.293\bar{U}_{\max}, \quad \alpha_0\delta = 0.94. \qquad (57)$$

The stream functions for the central and outer parts respectively are plotted in fig. 10, and the values of c_r and c_i are plotted in fig. 11(A). For a belt with $2\delta = 25$ degrees latitude, the wave length L_κ for the stable wave with $c = U_\kappa$ is equal to 39 degrees latitude while the wave with $c = U_0$ has the length $L_0 = 83$ degrees latitude.

Case II. Strong jet. Let $\bar{U}_{\max} = 5 \times 10^{-11}\delta^2$ m sec^{-1}. For $y_t = \delta/3$ we have $y_\kappa = 0.294\delta$ and

$$\bar{c}_\kappa = 0.360\bar{U}_{\max}, \quad \alpha_\kappa\delta = 2.07,$$
$$p\delta = 0.354\pi, \quad r\delta = 2.32, \quad \alpha_0\delta = 0.63. \qquad (58)$$

From these we get

$$\bar{c}_r/\bar{U}_{\max} = 0.113 + 0.058\alpha^2\delta^2, \qquad (59)$$

$$c_i/\bar{U}_{\max} = 0.228 - 0.053\alpha^2\delta^2. \qquad (60)$$

Equations (59) and (60) are plotted in fig. 11(B), together with the values for c_{r0} and c_{i0}, given by (49) and (50). From these examples we see that the profile of unlimited lateral extent is comparatively more unstable than that for a limited belt. Here the destabilizing effect of sharpening the profile can also be seen very clearly with the increase of c_r and c_i.

From the foregoing examples we see that for the unstable waves with $L_\kappa < L < L_0$ and $U_\kappa > c_r > U_0$, the amplification factor αc_i is of the order of 10^{-5} sec^{-1} for the last two cases, which shows that the amplitude will be doubled in the course of 24 hours. Thus we see that this kind of dynamic instability is at least of the right order of magnitude and may be one of the main factors responsible for the growth of disturbances in the upper atmosphere. For other cases, the amplifica-

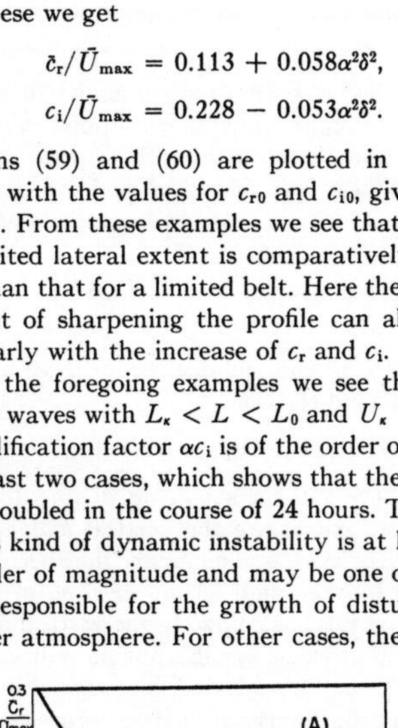

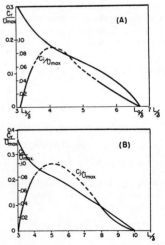

FIG. 11. c_r and c_i for the second sine-curve velocity profile. A: for the weaker jet; B: for the stronger jet, with the critical point at the same position.

tion factor may be much smaller, so that a much longer time would be required for the systems to double their amplitudes. Disturbances with a very small amplification factor will be difficult to distinguish from the stable waves. We have seen that for cases with very small amplification factors, the regions of instability are far away from each other and the value of U_κ is very near to U_0, *i.e.*, y_κ is near the boundary; these relatively stable waves thus merge into the long stable waves.

8. The dynamic instability of geostrophic flow for three-dimensional perturbations in a baroclinic atmosphere

We shall discuss briefly the possibility of extending this study to more general conditions. Consider a stratified atmosphere, with both vertical and horizontal wind shear, and solenoidal field. The basic state is a geostrophic flow and hydrostatic equilibrium, defined by

$$fU = -S\frac{\partial P}{\partial y}, \quad g = -S\frac{\partial P}{\partial z}, \qquad (61)$$

where S is the specific volume. From these we obtain the thermal wind relation

$$fU_z + g\sigma_y = fU\sigma_z, \qquad (62)$$

where $\sigma \equiv \ln S$, and the subscripts denote differentiation; thus, σ_y and σ_z are the vertical and horizontal stratifications. We assume that the perturbation, represented by the small letters u, v, w, p, and s, is superposed on this basic flow. In the vertical direction, we assume that static equilibrium is still valid, *i.e.*, $dw/dt - f_2U$ can be neglected. Through this assumption, the very short gravitational waves are eliminated. Using the symbol L for the operator $\partial/\partial t + U\partial/\partial x$, the equations of motion and of continuity are then as follows:

$$Lu + (U_y - f)v + (U_z + f_2)w + Sp_x = 0, \qquad (63)$$

$$Lv + fu - fUS^{-1}s + Sp_y = 0, \qquad (64)$$

$$-gS^{-1}s + Sp_z = 0, \qquad (65)$$

$$S^{-1}Ls + \sigma_y v + \sigma_z w - \text{div}\,(u, v, w) = 0. \qquad (66)$$

The motion is assumed to be adiabatic, so that

$$S^{-1}Ls + \sigma_y v + \sigma_z w + S\epsilon(Lp + vp_y + wp_z) = 0, \qquad (67)$$

where ϵ is the inverse square of the Laplacian velocity of sound, and is taken as constant. From (63) and (64) we get the vorticity equation

$$L\zeta + (\beta - U_{yy})v + (f - U_y)\,\text{div}\,(u, v) - fUS^{-1}s_x - \sigma_y Sp_x = 0, \qquad (68)$$

where the term $(f_2 - U_z)\partial w/\partial y$ has been neglected. If we use the geostrophic relation for the meridional velocity v,

$$fv = Sp_x, \qquad (69)$$

then by combining (65) and (69), we get

$$gs_x = fS(v_z - \sigma_z v). \qquad (70)$$

Assuming that each of the perturbation quantities is expressed as a function of y and z multiplied by the harmonic factor $\exp\,[ik_x(x - ct)]$, and combining (67), (62), (69), and (70), we get ultimately

$$w = -rf(U - c)v_z - f(g^{-1}c - rU_z)v, \qquad (71)$$

where $r^{-1} = g(\sigma_z - g\epsilon)$. From (66), (70), and (71), we get

$$\text{div}\,(u, v) = fr(U - c)(v_{zz} - \sigma_z v_z) + fg^{-1}Uv_z + [\sigma_y + fr(\sigma_z U_z - U_{zz}) - fg^{-1}U\sigma_z]v. \qquad (72)$$

Substituting (69), (70), and (72) into (68), and assuming $\partial\zeta/\partial x = \nabla^2 v$, which is substantially equivalent to the geostrophic approximation for the vorticity, we find on neglecting smaller terms,

$$(U - c)[\nabla^2 v + rfZ(v_{zz} - \sigma_z v_z)] + [\beta - U_{yy} - \sigma_y U_y + rfZ(\sigma_z U_z - U_{zz})]v = 0, \qquad (73)$$

where $Z = f - U_y$. A similar equation holds for the perturbation pressure p. It will be noted that, if we take the complete equations of motion without using the geostrophic relation, we arrive at a partial differential equation much more complicated than (73); but after neglecting terms of smaller magnitude by assuming that the waves are longer than 2000 km, we finally obtain (73).

Let us take the difference of the adiabatic and actual lapse rate equal to 3.5C km^{-1}, and the mean temperature equal to 250K; then we shall have the following values:

$$(gr)^{-1} = \sigma_z - g\epsilon = 1.4 \times 10^{-5}\ \text{m}^{-1};$$
$$\sigma_z = 1.3 \times 10^{-4}\ \text{m}^{-1}.$$

From (62),

$$f(\sigma_z U_z - U_{zz}) = g\sigma_{yz},$$

so the coefficient of the last term of (73) can be written

$$Z\frac{d}{dy}[\ln(SZ) + gr\sigma_z] - f\sigma_y,$$

if r is taken as constant. The terms in the expression above are all of the order 10^{-11} m^{-1} sec^{-1}, the same as β. If we neglect the variation in the meridional direction, (73) reduces to the fundamental equation discussed by Charney (1947). This equation should be solved under certain boundary conditions, but it is so complicated that it is almost impossible to solve in this form. However, we may solve equations of this form by certain approximations. Thus if we neglect the variation of U with height when it is undifferentiated, but retain the terms with U_z, we may assume the exponential solution $v = V(y)\exp\,(\frac{1}{2}\sigma_z + ik_z)z$;

(73) is then reduced to an ordinary differential equation with the independent variable y:

$$(U - c)\{V'' - [k_x^2 + rfZ(k_z^2 + \tfrac{1}{4}\sigma_z^2)]V\} + \{Z\, d[\ln (SZ) + gr\sigma_z]/dy - f\sigma_y\} V = 0. \quad (74)$$

The function V satisfies the upper boundary condition that the energy per unit volume will be zero at infinity, but does not satisfy the lower condition $w = 0$. This condition could be satisfied by taking into consideration a small friction near the ground, an artifice used by Rayleigh. If k_z is real, we have internal waves, with the amplitude increasing with height; if, on the other hand, k_z is imaginary, we shall have external waves, with amplitude decreasing with height. This difference is determined by the wave length and by the value of $U - c$, which determines the relative values of the terms in the coefficient of V. Thus we see that for waves with $L \approx 5000$ km, we shall have internal waves, while for waves with $L \lessapprox 2000$ km, we have external waves. With these differences, which will affect the value of k_x and therefore L, (74) is of the same form as (2), only with different constants as coefficients. Thus all the results we have obtained so far can also be applied to the case of three-dimensional flow in a baroclinic atmosphere, with the appropriate modifications for the position of the critical point and the value of the critical wave length. In this case, the critical point is characterized by the vanishing of the coefficient of the last term of (74), which, if we neglect $f\sigma_y$ against β, will occur when the quantity $\ln (SZ) + gr\sigma_z$ has an extreme value. If σ_z is constant, the critical point is the point where SZ has its extreme value. When σ_y is large, $f\sigma_y$ will no longer be negligible compared with β.

9. Synoptic examples

In conclusion, we shall offer some speculations concerning the development of cyclone waves along a jet of westerlies. Suppose we have two critical points (where the absolute vorticity has an extreme value), one on each side of the maximum wind; then the air to the north will have an excess of (cyclonic) absolute vorticity relative to the air to the south. Thus if a disturbance sets in and an exchange of air results, cyclonic and anticyclonic circulations will be produced. If the two critical points are not very far away from each other, the degree of instability will be great and the air in the central part of the current will be subject to much larger displacements, since it has a better chance to move across the critical points. If these wave disturbances move with a velocity roughly equal to the mean of U_κ and $U_{\min}$, rapid development should be expected.

In order to test this theory, let us consider some actual cases. During the period 29–31 January 1947 a strong jet of westerlies developed over the United States. The velocity profile for January 29 was computed along the meridian from Bismarck, N. D., to Brownsville, Tex., at the 500-mb level. This profile and the corresponding distribution of absolute vorticity Z are shown in fig. 12. According to the criterion obtained from the assumption of conservation of momentum, the situation should be absolutely stable, except at the 300-mb level, where a narrow zone of instability exists ($\partial U/\partial y > f$). But if we examine the distribution of Z, we find that the condition $\partial Z/\partial y = 0$ is satisfied at two latitudes, one to the south of the jet, at 34°N and one to the north, at 43°N, which shows that unstable and neutral waves can exist. The flow pattern was practically parallel on January 28; on the 29th, a small disturbance developed. This small disturbance developed into a closed center on the 30th and was moving ENE with a speed of about 15 m sec^{-1} (12 degrees latitude per day), less than the wind velocity at the critical point, which is about 26 m sec^{-1}

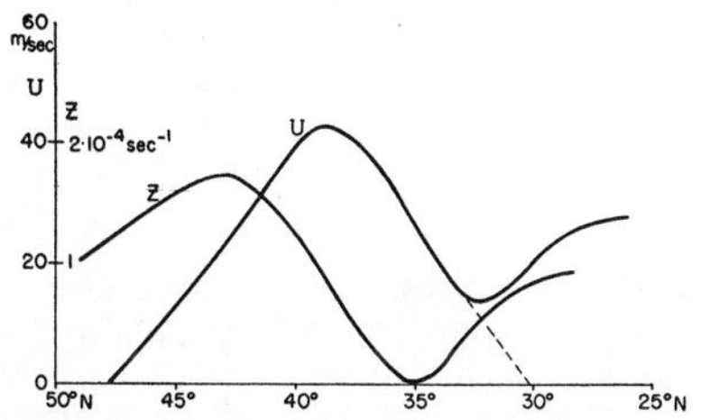

FIG. 12. The distribution of zonal velocity U and the absolute vorticity Z on the 500-mb surface for 29 January 1947. Note the symmetric position of the maximum and minimum Z in relation to the point with maximum current velocity.

(see fig. 13). Therefore, the cyclone was moving with a speed about one-half of U_κ, corresponding roughly to a maximum amplifying factor. The dimension and intensity of this storm almost doubled in the course of one day and this trend of increase continued during the next 24 hours; this, at least qualitatively, agrees with our results.

The wind profile for this case is very similar to a sine curve, except that the critical point is nearer to the center of the belt, indicating a more favorable condition for instability. For a rough estimation of the wave length, we may use the results of section 7, taking $y_t = b/2$ so that $\alpha_\kappa b = 2.7$. The observed width of the belt ($2b$) is about 15 degrees of latitude; hence, $L_\kappa = 1920$ km. Since the observed speed of the cyclone is less than U_κ and greater than $U_{\min}$, the corresponding wave length must be around 2500 km to 3000 km.

The present theory can also be applied to some extent in explaining seasonal conditions. Since we can regard the activity of highs and lows as large-scale eddies, we should expect some instability in the region of frequent occurrence of lows and highs. Fig. 14 gives

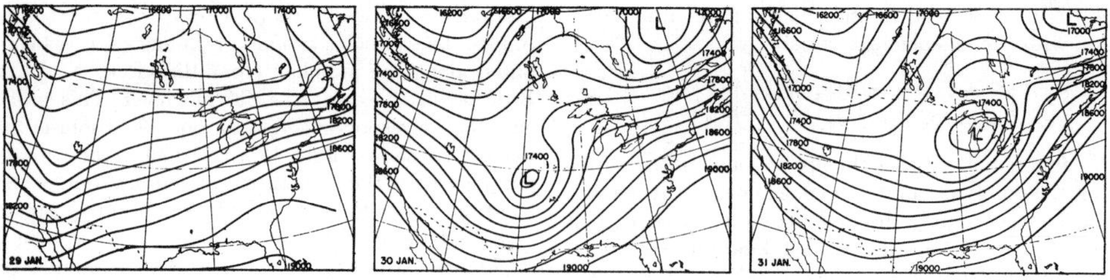

FIG. 13. 500-mb charts for 0300 GCT 29–31 January 1947. Note the formation and development of the cyclone center in the straight current and the rate of motion of this system.

the wind distribution at 12 km over North America during winter, which is plotted by using the values given by Willett (1944) and by Hess (1948). From the curve of Z, we see that there are two critical points, at about 40°N and 50°N. The region around 40°N to 50°N is actually the region of most frequent disturbances in winter. The curve for summer (fig. 14) shows that the region of instability has shifted northward to about 60°N. The vorticity profile is quite flat, indicating a lesser degree of instability according to the results we have obtained.

10. Summary

A general description of the method used in this study and the results obtained are presented in the following paragraphs.

Section 2 is concerned with the perturbation equations, the boundary conditions, and the types of velocity profiles. The study is mainly for horizontal nondivergent wave motions, so that the basic equation to be solved is the vorticity equation, which, when the harmonic wave solution is assumed, reduces to a differential equation for the stream function or the meridional velocity v. Since the velocity profiles of the westerlies generally have some symmetry with respect to a certain latitude, only symmetric profiles and boundary conditions are discussed. This results in symmetry of the perturbation, and leads to the simplification that only half of the profile need be considered. At the midpoint of the belt, where the maximum wind velocity is found, the perturbation should have its maximum value. Two different kinds of profiles are discussed: the first is a symmetric profile in a limited belt, with the boundary conditions that the perturbation vanishes at two latitudes $y = y_1$ and $y = y_2$; the second type is a belt extending to infinity in both directions so that the perturbation will be zero only at infinity.

In section 3 the analytic properties of the stream function are discussed. In this study our attention is centered on the range of phase velocities with a value between the maximum and minimum current velocity in the belt, so that we always have the point where $c = U$, which is a *singular point* of the vorticity equation, where the general solution ceases to be valid. Heretofore, meteorologists have always avoided this by assuming $c < U$; but by so doing have restricted their investigations to the slowly moving or retrograding waves.

In the immediate vicinity of this singular point (where $c = U$) the solution will give an infinite perturbation velocity and a sudden change of phase which can never occur in the real atmosphere. This difficulty is obviated by taking account of viscous (or eddy) stresses, which may be negligible as compared with the other effects when c is quite different from U, but must be of principal importance for the region in the vicinity of the singular point where $c = U$, and can not be neglected there. When the terms due to lateral mixing are included, the point where $c = U$ is no longer a singular point of the vorticity equation and infinite

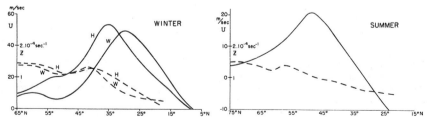

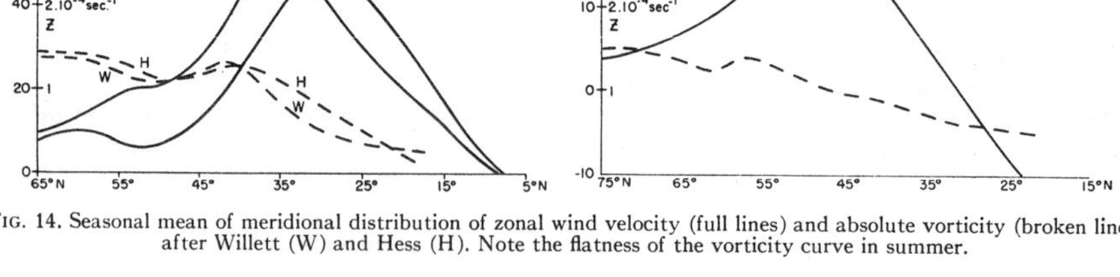

FIG. 14. Seasonal mean of meridional distribution of zonal wind velocity (full lines) and absolute vorticity (broken lines) after Willett (W) and Hess (H). Note the flatness of the vorticity curve in summer.

perturbation velocities do not occur. The change of phase will also be a gradual one. At a finite distance from the point where $c = U$, the frictional terms can be neglected entirely and the motion will be represented adequately by the solution of the ordinary vorticity equation. Thus it is only necessary to correct our results for the immediate vicinity of the singular point by considering the effect of virtual viscosity; this is the so-called method of cross-substitution.

Section 4 is devoted to the neutral waves (waves with amplitude independent of time). It is found that the phase velocity of these neutral waves can never be greater than the maximum wind velocity within the belt, but unlike the corresponding waves in a non-rotating system, they may have a phase velocity less than the minimum wind velocity, examples of which are the waves represented by Rossby's or Haurwitz' formula for the case with U = constant. When c has a value between the maximum and minimum current velocities, the occurrence of neutral waves requires that the absolute vorticity possess an extreme value $(dZ/dy \equiv \beta - U'' = 0)$ at some point. If no such *critical point* exists in the profile, then there can be no neutral wave with a phase velocity in the range between minimum and maximum current velocities. If only one distinct point (the two symmetric points, one on each side of the midpoint of the profile are identical) with this property exists, then only one such neutral wave will be possible, and its velocity will be given by the value of $U(= U_\kappa)$ at this point. Thus, in order to find the phase velocity of the neutral waves within this range of values, we need only plot the distribution of the absolute vorticity $Z = f - U'$ and find the point where $dZ/dy = 0$; the phase velocity is given by the current velocity at this point. The constant-vorticity profile is a special case for which this condition is satisfied at every point; in this case, all waves are neutral.

In section 5 it is found that the necessary condition for having amplified (unstable) waves is that the absolute vorticity Z must have an extreme value within the belt, *i.e.*, $dZ/dy \equiv \beta - U''$ must be zero at some point $y = y_\kappa$ (the critical point) in the belt, and change its sign there. The same conclusion also holds for motion over a spherical earth. If no such critical point exists, then all waves with phase velocity greater than the minimum current velocity will be damped.

Section 6 deals with waves having a phase velocity slightly different from that of the neutral wave (with phase velocity $c = U_\kappa$ and wave length $L = L_\kappa$), or slightly greater than $U_{\min}$. It is found that for waves longer than L_κ, the phase velocity c_r (the real part of c) will be smaller than U_κ and c_i (the imaginary part of c) will be positive, *i.e.*, their amplitude will increase with time, while for waves shorter than L_κ, we shall have $c_r > U_\kappa$ and $c_i < 0$, *i.e.*, the shorter and fast moving waves are damped. Thus, the neutral wave with phase velocity equal to the current velocity at the critical point divides the disturbances into amplified and damped waves. Equations are developed for calculating c_r and c_i in the neighborhood of this neutral solution.

The waves with a phase velocity slightly greater than that of the neutral wave with $c = U_{\min}$ are shown to be shorter and amplified.

Since the waves with $c = U_\kappa$ and $c = U_{\min}$ are the only neutral waves with a phase velocity within the range of current velocities, all waves with a value of the phase velocity between these two values will be amplified. Thus, a diagram with L as abscissa and c_r (or c_i) as ordinate is divided into three parts by the points $P(L_0, c_0 = U_{\min})$ and $Q(L_\kappa, c_\kappa = U_\kappa)$; to the right of P, with $L > L_0$, the waves are essentially neutral, with $c < U_{\min}$; to the left of Q, where $L < L_\kappa$ and $c_r > U_\kappa$, we shall have damped waves; in the central part, the waves are all amplified. The greatest degree of amplification will occur when c_r has a value somewhere between c_0 and c_κ, and the sharper the velocity profile the greater the instability; both fast and slowly moving waves will show little amplification.

When the waves are amplified, the troughs and ridges will not be straight lines but will be directed from southwest toward northeast to the south of the point where the absolute vorticity has its minimum value and from southeast toward northwest to the north of the point of maximum vorticity. This kind of flow pattern will give a negative correlation between the perturbation velocities u and v, and therefore indicates instability.

Section 7 is devoted to a study of numerical examples with sine-curve profiles. The wind distribution is fitted by the parameters $U_{\max}$, the width of the belt $2b$, and the position of the critical point. All the results obtained in section 6 are substantiated by these periodic profiles. The order of magnitude of c_i is such that a doubling of amplitude in the course of 24 hours could be expected in some cases.

In section 8, the study is extended to three-dimensional motions in a baroclinic atmosphere, and it is found that if certain approximations are made (which are justifiable for large-scale atmospheric motions), a second-order differential equation will be obtained for the meridional perturbation velocity v (also satisfied by the perturbation pressure), which is of the same form as the vorticity equation for two-dimensional motions, but with different coefficients. In this case, the critical point is determined not by the extreme value of the absolute vorticity Z, but by that of $\ln (SZ) + gr\sigma_z$, where S is the specific volume, σ_z the vertical stratification, and r a quantity depending on σ_z. Thus all the results obtained remain valid provided some modifications as to the values of c_κ, L_κ, and the other quantities are made.

In section 9, a synoptic example for the period of 28–31 January 1947 is studied. The situation was such that unstable waves could be expected. A cyclone center developed over the United States and moved with a velocity which, theoretically, indicated maximum amplification. Deepening and intensification of the cyclone actually took place in the following few days.

Acknowledgments.—The writer wishes to express his gratitude to Prof. C.-G. Rossby for his guidance and help during the course of this study, to Prof. Zd. Sekera, Prof. C. C. Lin, and T. C. Yeh for suggestions and discussions.

APPENDIX

A. The amplified waves in the vicinity of the neutral solution at the critical point.—In (11), $\Psi_1(0;\alpha,c)$, $\Psi_2(0;\alpha,c)$, $\Psi_1'(b;\alpha,c)$, and $\Psi_2'(b;\alpha,c)$ are all analytic functions of α and c ($y=0$ is the boundary, $y=b$ the midpoint); therefore, $F(\alpha,c)$ is also analytic and we can continue the solution for c in terms of $\lambda\equiv\alpha^2$ in the neighborhood of $\alpha=\alpha_\kappa$, $c=c_\kappa=U_\kappa$, and write

$$c=c_\kappa+\left(\frac{dc}{d\lambda}\right)_\kappa(\lambda-\lambda_\kappa)+\frac{1}{2}\left(\frac{d^2c}{d\lambda^2}\right)_\kappa(\lambda-\lambda_\kappa)^2+\cdots \tag{75}$$

The problem is then to find the differential coefficients of c with respect to λ in the vicinity of $\lambda=\lambda_\kappa$.

For this purpose, we write the Sturm–Liouville system in the form

$$\Psi''-\left(\lambda+\frac{U''-\beta}{U-c}\right)\Psi=0;\qquad \Psi(0)=0=\Psi'(b), \tag{76}$$

which has one characteristic solution $\Psi=\Psi_\kappa$ corresponding to $c=c_\kappa=U_\kappa$, $\lambda=\lambda_\kappa\equiv\alpha_\kappa^2$. If we have another solution $\Psi=\Psi_\kappa+(d\Psi/d\lambda)_\kappa\Delta\lambda$, which is slightly different from Ψ_κ, and if $c_\kappa+(dc/d\lambda)_\kappa\Delta\lambda$ is the corresponding value of c, then we find from (76) that Ψ_κ and $(d\Psi/d\lambda)_\kappa$ must satisfy the equations

$$\Psi''_\kappa-\left(\lambda_\kappa+\frac{U''-\beta}{U-c_\kappa}\right)\Psi_\kappa=0,$$

$$\left(\frac{d\Psi''}{d\lambda}\right)_\kappa-\left(\lambda_\kappa+\frac{U''-\beta}{U-c_\kappa}\right)\left(\frac{d\Psi}{d\lambda}\right)_\kappa=\left[1+\frac{U''-\beta}{(U-c_\kappa)^2}\left(\frac{dc}{d\lambda}\right)_\kappa\right]\Psi_\kappa.$$

Multiply the first by $(d\Psi/d\lambda)_\kappa$ and the second by Ψ_κ and subtract; since both Ψ_κ and $(d\Psi/d\lambda)_\kappa$ satisfy the boundary conditions, we have, on integrating the result from 0 to b, the following condition

$$\int_0^b\left[1+\frac{U''-\beta}{(U-c_\kappa)^2}\left(\frac{dc}{d\lambda}\right)_\kappa\right]\Psi_\kappa^2dy=0, \tag{77}$$

or

$$\Delta\lambda\int_0^b\Psi_\kappa^2dy+\Delta c\left(E+\int_{y_\kappa-\epsilon}^{y_\kappa+\epsilon}\frac{U''-\beta}{(U-c_\kappa)^2}\Psi_\kappa^2dy\right)=0, \tag{78}$$

where

$$E\equiv\lim_{\epsilon\to0}\left(\int_0^{y_\kappa-\epsilon}+\int_{y_\kappa+\epsilon}^b\right)\frac{U''-\beta}{(U-c_\kappa)^2}\Psi_\kappa^2dy. \tag{79}$$

Suppose that $U_\kappa'''-\beta'\neq0$ at $y=y_\kappa$, so that $y=y_\kappa$ is a simple root of $U''(y_\kappa)-\beta=0$, and take $\eta\equiv y-y_\kappa$; then, in the neighborhood of $\eta=0$,

$$\Psi_\kappa\approx1$$
$$U-U_\kappa=U-c_\kappa\approx U_\kappa'\eta$$
$$U''-\beta\approx U_\kappa'''\eta.$$

With these values for the vicinity of $y=y_\kappa$, and with $D\equiv(U_\kappa'''-\beta')/U_\kappa'^2$, we find

$$\int_{y_\kappa-\epsilon}^{y_\kappa+\epsilon}\frac{U''-\beta}{(U-c_\kappa)^2}\Psi_\kappa^2dy=D\pi i. \tag{80}$$

Writing $\Delta c=\Delta c_r+ic_i$, and using (80), equation (78) may be solved for Δc_r and c_i; by this process we are led to equations (32) and (33). As has been discussed in section 6, c_i is always positive for $\Delta\lambda<0$ and negative for $\Delta\lambda>0$, if $D<0$, which is generally the case.

For the second type of profile we may apply the same reasoning as for the first, but now we must integrate from zero to $y=-\infty$ instead of $y=\delta$, for although we can use the condition $\Psi'+r\Psi=0$ at the point of transition, this leaves $(d\Psi/d\lambda)_\kappa$ in the equation, which cannot be taken as Ψ_κ. If we integrate (77) from $y=-\infty$ to $y=\delta$ (taking the origin at the point of transition) and use the same procedure as before, we shall find that c_i and Δc_r are given by the same expressions (32) and (33), except that E is replaced by

$$E-a^2\beta/2r(U_\kappa-U_0)^2$$

and $\int_0^b\Psi_\kappa^2\,dy$ by

$$\int_0^\delta\Psi_{\kappa1}^2dy+\frac{a^2}{2r},$$

where $\Psi_{\kappa1}$ is the neutral solution for the central part of the profile and a its value at the point of transition $y=0$.

B. The amplified waves in the vicinity of the stationary neutral solution.—For $U(0) = 0$, (16) reduces to

$$c\left(\Psi'(0) + \alpha^2 \int_0^b \Psi\,dy\right) + \beta \int_0^b \Psi\,dy - \alpha^2 \int_0^b \Psi U\,dy = 0, \quad (81)$$

which is true for all values of c; the problem is to find Ψ. Let us differentiate (81) with respect to $\lambda \equiv \alpha^2$ in the neighborhood of $\Psi_{c=0}$:

$$\left(\frac{dc}{d\lambda}\right)_0 \left(\Psi_0'(0) + \alpha_0^2 \int_0^b \Psi_0\,dy\right) + \beta \int_0^b \left(\frac{d\Psi}{d\lambda}\right)_0 dy - \int_0^b U\Psi_0\,dy - \alpha_0^2 \int_0^b U\left(\frac{d\Psi}{d\lambda}\right)_0 dy = 0, \quad (82)$$

where Ψ_0 and α_0^2 are the values for $c = 0$ and therefore satisfy

$$\beta \int_0^b \Psi_0\,dy = \alpha_0^2 \int_0^b U\Psi_0\,dy. \quad (38)$$

In order to evaluate $(dc/d\lambda)_0$ in (82), we have to find the expressions for Ψ_0 and $(d\Psi/d\lambda)_0$. Let us consider the point very near to $c = 0$, with $c_r > 0$ and $|c_i| \ll c_r$. Take the new origin at the singular point where $U = c$ in the complex plane; expand U as a Taylor series with respect to the point $U = c$ (see fig. 3). Evaluating this series at the point $y = y_0$ where $U = 0$, we have

$$0 = c + U'_s y_0 + \cdots.$$

Reverting,

$$y_0 = -c/U'_s + \cdots;$$

also,

$$U'_0 = U'_s + U''_s y_0 + \cdots = U'_s - U''_s c/U'_s + \cdots.$$

By making use of the condition that $\Psi = 0$ at the boundary $y = y_0$, the ratio of the two arbitrary constants in $\Psi = A\Psi_1 + B\Psi_2$ is found to be

$$\frac{A}{B} = -\frac{\Psi_2(y_0)}{\Psi_1(y_0)} = \frac{1}{c}\left[U'_s - \frac{U''_s - \beta}{U'_s}\, c \ln\left(-\frac{c}{U'_s}\right) + \cdots\right].$$

Thus we may write, with $G_s \equiv (U''_s - \beta)/U'_s$,

$$\Psi = B_1 \left\{\left[U'_s - cG_s \ln\left(-\frac{c}{U'_s}\right) + \cdots\right]\Psi_1 + c(1 + G_s y \ln y + \cdots)\right\}. \quad (84)$$

Since the imaginary part of $\ln(-c/U'_s)$ is $-\pi i$ and that of $y \ln y$ and all other terms is small for small c_r and c_i, the main imaginary part of Ψ is, if we take $B_1 = 1$,

$$\Psi_{i0} \approx c_r G_s \Psi_1 \pi i \approx c_r G_s U(y) \pi i / U'_0. \quad (85)$$

If we assume that (83) is also satisfied by $(d\Psi/d\lambda)_0$ and take $U(y)$ as the approximate expression for Ψ_{r0}, then, after separating the real and imaginary parts of (82), we get

$$K_r c_r - K_i c_i = \Delta(\alpha^2) \int_0^b U^2\,dy, \quad (86)$$

$$K_r c_i + K_i c_r = \Delta(\alpha^2) \int_0^b U\Psi_{i0}\,dy, \quad (87)$$

where

$$K_r = U'(0) + \alpha_0^2 \int_0^b U\,dy, \quad (88)$$

$$K_i = \alpha_0^2 \int_0^b \Psi_{i0}\,dy. \quad (89)$$

In (89) we have used the condition $\Psi'_{i0} = 0$; further, on reference to (85), it is seen that K_i is of the order of c_r. Hence, since $c_i \ll c_r$, we may neglect $K_i c_i$ against $K_r c_r$ in (86), which then reduces to (35). Finally, the result given in (36) is obtained by substitution of (35) and (85) in (87).

REFERENCES

Charney, J. G., 1947: The dynamics of long waves in a baroclinic westerly current. *J. Meteor.*, **4**, 135–163.

Haurwitz, B., 1940: The motion of atmospheric disturbances. *J. marine Res.*, **3**, 35–50.

Heisenberg, W., 1924: Über Stabilität und Turbulenz von Flüssigkeitsströmen. *Ann. Physik* (4), **74**, 577–627.

Ince, E. L., 1944: *Ordinary differential equations.* New York, Dover Publications, 552 pp. (see ch. 10).

Kleinschmidt, E., 1941: Zur Theorie der labilen Anordnung. *Meteor. Z.*, **58**, 157–163.

Lamb, H., 1932: *Hydrodynamics*, 6 ed. Cambridge Univ. Press, 738 pp.

Lin, C. C., 1945: On the stability of two-dimensional parallel flows. *Quart. appl. Math.*, **3**, 117–142, 218–234.

Palmén, E., 1947: On the distribution of temperature and wind in the upper westerlies. *J. Meteor.*, **5**, 20–27.

Rayleigh, Lord, 1880: On the stability, or instability, of certain fluid motions. *Proc. London math. Soc.*, **11**, 57–70.

——, 1913: On the stability of the laminar motion of an inviscid fluid. *Phil. Mag.*, **26**, 1001–1010.

Rossby, C.-G., and collaborators, 1939: Relation between variations in the intensity of the zonal circulation of the atmosphere and the displacement of the semi-permanent centers of action. *J. marine Res.*, **2**, 38–55.

Solberg, H., 1936: Le mouvment d'inertie de l'atmosphère stable et son rôle dans la théorie des cyclones. *Proces-verbaux de l'assoc. de meteor., un. geod. geophys. Int., Edimbourg*, 66–82.

Thompson, P. D., 1948: The propagation of permanent-type waves in horizontal flow. *J. Meteor.*, **5**, 166–168.

Tollmien, W., 1929: Über die Entstehung der Turbulenz. 1. Mitteilung. *Nachr. Ges Wiss. Göttingen* (Neue Folge), **1**, 20–44.

Van Mieghem, J., 1944: Perturbation d'un courant atmosphérique permanent zonal. *Inst. R. météor. Belg., Mém.* **18**, 1–34.

Willett, H. C., 1944: *Descriptive meteorology.* New York, Academic Press, 310 pp. (see pp. 131–135).

Reprinted from *Compendium of Meteorology*, Boston, 1951. This volume was published by the American Meteorological Society through support of the Geophysics Research Directorate, Air Force Cambridge Research Laboratories, Air Research and Development Command.

STABILITY PROPERTIES OF LARGE-SCALE ATMOSPHERIC DISTURBANCES

By R. FJØRTOFT

*The Institute for Advanced Study**

Introduction

The large-scale motion of the earth's atmosphere is to the first approximation a solid rotation from west to east. Upon this are superimposed a more or less orderly zonal flow in the relative motion and the large-scale disturbances familiar in meteorology. In this article causes for the creation and maintenance of these disturbances will be discussed, excluding, however, the more or less permanent disturbances forced upon the atmosphere because of the earth's topographic inhomogeneity.

By the use of the phrase "disturbances in a zonal flow," a separation is implied between two components of the flow. This may seem artificial since the hydrodynamic equations are directly applicable to the total component of the flow. There are, however, several reasons for doing this: The immediate impression obtained by studying hemispherical weather maps is one of a more or less orderly zonal flow upon which are superimposed disturbances that behave to some degree as physical entities themselves. Further, the zonal flow and the disturbances undergo somewhat systematic changes, seemingly of great importance to weather. Therefore, by a separation of the atmospheric flow into some kind of orderly zonal flow and disturbances superimposed thereupon, one isolates at the outset certain phenomena which appear to be related to actual weather. Besides, this separation will enable one to deal satisfactorily with problems in which a detailed knowledge of the motion is unnecessary, as exemplified by the stability investigations carried out in the discussion of barotropic disturbances (pp. 460–463).

Granted that such a separation of the atmospheric flow may prove useful, it becomes important for quantitative treatment to express this separation in mathematical terms. How this should be done is to some extent arbitrary because there may be several ways of defining the orderly flow, and thereby the disturbances. In this article, the orderly flow will be characterized, for an arbitrary hydrodynamic element α, by the mean value of α at a fixed time along latitude circles:

$$\bar{\alpha} = \frac{1}{2\pi}\int_0^{2\pi} \alpha \, d\psi,$$

while the corresponding element in the flow of disturbances will be defined by

$$\alpha' = \alpha - \bar{\alpha}.$$

The flow therefore is composed of an orderly, axially symmetric motion and an irregular flow vanishing in the mean along zonal circles. The degree of irregularity may, however, vary widely. In this article it is assumed that all irregularities considerably smaller than the smallest-scale cyclones have already been smoothed out in some way. The corresponding turbulent stresses will be entirely neglected throughout this article.

As already pointed out above, the sum of the two components of flow must obey the hydrodynamic equations of motion. There must therefore exist a coupling between these two components. Actually, in many cases this coupling is so strong that a full understanding of what happens with one component cannot be achieved without taking into account simultaneous changes of the other.

It is an established procedure to separate the hydrodynamic equations into one set valid for the orderly motion and one for the irregular flow. To implement this process the equations will first be simplified by suppressing certain terms of minor importance. With the conventional simplification in the Coriolis acceleration, the equation of motion is

$$\rho\left[\frac{D\mathbf{v}}{dt} + f\mathbf{k}\times\mathbf{v} - \mathbf{g}\right] = -\nabla p,$$

where ρ is the density, f is the Coriolis parameter, $\mathbf{g}$ is the acceleration of gravity, $\mathbf{v}$ is the velocity, and p is the pressure. The coordinate system has been selected so that the x-axis is directed east, the y-axis north, and the z-axis upward; $\mathbf{i}$, $\mathbf{j}$, and $\mathbf{k}$ are unit vectors in the x, y, and z directions, respectively. By elimination of ∇p and substitution of $\varkappa = \ln \vartheta$ (where ϑ is the potential temperature) by means of the relationship $\nabla\rho - \Gamma\nabla p = -\rho\nabla\varkappa$, one obtains

$$\nabla\times\left[\frac{D\mathbf{v}}{dt} + f\mathbf{k}\times\mathbf{v}\right] = -\nabla\times\varkappa\mathbf{g}. \tag{1}$$

The neglected term $-\nabla\varkappa\times[D\mathbf{v}/dt + f\mathbf{k}\times\mathbf{v}]$ is small compared with the others. Equation (1) is equivalent to

$$\frac{D\mathbf{v}}{dt} = -\nabla\gamma - f\mathbf{k}\times\mathbf{v} - \varkappa\mathbf{g}, \tag{2}$$

where $\nabla\gamma$ is a certain laminar vector. It is easily understood that by introducing the simplification above, the effects from solenoids in horizontal planes have been neglected. Now let $Q(z)$ represent some standard distribution of density with height. The following approximate equation will then constitute the continuity equation:

$$\nabla\cdot Q\mathbf{v} = Q\nabla_h\cdot\mathbf{v}_h + \frac{\partial Qw}{\partial z} = 0. \tag{3}$$

* This article is to some extent based upon work performed under contract N6-ori-139, Task Order I between the Office of Naval Research and The Institute for Advanced Study.

In this article only adiabatic processes will be considered. The physical equation is therefore

$$\frac{\partial \varkappa}{\partial t} = -\mathbf{v}\cdot\nabla\varkappa. \tag{4}$$

From the foregoing equations one obtains by separation into the mean and irregular flows:

$$\frac{\partial \bar{\mathbf{v}}}{\partial t} + \bar{\mathbf{v}}\cdot\nabla\bar{\mathbf{v}} = -\nabla\bar{\gamma} - f\mathbf{k}\times\bar{\mathbf{v}} - \bar{\varkappa}\mathbf{g} - \overline{\mathbf{v}'\cdot\nabla\mathbf{v}'}, \tag{5a}$$

$$\nabla\cdot Q\bar{\mathbf{v}} = 0, \tag{5b}$$

$$\frac{\partial \bar{\varkappa}}{\partial t} = -\bar{\mathbf{v}}\cdot\nabla\bar{\varkappa} - \overline{\mathbf{v}'\cdot\nabla\varkappa'}, \tag{5c}$$

and

$$\frac{\partial \mathbf{v}'}{\partial t} + \mathbf{v}'\cdot\nabla\mathbf{v}' = -\nabla\gamma' - f\mathbf{k}\times\mathbf{v}' - \varkappa'\mathbf{g} - \bar{\mathbf{v}}\cdot\nabla\mathbf{v}' - \mathbf{v}'\cdot\nabla\bar{\mathbf{v}} + \overline{\mathbf{v}'\cdot\nabla\mathbf{v}'}, \tag{6a}$$

$$\nabla\cdot Q\mathbf{v}' = 0, \tag{6b}$$

$$\frac{\partial \varkappa'}{\partial t} = -\bar{\mathbf{v}}\cdot\nabla\varkappa' - \mathbf{v}'\cdot\nabla\bar{\varkappa} + \overline{\mathbf{v}'\cdot\nabla\varkappa'}. \tag{6c}$$

These equations reveal the coupling which must exist between the two components of the flow, as both components occur in each set of equations.

The Circular Vortex

According to the definitions above, the orderly flow may be considered as a pure zonal flow with velocity component $\bar{u}\mathbf{i}$, and a meridional flow with velocity $\bar{\mathbf{v}}_m = \bar{v}\mathbf{j} + \bar{w}\mathbf{k}$, which is identically the same in all meridional planes. The meridional component of (5) may be written

$$\frac{\overline{D\mathbf{v}_m}}{dt} = -\nabla\bar{\gamma} - \bar{\varkappa}\mathbf{g} - f\mathbf{k}\times\bar{u}\mathbf{i}.$$

The approximate balance existing in the large-scale relative motion in the atmosphere gives, when $\nabla\bar{\gamma}$ is eliminated from this equation:

$$\frac{\partial \bar{u}}{\partial z} = -\frac{g}{f}\frac{\partial \bar{\varkappa}}{\partial y}. \tag{7}$$

This is the so-called thermal wind equation applied to the mean flow.

One may study the axially symmetric meridional motions in a qualitative way by the method of velocity circulation used primarily by V. Bjerknes [4] and Høiland [16]. If $\nabla\bar{\gamma}$ is eliminated from the foregoing equation by taking the circulation along some arbitrary closed curve in a meridional plane, and the resulting equation differentiated once with respect to time, one gets

$$\frac{d}{dt}\oint\frac{\overline{D\mathbf{v}_m}}{dt}\cdot\delta\mathbf{r} = -\oint\frac{\partial\bar{\varkappa}}{\partial t}\mathbf{g}\cdot\delta\mathbf{r} - \oint f\frac{\partial\bar{u}}{\partial t}\mathbf{j}\cdot\delta\mathbf{r}. \tag{8}$$

The expression for $\partial\bar{u}/\partial t$ is obtained from the zonal component of (5*a*):

$$\frac{\partial \bar{u}}{\partial t} = -\bar{\mathbf{v}}_m\cdot(\nabla\bar{u} - f\mathbf{j}) - \overline{\mathbf{v}'\cdot\nabla u'}. \tag{9}$$

Substituting this expression for $\partial\bar{u}/\partial t$ in (8) and likewise for $\partial\bar{\varkappa}/\partial t$ from (5*c*), one gets

$$\frac{d}{dt}\oint\frac{\overline{D\mathbf{v}_m}}{dt}\cdot\delta\mathbf{r} = \oint\bar{\mathbf{v}}_m\cdot[f\nabla\bar{u}\mathbf{j} - f^2\mathbf{jj} + \nabla\bar{\varkappa}\mathbf{g}]\cdot\delta\mathbf{r} + \oint\overline{\mathbf{v}'\cdot\nabla\varkappa'}\mathbf{g}\cdot\delta\mathbf{r} + \oint f\overline{\mathbf{v}'\cdot\nabla u'}\mathbf{j}\cdot\delta\mathbf{r}. \tag{10}$$

A study of the first integral on the right-hand side of this equation leads to the conditions which must exist if in a pure, axially symmetric motion the meridional circulations should accelerate or decelerate, in other words to the now well-known stability criteria for a circular vortex for vortex-ring perturbations. It will be assumed in this article that all orderly flows which are treated are stable in this sense. Most likely this is usually the case in the atmosphere.

The remaining terms on the right-hand side of (10) represent the effects upon the acceleration of the meridional circulations which are due to the disturbances. The character of the resulting forced circulations will now also depend essentially upon the stability properties of the circular vortex for vortex-ring perturbations. Briefly, one may say that the presence of effects changing the fields of mass and velocity in the orderly zonal flow, other than effects of the meridional circulations themselves, will generally tend steadily to destroy the balance in the meridional motions. Because of the stability of the circular vortex the resulting added meridional circulations will act to restore the equilibrium, an equilibrium which will, however, be different from the original one. If the stability is large enough, the whole development may be thought of as one which goes through different equilibrium stages by smoothing out over sufficiently large periods the relatively high frequency oscillations superimposed upon this trend. The simplifications following from such a procedure are essentially the same as those introduced by the systematic use of the condition of quasi-geostrophic motion [7, 12]. With the simplifications above, A. Eliassen [11] has studied the forced meridional circulations produced by given sources of heat and angular momentum.

To see in a qualitative fashion how the irregular flow affects the mean meridional circulations one may use the simplifications mentioned above in connection with the circulation integrals in (10). One then obtains

$$\oint\bar{\mathbf{v}}_m\cdot[f\nabla\bar{u}\mathbf{j} - f^2\mathbf{jj} + \nabla\bar{\varkappa}\mathbf{g}]\cdot\delta\mathbf{r} = -\oint\overline{\mathbf{v}'\cdot\nabla\varkappa'}\mathbf{g}\cdot\delta\mathbf{r} - \oint f\overline{\mathbf{v}'\cdot\nabla u'}\mathbf{j}\cdot\delta\mathbf{r}. \tag{11}$$

It will now be assumed that $\nabla\bar{u}$ and $\partial\bar{\varkappa}/\partial y$ are small enough to be neglected where they occur in (9) and (11). It is further assumed that $\partial\bar{\varkappa}/\partial z \geqq 0$, which is necessary to insure the stability of the circular vortex in the present case. Equations (9) and (11) now reduce to

$$\frac{\partial \bar{u}}{\partial t} = f\bar{v} - \overline{\mathbf{v}' \cdot \nabla u'}, \tag{12}$$

$$- \oint f^2 \bar{v}\, \delta y - \oint g \frac{\partial \bar{\kappa}}{\partial z} \bar{w}\, \delta z = \oint \overline{\mathbf{v}' \cdot \nabla \kappa'} g\, \delta z - \oint f \overline{\mathbf{v}' \cdot \nabla u'}\, \delta y. \tag{13}$$

Let it now be assumed that the path of integration consists of the sides of a "rectangle" bounded below by the earth's surface and with the top at about tropopause height (Fig. 1). The direction of integration is indicated by arrows. With subscripts from 1 to 4 denoting average values along the sides of the rectangle correspondingly labelled, (13) may be written

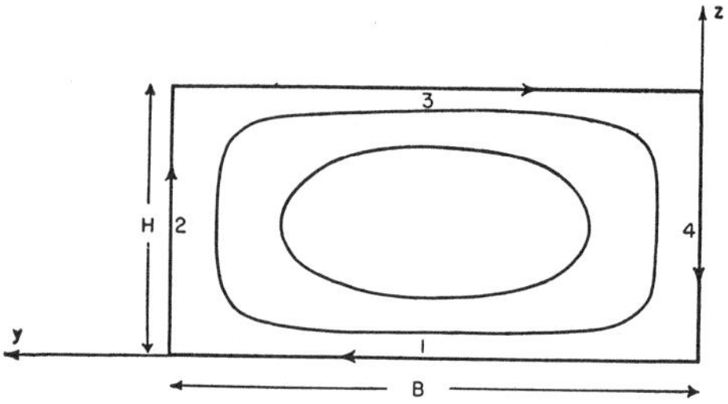

FIG. 1.—Idealized meridional circulation.

$$f^2(\bar{v}_3 - \bar{v}_1)B + g \frac{\partial \bar{\kappa}}{\partial z} (\bar{w}_2 - \bar{w}_4)H = g(\overline{\mathbf{v}' \cdot \nabla \kappa_2'} - \overline{\mathbf{v}' \cdot \nabla \kappa_4'})H + f(\overline{\mathbf{v}' \cdot \nabla u_3'} - \overline{\mathbf{v}' \cdot \nabla u_1'})B. \tag{14}$$

Here, B and H are the lengths of the sides of the rectangle. Suppose further that the rectangular-shaped boundary is a streamline in a corresponding simple cellular meridional motion, in which $\bar{v}$ and $\bar{w}$ are derived from a stream function

$$\psi_a \sim \sin \frac{\pi y}{B} \sin \frac{\pi z}{H}. \tag{15}$$

This implies that for the present the atmosphere is treated as incompressible. It may be anticipated, however, that the results to be obtained will also roughly apply to cellular motions whose kinematics are essentially the same as in this most simple cellular motion.

By deriving $\bar{v}$ and $\bar{w}$ from (15) and forming the averages $\bar{v}_1$, $\bar{v}_3$, $\bar{w}_2$, and $\bar{w}_4$, one obtains

$$(\bar{w}_4 - \bar{w}_2)B = (\bar{v}_3 - \bar{v}_1)H. \tag{16}$$

If one does not think of the velocities in this formula as averages along the sides of the rectangular boundary, but rather as averages over the whole region of the velocities in the ascending and descending motions, and in the north and south motions, the formula simply states the well-known continuity principle that the ratio between the magnitude of the vertical and horizontal velocities is proportional to the ratio between the vertical and horizontal scale of the motion. By a suitable choice of the integration curve in the circulation integrals given above, one could therefore also apply (16) to cellular motions of a much more general character than the one determined from (15). In view of (16), (14) may now be written

$$f(\bar{v}_3 - \bar{v}_1)\left(f^2 + g \frac{\partial \bar{\kappa}}{\partial z} \frac{H^2}{B^2}\right) = fg(\overline{\mathbf{v}' \cdot \nabla \kappa_2'} - \overline{\mathbf{v}' \cdot \nabla \kappa_4'}) \frac{H}{B} + f^2(\overline{\mathbf{v}' \cdot \nabla u_3'} - \overline{\mathbf{v}' \cdot \nabla u_1'}). \tag{17}$$

Taking likewise an average of (12) along the horizontal sides of the rectangle, one obtains by subtraction

$$\frac{\partial}{\partial t} (\bar{u}_3 - \bar{u}_1) = f(\bar{v}_3 - \bar{v}_1) - (\overline{\mathbf{v}' \cdot \nabla u_3'} - \overline{\mathbf{v}' \cdot \nabla u_1'}).$$

Substituting here for $f(\bar{v}_3 - \bar{v}_1)$ from (17), one obtains

$$\frac{\partial}{\partial t}\left(\frac{\bar{u}_3 - \bar{u}_1}{H}\right) = \left[\frac{g \frac{\partial \bar{\kappa}}{\partial z} \frac{H^2}{B^2}}{f^2 + g \frac{\partial \bar{\kappa}}{\partial z} \frac{H^2}{B^2}}\right] \left[\frac{\overline{\mathbf{v}' \cdot \nabla u_1'} - \overline{\mathbf{v}' \cdot \nabla u_3'}}{H}\right] + \left[\frac{f^2}{f^2 + g \frac{\partial \bar{\kappa}}{\partial z} \frac{H^2}{B^2}}\right] \left[\frac{g}{Bf}(\overline{\mathbf{v}' \cdot \nabla \kappa_2'} - \overline{\mathbf{v}' \cdot \nabla \kappa_4'})\right]. \tag{18}$$

This formula now determines, as a function of two terms, the time rate of change in the vertical wind shear of the mean zonal flow: The first term involves the wind shear that would directly result from the dynamic effects of the irregular motion; the second, the mean meridional temperature gradient resulting directly from the thermal effects of the disturbances. However, it is seen that only fractions of these quantities are effective in building up the resulting shear since they are multiplied by factors smaller than unity. This is clearly a result of the interference with the effects resulting from the forced meridional circulations, and could have been obtained by more direct considerations. The formula given above, however, may serve as a rough indicator of how this interference depends upon the stability of the circular vortex and the horizontal and vertical scales of the motion. In the present discussion it will only be pointed out how the dynamically conditioned increase in the wind shear becomes more and more compensated when the vertical stability goes to zero, or when H/B becomes smaller, while at the same time the thermally conditioned increase in wind shear becomes correspondingly more important. The relative importance, in regard to the general circulation, of the dynamic effects of the disturbances on the one hand, and the thermal effects on the other, naturally depends also upon the relative magnitudes of the terms $\overline{\mathbf{v}' \cdot \nabla u'}$ and $\overline{\mathbf{v}' \cdot \nabla \kappa'}$ and their distribution. This is intimately connected with the problems to be treated in the following sections.

Baroclinic Disturbances

One way of classifying atmospheric disturbances is with respect to the sources of energy which are at their disposal. The energy equation, when integrated over an isolated volume τ of the atmosphere, is obtained from (2) and (3) and becomes

$$\int Q\tfrac{1}{2}\mathbf{v}^2\, d\tau = \int Q\varkappa gz\, d\tau + \text{const.}$$

Substituting here $\mathbf{v} = \bar{u}\mathbf{i} + \bar{\mathbf{v}}_m + \mathbf{v}'$, one arrives at

$$\int Q\tfrac{1}{2}\mathbf{v}'^2\, d\tau = \int Q\varkappa gz\, d\tau - \int Q\tfrac{1}{2}\bar{u}^2\, d\tau + \text{const},$$

having neglected the relatively much smaller kinetic energy contained in the mean meridional circulations. Applying the same approximation, the time rate of change of this equation becomes, in view of (5) and (6),

$$\frac{d}{dt}\int Q\tfrac{1}{2}\mathbf{v}'^2\, d\tau = \int Q\varkappa' w' g\, d\tau - \int Q\frac{\partial\bar{u}}{\partial y}u'v'\, d\tau - \int Q\frac{\partial\bar{u}}{\partial z}u'w'\, d\tau. \tag{19}$$

Consequently, one may classify disturbances into three categories according to whether the main source of energy is potential, kinetic, or both. In this section the first one will be considered.

Clearly, it is the correlation between the fluctuations in temperature and vertical velocity which will be decisive in determining whether potential energy shall be a source or sink for the disturbances. It is in accordance with synoptic experience that in most cases cold air masses sink relative to the warmer ones. It is therefore to be expected that potential energy is, at least partly, an important factor in creating and maintaining the large-scale disturbances. In order to understand how a positive correlation between the fluctuations of temperature and vertical velocity may be brought about, one may write

$$\varkappa' = -\mathbf{l}\cdot\nabla\bar{\varkappa} = -K\mathbf{v}'\cdot\nabla\bar{\varkappa}, \qquad (K > 0).$$

Here, $\mathbf{l}$ is a kind of mixing length, and a positive correlation has been assumed between $\mathbf{l}$ and $\mathbf{v}'$. Consequently, one has

$$\int Q\varkappa' w' g\, d\tau = -K\int Q(\mathbf{v}'\cdot\nabla\bar{\varkappa})w' g\, d\tau$$

$$= -K\int Qv'w'\frac{\partial\bar{\varkappa}}{\partial y}g\, d\tau - K\int Qw'^2\frac{\partial\bar{\varkappa}}{\partial z}g\, d\tau.$$

Having assumed vertical stability, it is therefore seen that as requirements for potential energy to be fed into the disturbances (*i*) horizontal temperature gradients must exist, and (*ii*) the slope of the streamlines in the meridional planes, w'/v', must be of the same sign as the slope $(-\partial\bar{\varkappa}/\partial y)/(\partial\bar{\varkappa}/\partial z)$ of the isentropic surfaces of the mean flow, but have a smaller magnitude. This last requirement may also be stated as saying that in the identity $\mathbf{v}'\cdot\nabla\bar{\varkappa} = v'\partial\bar{\varkappa}/\partial y + w'\partial\bar{\varkappa}/\partial z$ there must be a tendency for the vertical transport of entropy to compensate the horizontal transport. The latter, however, has to be the dominating effect, so that approximately $\mathbf{v}'\cdot\nabla\bar{\varkappa} = v'\partial\bar{\varkappa}/\partial y$.

For reasons of continuity it is to be expected that for decreasing horizontal dimensions of the disturbances the magnitude of the vertical velocities will increase relative to the horizontal velocities. It would therefore not be surprising if, for sufficiently small horizontal dimensions of the disturbances, w'/v' would exceed the values for which a conversion of potential energy into kinetic energy of the disturbances could take place. This effect will now be studied in more detail. To obtain results comparable with others which will be referred to at the end of this section, an incompressible atmosphere will be considered, bounded by two horizontal rigid planes at distance h apart. Also it will be assumed that

$$\frac{\partial u}{\partial y} = \frac{\partial v}{\partial y} = \frac{df}{dy} = 0; \qquad \frac{d^2u}{dz^2} = 0.$$

By eliminating $\nabla_h\gamma$ from the horizontal component of (2), one now obtains

$$\left(\frac{\partial}{\partial t} + u\frac{\partial}{\partial x}\right)\frac{\partial v}{\partial x} = -f\frac{\partial u}{\partial x} = f\frac{\partial w}{\partial z}. \tag{20}$$

Let it be assumed that instantaneously v and its derivatives may be obtained from the identity

$$v = \text{const}\cdot\sin\frac{2\pi}{L}\left[x - u\left(\frac{h}{2}\right)t\right],$$

representing instantaneously a simple wave propagating with a speed given by the value of u halfway between the boundaries. By substituting into (20), one obtains

$$-\frac{4\pi^2}{L^2}\frac{du}{dz}\left(z - \frac{h}{2}\right)v = f\frac{\partial w}{\partial z}.$$

Applying the boundary condition $w = 0$ for $z = 0$, one obtains by integration between $z = 0$ and the height $h/2$ where w reaches its maximum value:

$$\frac{w_{z=h/2}}{v} = \frac{\pi^2 h^2}{2L^2 f}\frac{du}{dz}.$$

Applying now the condition (*ii*) above to $w_{z=h/2}/v$, one obtains

$$\frac{\pi^2 h^2}{2L^2 f}\frac{du}{dz} < -\frac{\partial\varkappa/\partial y}{\partial\varkappa/\partial z},$$

or, by substitution from the thermal wind relationship $du/dz = -(g/f)(\partial\varkappa/\partial y)$:

$$\frac{L^2}{h^2} > \frac{\pi^2}{2f^2}\left(g\frac{\partial\varkappa}{\partial z}\right). \tag{21}$$

This now constitutes approximately the restriction on the horizontal scale of the disturbances if potential energy is to be converted into kinetic energy of the disturbances.

It will now be shown how one may express the conditions for a positive correlation between $\varkappa'$ and w'

in terms of the horizontal fields of velocity and temperature only. The conclusions arrived at are very much like those of Bjerknes and Holmboe [3]. The line of argument followed below is in some respects similar to that of Sutcliffe [26, 27]. (See also [8] and the article by J. G. Charney in this Compendium.[1])

From (2) one finds the vorticity equation in the vertical component to be

$$\frac{\partial \zeta}{\partial t} + \mathbf{v}_h \cdot \nabla \zeta + \beta v + f \nabla_h \cdot \mathbf{v} = 0,$$

when the presumably small terms

$$w(\partial \zeta / \partial z) + \zeta \nabla_h \cdot \mathbf{v} + \nabla_h w \times (\partial \mathbf{v} / \partial z) \cdot \mathbf{k}$$

are neglected. In this equation ζ is the vorticity and β is the variation of the Coriolis parameter with latitude. Let α^* be defined from $\alpha^* \int_0^\infty Q\, dz = \int_0^\infty Q\alpha\, dz$, where Q is now supposed to be the standard density in some isothermal atmosphere.[2] The term α^* will represent the mean, in the vertical, of α with respect to mass. Taking this mean of the vorticity equation, one obtains, by virtue of the continuity equation (3) and the boundary conditions $Qw = 0$ for $z = 0, z = \infty$,

$$\frac{\partial \zeta^*}{\partial t} + \mathbf{v}_h^* \cdot \nabla \zeta^* + \beta v^* + [(\mathbf{v}_h - \mathbf{v}_h^*) \cdot \nabla (\zeta - \zeta^*)]^* = 0. \tag{22}$$

In this equation the last term depends upon the existence of vertical wind shears, or in consequence of the thermal wind equation, upon the horizontal temperature gradients. It must therefore be this term that provides for the effects responsible for conversion of potential into kinetic energy. For a rough estimate of this term one may assume $d^2\mathbf{v}_h/dz^2 = 0$. From the thermal wind equation this implies that $\nabla_h \varkappa = \nabla_h \varkappa^*$. Equation (22) now takes the form

$$\frac{\partial \zeta^*}{\partial t} = -\mathbf{v}_h^* \cdot \nabla \zeta^* - \beta v^* - \mathbf{v}_T \cdot \nabla \zeta_T, \tag{23}$$

where

$$\mathbf{v}_h^* = \mathbf{v}_{z=0} + \mathbf{v}_T,$$

$$\mathbf{v}_T = H \frac{d\mathbf{v}_h}{dz} = -\frac{gH}{f} \nabla \varkappa^* \times \mathbf{k}, \tag{24}$$

and H = height of the homogeneous atmosphere. By taking the mean in the vertical of the physical equation (4), one further obtains

$$\frac{\partial \varkappa^*}{\partial t} = -\mathbf{v}_h^* \cdot \nabla \varkappa^* - \left(w \frac{\partial \varkappa}{\partial z} \right)^*. \tag{25}$$

To these equations one may add

$$\nabla \cdot \mathbf{v}_h^* = 0, \qquad \nabla \cdot \mathbf{v}_T = 0, \tag{26}$$

of which the first is exactly true owing to the definition of $\mathbf{v}_h^*$, and the second approximately true because of the identity (24).

It may be inferred from (22) that, under the foregoing assumptions, vorticity in the vertical-mean motion can vary individually only as a result of an advection of the vorticity of the thermal wind by the thermal wind $\mathbf{v}_T$. It is also apparent that if in the thermal wind field there is a transport of cyclonic thermal wind vorticity into regions of high vorticities in the actual motion, these vorticities will intensify. This corresponds to one of the rules developed by Sutcliffe for the sea-level motion [26, p. 205]. Applied to troughs which are symmetrical with respect to meridians, this leads, as Fig. 2 illustrates, to the synoptically well-known rule that troughs in the upper-air flow pattern intensify if troughs in the temperature patterns lag behind the troughs in the streamline patterns. A similar rule applies to ridges. It should be noted that these intensifications cannot be a result of the solenoids in horizontal planes, since these were neglected in the derivation of (2). The corresponding increase in the kinetic energy must have resulted from a conversion of potential energy. With reference to the discussion earlier in this section, it may therefore be concluded that, under the conditions mentioned above, the cold air must be subsiding relative to the warmer air, and further that the temperature changes due to the vertical motions can only partly compensate the advective changes. This rather definite knowledge of the three-dimensional flow structure based only upon a knowledge of the structure of the horizontal temperature and flow patterns is noteworthy. Clearly, nothing could in principle prevent a horizontal flow as illustrated in Fig. 2 from having any distribution of vertical velocities initially. This seeming discrepancy is due to the specific use which has been made of the conditions for quasi-geostrophic motion, which actually may be interpreted as effecting a smoothing similar to the one mentioned under the study of the mean meridional motions. As there, the success of such a smoothing, and therefore of the specific use of the conditions for quasi-geostrophic motion, depends upon the stability of the noise motion which is superimposed upon the "geostrophically" conditioned trend.

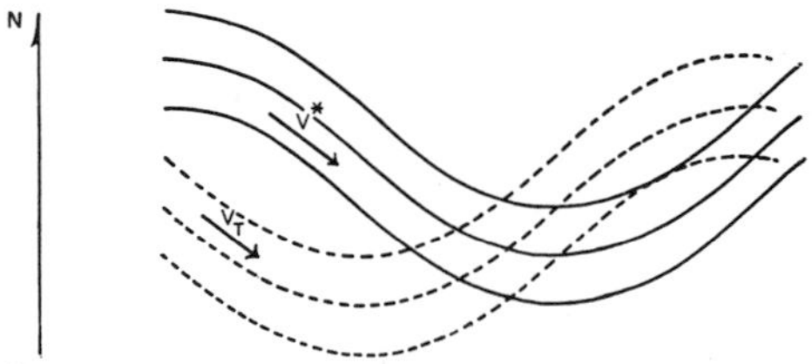

Fig. 2.—Flow pattern (solid lines) and temperature pattern (dashed lines) in an intensifying trough.

The question may now be raised as to what are the different mechanisms leading to the conditions mentioned above, under which potential energy can be converted into kinetic energy of the disturbances. Ad-

1. "Dynamic Forecasting by Numerical Process" by J. G. Charney, pp. 470–482.

2. The assumption of isothermalcy is not necessary, but convenient.

mitting that several such mechanisms may exist, the discussion here will be confined to the self-exciting one, by means of which small disturbances may amplify because of an instability of the underlying basic zonal flow. A theoretical attack on the problem of waves in a baroclinic atmosphere was first undertaken in the Norwegian polar front school of meteorology, principally by H. Solberg [25] (in addition, see [2, 5]). Waves were examined on an inclined surface of discontinuity separating two barotropic layers. Thus, all the baroclinity was considered as concentrated in a surface of discontinuity. In principle, however, with regard to the possibility of converting potential into kinetic energy, there is no difference between such a basic flow and one with continuously distributed baroclinity. In contrast to the pure, polar front waves, which may possibly feed also upon the kinetic energy of the basic current, are the baroclinic waves for a horizontally uniform basic flow, first examined by Charney [6]. The essential stability properties of these waves may be found easily by means of equations (23)–(26), if one neglects the vertical transport of potential temperature. As remarked in an earlier connection, and confirmed by the more rigorous solutions [10; 14, pp. 46–51], this approximation will be justified for the relatively large wave lengths. The adiabatic equation (3) may then be written

$$\left(\frac{\partial}{\partial t} + u^* \frac{\partial}{\partial x}\right) \varkappa^* + \frac{\partial \varkappa^*}{\partial y} v^* = 0, \qquad (27)$$

or, by differentiation with respect to x and use of (24),

$$\left(\frac{\partial}{\partial t} + u^* \frac{\partial}{\partial x}\right) v_T - u_T \frac{\partial v^*}{\partial x} + \frac{\partial v_T}{\partial y} v^* + \frac{\partial u^*}{\partial x} v_T = 0.$$

Let it now be assumed by way of example that

$$\frac{\partial v^*}{\partial y} = \frac{\partial v_T}{\partial y} = 0,$$

so that the results arrived at may be said to apply approximately to disturbances whose scale in the y-direction is large compared with the scale in the x-direction. It follows then from (26) that $\partial u^*/\partial x = \partial u_T/\partial x = 0$. With the assumption of no horizontal shear for the zonal flow, u^* and u_T will now have to be independent of x and y. It is also easily understood that neither can they depend upon time. Equations (23) and (25) now reduce to

$$\left[\left(\frac{\partial}{\partial t} + u^* \frac{\partial}{\partial x}\right)\frac{\partial}{\partial x} + \beta\right] v^* + \left(u_T \frac{\partial^2}{\partial x^2} - \frac{\partial}{\partial x}\right) v_T = 0, \qquad (28)$$

$$u_T \frac{\partial}{\partial x} v^* - \left(\frac{\partial}{\partial t} + u^* \frac{\partial}{\partial x}\right) v_T = 0.$$

Suppose

$$v^* \sim \exp\,[i(\mu x + \omega t)]$$

and

$$v_T \sim \exp\,[i(\mu x + \omega t)]$$

to be solutions of (28). By substitution into (28) one gets as the condition that v^* and v_T do not vanish identically,

$$\omega = -\mu u^* + \frac{\beta}{2\mu} \pm \sqrt{\left(\frac{\beta}{2\mu}\right)^2 - \mu^2 u_T^2}.$$

When the square root becomes imaginary, and the negative sign is taken, v^* and v_T will increase exponentially. When the substitution for u_T is made from (24), the criterion for stability and instability therefore becomes

$$\left(\frac{\beta}{2\mu}\right)^2 - \mu^2 H^2 \left(\frac{du}{dz}\right)^2 \begin{matrix} < 0 & \text{(unstable)} \\ > 0 & \text{(stable).} \end{matrix} \qquad (29)$$

Formula (29) reveals the high degree of instability of a horizontally uniform current in a baroclinic atmosphere. This result is common to all the different studies of baroclinic waves, which otherwise differ widely both with respect to the manner of formulating the problem of instability, and with respect to some of the conclusions obtained [1; 6; 10; 14, pp. 35–51]. Below is a summary of some of the assumptions and conclusions.

Charney

Assumptions:

1. Geostrophic approximation.
2. Compressibility.
3. Infinite atmosphere.
4. Vertical stability.

Conclusion:

All waves, at least down to about 1200 km, are unstable for a sufficiently large meridional temperature gradient.

Eady

Assumptions:

1. Geostrophic assumption.
2. Incompressibility.
3. Vertical stability.
4. Inertia effects of inhomogeneity neglected:

$$Q\left(\frac{D\mathbf{v}}{dt} + f\mathbf{k}\times\mathbf{v}\right) = \text{const}\left(\frac{D\mathbf{v}}{dt} + f\mathbf{k}\times\mathbf{v}\right).$$

5. Constant Coriolis parameter: $df/dy = 0$.
6. (*a*) Finite atmosphere bounded by two rigid walls at distance h apart.
   (*b*) Infinite atmosphere.

Conclusions from assumption (6) are:

(*a*) All waves are unstable[3] if and only if

$$\left(\frac{L}{h}\right)^2 > \frac{\pi^2}{2f^2}\left(g\frac{\partial \bar{\varkappa}}{\partial z}\right).$$

(*b*) No waves are unstable unless a layer of smaller vertical stability is underlying one of greater stability.

3. Compare with the result obtained on p. 457.

Fjørtoft

Assumptions:

1. Incompressibility.
2. Vertical stability zero.
3. Constant Coriolis parameter: $df/dy = 0$.
4. Finite atmosphere bounded by horizontal walls at distance h apart.

Conclusion:

All waves are unstable if and only if

$$\left(\frac{L}{h}\right)^2 > \frac{\pi^2}{2f^2}\left(\frac{du}{dz}\right)^2.$$

It may be remarked that Eady's second conclusion will no longer hold if the simplification mentioned in his fourth assumption is not made, in other words, even the infinite atmosphere with uniform vertical stability will be unstable if account is taken of the fact that density diminishes to zero for increasing heights. The appearance of a stabilizing influence from the vertical shear for short wave lengths in Fjørtoft's conclusion is due to effects to be discussed at the end of the following section. This stabilizing effect could not possibly appear in the other studies because there $(\omega + 2\pi u/L)^2$ was neglected compared with f^2 [14, pp. 41–42].

Barotropic Disturbances

In the case of barotropy there can be no vertical wind shear in the state of quasi-balance which characterizes the motions with which this article is concerned. Equations (18) and (21) therefore reduce to

$$\frac{D\zeta_{\text{abs}}}{dt} = 0; \qquad \nabla\cdot\mathbf{v} = 0, \tag{30}$$

with the asterisks now dropped as superfluous. These equations represent the classical equations for conservation of vorticity in a two-dimensional nondivergent flow of a nonviscous fluid. The fundamental investigation of wave motions in such flows was carried out by Rayleigh [22]. Although in the studies of polar front waves the destabilizing effects of a gliding discontinuity were considered to be important, it has not been until recently that barotropic phenomena in their full and complex generality have been taken up for systematic investigations, primarily by the Chicago school of meteorology. Starting with Rossby's work on planetary waves [24], in which the specific importance of the variability of the Coriolis parameter was discovered, a series of papers have followed in which different barotropic phenomena have been discussed. Briefly, one may say that while some of them, apart from the modifications following from the spherical shape of the earth, are analogous to the classical works by Rayleigh, others represent original investigations as exemplified by those treating stationary solutions of the nonlinear vorticity equation [9, 13, 17, 20]. The mathematical solution of (30) involves, of course, all the difficulties connected with the solution of nonlinear equations. The difficulties may even be very great for the linearized equations, particularly when there is a variable zonal current [18]. It is, however, possible and also useful to obtain an understanding of several of the most important barotropic phenomena by direct physical considerations [14, pp. 15–35]. In the following discussion this kind of argument will be used. We will make the purely formal simplification of assuming that the horizontal motion takes place as if on a circular disk; however, f will be kept a variable parameter.

One of the physical principles which may be used for a general discussion of some barotropic phenomena is the conservation of total angular momentum:

$$\int uR\,dF = \text{const.} \tag{31}$$

Here R is the distance from the pole, and dF a surface element in the plane of motion. By introducing the velocity circulation $c = \int_0^{2\pi} uR\,d\psi$ along zonal circles, (31) becomes equivalent to

$$\int c\,dF = \text{const.} \tag{32}$$

Another equivalent expression can easily be shown to be [14, p. 21]

$$G = \int \zeta_{\text{abs}}(R_0, \psi_0)R^2\,dF = \text{const.} \tag{33}$$

Here, ζ_{abs} is represented as a function of Lagrangian coordinates, and is therefore independent of time because the absolute vorticity is conserved, and R represents the generally time-variable radial positions of the fluid particles. Equation (33) is now a condition which restricts all future radial positions. In Fig. 3

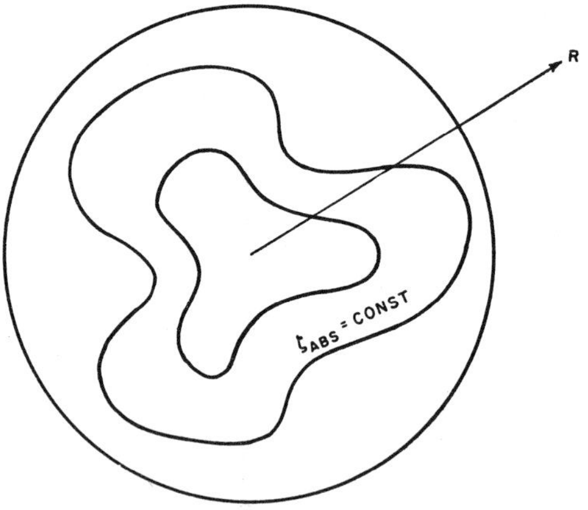

Fig. 3.—Isolines for the vertical component of absolute vorticity.

the irregular lines are curves of equal absolute vorticity for the case that ζ_{abs} varies monotonically from one isoline to the other. Clearly, a necessary and sufficient condition for having a pure zonal flow is that the lines of equal vorticity have a zonal distribution. The motion corresponding to the vorticity distribution in Fig. 3 is therefore certainly not zonal. It may now be inferred from (33) that neither can it be so at any later time. The reason for this is that by varying the positions of the fluid particles, G assumes an extreme value if and only if the lines of equal vorticity are zonal. In the present case this extremum would be either an absolute minimum or maximum. Therefore, the isolines of ζ_{abs} could not possibly become zonal unless at the same time G varied in contradiction to (33). Thus, at all times one must have

$$\int \zeta'^2 \, dF \geqq m, \qquad (m > 0), \tag{34}$$

where a prime again has been used to indicate deviations from zonal means. With possible exceptions for some singular cases, it can be shown that (34) must be true for a quite general distribution of vorticities.

A problem of considerable interest is involved in the question as to what will happen in a barotropic atmosphere left with a certain distribution of vorticities that do not correspond to a motion which is stationary, either absolutely or with respect to a coordinate system rotating at a constant speed. Will the structure of the subsequent motion tend to approach a more or less definite limit, or will different structures be repeated more or less periodically? Synoptic experience is probably most in favor of the first point of view, though there have been attempts to interpret some cycles in the general circulation on a strictly barotropic basis. In favor of the first point of view one can at least say with certainty that theoretically no oscillations in the strict sense are possible. This is because in a purely oscillatory motion the fluid particles would simultaneously have to reassume earlier positions, but with different velocities. However, this is impossible because, according to the conservation of vorticity, the positions of the fluid particles determine uniquely the vorticity distribution which in turn determines the velocities.

From the condition $\int \zeta'^2 \, dF + \int \bar{\zeta}_{abs}^2 \, dF = \text{const}$, there is also an upper limit to $\int \zeta'^2 dF$, so that (34) may be extended to

$$M \geqq \int \zeta'^2 \, dF \geqq m, \qquad (m > 0). \tag{35}$$

Returning now to the kind of vorticity distributions which are illustrated in Fig. 3, it will be assumed as a particular case that the vorticity distribution deviates only slightly from a zonal one. The corresponding flow is a zonal flow upon which there are superimposed small disturbances. The time-invariant value of G will now be but slightly different from a maximum or minimum value, which implies that no change in the vorticity pattern from the nearly zonal one to one characterized as in Fig. 3 can take place without necessarily changing the value of G. The proof for this is simply the reversal of the one stating that it was not possible to come arbitrarily near to a zonal distribution. The corresponding zonal flow is, therefore, stable in this case. Let $\bar{\zeta}_0 + f$ and ζ_0' be the initial vorticities in the mean zonal flow and in the disturbances. An expression and criterion for the present stability is

$$M \geqq \int \zeta'^2 \, dF \geqq m, \qquad (m > 0), \tag{36a}$$

$$M \to 0 \quad \text{when} \quad \int \zeta_0'^2 \, dF \to 0, \tag{36b}$$

if

$$\bar{\zeta}_0 + f \quad \text{varies monotonically with latitude.} \tag{36c}$$

It should be mentioned that the result which has been found that polar anticyclones are always unstable in a barotropic atmosphere [23] cannot be true if (36) is true. That is because anticyclones may exist for which condition (36c) still may be true.

Suppose now again that the absolute vorticity for the mean zonal flow varies monotonically with latitude and consider the possible changes in the mean zonal flow which will result from the meridional exchange of air. It may be assumed, in accordance with the most frequent conditions, that $d(\bar{\zeta}_0 + f)/dy > 0$. One has

$$\bar{u} = \frac{c}{2\pi R} = \frac{1}{2\pi R} \int_F \zeta \, dF,$$

where F is the area north of the latitude circle which is being considered. Since equal areas of fluid are going in and out of a latitude circle, $\bar{u}$ will have to decrease or increase according as the vorticities leaving the circle are replaced by vorticities of lower or higher magnitudes, respectively. Now, each fluid particle is assigned a certain absolute vorticity $\bar{\zeta}_0 + f + \zeta_0'$ which is moving with the particle. The effect of this transport may be considered as a separate effect from those of the transport of $\bar{\zeta}_0 + f$ and of ζ_0' As to the first effect it is easily understood that because $\bar{\zeta}_0 + f$ is increasing northwards, air streaming out of a zonal circle will have to be replaced by air with lower value of the absolute vorticity. This effect, when considered alone, will therefore amount to a decrease in c at all latitudes. This is in conflict with the principle of the conservation of total angular momentum, equation (32). It can, therefore, immediately be inferred that the effect from the transport of the initial irregular vorticities must be to compensate exactly this loss in angular momentum, that is, to create in the mean a compensating westerly flow [14, p. 28]. In consequence of this it may be concluded that, in the mean at least, the air with positive ζ_0' has to be transported to the north, and that with negative ζ_0' to the south. In the special case of a stationary flow pattern, as for instance for the Rossby waves, the two effects compensate each other exactly at each latitude. In other cases, however, one can only expect that the compensation is accomplished after integration over all latitudes. It has been assumed by Kuo [19] that the effect of the transport of the irregular vorticities will be the dominating one at middle latitudes, resulting there in an increase of the westerlies. However, the arguments used are not convincing, and without carrying out numerical calculations nothing certain can be said with respect to the resulting changes in the mean zonal flow. Preliminary calculations [15] seem to indicate that rather than increasing the westerlies at middle latitudes, the tendency under certain conditions may as well be to decrease the westerlies at middle latitudes and increase them in belts to the north and south, particularly to the north.

In a barotropic atmosphere the energy equation reduces to

$$\int \tfrac{1}{2}\mathbf{v}'^2\, dF = -\int \tfrac{1}{2}\bar{u}^2\, dF + \text{const.}$$

Consequently, there is an upper bound to the kinetic energy of the disturbances. In the case where ζ_{abs} varied monotonically from one isoline of vorticity to the next it was found that there must be a lower bound to $\int \zeta'^2\, dF$ which is different from zero. The same must, therefore, be the case for the kinetic energy of the irregular flow. Thus, in this case

$$A \geqq \int \tfrac{1}{2}\mathbf{v}'^2\, dF \geqq a, \qquad (a > 0). \tag{37}$$

The stability under condition (36*c*) therefore does not imply that the disturbances are entirely damped out. Whether the total kinetic energy of the disturbances will increase or decrease is usually difficult to ascertain and will depend upon the character of the changes in $\bar{u}$. Writing

$$\begin{aligned} \tfrac{1}{2}\int (\mathbf{v}'^2 - \mathbf{v}_0'^2)\, dF &= -\tfrac{1}{2}\int (\bar{u}^2 - \bar{u}_0^2)\, dF \\ &= -\int \frac{\bar{u}_0}{R}(\bar{u}R - \bar{u}_0R)\, dF - \tfrac{1}{2}\int (\bar{u} - \bar{u}_0)^2\, dF, \end{aligned} \tag{38}$$

one finds easily [14, p. 23] by using condition (31) in the form

$$\int (\bar{u}R - \bar{u}_0R)\, dF = 0 \tag{39}$$

that $\bar{u}$ has to decrease where $\bar{u}_0/R$ is large and increase where $\bar{u}_0/R$ is small, if the kinetic energy of the disturbances is to increase. Particularly if one has to do with small disturbances in a zonal flow, the upper bound to the changes in $\bar{u}$ which can be caused by a transport of the initial irregular vorticities is also a small quantity. In order to find necessary conditions for real instability one has therefore to investigate the effect from the transport of $\bar{\zeta}_0 + f$. It was found earlier that $\bar{u}$ would decrease if $d(\bar{\zeta}_0 + f)/dy > 0$. By similar arguments one will find that $\bar{u}$ on the other hand has to increase where $d(\bar{\zeta}_0 + f)/dy < 0$. So, the necessary conditions for real instability will be that

$$\begin{aligned} &\frac{d}{dy}(\bar{\zeta}_0 + f) > 0 \quad \text{where } \frac{\bar{u}_0}{R} \text{ is large,} \\ &\frac{d}{dy}(\bar{\zeta}_0 + f) < 0 \quad \text{where } \frac{\bar{u}_0}{R} \text{ is small.} \end{aligned} \tag{40}$$

The trivial case with solid rotation in the mean flow, $\bar{u}_0/R = \text{const}$, implies, of course, according to (38) and (39), that $\int \tfrac{1}{2}\mathbf{v}'^2\, dF$ at most can remain constant in time, but will decrease if some changes in $\bar{u}$ result.

Hitherto, the most complete mathematical treatment of barotropic waves in a basic flow which is unstable in the above sense has been undertaken by Kuo [18]. This instability is fundamentally the same as the one occurring when a gliding discontinuity exists. However, by treating the realistic case with a continuous shear and including the variation of the Coriolis parameter, two important modifications result:

1. As results of an assumed continuous shear under average atmospheric conditions:

a. All waves below approximately 300 km are stable.

b. An intermediate wave length of maximum instability exists.

2. As a result of the inclusion of $df/dy \neq 0$, the longest waves become stable.

It is important to notice that the most unstable waves of the type discussed above are relatively long waves compared with the most unstable baroclinic waves [10; 14, p. 50].

How can the stability occurring for short waves mentioned above be understood? It was previously seen that provided conditions (40) were fulfilled the kinetic energy of the disturbances would necessarily increase as a result of a transport of $\bar{\zeta}_0 + f$. Therefore, when the shortest waves become stable this can only be a result of the transport of the initial irregular vorticities, ζ_0', which furthermore must tend to be the dominating effect for the shortest wave lengths. An understanding of the stabilizing influence arising from the transport of irregular vorticities may be obtained in the following way: Suppose a wavelike disturbance with untilted troughs and ridges to exist initially in a nonuniform zonal current. The instantaneous transport of the irregular vorticities is accomplished by a component $\bar{u}_0\mathbf{i}$ of the mean flow and a component $\mathbf{v}_0'$ of the irregular flow. When small disturbances are considered, or disturbances in which $\mathbf{v}_0'$ is essentially parallel to the lines $\zeta_0' = \text{const}$, only the transport by the first component has to be considered. It is now obvious that if the angular velocity $\bar{u}_0/R$ varies with latitude, the lengths of the lines $\zeta' = \text{const}$ have to increase as a result of this transport. On the other hand, the areas enclosed by these lines are conserved as are also the values of ζ' because the effects of the transverse displacements of the vorticities $\bar{\zeta}_0 + f$ are disregarded in this connection. Consequently, it follows from Stokes' theorem that the velocity circulation for the disturbances taken along the closed curves $v\zeta' = \text{const}$, which approximately are also streamlines for $\mathbf{v}'$, must remain constant. But since the lengths of the streamlines for $\mathbf{v}'$ increase, the average intensity of $|\mathbf{v}'|$ must decrease correspondingly. When this stabilizing influence dominates the destabilizing influence from the transverse transport of vorticities of the basic flow, which can be shown to be the case for the shortest waves [14, p. 31], kinetic energy must flow from the disturbances to the mean flow so that in accordance with what was said above, $\bar{u}$ will have to increase where $\bar{u}/R$ is large and decrease where $\bar{u}/R$ is small.

Combined Baroclinic and Barotropic Disturbances

While there is enough evidence for the importance both of baroclinic and barotropic effects, there must be a limit to the extent to which phenomena can be explained purely barotropically or baroclinically. In general, one must expect that barotropic and baroclinic effects either add together in a more or less simple fashion, or they may be coupled to such a degree that the consideration of both effects simultaneously may give rise to entirely new types of phenomena.

The only studies until now on waves for which both potential and kinetic energy are possible sources for the growth of the disturbance are those on polar front waves. Because of the complexity in the solutions for these waves one does not know whether the one or the other of these two possible sources is the more important, although the shearing instability has been interpreted as the decisive one, seemingly, however, without any convincing justification. The unstable baroclinic waves treated in this article have accordingly been looked upon as physically entirely different waves. It is the writer's opinion that this probably is not true. Further investigations on this subject can be carried out with relative ease when the quasi-geostrophic approximation is made. Relatively simple equations appropriate for the most simple polar front model have been worked out by Phillips [21].

It is not unlikely that the study of an atmosphere where typical barotropic and baroclinic effects are operating in full generality may contribute considerably to a further understanding of the behavior of the atmosphere. For this purpose equations (23) and (25), or essentially similar equations, may prove useful, at least for theoretical investigations, because of their great simplicity and generality.

REFERENCES

1. Berson, F. A., "Summary of a Theoretical Investigation into the Factors Controlling the Instability of Long Waves in Zonal Currents." *Tellus*, Vol. 1, No. 4, pp. 44–52 (1949).
2. Bjerknes, J., and Godske, C. L., "On the Theory of Cyclone Formation at Extra-tropical Fronts." *Astrophys. norveg.*, Vol. 1, No. 6 (1936).
3. Bjerknes, J., and Holmboe, J., "On the Theory of Cyclones." *J. Meteor.*, 1:1–22 (1944).
4. Bjerknes, V., "Application of Line Integral Theorems to the Hydrodynamics of Terrestrial and Cosmic Vortices." *Astrophys. norveg.*, 2:263–339 (1937).
5. —— and others, *Hydrodynamique physique*. Paris, Presses Universitaires de France, 1934.
6. Charney, J. G., "The Dynamics of Long Waves in a Baroclinic Westerly Current." *J. Meteor.*, 4:135–162 (1947).
7. —— "On the Scale of Atmospheric Motions." *Geofys. Publ.*, Vol. 17, No. 2, 17 pp. (1948).
8. —— Fjørtoft, R., and Neumann, J. v., "Numerical Integration of the Barotropic Vorticity Equation." *Tellus*, 2:237–254 (1950).
9. Craig, R. A., "A Solution of the Nonlinear Vorticity Equation for Atmospheric Motion." *J. Meteor.*, 2:175–178 (1945).
10. Eady, E. T., "Long Waves and Cyclone Waves." *Tellus*, Vol. 1, No. 3, pp. 33–52 (1949).
11. Eliassen, A., "Slow Thermally or Frictionally Controlled Meridional Circulation in a Circular Vortex." Unpublished manuscript (1951).
12. —— "The Quasi-static Equations of Motion with Pressure as Independent Variable." *Geofys. Publ.*, Vol. 17, No. 3, 44 pp. (1949).
13. Ertel, H., "Die Westwindgebiete der Troposphäre als Instabilitätszonen." *Meteor. Z.*, 60:397–400 (1943).
14. Fjørtoft, R., "Application of Integral Theorems in Deriving Criteria of Stability for Laminar Flows and for the Baroclinic Circular Vortex." *Geofys. Publ.*, Vol. 17, No. 6 (1950).
15. —— Unpublished manuscript, 1950.
16. Høiland, E., "On the Interpretation and Application of the Circulation Theorems of V. Bjerknes." *Arch. Math. Naturv.*, Vol. 42, No. 5, pp. 25–57 (1939).
17. —— "On Horizontal Motion in a Rotating Fluid." *Geofys. Publ.*, Vol. 17, No. 10 (1950).
18. Kuo, H.-L., "Dynamic Instability of Two-Dimensional Nondivergent Flow in a Barotropic Atmosphere." *J. Meteor.*, 6:105–122 (1949).
19. —— "The Motion of Atmospheric Vortices and the General Circulation." *J. Meteor.*, 7:247–258 (1950).
20. Neamtan, S. M., "The Motion of Harmonic Waves in the Atmosphere." *J. Meteor.*, 3:53–56 (1946).
21. Phillips, N. A., Unpublished manuscript, 1950.
22. Rayleigh, Lord, *Scientific Papers*, 6 Vols. Cambridge, University Press, 1899–1920. (See Vol. I, pp. 474–490; Vol. III, pp. 17–23, 575–584; Vol. VI, pp. 197–204.)
23. Rossby, C.-G., "On a Mechanism for the Release of Potential Energy in the Atmosphere." *J. Meteor.*, 6:163–180 (1949).
24. —— and Collaborators, "Relation between Variations in the Intensity of the Zonal Circulation of the Atmosphere and the Displacements of the Semi-permanent Centers of Action." *J. mar. Res.*, 2:38–55 (1939).
25. Solberg, H., "Das Zyklonenproblem." *Verh. III intern. Kongress für techn. Mechanik* (1930).
26. Sutcliffe, R. C., "A Contribution to the Problem of Development." *Quart. J. R. meteor. Soc.*, 73:370–383 (1947).
27. —— and Forsdyke, A. G., "The Theory and Use of Upper Air Thickness Patterns in Forecasting." *Quart. J. R. meteor. Soc.*, 76:189–217 (1950).

Reprinted from *Journal of Meteorology*, Vol. 11, No. 5, Oct., 1954, published by the American Meteorological Society.

SYMMETRICAL DISTURBANCES IN A THIN LAYER OF FLUID SUBJECT TO A HORIZONTAL TEMPERATURE GRADIENT AND ROTATION

By H.-L. Kuo

Massachusetts Institute of Technology[1]

(Manuscript received 11 December 1953)

ABSTRACT

The symmetrical thermal convection of a rotating fluid subject to a horizontal temperature difference is examined. It is shown that the effect of rotation is to inhibit the convection. The extent of this inhibition depends upon the non-dimensional parameter $T = 4\Omega^2 d^4 \nu^{-2}$, where d denotes the depth of the layer, Ω the rotation rate, and ν is the kinematic viscosity. For a given value of T, the onset of convection requires the non-dimensional parameter $Q = gd^4 \Delta\rho\,(\kappa\nu a\rho)^{-1}$ to be higher than a critical value Q_c, and there is a most favorable cell size l_c for which the critical Q is lowest. Here $\rho^{-1}\Delta\rho$ is the horizontal density contrast, κ the thermometric conductivity, and a is horizontal extent (radius of the pan used). When T is very large, $4Qd(lT)^{-1}$ approaches a constant value, suggesting that the onset of convection may be determined by the product of a properly defined Rossby number and the Prandtl number, $\nu\kappa^{-1}$. The forms of the flow pattern and the temperature distribution are also discussed.

1. Introduction

The present work is a preliminary attempt to solve some problems concerning the symmetrical convective motion of a thin fluid layer which is subject to the influences of a horizontal temperature contrast and of rotation, particularly the stability problem of this motion and the distribution of the zonal velocity produced. This type of motion is of particular interest to meteorologists, largely because it is commonly believed that the general circulation of the atmosphere is maintained by such a large-scale convective process, with ascending motions in lower latitudes and descending motions in higher latitudes, driven directly by the heating. Such thermal convection was first discussed theoretically by Oberbeck (1888), whose results have been given in a more simple form by Arakawa (1940). The problem also has been discussed by Kropatscheck (1935), Prandtl (1939) and Davies (1953). The fundamental assumption used in these investigations is to take the temperature distribution either as given or as determined entirely by heat conduction or radiation, and not affected by the motion. Under this assumption, the temperature distribution appears in the equations of motion as an unchanging forcing function, and the motion becomes a forced motion. If this assumption is correct, the kind of convection mentioned will exist whenever there is a temperature contrast in the fluid. However, a rough computation shows that, when there is a finite temperature contrast in the fluid and when the fluid is in motion, the local change of temperature is determined mainly by the motion, and not much by molecular heat conduction except very near to solid boundaries. Thus, in order that the theoretical result obtained should be consistent both dynamically and thermodynamically, we must use the complete heat-flow equation, with the heat convection terms included. In other words, the motion is a "natural flow," in which the velocity field and the temperature field are mutually dependent and must be determined simultaneously. When this mutual dependence between the temperature field and the velocity field is considered, the question arises whether such a motion can be sustained by the temperature contrast or whether the motion will take forms other than symmetric direct circulation.

To understand the physical processes involved in this problem, let us consider a fluid which is under the influence of heating and of rotation, the main function of the former being to produce and to maintain a horizontal temperature — and therefore density — contrast in the fluid and thereby introducing a buoyancy force. When the heating rate is large, there must be a heat transport from the heat source to the cold source by motions in the cross-isothermal direction in addition to heat conduction. In other words, if friction is overcome, the density contrast sets up certain motions to perform the function of heat transfer. However, although a direct symmetric thermal convection which moves the fluid directly from heat source to cold source is the simplest form of motion that can transport heat, such a motion is prevented by the deflecting force of rotation which tends to cause the fluid particles to describe some type of inertial circles and follow paths which are more horizontal. Thus, the type of motion that will appear under a given rate of rotation and heating must depend upon its adjustment to two different effects, the effects of

[1] The research reported in this article was sponsored by the Geophysics Research Directorate, Air Force Cambridge Research Center, under Contract No. AF 19(122)-153.

the temperature contrast and that of rotation. Only when the temperature contrast is large and the rotation rate is small can symmetrical direct thermal convection take place. When the rotation rate is high and the temperature contrast is relatively small, the fluid particles are not able to follow such a direct circulation; the motion must then be asymmetrical and more horizontal, and therefore will appear as waves in the zonal direction, as is shown by the experiments of Fultz (1951b).

Because of the very complicated nature of the motion of this fluid system, in this article we shall discuss only problems concerning the symmetric convective flow. To simplify the analysis, we consider that a temperature contrast in the radial direction is introduced, and to a degree later maintained within the fluid by heat conduction. At the initial moment, we may assume that the fluid is in purely zonal motion which balances the radial pressure gradient due to the mean temperature contrast, or more simply we may assume that the fluid is initially at relative rest. The latter case can be realized by imagining that the finite horizontal temperature contrast is produced suddenly, or that the fluid is in a highly viscous state before the initial moment. Our problems are to find the criterion for the onset of symmetric motion in this fluid and to determine the velocity distribution in the early stages of the development of such motion, during which the relative velocities are still small. This restriction permits us to linearize the equations of motion by neglecting all the terms involving the products of velocity components. The criterion thus obtained may also be the one that marks the transition from the low- to the high-rotation regime with the lowest wave number, if the state of solid rotation is to be disturbed at all. It is also assumed that the depth of the layer is much smaller than its horizontal dimension, so that the effect of the vertical walls may be replaced by a harmonic requirement. Because of this latter simplification, our final results cannot give a good representation of the distributions of certain quantities in the regions near the vertical walls. However, it is assumed that these simplifications do not affect the character of the instability very much.

The result shows that the onset of the convective motion requires the non-dimensional parameter $Q = gd^4\,\Delta\rho\,(\kappa\nu a\rho)^{-1}$ to be above a critical value Q_c, which increases with the rate of rotation. The effect of rotation is therefore to inhibit the convection. The extent of this inhibition depends upon the non-dimensional parameter $T = 4\Omega^2 d^4 \nu^{-2}$. The lowest value of Q is associated with a certain wave number k. When T is very large ($T > 2 \times 10^3$), we have $4Q_c d(lT)^{-1} \rightarrow$ constant, showing that the onset of convection is determined by the product of a properly defined Rossby number and the Prandtl number, $\nu\kappa^{-1}$. A finite Q is also required for zero rotation, showing the inhibiting effect of viscosity.

The mean values of the parameters Q and T obtained from the most recent, unpublished experimental data of Dr. Fultz for the symmetrical flow all lie above the critical curve and are not very far away from it, although different depths were used in the experiments. The observed zonal velocity distribution also agrees well with the theoretical results.

2. Equations of the problem

Let us consider a layer of nearly incompressible fluid of depth d, contained between two concentric cylindrical vessels of radii a_1 and a_2, which rotate with a uniform angular speed Ω about their common axis. The equations of motion, continuity and heat conduction appropriate to the problem, in cylindrical coordinates r, ϕ and z, are

$$\frac{\partial u}{\partial t} + u\frac{\partial u}{\partial r} + \frac{v}{r}\frac{\partial u}{\partial \phi} + w\frac{\partial u}{\partial z} - \frac{v^2}{r} - 2\Omega v = -\frac{1}{\rho}\frac{\partial p}{\partial r} + r\Omega^2 + \nu\left(\nabla^2 u - \frac{u}{r^2} - \frac{2}{r^2}\frac{\partial v}{\partial \phi}\right), \quad (1)$$

$$\frac{\partial v}{\partial t} + \frac{u}{r}\frac{\partial rv}{\partial r} + \frac{v}{r}\frac{\partial v}{\partial \phi} + w\frac{\partial v}{\partial z} + 2\Omega u = -\frac{1}{\rho r}\frac{\partial p}{\partial \phi} + \nu\left(\nabla^2 v - \frac{v}{r^2} + \frac{2}{r^2}\frac{\partial u}{\partial \phi}\right), \quad (2)$$

$$\frac{\partial w}{\partial t} + u\frac{\partial w}{\partial r} + \frac{v}{r}\frac{\partial w}{\partial \phi} + w\frac{\partial w}{\partial z} = -\frac{1}{\rho}\frac{\partial p}{\partial z} - g + \nu\,\nabla^2 w, \quad (3)$$

$$\frac{1}{r}\frac{\partial ru}{\partial r} + \frac{1}{r}\frac{\partial v}{\partial \phi} + \frac{\partial w}{\partial z} = 0, \quad (4)$$

and

$$\frac{\partial \theta}{\partial t} + u\frac{\partial \theta}{\partial r} + \frac{v}{r}\frac{\partial \theta}{\partial \phi} + w\frac{\partial \theta}{\partial z} = \kappa\,\nabla^2\theta, \quad (5)$$

where u, v and w are the radial, zonal and vertical velocity components, respectively, ρ is the density, p the pressure, θ the temperature, and ν and κ are the coefficients of kinematic viscosity and thermometric conductivity, respectively. In these equations, ∇^2 stands for the three-dimensional Laplacian operator

$$\partial^2(\ )/\partial r^2 + r^{-1}\partial(\ )/\partial r + r^{-2}\partial^2(\ )/\partial\phi^2 + \partial^2(\ )/\partial z^2.$$

As has been discussed before, we consider that at the initial moment the fluid is at relative rest or in purely zonal motion, and that a variable mean temperature θ_0 is produced and maintained within the fluid by external heating, so that θ_0 satisfies the steady-state heat-conduction equation,

$$\nabla^2\theta_0 = 0. \quad (6)$$

Our problem is to investigate whether a symmetric

thermal convection can be set up by this temperature contrast, and if so, to find the velocity distribution during the early stage of the development.

As is permissible in this problem, we allow for the variation of density due to thermal expansion only in so far as it modifies gravity and introduces a buoyancy force. Thus, in (3) we replace ρ, which occurs as a factor of g, by

$$\rho = \bar{\rho}_0(1 - \alpha\,\Delta\theta), \tag{7}$$

where α denotes the coefficient of volume expansion, $\bar{\rho}_0$ the density corresponding to a mean temperature $\bar{\theta}_0$, and $\Delta\theta$ is the deviation of the local temperature from θ_0. We regard ρ occurring elsewhere in (1) to (3) as a constant equal to $\bar{\rho}_0$, and consider the fluid as incompressible during the motion.

For this problem, we may neglect all the terms in (1) to (5) that involve the products of the velocity components u, v and w, and also θ, where v is the deviation of the zonal velocity from v_0, and θ is the deviation of the local temperature from θ_0. Replacing ρ by $\bar{\rho}_0$, and g by $g\alpha\theta$, which represents the buoyancy force due to the local density anomaly, and assuming all the quantities to be independent of longitude ϕ, we note that these equations reduce to

$$\frac{\partial u}{\partial t} - 2\left(\Omega + \frac{v_0}{r}\right)v = -\frac{1}{\rho_0}\frac{\partial p}{\partial r} + \nu\left(\nabla^2 u - \frac{u}{r^2}\right), \tag{8}$$

$$\frac{\partial v}{\partial t} + \left(2\Omega + \frac{\partial v_0}{\partial r} + \frac{v_0}{r}\right)u + w\frac{\partial v_0}{dz} = \nu\left(\nabla^2 v - \frac{v}{r^2}\right), \tag{9}$$

$$\partial w/\partial t = g\alpha\theta - \rho_0^{-1}\,\partial p/\partial z + \nu\,\nabla^2 w, \tag{10}$$

$$r^{-1}\,\partial(ru)/\partial r + \partial w/\partial z = 0, \tag{11}$$

and

$$\partial\theta/\partial t + u\,\partial\theta_0/\partial r + w\,\partial\theta_0/\partial z = \kappa\,\nabla^2\theta, \tag{12}$$

where p now represents the deviation of the local pressure from the pressure in the initial state, and ∇^2 stands for the appropriate form of the Laplacian operator. Since v_0 satisfies the steady-state hydrodynamic equations, its vertical variation is determined by the thermal-wind relation,

$$\frac{\partial}{\partial z}\left(2\Omega v_0 + \frac{v_0^2}{r}\right) = g\alpha\frac{\partial\theta_0}{\partial r}. \tag{13}$$

The radial variation of v_0 in a rotating cylindrical vessel with arbitrary radius will be discussed in section 7, below.

To simplify the mathematics, we assume that the radii of the cylindrical vessels are large, so that the operator $\partial/\partial r + 1/r$ may be approximated by $\partial/\partial r$, and the terms u/r^2 and v/r^2 in (8) and (9) may be neglected. We shall also neglect $\partial v_0/\partial r$ and v_0/r against 2Ω. The only term involving v_0 is then $\partial v_0/\partial z$ in (9), which may be replaced by $(2\Omega)^{-1}g\alpha\,\partial\theta_0/\partial r$. We assume that θ_0 varies linearly with r and z. For the sake of convenience, we may introduce a stream function ψ, defined by

$$\partial\psi/\partial r = w \quad \text{and} \quad \partial\psi/\partial z = -u. \tag{14}$$

Eliminating v from (8) and (9), and expressing the velocity components u and w in terms of ψ, we obtain

$$\left(\frac{\partial}{\partial t} - \nu\nabla^2\right)^2\frac{\partial\psi}{\partial z} + 4\Omega^2\frac{\partial\psi}{\partial z} - g\alpha\frac{\partial\theta_0}{\partial r}\frac{\partial\psi}{\partial r} = -\frac{1}{\rho}\frac{\partial}{\partial r}\left(\frac{\partial}{\partial t} - \nu\nabla^2\right)p. \tag{15}$$

Eliminating p from (10) and (15), and then making use of (12), we obtain

$$\begin{aligned}\left(\frac{\partial}{\partial t} - \nu\nabla^2\right)^2\nabla^2\psi + 4\Omega^2\frac{\partial^2\psi}{\partial z^2} - g\alpha\frac{\partial\theta_0}{\partial r}\frac{\partial^2\psi}{\partial r\,\partial z} &= g\alpha\frac{\partial}{\partial r}\left(\frac{\partial}{\partial t} - \nu\nabla^2\right)\theta \\ &= g\alpha\left[\frac{\partial^2\psi}{\partial r\,\partial z}\frac{\partial\theta_0}{\partial r} - \frac{\partial^2\psi}{\partial r^2}\frac{\partial\theta_0}{\partial z}\right] - g\alpha(\nu - \kappa)\nabla^2\frac{\partial\theta}{\partial r}.\end{aligned} \tag{16}$$

Here ∇^2 stands for the ordinary two-dimensional Laplacian operator, $\partial^2(\ )/\partial r^2 + \partial^2(\ )/\partial z^2$.

The temperature θ may be eliminated from this equation by applying the operator $(\partial/\partial t - \kappa\nabla^2)$ and combining with (12). However, since we are going to discuss the limiting case of marginal instability when $\partial/\partial t$ approaches zero, the final differential equation is obtained by combining (16) and (12) without further differentiation. We shall discuss the meaning of this marginal instability by a manipulation of (16) for the particular case when $\kappa = \nu$, which holds approximately for the atmosphere.

In seeking solutions of these equations we must satisfy certain boundary conditions on the planes $z = 0$ and $z = d$, and the vertical walls $r = a_1$ and $r = a_2$. Certainly we must require the vanishing of the normal velocity components along these surfaces, which necessitates ψ to be constant at these boundaries. We denote this stream line by $\psi = 0$. If these boundaries are rigid, the tangential velocity components should also vanish, *i.e.*, the normal derivative $\partial\psi/\partial n$ must vanish, and also $\partial^2\psi/\partial r\,\partial z$, because of the continuity equation. On the other hand, the tangential stresses vanish on a free surface, which requires $\partial^2\psi/\partial n^2$ to be zero. Since the normal velocity is zero at all points on the boundaries, this is equivalent to $\nabla^2\psi = 0$. Additional boundary conditions follow from the basic equations. Elimination of p from (1) and (3) gives

$$\nu \nabla^4\psi - 2\Omega\, \partial v/\partial z = -g\alpha\, \partial\theta/\partial r. \qquad (17)$$

Certain restrictions can be obtained from this equation. On the top free surface, $\partial v/\partial z$ vanishes. We also assume that the radial temperature gradient is kept constant on the boundaries, so that we should require $\nabla^4\psi$ to vanish on the horizontal free surface. For simplicity, we shall treat all the boundaries as free surfaces and require the vanishing of $\nabla^4\psi$ on each of them. Thus, our boundary conditions are

$$\psi = 0, \quad \nabla^2\psi = 0,$$

and

$$\nabla^4\psi = 0 \text{ on the boundaries.} \qquad (18)$$

3. Marginal instability with the motion setting in as symmetric convection in the meridional plane

As has been discussed in the introduction, the primary concern of this study is to find the condition for the onset of the symmetric convection, or to find the lowest temperature contrast that is required for the occurrence of the symmetrical convection at a given rate of rotation. If we assume the rate of development of the motion to be represented by the factor exp (σt), this lowest temperature contrast is obtained by letting σ approach zero, which is equivalent to putting $\partial/\partial t = 0$ in the foregoing equations. We may now demonstrate that this limiting case actually separates the amplifying disturbances from the damped disturbances. For this purpose, it seems sufficient to consider the particular case when $\kappa = \nu$, so that the last term on the right side of (16) is absent. If the time factor σ is assumed to be complex, $\sigma = \sigma_r + i\sigma_i$, the solution ψ must also be complex, and may be written as

$$\psi_1 = \Psi_1(r, z)\, e^{\sigma t} = (W + iW')\, e^{(\sigma_r + i\sigma_i)t}.$$

However, the conjugate function,

$$\psi_2 = \Psi_1{}^* e^{\sigma^* t} = (W - iW')\, e^{(\sigma_r - i\sigma_i)t},$$

is also a solution of (16) and must satisfy the same boundary conditions. Let us denote (16) for ψ_1 by (16a), and the corresponding equation for ψ_2 by (16b). Multiplying (16a) by ψ_2, (16b) by ψ_1, and then subtracting the results, we obtain

$$\begin{aligned}\nu^2(\psi_2 \nabla^6\psi_1 - \psi_1 \nabla^6\psi_2) &- 2\nu(\sigma\psi_2 \nabla^4\psi_1 - \sigma^*\psi_1 \nabla^4\psi_2) \\ &+ (\sigma^2\psi_2 \nabla^2\psi_1 - \sigma^{*2}\psi_1 \nabla^2\psi_2) \\ &+ 4\Omega^2\left(\psi_2 \frac{\partial^2\psi_1}{\partial z^2} - \psi_1 \frac{\partial^2\psi_2}{\partial z^2}\right) \\ &- 2g\alpha \frac{\partial\theta_0}{\partial r}\left(\psi_2 \frac{\partial^2\psi_1}{\partial r\,\partial z} - \psi_1 \frac{\partial^2\psi_2}{\partial r\,\partial z}\right) \\ &+ g\alpha \frac{\partial\theta_0}{\partial z}\left(\psi_2 \frac{\partial^2\psi_1}{\partial r^2} - \psi_1 \frac{\partial^2\psi_2}{\partial r^2}\right) = 0. \qquad (19)\end{aligned}$$

We now integrate this equation over the entire cross-sectional area A, bounded by $z = 0$, $z = d$, $r = a_1$, and $r = a_2$. By use of Green's theorem, and because of the boundary conditions given by (18), the integration of the first two terms gives

$$\iint [\psi_2 \nabla^6\psi_1]\, dA - \iint [\nabla^2\psi_2 \cdot \nabla^4\psi_1]\, dA = \int_c \left(\psi_2 \frac{\partial}{\partial n} \nabla^4\psi_1 - \nabla^4\psi_1 \frac{\partial\psi_2}{\partial n}\right) ds = 0,$$

and

$$\iint (\psi_1 \nabla^6\psi_2 - \nabla^2\psi_2 \cdot \nabla^4\psi_1)\, dA = \int_c \left[\psi_1 \frac{\partial \nabla^4\psi_2}{\partial n} - \nabla^4\psi_2 \frac{\partial\psi_1}{\partial n} + \nabla^2\psi_1 \frac{\partial \nabla^2\psi_2}{\partial n} - \psi_2 \frac{\partial \nabla^4\psi_1}{\partial n}\right] ds = 0,$$

where n is the outward normal, and ds is the line element of the boundary c. The line integrals vanish because of the boundary conditions. Therefore, we have

$$\iint (\psi_1 \nabla^6\psi_2 - \psi_2 \nabla^6\psi_1)\, dA = 0.$$

In a similar manner, we obtain the following integrals of the other terms of (19):

$$\begin{aligned}\iint (\sigma\psi_2 \nabla^4\psi_1 - \sigma^*\psi_1 \nabla^4\psi_2)\, dA &= (\sigma - \sigma^*) \iint (\nabla^2\psi_1 \cdot \nabla^2\psi_2)\, dA \\ &= 2i\sigma_i \iint [(\nabla^2 W)^2 + (\nabla^2 W')^2]\, dA,\end{aligned}$$

$$\begin{aligned}\iint (\sigma^2\psi_2 \nabla^2\psi_1 - \sigma^{*2}\psi_1 \nabla^2\psi_2)\, dA &= (\sigma^2 - \sigma^{*2}) \iint \left(\frac{\partial\psi_1}{\partial r}\frac{\partial\psi_2}{\partial r} + \frac{\partial\psi_1}{\partial z}\frac{\partial\psi_2}{\partial z}\right) dA \\ &= -2\sigma_r\sigma_i i \iint \left[\left(\frac{\partial W}{\partial r}\right)^2 + \left(\frac{\partial W'}{\partial r}\right)^2 + \left(\frac{\partial W}{\partial z}\right)^2 + \left(\frac{\partial W'}{\partial z}\right)^2\right] dA,\end{aligned}$$

$$\iint \left(\psi_2 \frac{\partial^2\psi_1}{\partial z^2} - \psi_1 \frac{\partial^2\psi_2}{\partial z^2}\right) dA = \iint \left[\frac{\partial}{\partial z}\left(\psi_2 \frac{\partial\psi_1}{\partial z}\right) - \frac{\partial}{\partial z}\left(\psi_1 \frac{\partial\psi_2}{\partial z}\right)\right] dA = 0,$$

$$\iint \left(\psi_2 \frac{\partial^2\psi_1}{\partial r\,\partial z} - \psi_1 \frac{\partial^2\psi_2}{\partial r\,\partial z}\right) dA = \iint \left[\frac{\partial}{\partial z}\left(\psi_2 \frac{\partial\psi_1}{\partial r}\right) - \frac{\partial}{\partial r}\left(\psi_1 \frac{\partial\psi_2}{\partial z}\right)\right] dA = 0,$$

and

$$\iint \left(\psi_2 \frac{\partial^2 \psi_1}{\partial r^2} - \psi_1 \frac{\partial^2 \psi_2}{\partial r^2}\right) dA = \iint \frac{\partial}{\partial r}\left[\psi_2 \frac{\partial \psi_1}{\partial r} - \psi_1 \frac{\partial \psi_2}{\partial r}\right] dA = 0.$$

Thus, integration of the whole equation (19) gives

$$\sigma_i\{\kappa_1^2 + \sigma_r \kappa_2^2\} = 0, \qquad (20)$$

where

$$\kappa_1^2 = 2\iint [(\nabla^2 W)^2 + (\nabla^2 W')^2]\, dA$$

and

$$\kappa_2^2 = \iint \left[\left(\frac{\partial W}{\partial r}\right)^2 + \left(\frac{\partial W'}{\partial r}\right)^2 + \left(\frac{\partial W}{\partial z}\right)^2 + \left(\frac{\partial W'}{\partial z}\right)^2\right] dA.$$

Equation (20) requires that we either have $\sigma_i = 0$ or $\sigma_r = -(\kappa_1/\kappa_2)^2$. Thus, oscillating motions only occur with decaying symmetric disturbances, while for the amplifying disturbances we must have $\sigma_r > 0$ and $\sigma_i = 0$. Therefore, the slowest rate of development can be obtained by setting σ to zero. The corresponding critical temperature contrast then represents the lowest one that is capable of producing a symmetric motion. In the following we shall discuss only this limiting case.

Putting $\partial/\partial t = 0$ in (12) and (16), and eliminating the last term on the right side of (16), we obtain the following partial differential equation for ψ:

$$\nabla^6\psi + \frac{4\Omega^2}{\nu^2}\frac{\partial^2\psi}{\partial z^2} - \frac{g\alpha}{\kappa\nu}\left(1 + \frac{\kappa}{\nu}\right)\frac{\partial\theta_0}{\partial r}\frac{\partial^2\psi}{\partial r\,\partial z} + \frac{g\alpha}{\kappa\nu}\frac{\partial\theta_0}{\partial z}\frac{\partial^2\psi}{\partial r^2} = 0. \qquad (21)$$

This equation is to be solved, together with the boundary conditions (18), as a characteristic-value problem. We observe that the term with $\partial\theta_0/\partial r$ as a factor has two parts. The first part comes from the energy equation, while the second part comes from the term $w(\partial v_0/\partial z)$ of (9). The ratio of these two parts is κ/ν. Since this ratio is small for water, the result is not very different from that obtained by assuming that the fluid is initially at relative rest ($v_0 = 0$).

We note that, if there is no radial temperature contrast, (21) is very similar to the equation for ordinary convection discussed by Chandrasekhar (1953), which can be solved by separation of variables. However, when the motion is mainly driven by the radial temperature contrast, this method is no longer applicable. This means that it is impossible to reduce this equation to an ordinary differential equation, and it therefore is more difficult to solve. This mathematical difference can be explained by a physical consideration. When the motion is driven by the radial temperature contrast, the fluid particles are gaining kinetic energy from the release of the potential energy associated with this temperature contrast. Let us suppose a parcel of fluid has attained a temperature which is slightly higher than that of the immediate surroundings, so that it will then tend to rise. However, to maintain this temperature contrast against the effect of heat conduction and therefore to maintain the motion against friction, this parcel must move from a warmer to a colder region. Similarly, a slightly colder parcel can maintain or increase its downward motion only by moving into a warmer region. This means that the axis of the motion must be inclined with respect to the vertical, and therefore the stream function ψ cannot be represented by the product of two separate functions of r and z.

However, although the ordinary method of separation of variables is not applicable to (22), it is readily seen that this equation is satisfied by the function

$$\psi = \sum A_j \exp i[(kr/b) + m_j\xi], \qquad (22)$$

provided m_j is a root of the following equation:

$$m^6 + 3k^2m^4 + (T_0 + 3k^4)m^2 - kQ_0m + k^6 + k^2R_0 = 0, \qquad (23)$$

for a fixed k. Conversely, we may also consider k as the roots of this equation with m fixed. Here the A_j are arbitrary constants, $\xi = z/b$ where $b = d/2$ is a new vertical coordinate, and the quantities T_0, Q_0 and R_0 are defined by

$$T_0 = \frac{4\Omega^2}{\nu^2}b^4, \quad Q_0 = \frac{g\alpha}{\kappa\nu}b^4\left(1 + \frac{\kappa}{\nu}\right)\frac{\partial\theta_0}{\partial r}$$

and

$$R_0 = \frac{g\alpha}{\kappa\nu}b^4\frac{\partial\theta_0}{\partial z}. \qquad (24)$$

Thus T_0 is the square of a Reynolds number in terms of which the effect of rotation is measured, Q_0 is a new parameter which represents the effect of the horizontal temperature contrast, and $-R_0$ is the Rayleigh number which occurs also in the problem of thermal convection produced by vertical temperature contrast. The characteristic length used here is the half depth $b = d/2$. We shall use T, Q and R without the subscript 0 to denote these parameters with b replaced by d.

Since the effect of the vertical temperature gradient for ordinary convection has been studied very thoroughly, we shall discuss the effect of the last term of (21) only briefly. It can easily be shown that a negative vertical temperature gradient facilitates the symmetric motion, while a positive vertical temperature gradient inhibits such motion. For a not too large R_0, we may consider that its effect is merely to modify the value T_0, the presence of which inhibits the symmetric motion. As a matter of fact, for the case of a fluid contained in a cylindrical vessel of square axis-to-rim cross-section, the effect of the vertical stability is included if we simply replace T_0 by $T_0 + R_0$. We shall therefore omit the last term of (21) in the following.

4. Solution of the problem for a shallow layer of fluid

Generally, since it requires an infinite number of terms consisting of the fundamental solutions of (22) to satisfy all the boundary conditions, it is difficult to obtain an exact treatment. However, if the distance $(a_2 - a_1)$ between the two vertical walls is very large in comparison with the depth, the boundary conditions along these vertical walls can be relaxed and replaced by a single condition that the motion must be simple harmonic in r, *i.e.*, $\psi \sim \exp(ikr/d)$. We may then consider k as given, representing the number of cells in a horizontal distance πd, and write (22) in the following form:

$$\psi = e^{2ikrd^{-1}}\Psi(\xi) = e^{2ikrd^{-1}} \sum_{j=1}^{6} A_j e^{im_j\xi}. \qquad (25)$$

The six arbitrary constants A_j are determined by the following six conditions on the top and the bottom surfaces:

$$\Psi = 0, \quad \frac{d^2\Psi}{d\xi^2} = 0 \quad \text{and} \quad \frac{d^4\Psi}{d\xi^4} = 0$$

at

$$\xi = \pm 1, \qquad (26)$$

where we have shifted the origin of ξ to $z = d/2$. Substitution of (25) into these conditions leads to the following six linear homogeneous equations for these six constants:

$$\sum_{j=1}^{6} b_{ij}A_j = 0, \quad i = 1, 2, \cdots, 6, \qquad (27)$$

where the coefficients b_{ij} are functions of the six roots m_j. The condition for the existence of the symmetric convective flow is that not all the six A_j are identically zero, which requires the determinant formed by the coefficients b_{ij} to be zero, *i.e.*,

$$\Delta \equiv \begin{vmatrix} b_{11} & b_{21} & \cdots & b_{61} \\ b_{12} & b_{22} & \cdots & b_{62} \\ \cdot & \cdot & \cdot\ \cdot\ \cdot & \cdot \\ b_{16} & b_{26} & \cdots & b_{66} \end{vmatrix} = 0, \qquad (28)$$

which relates the parameters T, k and Q through the roots m_j of (23).

To solve this relation, we must first find the roots m_j of (23). For values of k not too large, one root of this equation is very small, *i.e.*, $m_1 \approx 0$, and the other five are the roots of

$$F(m) = m^5 + 3k^2m^3 + (T_0 + 3k^4)m - kQ_0 = 0. \qquad (29)$$

It can easily be shown that this equation has one and only one real root, which we denote by m_2. The other four roots are two conjugate complex pairs, which can be expressed in terms of m_2. Thus, if we put

$$m_{3,4,5,6} = m_2 \cdot n_{3,4,5,6},$$

the n's are the roots of the quartic equation

$$n^4 + n^3 + Bn^2 + Bn + (B + E) = 0, \qquad (30)$$

where $B = 1 + 3k^2m_2^{-2}$, and $E = (T_0 + 3k^4)m_2^{-4}$. These roots can be found by Ferrari's method (see Uspensky, 1948), and may be written in the following form:

$$n_{3,4} = \lambda_3' \pm \mu_3' i$$
$$= -\tfrac{1}{4}(1 - t) \pm \frac{i}{8^{\frac{1}{2}}}\left(1 + 2y + \frac{5}{t}\right)^{\frac{1}{2}},$$

and

$$n_{5,6} = \lambda_5' \pm \mu_5' i$$
$$= -\tfrac{1}{4}(1 + t) \pm \frac{i}{8^{\frac{1}{2}}}\left(1 + 2y - \frac{5}{t}\right)^{\frac{1}{2}}, \qquad (31)$$

where y is one of the real roots of the cubic equation

$$y^3 - By^2 - (3B + 4E)y + (3B^2 + 4BE - B - E) = 0, \qquad (32)$$

and can be obtained from a table given by Jahnke and Emde (1945), and t is given by

$$t^2 = 4y - 3. \qquad (33)$$

We have, thus,

$$m_1 = 0, \quad m_2 = m_2, \quad m_{3,4} = m_2n_{3,4} = \lambda_3 \pm \mu_3 i,$$

and

$$m_{5,6} = m_2n_{5,6} = \lambda_5 \pm \mu_5 i. \qquad (34)$$

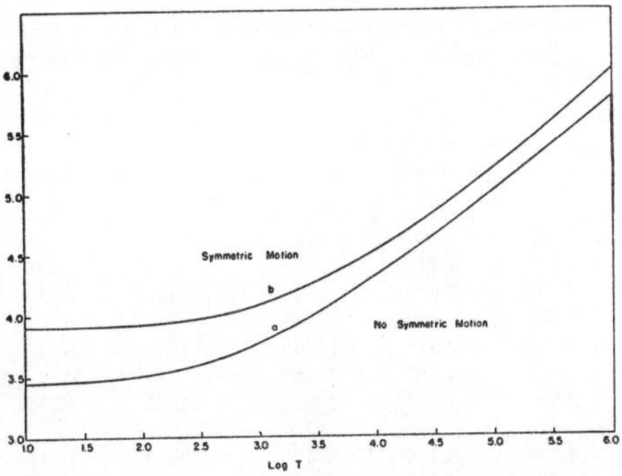

FIG. 1. Variation of critical value of Q for onset of symmetric convection as function of T for the two cases: (a) horizontal extent of fluid is infinitely large as compared with depth, and (b) horizontal extent is equal to depth.

5. Determination of the criterion

Expanding the determinant (28) in terms of these roots, we finally arrive at the following equation:

$$
\begin{aligned}
m_5^2 m_6^2(m_3^2 - m_4^2)s_3 s_4 &\left\{\frac{\sin(m_2 - m_5)\sin(m_3 - m_6)}{m_2^2 - m_5^2} - \frac{\sin(m_2 - m_6)\sin(m_3 - m_5)}{m_2^2 - m_6^2}\right\} \\
+ m_4^2 m_6^2(m_3^2 - m_5^2)s_3 s_5 &\left\{\frac{\sin(m_2 - m_6)\sin(m_3 - m_4)}{m_2^2 - m_6^2} - \frac{\sin(m_2 - m_4)\sin(m_3 - m_6)}{m_2^2 - m_4^2}\right\} \\
+ m_4^2 m_5^2(m_3^2 - m_6^2)s_3 s_6 &\left\{\frac{\sin(m_2 - m_4)\sin(m_3 - m_5)}{m^2{}_2 - m_4^2} - \frac{\sin(m_3 - m_4)\sin(m_2 - m_5)}{m_2^2 - m_5^2}\right\} \\
+ \frac{m_3^2}{m_2^2 - m_3^2} s_4 \sin(m_2 - m_3)&\{m_6^2(m_4^2 - m_5^2)s_5\sin(m_3 - m_6) - m_5^2(m_4^2 - m_6^2)s_6\sin(m_3 - m_5)\} \\
+ \frac{m_3^2 m_4^2(m_5^2 - m_6^2)}{m_2^2 - m_3^2} s_5 s_6 &\sin(m_2 - m_3)\sin(m_3 - m_4) = 0, \qquad (35)
\end{aligned}
$$

where $s_j = \sin m_j$. It may be remarked that, although this equation is of complex form, the imaginary part is identically zero; therefore, it contains only real terms. To determine the roots of this equation, certain approximations may be introduced. Thus, since all the solutions give $\mu_3 > 2.50$ and $\mu_5 > 2.50$, we may put

$$\cosh \mu_3 \approx \tfrac{1}{2}e^{\mu_3} \approx \sinh \mu_3,$$

and

$$\cosh \mu_5 \approx \tfrac{1}{2}e^{\mu_5} \approx \sinh \mu_5.$$

We may also neglect $\frac{1}{2}$ against these quantities. Through these approximations, (35) simplifies to the following:

$$
\begin{aligned}
[m_2^2\{(\lambda_3^2 + \mu_3^2)(\lambda_5^2 - \mu_5^2) &- (\lambda_5^2 + \mu_5^2)(\lambda_3^2 - \mu_3^2)\}(M_{56} - M_{34}) + (\lambda_3^2 + \mu_3^2)^2(\lambda_5^2 + \mu_5^2)^2(M_{56} + M_{34}) \\
&- \{(\lambda_3^2 - \mu_3^2)(\lambda_5^2 - \mu_5^2) + 4\lambda_3\mu_3\lambda_5\mu_5\}\{(\lambda_3^2 + \mu_3^2)^2 M_{56} + (\lambda_5^2 + \mu_5^2)^2 M_{34}\}]\tan m_2 \\
&+ 2\{\lambda_3\mu_3(\lambda_5^2 - \mu_5^2) - \lambda_5\mu_5(\lambda_3^2 - \mu_3^2)\}\{(\lambda_3^2 + \mu_3^2)^2 M_{56} - (\lambda_5^2 + \mu_5^2)^2 M_{34}\} \\
&+ 2m_2^2\{(\lambda_3^2 + \mu_3^2)^2\lambda_5\mu_5 - (\lambda_5^2 + \mu_5^2)^2\lambda_3\mu_3\}(M_{56} - M_{34}) = 0, \qquad (36)
\end{aligned}
$$

where $M_{34} = m_2^4 - 2m_2^2(\lambda_3^2 - \mu_3^2) + (\lambda_3^2 + \mu_3^2)^2$, and $M_{56} = m_2^4 - 2m_2^2(\lambda_5^2 - \mu_5^2) + (\lambda_5^2 + \mu_5^2)^2$. A common factor, $\exp(3\mu_5 + 2\mu_3 - i\lambda_3)$, has been omitted from this equation. Since the values of λ_3, μ_3, λ_5 and μ_5 depend only on m_2 when T and k are given, we may look upon (36) as an equation for m_2 alone for fixed values of T and k.

In the following, we shall determine the critical horizontal temperature contrast for different values of T. The procedure adopted is as follows. For a fixed T, we first choose one k and one m_2, and then find the values of λ_3, μ_3, λ_5 and μ_5, and substitute these quantities in (36). If this set of values does not satisfy this equation, we then choose another m_2 and compute the corresponding λ_3, μ_3, λ_5 and μ_5, repeating the process until the set of m_j satisfies (36). The value of the required Q_0 for this T and k can then be obtained from (23), or from

$$kQ_0 = m_2^5 + 3k^2 m_2^3 + (T_0 + 3k^4)m_2 + k^6/m_2. \qquad (37)$$

We now repeat the computation for the same T but for other values of k. It will be found that there is one particular $k = k_c$ which gives the lowest Q_0. This is the critical Q_{0cm}, and k_c is thus the most favorable wave number for the given T, while the corresponding most favorable half-wavelength is given by $l_c = \pi d/2k_c$. The results of this computation for different values of T are given in table 1. To illustrate that l_c is the most favorable half-wavelength which requires the smallest Q, included in table 1 are two other sets of values for $T = 5000$ and $T = 50{,}000$, one set for k smaller than k_c and one set for k larger than k_c. In this table, the

TABLE 1. Critical values of k, Q_{cm}, P, K and m_j for different T.

T	k_c	m_2	λ_3	μ_3	λ_5	μ_5	Q_{cm}	P_c	K_c
0	0.922	2.560	0.799	2.677	− 2.067	1.735	2747	6448	
100	1.067	2.640	0.883	2.980	− 2.205	1.916	3288	8932	89.32
1,000	1.515	2.863	1.257	3.606	− 2.689	2.606	6100	23535	23.54
	1.571	3.033	1.970	4.112	− 3.489	3.410	14987		
5,000	2.110	3.012	1.884	4.471	− 3.390	3.598	13365	71583	14.32
	3.142	3.000	1.776	5.483	− 3.276	4.235	16180		
10,000	2.440	3.062	2.296	4.993	− 3.827	4.187	20264	125880	12.59
	2.221	3.149	4.102	6.049	− 5.676	5.676	78370		
50,000	3.433	3.127	3.832	6.759	− 5.396	6.134	60480	528840	10.58
	4.712	3.100	3.038	7.673	− 4.591	6.547	68240		
100,000	3.942	3.137	4.680	7.770	− 6.255	7.230	100730	1011100	10.11
500,000	5.390	3.143	7.560	11.000	− 9.130	10.565	347330	4773680	9.55
1,000,000	6.120	3.145	9.230	12.830	−10.830	12.450	603200	9407510	9.41

parameters used are $T = 16\,T_0$ and $Q = 16\,Q_0$, *i.e.*, those parameters with d as the characteristic length instead of $d/2$. In the last two columns of this table are given the critical values of the parameter P, defined as $P_c = 8kQ_c m/\pi$, and its ratio to T,

$$K_c = \frac{P_c}{T} = \left(\frac{\nu}{\kappa} + 1\right)\frac{gd}{l\Omega^2}\alpha\left(\frac{\partial\theta_0}{\partial r}\right)_c. \qquad (38)$$

It is seen that Q_{cm}, P_c and k_c all increase as T increases, indicating that. when the rotation rate is high, not only a larger horizontal temperature contrast is required to produce and to maintain the symmetric motion, but the motion also tends to break up into cells of smaller horizontal dimension.

The variations of Q_{cm} and P_c with T are illustrated in fig. 1 (curve a) and fig. 2, respectively. These diagrams show that, as $T \rightarrow \infty$, we have $Q_{cm} \alpha T^{0.79}$, $k_c \alpha T^{0.21}$, and $P_c \alpha T$, so that the parameter K_c approaches a constant value of about 8.1 asymptotically. This asymptotic value of K_c is approached very fast as T becomes larger than 5000. Therefore, when T is large, the criterion may be represented by this parameter K. We note that the second factor of K may be considered as a Rossby number, defined as $R_0 = gd\alpha l^{-1}\Omega^{-2}\partial\theta_0/\partial r$, and $\nu\kappa^{-1}$ is the Prandtl number.

It should be pointed out that, although the values of K_c given in table 1 are those corresponding to l_c, the asymptotic value of K_c depends very little on l for values of l larger than l_c; therefore this asymptotic value can also be used to compute the necessary horizontal temperature contrast for the development of symmetric motions of larger horizontal dimensions, or to compute the maximum horizontal dimension of the symmetric motion for a given temperature contrast.[2]

The importance of this parameter becomes clear when the theory is applied to the large symmetric convective motions in the atmosphere, because the Taylor number T is so large that it may be considered as infinite even very near the equator, if we take d as the depth of an equivalent homogeneous atmosphere, which is roughly equal to 7 km. As an example, let us estimate the maximum horizontal dimension of a meridional cell that may exist in the tropics, centered at latitude 10°N or S, where $\Omega = \omega \sin\phi = 1.267 \times 10^{-5}$ sec^{-1}. Using 0.72 as the appropriate Prandtl number and $\alpha = 0.00367$ (deg C)$^{-1}$, and assuming a mean meridional temperature gradient of 0.5C (deg lat)$^{-1}$, and neglecting the effect of the stable vertical stratification, we find that the maximum possible horizontal dimension of the symmetric motion is only about 13 deg lat. When the effect of the stable stratification is considered, the possible horizontal dimension must be smaller. Also, since l is inversely proportional to Ω^2, the possible horizontal dimension l decreases rapidly with increasing latitude.

[2] This statement can easily be verified by the approximate formula for Q_c for arbitrary T, l and R, given by

$$Q_c = 0.597\,\pi^6 l d^{-1}(\varphi_1\varphi_2\varphi_3)^{\frac{1}{2}}(81\,\varphi_1 + 25\,\varphi_3)^{-\frac{1}{2}},$$

where $\varphi_n = (n^2T + d^2l^{-2}R)\pi^{-4} + (n^2 + d^2l^{-2})^3$. [See Kuo (1953).]

In fig. 1, another curve (b) is also plotted, which is for the case when the depth is equal to the distance between the two cylindrical vessels. For this case, the lateral boundary conditions cannot be replaced by the harmonic condition. The result for this case is obtained by a different method and is discussed in another paper (Kuo, 1953). It is included here for comparison. It is seen that the critical value of Q for this case is two to three times larger than that represented by curve a. This is partly due to the smaller value of k, and partly due to the effect of the lateral boundaries. For small rotation rate, the corresponding value of K_c is also higher than those given in table 1; however, for higher rotation rate the value of K_c for this case is lower than those given in table 1, and has the asymptotic value 4.8 instead of 8.1. The reason is that the value of k is predetermined and has the smaller value $\pi/2$.

In fig. 2, a number of the parameters P and T obtained from Dr. Fultz's (University of Chicago) most recent (as yet unpublished) experimental data on the symmetric motions have also been entered. It is seen that they all lie above the critical curve and are not very far away from it.

6. Flow pattern and the distributions of temperature and zonal velocity

When the horizontal temperature contrast is large and the rotation rate is small, the motion will actually set in as symmetric convection. In this section we shall obtain the flow pattern and the distributions of temperature and zonal velocity in this motion. Although the results obtained from the linear equations hold only during the early stages of the motion, when the relative velocity is small, one may expect that they

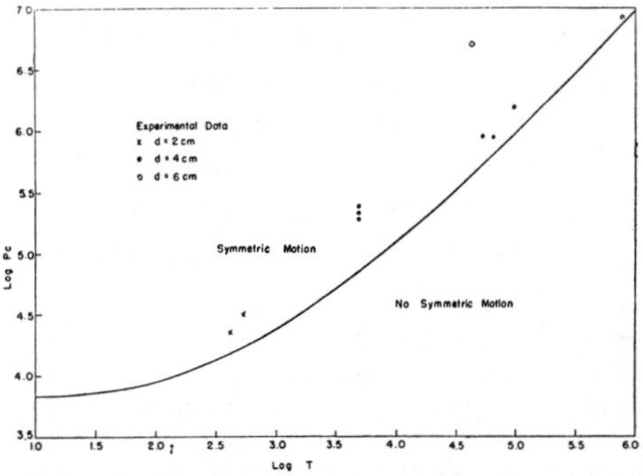

FIG. 2. Variation of parameter P as function of T. Points and crosses are obtained from some of Dr. Fultz's unpublished experimental data on fully developed symmetric motions.

will also throw some light on the problems concerning the later stages of the motion.

The streamline pattern in the meridional plane.—As has been discussed in section 4, above, the stream function ψ is given by

$$\psi = e^{2ikr/d} \sum_{j=1}^{6} A_j e^{im_j\xi}, \tag{39}$$

where m_j are the six roots of (23). Now, if (23) is satisfied by (k, m_j), it will also be satisfied by $(-k, -m_j)$. Thus, we have an alternative solution,

$$\psi' = e^{-2ikr/d} \sum_{j=1}^{6} A_j e^{-im_j\xi}. \tag{40}$$

Adding these two solutions and dividing by two, we obtain a solution of real form,

$$\begin{aligned} \psi = A_1 \cos \frac{\pi r}{l} &+ A_2 \cos \left(\frac{\pi r}{l} + m_2\xi\right) \\ &+ A_3' \cosh \mu_3\xi \cos \left(\frac{\pi r}{l} + \lambda_3\xi\right) \\ &+ A_4' \sinh \mu_3\xi \sin \left(\frac{\pi r}{l} + \lambda_3\xi\right) \\ &+ A_5' \cosh \mu_5\xi \cos \left(\frac{\pi r}{l} + \lambda_5\xi\right) \\ &+ A_6' \sinh \mu_5\xi \sin \left(\frac{\pi r}{l} + \lambda_5\xi\right), \end{aligned} \tag{41}$$

where l $(=\pi d/2k)$ is the half-wavelength, and

$$\begin{aligned} A_3' &= A_3 + A_4, \qquad A_4' = i(A_4 - A_3), \\ A_5' &= A_5 + A_6, \quad \text{and} \quad A_6' = i(A_6 - A_5). \end{aligned} \tag{42}$$

Five of the six coefficients A_j can be determined and expressed in terms of the remaining one by any five of the six boundary conditions (26); the remaining condition must then be satisfied, because m_j constitute a solution of the determinant (28).

For the case with $T = 5000$, we have

$$\begin{aligned} k = k_c = 2.11, \quad m_1 &= 0, \quad m_2 = 3.012, \\ \lambda_3 = 1.884, &\quad \mu_3 = 4.471, \\ \lambda_5 = -3.390, &\quad \mu_5 = 3.598, \\ A_1 = -0.58365, &\quad A_2 = -0.41206, \\ A_3' = -0.0010519, &\quad A_4' = +0.0019688, \\ A_5' = -0.0032415 \quad \text{and} &\quad A_6' = +0.0048036. \end{aligned} \tag{43}$$

The value of the remaining arbitrary constant is determined so as to make $\psi(0, 0) = -1.00$.

The flow pattern for this case is represented in fig. 3, in which the right side corresponds to the warmer part and the left side corresponds to the colder part. It is seen that the axis of the streamlines slopes upward toward the colder side, so that the ascending fluid is moving into a colder region while the descending fluid is moving into a warmer region. Thus, both the ascending and the descending particles are gaining kinetic energy through the release of the potential energy associated with the horizontal temperature contrast. This is also true in a so-called reverse cell, as partly represented by the streamlines at the two ends of the diagram.

It is to be noted that the maximum inward radial velocity occurs near the top and the center (left), while the maximum outward flow occurs near the bottom and the outer wall (right). When the convergence of the radii is also considered (this effect has been omitted in this study), the shift of the maximum of radial velocity inward and outward must be more pronounced. The maximum vertical motions occur near the two ends.

When the horizontal dimension is not very large compared with the depth, only a single, large direct cell will occur. However, two small reverse cells will be present in the upper-right and lower-left corners. In reality, these small reverse cells merely represent relatively stagnant small pockets of warm and cold fluid.

The temperature distribution.—Putting

$$\theta = \Theta(\xi) \exp(2ikrd^{-1})$$

and substituting in the energy equation (12), with the last term omitted (we are considering the case when $\partial\theta_0/\partial z = 0$; the general case can be discussed without any difficulty), we obtain the following differential equation for Θ:

$$\begin{aligned} \frac{d^2\Theta}{d\xi^2} - k^2\Theta &= -\frac{d}{2k}\frac{\partial\theta_0}{\partial r}\frac{\partial\Psi}{\partial\xi} \\ &= -\frac{d}{2k}\frac{\partial\theta_0}{\partial r} i \sum_{j=1}^{6} m_j A_j e^{im_j\xi}, \end{aligned} \tag{44}$$

where $\xi = 2d^{-1}z - 1$. We seek solutions of this equa-

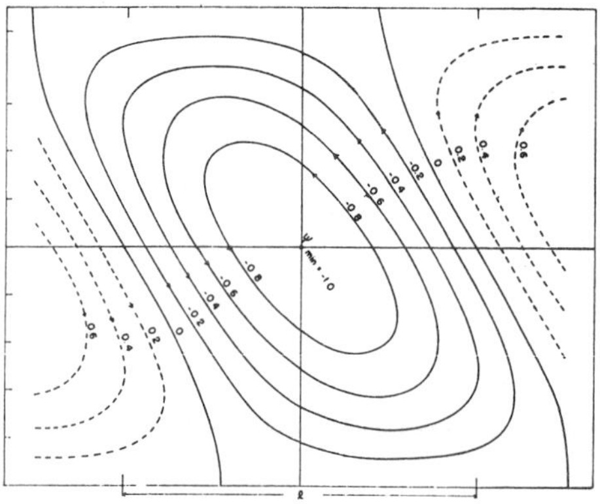

FIG. 3. Streamline pattern of meridional motion for case $T = 5000$.

tion that satisfy certain appropriate boundary conditions. Let us first consider the case when the top surface is insulated and a given horizontal temperature contrast is maintained over the bottom surface. The boundary conditions for this case are $\partial\Theta/\partial\xi = 0$ at $\xi = 1$, and $\Theta = 0$ at $\xi = -1$. The solution of (44) that satisfies these conditions is

$$\Theta = \frac{1}{\coth 2k} \sum_{j=1}^{6} \frac{B_j}{m_j^2 + k^2} \times \left\{ \cosh 2k \cdot e^{im_j\xi} - \cosh k(1-\xi)e^{-im_j} - \sinh k(1+\xi) \cdot \frac{im_j}{k} e^{im_j} \right\}, \quad (45)$$

where $B_j = (id/2\kappa)(\partial\theta_0/\partial r)m_jA_j$. We also have an alternative solution, with (k, m_j, B_j) replaced by $(-k, -m_j, -B_j)$. Taking the sum of these two solutions and dividing by two, we obtain

$$\theta = \frac{1}{\cosh 2k} \sum_{j=1}^{6} \frac{iB_i}{m_i^2 + k^2} \times \left\{ \cosh 2k \cdot \sin\left(\frac{\pi r}{l} + m_j\xi\right) - \cosh k(1-\xi) \cdot \sin\left(\frac{\pi r}{l} - m_j\right) - \frac{im_j}{k} \sinh k(1+\xi) \cos\left(\frac{\pi r}{l} + m_j\right) \right\}. \quad (46)$$

When m_j and A_j are known, all the coefficients are known. We note that this perturbation temperature is proportional to $\partial\theta_0/\partial r$. If there is also a basic vertical temperature gradient, an additional solution proportional to $\partial\theta_0/\partial z$ will also be present.

The total temperature at any point is given by $\theta_0 + \theta$. However, since one A_j is still arbitrary, the magnitude of θ is also arbitrary. In fig. 4 is plotted the total temperature distribution for the same case with $T = 5000$, in the region of a direct cell. The arbitrary constant factor of θ is chosen so as to make the maximum temperature contrast given by θ equal to two-thirds of the basic temperature contrast. It may be remarked that, if the lower boundary is also insulated, the isotherms will become vertical near the bottom instead of bending toward the left.

The essential feature of this temperature distribution is the presence of a warm tongue extending upward from the warm side toward the cold side, and a cold tongue extending downward from the cold side toward the warm side. Such tongues of warm and cold fluid are present in almost all of Dr. Fultz's experimental data for the symmetric motion. Such an observed temperature distribution, obtained by Mr. A. Faller of the Massachusetts Institute of Technology, is given in fig. 5. It is seen that the overall distributions in these two diagrams are very similar, although certain conditions are quite different. The Taylor number for this experiment is $T = 8.55 \times 10^6$, while the parameter K obtained from the measurement is 9.35, which is very close to the theoretical value.

Another interesting case is the one with both the top and the bottom boundaries kept at a given horizontal temperature contrast, which requires $\Theta = 0$ at $\xi = \pm 1$. The perturbation temperature for this case is given by

$$\theta = \frac{1}{\sinh 2k} \sum_{j=1}^{6} \frac{iB_j}{m_j^2 + k^2} \times \left\{ \sinh 2k\left(\sin\frac{\pi r}{l} + m_j\xi\right) - \sinh k(1-\xi) \sin\left(\frac{\pi r}{l} - m_j\right) - \sinh k(1+\xi) \sin\left(\frac{\pi r}{l} + m_j\right) \right\}. \quad (47)$$

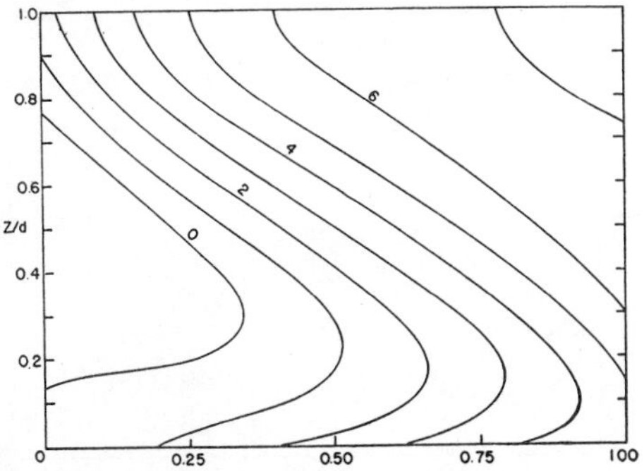

FIG. 4. Theoretical temperature distribution for case with $T = 5000$ when top surface is insulated and a given temperature contrast is maintained over bottom surface.

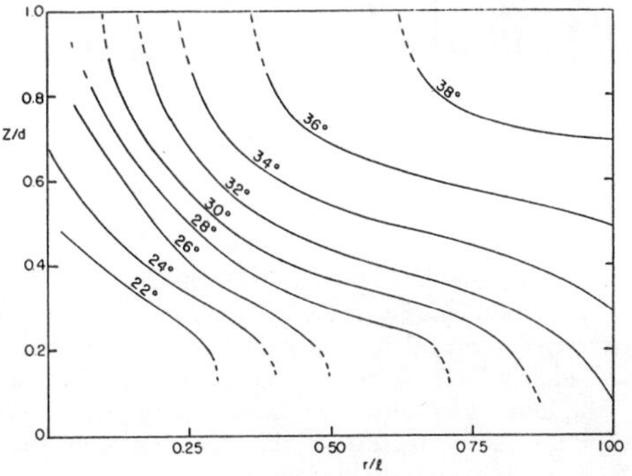

FIG. 5. Observed temperature distribution in symmetric motion with $d = 6.2$ cm, $l = a = 14$ cm, $\partial\theta_0/\partial r = 1.03$C/cm, $\Omega = 0.31$ sec^{-1} and $\bar{\theta}_0 = 30$C.

The temperature distribution given by this solution has also been computed. It is not very different from that given by (46) except near the top surface, where the isotherms bend toward the right, depressing the warm tongue downward.

The zonal velocity distribution.—Eliminating p from the first two equations of motion and making use of the continuity equation, we obtain the equation for the vertical component of the relative vorticity,

$$\left(\frac{\partial}{\partial t} - \nu\nabla^2\right)\zeta = 2\Omega\frac{\partial w}{\partial z}, \quad (48)$$

where $\zeta = r^{-1}\,\partial(rv)/\partial r$. According to the previous discussion, we may approximate ζ by $\partial v/\partial r$. Putting $v = V(\xi)\exp(2ikrd^{-1})$, and expressing w in terms of the stream function ψ, we find, for the limiting case of marginal instability, that V must satisfy the differential equation

$$\frac{d^2V}{d\xi^2} - k^2V = -\frac{T^{\frac{1}{2}}}{2d}\frac{d\Psi}{d\xi} = -\frac{T^{\frac{1}{2}}}{2d}i\sum_{j=1}^{6} m_jA_je^{im_j\xi}. \quad (49)$$

This equation is of the same form as (44) for the temperature function Θ. Since the upper and lower boundaries are considered as free surfaces, V must satisfy the boundary conditions $\partial V/\partial\xi = 0$ at $\xi = \pm 1$. The solution of (49) that satisfies these conditions is

$$V = \sum_{j=1}^{6}\frac{D_j}{m_j^2 + k^2}\left\{e^{im_j\xi} + \frac{im_j}{k\sinh 2k}\times\left[e^{-im_j}\cosh k(1-\xi) - e^{im_j}\cosh k(1+\xi)\right]\right\}, \quad (50)$$

where $D_j = im_jA_jT^{\frac{1}{2}}/2d$. Multiplying by $\exp(2ikrd^{-1})$, and combining with the alternative solution where (k, m_j, D_j) are replaced by $(-k, -m_j, -D_j)$, we obtain v in a purely real form:

$$v = \sum_{j=1}^{6}\frac{iD_j}{m_j^2+k^2}\left\{\sin\left(\frac{\pi r}{l} + m_j\xi\right) + \frac{m_j}{k\sinh 2k}\times\left[\cosh k(1-\xi)\cos\left(\frac{\pi r}{l} - m_j\right) - \cosh k(1+\xi)\cos\left(\frac{\pi r}{l} + m_j\right)\right]\right\}. \quad (51)$$

This function has been computed for the case $T = 5000$ and is plotted in fig. 6. As is to be expected, there is a westerly current in the upper part of the fluid where the radial velocity is inward, and an easterly current in the lower part where the motion is outward. Another interesting feature of this distribution is that the maximum westerly current occurs at the top surface, at a point whose distance from the cold center is only half of its distance from the warm rim. The maximum easterly current occurs at the bottom, at a point which is nearer to the rim. When the convergence of the radii is included, this shift on the point of maximum westerlies inward and easterlies outward must be more pronounced.

If the top surface is free and the bottom surface is rigid, the boundary conditions for V are $\partial V/\partial\xi = 0$ at $\xi = 1$ and $V = 0$ at $\xi = -1$. The zonal velocity distribution is then the same as that of the temperature given by (47), with B_j replaced by D_j. This distribution differs very little from that given by (51) except very near the bottom, where the region of the maximum easterlies is shifted upward and toward the colder side.

As has been discussed before, the results obtained from the linear equations can only be expected to hold when the relative velocities are small. When the velocities become large, the form of the motion may be greatly modified because of the contribution from the nonlinear terms. We shall now examine the effect of the term $w\,\partial v/\partial z$ on the zonal velocity distribution, since this is the dominating non-linear term in (2). As a direct application of the method of successive approximations to the present problem is too cumbersome, we shall discuss only qualitatively the local change of v produced by this term, as is given by $\partial v/\partial t = -w\,\partial v/\partial z$. As is seen from fig. 5, v increases upward in almost all parts of the fluid; therefore this term has the effect of increasing the zonal velocity in the inner region where the motion is downward, and of decreasing the zonal velocity in the outer region where the motion is upward. Thus, as the motion develops, the westerly current tends to spread downward in the inner portions of the fluid, and the easterly current extends upward in the outer portions of the fluid. Finally the easterly current will be confined in the lower and outer portion of the fluid, with the surface that separates the westerly from the easterly currents sloping outward and upward.

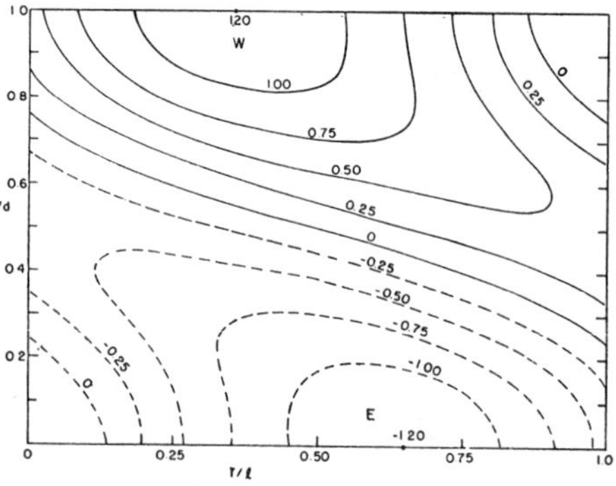

FIG. 6. Zonal velocity distribution when both top and bottom surfaces are free.

7. An equilibrium solution for the zonal motion

The solution (51) shows that the zonal velocity produced in symmetric motion is proportional to $T^{\frac{1}{2}}$, or proportional to the rate of rotation. Therefore, when the rotation rate is large, most of the kinetic energy must be contained in the kinetic energy of the zonal motion. In this section we shall discuss another zonal wind distribution which may exist in an equilibrium state when the meridional motion is exceedingly small, *i.e.*, when $u \approx w \approx \partial/\partial t \approx \partial/\partial\phi \approx 0$. Under these conditions, all the other terms of (2) can be neglected except the viscous term, so that the equation reduces to

$$\frac{\partial^2 v}{\partial r^2} + \frac{1}{r}\frac{\partial v}{\partial r} - \frac{v}{r^2} + \frac{\partial^2 v}{\partial z^2} = 0. \qquad (52)$$

The elimination of p from (1) and (3) give the thermal-wind relation (13). Thus, if v satisfies (52) and (13), it represents a possible equilibrium solution. It is readily seen that the function

$$v = \sum_{\beta} A_\beta J_1(\beta r/a) \sinh \beta z/a \qquad (53)$$

satisfies (52) and the boundary condition $v = 0$ at $z = 0$. In (53), the summation extends over the positive roots β of the Bessel function $J_1(x) = 0$, a is the radius of the cylindrical vessel, and the coefficients A_β may be chosen so as to satisfy (13). However, although this solution is rather general, it usually requires quite a number of terms to approximate the observed distribution, and we shall therefore seek still another solution. Observations show that v increases nearly linearly with height except near the bottom and the vertical walls. If a linear variation with height is assumed, (52) yields

$$v = (A_1\eta + B_1/\eta)\zeta + A_2\eta + B_2/\eta, \qquad (54)$$

where $\eta = r/a$ and $\zeta = z/d$. It is seen that, when Ω is not too small, this solution also satisfies (13) approximately. The four constants can be chosen so as to fit the observations. We assume that there is an easterly current in the outer, lower portions of the fluid, and a westerly current in the inner and upper portions of the fluid. Thus, we require v to be zero at the three points ($\eta = 1, \zeta = 1$), ($\eta = \eta_1, \zeta = 1/2$) and ($\eta = \eta_2, \zeta = 0$), and to be finite for very small η. We also specify that the maximum zonal velocity occurs at $\eta = \eta_0 < 1$ and $\zeta = 1$. The four constants then can be expressed in terms of $\bar{v}_{max}$, η_0, η_1 and η_2. Thus, in the region $\eta > \eta_0$, v is given by

$$v = v_1 = \frac{\bar{v}_{max}}{(1-\eta_0^2)(\eta_1^2-\eta_2^2)}\frac{\eta_0}{\eta} \times \{(1-\eta_1^2)(\eta_2^2-\eta^2) - \zeta[2\eta_2^2 - \eta_1^2\eta_2^2 - \eta_1^2 - (1+\eta_2^2-2\eta_1^2)\eta^2]\}, \qquad (55)$$

while in the region $\eta < \eta_0$ it is given by

$$v = v_2 = \bar{v}_{max}\frac{\eta}{\eta_0} \times \left\{\left(\frac{1-\eta_1^2}{1-\eta_0^2}\right)\left(\frac{\eta_2^2-\eta_0^2}{\eta_1^2-\eta_2^2}\right)(1-\zeta)+\zeta\right\}. \qquad (56)$$

If one chooses $\bar{v}_{max}$ slightly larger than the actual maximum value of v, *e.g.*, $\bar{v}_{max} = 1.1\, v_{max}$, these solutions give a very good approximation to the observed zonal wind distribution above the bottom layer, as illustrated in fig. 7.

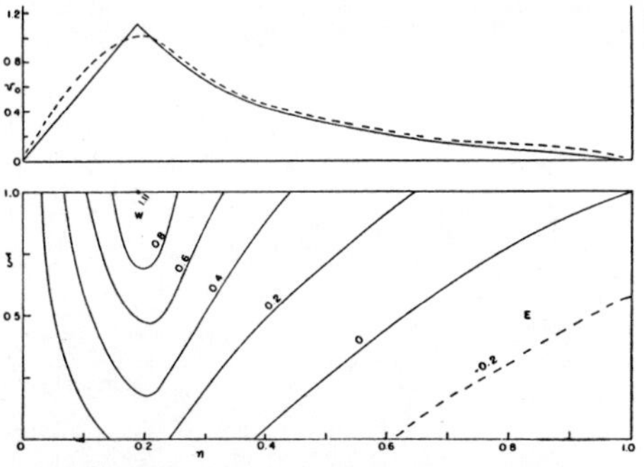

FIG. 7. Possible equilibrium zonal velocity distribution. In upper diagram, fully drawn curve is calculated zonal current on top surface, dashed curve is typical observed distribution. Lower diagram illustrates distribution in meridional cross-section.

8. Concluding remarks

In this article it has been shown that a finite horizontal temperature contrast is required to produce a symmetric convective motion in a stably stratified rotating fluid. This necessary minimum temperature contrast increases with the rate of rotation and with the static stability, and also increases with the horizontal scale of the motion. When applied to the motions in the atmosphere, this study shows that very large meridional cells cannot exist under the normal temperature distribution, especially in middle and higher latitudes. However, such convective motions of a relatively smaller scale can be produced by a horizontal temperature contrast, for example, along the strong jet streams of westerlies in the upper atmosphere. The applicability of the theory to the land-and-sea breezes and also to certain features of the monsoon circulation is apparent. Certain smaller-scale convective processes that cannot be explained by vertical instability may also find their explanation in the effect of the horizontal temperature contrast.

Acknowledgment.—The writer wishes to thank Prof. D. Fultz for supplying his as yet unpublished experimental results concerning the symmetric motion and the determination of the transition from the unsymmetric to the symmetric motion.

REFERENCES

Arakawa, H., 1940: Die Arbeiten zur allgemeinen Zirkulation der Atmosphäre von A. Oberbeck. *Gerlands Beitr. Geophysik*, **57**, 20–28.

Chandrasekhar, S., 1953: The instability of a layer of fluid heated below and subject to Coriolis forces. *Proc. roy. Soc. London*, A, **217**, 306.

Davies, T. V., 1953: The forced flow of a rotating viscous liquid which is heated from below. *Phil. Trans. roy. Soc.*, A, **246**, 81–112.

Fultz, D., 1951a: Non-dimensional equations and modeling criteria for the atmosphere. *J. Meteor.*, **8**, 262–267.

Fultz, D., 1951b: Experimental analogies to atmospheric motion. *Compendium Meteor.* Boston, Amer. meteor. Soc., 1235.

Jahnke, E., and F. Emde, 1945: *Tables of functions.* New York, Dover Publ., 303 pp.

Kuo, H.-L., 1953: *On convective instability of a rotating fluid with a horizontal temperature contrast.* Paper presented at "Symposium on model experiments," Johns Hopkins Univ., Baltimore, 1–4 September, 1953.

Kropatscheck, F., 1935: Die Mechanik der gross Zirkulation der Atmosphäre. *Beitr. Physik. fr. Atmos.*, **22**, 272.

Oberbeck, A., 1888: In *Sitzungber. Preuss. Akad. Wiss.*, pp. 383–395 and 1129–1138.

Prandtl, L., 1939: *Beiträge zur Mechanik der Atmosphäre.* Paris, P. Dupont, 32 pp.

Uspensky, J. V., 1948: *Theory of equations.* New York, McGraw-Hill Book Co., 352 pp.

Reprinted from *Philosophical Transactions of the Royal Society of London*, Series A, Vol. 249, Mar. 22, 1956.

THE FORCED FLOW DUE TO HEATING OF A ROTATING LIQUID

By T. V. DAVIES, *King's College, London*

(*Communicated by G. Temple, F.R.S.—Received* 14 *June* 1955)

CONTENTS

An investigation is made of the forced liquid motion in a rotating cylindrical vessel with a horizontal base when a temperature difference exists between the outer and inner cylindrical boundaries of the liquid. It has been observed experimentally that at critical values of a certain non-dimensional parameter, known as the Rossby number, the flow patterns change abruptly in character. The present investigation derives a stability criterion which agrees qualitatively with the experimental results and also gives reasonable quantitative results. In the derivation of this result it is shown that there exists a relation between the mean vertical temperature gradient, the mean horizontal temperature gradient and the angular velocity of rotation of the system.

1. Introduction

The dishpan experiments by Fultz in Chicago and Hide's heated rotating cylinder experiment at Cambridge have been described by Fultz (1953), and the importance of the experiments to meteorology has been established by Starr & Long's (1953) investigation of the transfer of momentum. Theoretical work which has as its aim the understanding of the thermodynamical and dynamical processes has been initiated by Kuo (1955), Lorenz (1953) and by the present author (1953). In this paper it is proposed to investigate theoretically what has become known as the Rossby régime in these experiments which is the régime of principal interest to meteorology.

In the typical experiment a shallow liquid of suitable low viscosity is contained in a cylindrical vessel, or in the annulus between two concentric cylinders, the usual dimensions in the former case being a radius of 15 cm and a liquid depth of about 3 cm. The effects of heating the horizontal base of the vessel near the side have been observed for various rates of rotation of the vessel about its central axis. The heating in such experiments is approximately symmetrical about the central axis, and the difference in temperature between the outer portions of the liquid and the central portions is usually between 5 and 15° C. In Hide's experiment and in recent experiments by Fultz the outer and inner cylinders are maintained at constant temperatures, T_0 and T_i ($T_0 > T_i$) respectively, and the observed flow patterns are then considerably more steady and more controlled. Two principal régimes have emerged which are referred to as the Hadley or spiral régime or low-rotation régime and the Rossby or wave régime or high-rotation régime. In the former the motion near the free upper surface is predominantly symmetrical about the central axis, and the stream-lines and the paths of the particles spiral inwards towards the central axis. Within the liquid and near the base of the vessel the liquid spirals outwards, and in the case of two concentric cylinders this outward spiral persists at all distances from the central axis. When the vessel rotates from west to east, as in the case of the earth's rotation, there is a deflexion to the right as in 'Ferrel's rule', so that the inflowing spiral at the top winds counterclockwise when viewed from above and the outflowing spiral near the base winds clockwise. In the case of one outer cylinder and liquid occupying the whole of the interior, the outflowing spiral near the base does not wind clockwise for all radii, and it has been shown by Fultz that in this case the flow near the outer cylindrical wall is in the reverse direction. This reversal is necessary in order to preserve the angular momentum balance and is a feature of the mathematical solution investigated by the present author (1953). In the Rossby régime, on the other hand, the motion is markedly asymmetrical in character, and the stream-line pattern of the free upper surface, observed relative to the rotating vessel, consists of distinct finite-amplitude wave patterns which progress slowly relative to the vessel in the same direction as the rotation. With a fixed heating system at the base or with a constant maintained temperature difference between the outer and inner cylinders, the transition from the Hadley to the Rossby régime occurs at a critical angular velocity of rotation Ω_c of the vessel. The range $0<\Omega<\Omega_c$ of the angular velocity then corresponds to the Hadley régime and $\Omega>\Omega_c$ to the Rossby régime. When Ω is just slightly above Ω_c the number of wave petals in the stream-line pattern is usually small, and as Ω increases from this value the number of petals increases, a three-wave pattern, say, giving way to a four-wave pattern and so on. This is evidently a stability problem, and one of the aims of this investigation is to seek to explain why the spiral régime becomes unstable at a critical angular velocity and why an m-wave régime moves over to an $(m+1)$-wave régime at a different critical value. Qualitatively, it is fairly clear that the spiral régime cannot exist indefinitely as Ω is increased; for with increasing rotation there is a tightening of the spiral in the inflow towards the central axis in the upper portion of the liquid, and thus the efficiency of the liquid as a convector of heat steadily diminishes; therefore, a critical stage necessarily arises when the liquid chooses a new method of convecting the heat. In addition to the stability problem, the theory must predict a formula for the angular velocity of the waves relative to the rotating vessel which must bear comparison with certain empirical formulae derived by Hide (1953).

The three-dimensional structure of the wave patterns in the Rossby régime have now been explored to a certain extent, and it would appear that the structure is similar to the long atmospheric waves in that the liquid which is moving inward (towards the central axis) is ascending while the outward moving liquid is descending. In addition, there is a phase shift of the waves in the vertical direction.

One feature of the experiments which cannot be investigated here is that called 'vacillation' by Hide. This is an oscillation of the long wave about its original horizontal axis of symmetry which occurs when the amplitude/wavelength ratio exceeds a critical quantity 0·67. This is probably a non-linear phenomenon, and the present investigation, which is entirely 'linear', cannot hope to cast any light upon the feature.

In their discussion of the experimental results both Fultz and Hide adequately express their results in terms of a single parameter called the Rossby number, which is introduced in the present paper in (1·18) where it is denoted by R_H. Fultz (1953) uses the Rossby number Ro_T which is identical with the present R_H, and broadly his experimental results can be summarized as follows. The Hadley or spiral régime is 'associated with values of Ro_T in general greater than some limit in the interval 0·2 to 0·6' and 'in the Rossby régime Ro_T has values of the order of 0·1'. In general, higher wave numbers appear as Ro_T (or R_H) is decreased although experimentally there is an overlap of the Ro_T intervals in which two neighbouring wave numbers can exist. Some of the experimental figures quoted by Fultz (1953) are incorporated in table 5 later in this paper, and there is a further discussion of the experimental results also towards the end of this paper.

In setting up the problem, which is essentially three-dimensional, I use cylindrical co-ordinates (r, ϕ, z), and there are six dependent variables $(u_1, v_1, w_1, p_1, \rho_1, T_1)$, where u_1 represents the velocity component in the direction r increasing, v_1 in the direction ϕ increasing, w_1 in the direction z increasing, where p_1 is the pressure, ρ_1 the density and T_1 the temperature. Connecting these six dependent variables are the following six equations:

$$\rho_1\left(\frac{\mathrm{d}u_1}{\mathrm{d}t}-\frac{v_1^2}{r}\right) = -\frac{\partial p_1}{\partial r}+\mu\left(\nabla_1^2 u_1-\frac{u_1}{r^2}-\frac{2}{r^2}\frac{\partial v_1}{\partial \phi}\right)+\tfrac{1}{3}\mu\frac{\partial \chi_1}{\partial r} = -\frac{\partial p_1}{\partial r}+\mu F_r, \tag{1·1}$$

$$\rho_1\left(\frac{\mathrm{d}v_1}{\mathrm{d}t}+\frac{u_1 v_1}{r}\right) = -\frac{\partial p_1}{r\,\partial \phi}+\mu\left(\nabla_1^2 v_1-\frac{v_1}{r^2}+\frac{2}{r^2}\frac{\partial u_1}{\partial \phi}\right)+\tfrac{1}{3}\mu\frac{\partial \chi_1}{r\,\partial \phi} = -\frac{\partial p_1}{r\,\partial \phi}+\mu F_\phi, \tag{1·2}$$

$$\rho_1\frac{\mathrm{d}w_1}{\mathrm{d}t} = -\frac{\partial p_1}{\partial z}-g\rho_1+\mu\nabla_1^2 w_1+\tfrac{1}{3}\mu\frac{\partial \chi_1}{\partial z} = -\frac{\partial p_1}{\partial z}-g\rho_1+\mu F_z, \tag{1·3}$$

$$\frac{\mathrm{d}\rho_1}{\mathrm{d}t}+\rho_1\chi_1 = 0, \quad \chi_1 = \frac{\partial u_1}{\partial r}+\frac{u_1}{r}+\frac{\partial v_1}{r\,\partial \phi}+\frac{\partial w_1}{\partial z}, \tag{1·4}$$

$$f(\rho_1, T_1) = 0, \tag{1·5}$$

$$\rho_1 J c_v \frac{\mathrm{d}T_1}{\mathrm{d}t} = Jk\nabla_1^2 T_1+\Phi_1, \tag{1·6}$$

where

$$\nabla_1^2 \equiv \frac{\partial^2}{\partial r^2}+\frac{1}{r}\frac{\partial}{\partial r}+\frac{1}{r^2}\frac{\partial^2}{\partial \phi^2}+\frac{\partial^2}{\partial z^2}. \tag{1·7}$$

Equations (1·1) to (1·3) are the equations of motion, (1·4) is the equation of continuity, (1·5) is the equation of state for a liquid and (1·6) is the equation of heat transfer for a liquid. We consider first of all the equation of state which, within the temperature range of the experiment, can be chosen to be a linear relation between density and temperature. One of the important features of the experiment is that when the mean temperature field of all the planes ϕ = constant is obtained it reveals that there is an increase of temperature from the base to the free surface of the liquid and an increase of temperature from the central axis (or inner cylinder) to the outer cylindrical wall. It is quite evident that we may regard the temperature pattern in any ϕ plane to be a small departure from this mean temperature pattern. Accordingly, we shall write the density and temperature in the forms

$$\rho_1 = \rho^*(r, z)+\rho(r, \phi, z, t), \tag{1·8}$$

$$T_1 = T^*(r, z)+T(r, \phi, z, t), \tag{1·9}$$

where ρ^* and T^* represent the mean meridional fields of density and temperature respectively and are functions of r, z only, while ρ and T represent the small departures from the mean values. Using the linearity of the relation between density and temperature, we thus have the relations

$$\rho^* = \rho_0 - \alpha(T^* - T_0), \tag{1·10}$$

$$\rho = -\alpha T, \tag{1·11}$$

where ρ_0 is the constant density of the liquid at the temperature T_0 and α is the inverse of the coefficient of cubical expansion. Using the results quoted in Davies (1953), the appropriate value of α for the range 20 to 30° C is $\alpha = 2{\cdot}5563 \times 10^{-4}$.

Owing to the presence of this mean temperature field there will be established a mean zonal motion, in the ϕ-increasing direction, relative to the rotating cylinder. Accordingly, we shall assume that the complete velocity field is given by

$$u_1 = u(r, \phi, z, t), \quad v_1 = r\Omega + V_0(r, z) + v(r, \phi, z, t), \quad w_1 = w(r, \phi, z, t), \tag{1·12}$$

where $V_0(r, z)$ is the mean zonal flow relative to the cylinder which rotates with an angular velocity Ω. The expression for the pressure will be

$$p_1 = P_0(r, z) + p(r, \phi, z, t), \tag{1·13}$$

where P_0 is the mean pressure arising from the mean zonal flow and hydrostatic sources.

The equations which govern the mean zonal flow patterns are as follows:

$$\left.\begin{aligned} -\rho_0(r\Omega+V_0)^2/r &= -\frac{\partial P_0}{\partial r}, && (a)\\ 0 &= \nabla_1^2 V_0 - \frac{V_0}{r^2}, && (b)\\ 0 &= -\frac{\partial P_0}{\partial z} - g\rho^*, && (c)\\ \rho^* &= \rho_0 - \alpha(T^*-T_0), && (d)\\ 0 &= Jk\nabla_1^2 T^* + \Phi_0. && (e) \end{aligned}\right\} \tag{1·14}$$

In (1·14 e) the function Φ_0 which represents the dissipation of energy due to molecular viscosity is here given by

$$\Phi_0 = \mu\left\{\left(\frac{\partial V_0}{\partial r} - \frac{V_0}{r}\right)^2 + \left(\frac{\partial V_0}{\partial z}\right)^2\right\},$$

and in (1·14 a) it will be noted that the constant density ρ_0 of the liquid appears on the left-hand side in place of the exact ρ^*. Since the difference is small, equation (1·14 a) is sufficiently exact in this form. It is not practicable to seek or to use any exact solution of the equations (1·14) for the resulting equations for the perturbation field become completely intractable in this case. We postulate therefore a basic temperature field in the form

$$T^* = T_0 + \Theta_V z + \tfrac{1}{2}r^2\Theta_H, \tag{1·15}$$

where Θ_V and Θ_H are positive constants. A recent set of temperature measurements by Fultz in the case of a three-wave pattern between concentric cylinders gives some idea of the magnitude of these constants, these being $\Theta_V = 1{\cdot}45°/\text{cm}$, $\Theta_H = 0{\cdot}16°/\text{cm}^2$. It is important here to emphasize the positive sign of Θ_V, and it is necessary to bear in mind that in making any comparisons with meteorology the quantity that corresponds to T^* is the potential temperature, which increases in value in the vertical direction. In order to derive the velocity field arising from (1·15) we write (1·14 *a*) in the approximate form

$$\rho_0(r\Omega^2+2\Omega V_0) = \frac{\partial P_0}{\partial r},$$

since V_0 is everywhere considerably less than $2r\Omega$ at the corresponding value of r. It then follows that

$$2\Omega\rho_0 \frac{\partial V_0}{\partial z} = g\alpha \frac{\partial T^*}{\partial r}, \qquad (1·16)$$

and thus the solution for V_0 which satisfies (1·14 *b*) and the condition $V_0 = 0$ at $z = 0$ is

$$V_0 = 2\Omega R_H(z/h)\, r, \qquad (1·17)$$

where h is the depth of the liquid in the experiment and R_H is a non-dimensional constant defined by

$$R_H = \frac{g\alpha h\Theta_H}{4\rho_0 \Omega^2}. \qquad (1·18)$$

The velocity field (1·17) cannot be correct for all values of r, since at the boundary $r = r_0$, V_0 actually vanishes, but within a region $0 \leqslant r \leqslant r_b < r_0$, which includes the central axis, it can be accepted as an approximation to the mean velocity field (see table 1). An alternative procedure would be to choose V_0 to be that zonal flow which is derived in Davies (1953), so that $V_0 \propto J_1(\beta r)$, which is known to represent the zonal field reasonably well; this, however, makes the perturbation equations intractable. With the temperature field (1·15) and the velocity field (1·17), equation (1·14 *e*) cannot be satisfied, and it is necessary to supply heat to the liquid in order to maintain this distribution. Although many of the assumptions introduced in this basic flow are rather crude, the important feature of 'baroclinity', which is the meteorological term for the non-coincidence of the isobaric and isothermal surfaces, is certainly incorporated in the above basic fields through the constant Θ_H, and we shall later find that the non-dimensional parameter R_H in (1·18), which depends upon Θ_H, plays an important role throughout the work. Both Fultz and Hide introduce a non-dimensional parameter similar to (1·18); this will be discussed at greater length later in the paper. It may be observed here, however, that R_H is a type of Richardson number although not in the conventional sense which refers to density and velocity gradients in the vertical; it is later interpreted as the Rossby number of the problem.

TABLE 1. MEAN VALUES OF V_0 MEASURED ON THE FREE SURFACE AT VARIOUS RADIAL DISTANCES r MEASURED FROM THE CENTRAL AXIS. (AFTER STARR & LONG)

V_0 (cm/s)	0·0705	0·1413	0·2449	0·4119	0·7290	0·6375
r (cm)	2·50	5·00	7·50	10·00	12·50	13·75

The equations which govern the perturbation field are now assumed to be the linearized form of the set (1·1) to (1·6) when products and squares of the terms u, v, w, p, ρ and T are neglected. The three equations of motion which result are then found to be as follows for the motion *relative* to the rotating cylinder, in which ϕ now refers to longitude relative to a fixed radius in the cylinder:

$$\rho_0\left\{\left(\frac{\partial}{\partial t}+\frac{V_0}{r}\frac{\partial}{\partial\phi}\right)u-v\left(2\Omega+\frac{2V_0}{r}\right)\right\}=-\frac{\partial p}{\partial r}+\mu\left\{\nabla_1^2u-\frac{u}{r^2}-\frac{2}{r^2}\frac{\partial v}{\partial\phi}+\frac{1}{3}\frac{\partial\chi}{\partial r}\right\}, \tag{1·19}$$

$$\rho_0\left\{\left(\frac{\partial}{\partial t}+\frac{V_0}{r}\frac{\partial}{\partial\phi}\right)v+u\left(2\Omega+\frac{V_0}{r}+\frac{\partial V_0}{\partial r}\right)\right\}=-\frac{\partial p}{r\partial\phi}+\mu\left\{\nabla_1^2v-\frac{v}{r^2}+\frac{2}{r^2}\frac{\partial u}{\partial\phi}+\frac{1}{3}\frac{\partial\chi}{r\partial\phi}\right\}, \tag{1·20}$$

$$\rho_0\left(\frac{\partial}{\partial t}+\frac{V_0}{r}\frac{\partial}{\partial\phi}\right)w=-\frac{\partial p}{\partial z}+g\alpha T+\mu\left(\nabla_1^2w+\frac{1}{3}\frac{\partial\chi}{\partial r}\right), \tag{1·21}$$

where χ is the divergence defined by

$$\chi=\frac{\partial u}{\partial r}+\frac{u}{r}+\frac{\partial v}{r\partial\phi}+\frac{\partial w}{\partial z}. \tag{1·22}$$

It will be observed that the density in these equations has been replaced everywhere by its constant value ρ_0 at temperature T_0 except, of course, in the buoyancy term, where it is replaced by the value $-\alpha T$ from (1·11). Furthermore, in (1·20) the term $w\,\partial V_0/\partial z$ has been ignored in comparison with the other terms on the left-hand side which are horizontal velocity terms; it will be evident later that this approximation is fully justified. In the equations of continuity and heat transfer a new type of approximation is incorporated in the following way. We have

$$\begin{aligned}\frac{\mathrm{d}T_1}{\mathrm{d}t}&=\left(\frac{\partial}{\partial t}+\frac{V_0+v}{r}\frac{\partial}{\partial\phi}+u\frac{\partial}{\partial r}+w\frac{\partial}{\partial z}\right)(T^*+T)\\&=\frac{\partial T}{\partial t}+\frac{V_0}{r}\frac{\partial T}{\partial\phi}+u\frac{\partial T^*}{\partial r}+w\frac{\partial T^*}{\partial z}+\text{second-order terms.}\end{aligned}$$

Using (1·15) we may here replace $\partial T^*/\partial z$ by Θ_V and $\partial T^*/\partial r$ by $r\Theta_H$. If the resulting equations are considered with this operator in the heat-transfer equation it is found that they are quite intractable, since the method of separation of variables is not applicable. It is proposed, therefore, to replace the velocity component u by its 'geostrophic value' in the unsteady case. Precisely what this implies will be seen in the next section, and here it is sufficient to state that ru is to be replaced by $-F(z)\,\partial p/\partial\phi$, and accordingly we may write the above expression in the form

$$\frac{\mathrm{d}T_1}{\mathrm{d}t}=\left(\frac{\partial}{\partial t}+\frac{V_0}{r}\frac{\partial}{\partial\phi}\right)T-\Theta_HF(z)\frac{\partial p}{\partial\phi}+\Theta_Vw+\text{second-order terms,} \tag{1·23}$$

and in this case the equations of continuity and heat transfer become

$$\alpha\left\{\left(\frac{\partial}{\partial t}+\frac{V_0}{r}\frac{\partial}{\partial\phi}\right)T-\Theta_HF(z)\frac{\partial p}{\partial\phi}+\Theta_Vw\right\}=\rho_0\chi \tag{1·24}$$

and

$$\rho_0c_v\left\{\left(\frac{\partial}{\partial t}+\frac{V_0}{r}\frac{\partial}{\partial\phi}\right)T-\Theta_HF(z)\frac{\partial p}{\partial\phi}+\Theta_Vw\right\}=k\nabla_1^2T. \tag{1·25}$$

We now have five equations, namely, (1·19), (1·20), (1·21), (1·24) and (1·25), between the five dependent variables u, v, w, p, T, and these equations form a consistent set.

2. The method of solution of the perturbation equations

We first of all assume that the dependent variables are of the form

$$(u, v, w, p, T, \chi) = (u, v, w, p, T, \chi) \exp(im\phi + i\sigma t), \tag{2·1}†$$

where m is the wave number of the perturbation and σ its frequency. The five equations governing the perturbation motion are then

$$i\rho_0 \sigma' u - 2\rho_0 \Omega' v = -\frac{\partial p}{\partial r} + \gamma \frac{\partial \chi}{\partial r} + \mu\left(\nabla^2 u - \frac{u}{r^2} - \frac{2imv}{r^2}\right), \tag{2·2}$$

$$i\rho_0 \sigma' v + 2\rho_0 \Omega' u = -\frac{imp}{r} + \frac{im\gamma\chi}{r} + \mu\left(\nabla^2 v - \frac{v}{r^2} + \frac{2imu}{r^2}\right), \tag{2·3}$$

$$i\rho_0 \sigma' w = -\frac{\partial p}{\partial z} + \gamma \frac{\partial \chi}{\partial z} + g\alpha T + \mu \nabla^2 w, \tag{2·4}$$

$$\alpha\{i\sigma' T - im\Theta_H F(z)\, p + \Theta_V w\} = \rho_0 \left\{\frac{\partial u}{\partial r} + \frac{u}{r} + \frac{imv}{r} + \frac{\partial w}{\partial z}\right\} = \rho_0 \chi, \tag{2·5}$$

$$\rho_0 c_v \{i\sigma' T - im\Theta_H F(z)\, p + \Theta_V w\} = k \nabla^2 T, \tag{2·6}$$

where $\gamma = \frac{1}{3}\mu$,
$$\nabla^2 \equiv \frac{\partial^2}{\partial r^2} + \frac{1}{r}\frac{\partial}{\partial r} + \frac{\partial^2}{\partial z^2} - \frac{m^2}{r^2}, \tag{2·7}$$

and where σ' and Ω' are defined by

$$\left.\begin{aligned} \sigma' &= \sigma + 2\Omega R_H(z/h)\, m, \\ \Omega' &= \Omega + 2\Omega R_H(z/h). \end{aligned}\right\} \tag{2·8}$$

It is of interest to note at this stage that the incorporation of the 'baroclinicity' through the term R_H has the effect of making both the frequency term σ' and the Coriolis term Ω' depend upon z, so that the effective frequency and effective angular velocity will vary from one level to the next.

The next step consists in separating the variables r and z in equations (2·2) to (2·6). This was done originally by recasting the equations in such a way that $u+iv$ and $u-iv$ replace u and v as dependent variables. The detailed method need not be explained, and it is sufficient to state that when two new variables $\xi(z)$ and $\eta(z)$ are introduced so that

$$2u = \xi(z) \frac{mC_m(\beta r)}{\beta r} - \eta(z)\, C'_m(\beta r), \tag{2·9}$$

$$2iv = -\xi(z)\, C'_m(\beta r) + \eta(z) \frac{mC_m(\beta r)}{\beta r}, \tag{2·10}$$

$$w = W(z)\, C_m(\beta r), \tag{2·11}$$

$$p = P(z)\, C_m(\beta r), \tag{2·12}$$

$$T = \tau(z)\, C_m(\beta r), \tag{2·13}$$

$$\chi = \chi_0(z)\, C_m(\beta r), \tag{2·14}$$

where $C_m(\varpi)$ is a solution of Bessel's differential equation of order m

$$\frac{d^2 C_m}{d\varpi^2} + \frac{1}{\varpi}\frac{dC_m}{d\varpi} + \left(1 - \frac{m^2}{\varpi^2}\right) C_m = 0, \tag{2·15}$$

† No confusion will arise from the use of the same variables on each side of this equation.

the variables r and z in (2·2) to (2·6) become separable. The five resulting equations for $\xi(z)$, $\eta(z)$, $W(z)$, $P(z)$ and $\tau(z)$ are then the following five ordinary simultaneous equations:

$$i\rho_0\sigma'\xi+2i\rho_0\Omega'\eta=\mu\left(\frac{d^2\xi}{dz^2}-\beta^2\xi\right), \tag{2·16}$$

$$i\rho_0\sigma'\eta+2i\rho_0\Omega'\xi=2\beta(P-\gamma\chi_0)+\mu\left(\frac{d^2\eta}{dz^2}-\beta^2\eta\right), \tag{2·17}$$

$$i\rho_0\sigma'W-g\alpha\tau=-\left(\frac{dP}{dz}-\gamma\frac{d\chi_0}{dz}\right)+\mu\left(\frac{d^2W}{dz^2}-\beta^2W\right), \tag{2·18}$$

$$\alpha\{i\sigma'\tau-im\Theta_HF(z)\,P+\Theta_VW\}=\tfrac{1}{2}\rho_0\beta\eta+\rho_0\frac{dW}{dz}=\rho_0\chi_0, \tag{2·19}$$

$$c_v\rho_0\{i\sigma'\tau-im\Theta_HF(z)\,P+\Theta_VW\}=k\left(\frac{d^2\tau}{dz^2}-\beta^2\tau\right). \tag{2·20}$$

In their present form these five equations apply to a wide variety of heating problems in cylindrical co-ordinates.

It is of interest to note at this stage that the function $C_m(\beta r)$ is any solution of (2·15), so that for a liquid bounded by one outer cylindrical wall, we may utilize the function $J_m(\beta r)$, which is finite at $r=0$, and for a liquid between two concentric cylinders we may utilize the function $\alpha_mJ_m(\beta r)+\beta_mY_m(\beta r)$. In each case the resulting form of the equations (2·16) to (2·20) is unchanged. This implies that there is no essential difference between the two types of experiment as far as the stability characteristics are concerned, for these depend entirely upon the parameters entering into equations (2·16) to (2·20) and upon the similar boundary conditions at $z=0$ and $z=h$.

We consider next the boundary conditions of the problem. At the side wall of the vessel the exact boundary conditions will evidently be $u=v=w=0$ at $r=r_0$, but since the equations themselves are not valid right up to $r=r_0$, this stringent condition will be relaxed and we shall take the condition to be the vanishing of the normal velocity at $r=r_0$, that is,

$$u=0, \quad r=r_0. \tag{2·21}$$

This is the condition at the edge of the boundary layer, and (2·21) implies in fact that the boundary layer at the side wall is ignored. If there are two concentric cylinders then there will be a second condition similar to (2·21); but most of the work hereafter will refer to the single-sided problem. If we were able to solve the problem exactly from this point onwards the appropriate conditions at $z=0$, the base of the liquid at $z=h$ the free upper surface of the liquid would be as follows:

$$u=v=w=0, \quad z=0;$$

$$\frac{\partial u}{\partial z}=\frac{\partial v}{\partial z}=w=0, \quad z=h;$$

and these velocity conditions transform simply into

$$\xi=\eta=W=0, \quad z=0;$$

$$\frac{d\xi}{dz}=\frac{d\eta}{dz}=W=0, \quad z=h.$$

Likewise there will be conditions imposed at $z = 0$ and $z = h$ on the heat flow passing through these surfaces. If it is assumed that no heat flows across the upper free surface then

$$\frac{d\tau}{dz} = 0 \quad \text{at} \quad z = h,$$

and if it is assumed that the perturbation receives no heat supply from the base $z = 0$, so that it must acquire its energy from the liquid interior, then we could take

$$\frac{d\tau}{dz} = 0 \quad \text{at} \quad z = 0$$

also. However, the set of equations (2·16) to (2·20), even though they are ordinary simultaneous equations, are difficult to handle in the general case, being of the eighth order when eliminations are completely carried out. Consequently it is necessary to simplify the approach, in the first instance at least, by using physical arguments.

It is quite certain that the velocity field in its vertical variation will contain at least three important regions. Near the base of the cylinder where boundary-layer effects predominate, it is quite certain that the second-order differential terms such as $\mu d^2\xi/dz^2$, $\mu d^2\eta/dz^2$ and $\mu d^2W/dz^2$ will be of considerable importance. Likewise in a narrow region near the free upper surface these terms will be of importance but in the intermediate region, which is the greatest region in extent, it is likely that these terms play a secondary role only. It has been shown (Davies 1953) that in the symmetric problem the boundary-layer thickness is, in fact, $h/R^{\frac{1}{2}}$, where $R = \Omega\rho_0 h^2/\mu$, and in a typical case when $\Omega = 6\pi/60$ per sec., $\rho_0 = 1$, $h = 3$ cm and $\mu = 0{\cdot}01$, this gives $R = 300$ approximately and the boundary-layer thickness is about 2 mm. Accordingly, for the flow outside the narrow boundary layers we shall take the equations in the modified form given by

$$(i\rho_0\sigma' + \mu\beta^2)\,\xi + 2i\rho_0\Omega'\eta = 0, \tag{2·22}$$

$$(i\rho_0\sigma' + \mu\beta^2)\,\eta + 2i\rho_0\Omega'\xi = 2\beta(P - \gamma\chi_0), \tag{2·23}$$

$$(i\rho_0\sigma' + \mu\beta^2)\,W - g\alpha\tau = -\frac{d}{dz}(P - \gamma\chi_0), \tag{2·24}$$

$$\alpha\{i\sigma'\tau - im\Theta_H F(z)\,P + \Theta_V W\} = \tfrac{1}{2}\rho_0\beta\eta + \rho_0\frac{dW}{dz}, \tag{2·25}$$

$$\left(i\rho_0\sigma' + \frac{k\beta^2}{c_v}\right)\tau - i\rho_0 m\Theta_H F(z)\,P + \rho_0\Theta_V W = 0, \tag{2·26}$$

and we can now define the function $F(z)$ which was introduced in (1·23) to be

$$F(z) = \frac{2\rho_0\Omega'}{4\rho_0\Omega'^2 + (i\rho_0\sigma' + \mu\beta^2)^2}, \tag{2·27}$$

this being the approximate unsteady geostrophic value obtained from the pair of equations

$$(i\rho_0\sigma' + \mu\beta^2)\,u - 2\rho_0\Omega' v = 0,$$

$$(i\rho_0\sigma' + \mu\beta^2)\,v + 2\rho_0\Omega' u = -\frac{1}{r}\frac{\partial p}{d\phi},$$

in which
$$u = -\frac{1}{r}F(z)\frac{\partial p}{\partial\phi}.$$

Since in equations (2·22) to (2·26) the second differentials of velocity and temperature have been ignored the appropriate boundary conditions will be

$$\left.\begin{aligned} w = 0, \quad z = 0, \\ w = 0, \quad z = h, \end{aligned}\right\} \tag{2·28}$$

which are the inviscid conditions, and the problem is then self-consistent. The equations (2·22) to (2·26) contain the viscosity through the term $\mu\beta^2$ and the conduction through the term $k\beta^2/c_v$, and the presence of these terms will indicate the direction in which viscosity and conductivity influence the large-scale motion. The ignoring of the second derivative terms in fact is equivalent to the assumption that the viscous effect is directly proportional to the velocity and the conduction effect is directly proportional to the temperature. The viscous effect and conductivity effect is probably small in this problem, but we shall retain these modified forms of viscosity and conductivity, since they play an important part in the later discussion of the singularities. At this point, however, we shall ignore the term χ_0 on the right-hand sides of (2·23) and (2·24), since it is equal to $-\alpha k\beta^2\tau/\rho_0^2 c_v$, and the combination of $\alpha k\mu$ in the term $\gamma\chi$ makes this quite negligible. This term could well have been ignored earlier in fact, but it is of interest to have shown that the complete perturbation equations, with χ included, could be successfully tackled by the present method.

Before proceeding any further with the development of the equations (2·22) to (2·26) it is convenient to introduce non-dimensional variables $\bar{\xi}$, $\bar{\eta}$, $\overline{W}$, $\bar{\tau}$, $\bar{P}$ in place of ξ, η, W, τ and P; accordingly, we shall write

$$z = h\zeta, \quad a = \beta h, \tag{2·29}$$

so that the liquid now is contained in the range $0 \leqslant \zeta \leqslant 1$;

$$\left.\begin{aligned} \xi &= 2R_H\Omega r_0\bar{\xi}, & P &= 2\rho_0 R_H\Omega^2 r_0^2\bar{P}, \\ \eta &= 2R_H\Omega r_0\bar{\eta}, & \chi_0 &= 2aR_H\Omega r_0\bar{\chi}/h, \\ W &= 2R_H\Omega r_0 a\overline{W}, & \tau &= \tfrac{1}{2}r_0^2\Theta_H\bar{\tau}; \end{aligned}\right\} \tag{2·30}$$

and we introduce the following non-dimensional parameters:

$$f = \frac{\sigma}{2\Omega}, \quad R = \frac{\Omega\rho_0 h^2}{\mu}, \quad K = \frac{\Omega\rho_0 h^2 c_v}{k}, \quad R_H = \frac{g\alpha h\Theta_H}{4\rho_0\Omega^2}, \quad R_v = \frac{g\alpha\Theta_V}{4\rho_0\Omega^2}. \tag{2·31}$$

In (2·31) R is a Reynolds number for the flow, K a Péclet number, R_H has already been mentioned in (1·18), R_v is a Richardson number (being of the form $g(\partial\rho/\partial z)/\rho(\partial u/\partial z)^2$), and f is a non-dimensional frequency. The equations (2·22) to (2·26) then become

$$s\bar{\xi} + \mathrm{i}(1+2R_H\zeta)\,\bar{\eta} = 0, \tag{2·32}$$

$$s\bar{\eta} + \mathrm{i}(1+2R_H\zeta)\,\bar{\xi} = \beta r_0\bar{P}, \tag{2·33}$$

$$\frac{2ah}{r_0}s\overline{W} - \tau = -\frac{\mathrm{d}P}{\mathrm{d}\zeta}, \tag{2·34}$$

$$\frac{2r_0\Omega^2}{g}\left\{\mathrm{i}(f+mR_H\zeta)\,\bar{\tau} - \frac{\mathrm{i}mR_H(1+2R_H\zeta)}{(1+2R_H\zeta)^2+s^2}\bar{P} + \frac{2ah}{r_0}R_v\overline{W}\right\} = a\left(\tfrac{1}{2}\bar{\eta} + \frac{d\overline{W}}{d\zeta}\right), \tag{2·35}$$

$$s'\tau - \frac{\mathrm{i}mR_H(1+2R_H\zeta)}{(1+2R_H\zeta)^2+s^2}\bar{P} + \frac{2ah}{r_0}R_v\overline{W} = 0, \tag{2·36}$$

where, for convenience, we have written

$$s = \mathrm{i}(f+mR_H\zeta)+\frac{a^2}{2R}, \tag{2·37}$$

$$s' = \mathrm{i}(f+mR_H\zeta)+\frac{a^2}{2K}. \tag{2·38}$$

It is most convenient now to derive the differential equation for $\overline{W}$ from the set (2·32) to (2·36), since the boundary conditions are expressly imposed upon $\overline{W}$ being

$$\left.\begin{array}{ll}\overline{W}=0, & \zeta=0,\\ \overline{W}=0, & \zeta=1.\end{array}\right\} \tag{2·39}$$

From (2·32) and (2·33) we obtain

$$\frac{\mathrm{i}\bar{\xi}}{1+2R_H\zeta}=\frac{\bar{\eta}}{s}=\frac{\beta r_0\overline{P}}{(1+2R_H\zeta)^2+s^2}. \tag{2·40}$$

Likewise from (2·35) and (2·36) we have

$$-\frac{ar_0\Omega^2}{Kg}\bar{\tau}=\tfrac{1}{2}\bar{\eta}+\frac{\mathrm{d}\overline{W}}{\mathrm{d}\zeta}, \tag{2·41}$$

and substituting for $\bar{\eta}$ from (2·40) this gives

$$-\frac{ar_0\Omega^2}{Kg}\bar{\tau}=\frac{\frac{1}{2}\beta r_0 s}{(1+2R_H\zeta)^2+s^2}\overline{P}+\frac{\mathrm{d}\overline{W}}{\mathrm{d}\zeta}. \tag{2·42}$$

When we substitute for $\bar{\tau}$ from (2·34) in (2·42) we obtain the following relation between $\overline{P}$ and $\overline{W}$:

$$-\frac{ar_0\Omega^2}{Kg}\left\{\frac{\mathrm{d}\overline{P}}{\mathrm{d}\zeta}+\frac{2ah}{r_0}s\overline{W}\right\}=\frac{\frac{1}{2}\beta r_0 s}{(1+2R_H\zeta)^2+s^2}\overline{P}+\frac{\mathrm{d}\overline{W}}{\mathrm{d}\zeta}. \tag{2·43}$$

Similarly, by eliminating $\bar{\tau}$ between (2·36) and (2·34) we obtain a second relation between $\overline{P}$ and $\overline{W}$, namely,

$$s'\left(\frac{\mathrm{d}\overline{P}}{\mathrm{d}\zeta}+\frac{2ah}{r_0}s\overline{W}\right)=\frac{imR_H(1+2R_H\zeta)}{(1+2R_H\zeta)^2+s^2}\overline{P}-\frac{2ah}{r_0}R_v\overline{W}. \tag{2·44}$$

The elimination of $\overline{P}$ between (2·43) and (2·44) leads to the desired second-order differential equations for $\overline{W}$. In the general case we can express this equation in the form

$$s'\frac{\mathrm{d}}{\mathrm{d}\zeta}\left\{\frac{\lambda_1}{\lambda_2}\left(s'\frac{\mathrm{d}\overline{W}}{\mathrm{d}\zeta}-A\overline{W}\right)\right\}+\frac{imR_H(1+2R_H\zeta)}{\lambda_2}\left\{A\overline{W}-s'\frac{\mathrm{d}\overline{W}}{\mathrm{d}\zeta}\right\}-\frac{2ah}{r_0}(R_v+ss')\,\overline{W}=0, \tag{2·45}$$

where

$$\left.\begin{aligned}A&=2a^2h\Omega^2R_v/Kg,\\ \lambda_1&=(1+2R_H\zeta)^2+s^2,\\ \lambda_2&=imR_H\left(\frac{ar_0\Omega^2}{Kg}\right)(1+2R_H\zeta)+\tfrac{1}{2}\beta r_0 ss',\end{aligned}\right\} \tag{2·46}$$

but we may simplify this equation considerably by investigating the orders of magnitude of the various terms. In order to do this we shall use the typical values $\Omega=0{\cdot}3$ rad/s, $f=0{\cdot}05$, $\rho_0=1$, $r_0=15$ cm, $h=3$ cm, $g=10^3$, $\Theta_H=0{\cdot}16$, $\Theta_V=1{\cdot}45$, $R_H=0{\cdot}3$, $R_v=1{\cdot}0$, $R=300$, $K=3000$; the second quantity in this list is a typical observed value for f. In the expression for λ_2 the term $mR_H(ar_0\Omega^2/Kg)$ bears to $\frac{1}{2}\beta r_0 ss'$ the ratio 10^{-2} to 1 when s and s' are chosen to be each equal to $\mathrm{i}f$. Thus there will be no important error introduced if we write

$$\lambda_2=\tfrac{1}{2}\beta r_0 ss'. \tag{2·47}$$

Likewise, if we compare the term $imR_H(1+2R_H\zeta)\,A\overline{W}/\lambda_2$ with $2ahR_v\overline{W}/r_0$ we find that the coefficients of $\overline{W}$ here are in the ratio 10^{-3} to 1. Similarly the term containing A in the leading expression of (2·45), namely $As'\,\mathrm{d}(\lambda_1\overline{W}/\lambda_2)/\mathrm{d}\zeta$, may be safely ignored compared with later terms in $\overline{W}$ and $\mathrm{d}\overline{W}/\mathrm{d}\zeta$. Thus we may write (2·45) in the form

$$s'\frac{\mathrm{d}}{\mathrm{d}\zeta}\left(\frac{\lambda_1}{s}\frac{\mathrm{d}\overline{W}}{\mathrm{d}\zeta}\right)-\frac{imR_H}{s}(1+2R_H\zeta)\frac{\mathrm{d}\overline{W}}{\mathrm{d}\zeta}-a^2(R_v+ss')\,\overline{W}=0, \tag{2·48}$$

and it is easily seen that the reason for this simplification of the differential equation is essentially the smallness of the factor $ar_0\Omega^2/Kg$ which appears on the left-hand side of (2·41), (2·42) and (2·43). When the term on the left-hand side of (2·41) is ignored we obtain the result $\frac{1}{2}\overline{\eta}+\mathrm{d}W/\mathrm{d}\zeta=0$; in its original context this would read $\operatorname{div}\mathbf{V}=0$, so that the above simplification is merely an expression of the physical result that the process of conductivity is negligible here in its influence upon the divergence of a fluid element. This could probably have been surmised initially, but it is more satisfactory to do so at this stage.

We now discuss equation (2·48). It may be written in the form

$$\lambda_1 ss'\frac{\mathrm{d}^2\overline{W}}{\mathrm{d}\zeta^2}+\frac{\mathrm{d}\overline{W}}{\mathrm{d}\zeta}\left\{-imR_H s(1+2R_H\zeta)+ss'\frac{\mathrm{d}\lambda_1}{\mathrm{d}\zeta}-s'\lambda_1\frac{\mathrm{d}s}{\mathrm{d}\zeta}\right\}-a^2s^2(R_v+ss')\,\overline{W}=0, \tag{2·49}$$

and it is clear from this form that the equation has singularities at the points where s, s' and λ_1 vanish. From the definition of s in (2·37) we see that s vanishes at $\zeta=\zeta_1$, where

$$\zeta_1=-\frac{f}{mR_H}+\frac{ia^2}{2RmR_H}; \tag{2·50}$$

similarly, from (2·38), s' vanishes at $\zeta=\zeta_2$, where

$$\zeta_2=-\frac{f}{mR_H}+\frac{ia^2}{2KmR_H}; \tag{2·51}$$

and, from (2·46), λ_1 vanishes at $\zeta=\zeta_3$ and $\zeta=\zeta_4$, where

$$\zeta_3R_H(m+2)=-1-f+\frac{ia^2}{2R}, \tag{2·52}$$

$$\zeta_4R_H(m-2)=1-f+\frac{ia^2}{2R}. \tag{2·53}$$

The quantity ζ in the present problem is real and varies between 0 and 1, and thus all the singularities lie at points in a complex ζ plane which are not on the real axis if a^2 is a real quantity. It is interesting to note, however, that if $R\to\infty$ and $K\to\infty$ then there will certainly be at least one singularity in the real range $0\leqslant\zeta\leqslant1$ when m is sufficiently large, and the presence of such a singularity gives rise to peculiar difficulties in satisfying the boundary conditions (2·39). Thus the retention of viscosity and conductivity, though in a form which is not exact, serves a most useful purpose in the problem. The remaining sections of this paper will discuss various aspects of equation (2·48).

3. The barotropic solution

In the expressions for σ' and Ω' given in (2·8) and (2·9) it has been observed that an interpretation of their variation is that the effective frequency and effective angular velocity depend upon z. A very much simplified theory will evidently result if we assume that the effective frequency and effective angular velocity show no variation with height. This is an assumption made frequently in the corresponding meteorological problems. The immediate advantage of this barotropic assumption is that there is no possibility of any singularity arising in the differential equation (2·48), and we shall investigate this case in detail when R and K are sufficiently large to ignore the terms $a^2/2R$ and $a^2/2K$. The case in which $a^2/2R$ and $a^2/2K$ are retained will be discussed briefly at the end of this section.

In equation (2·48) we now replace $s = if$, $s' = if$, $\lambda_1 = 1-f^2$, and it then becomes

$$(1-f^2)\frac{d^2\overline{W}}{d\zeta^2}-\frac{mR_H}{f}\frac{d\overline{W}}{d\zeta}-a^2(R_v-f^2)\,\overline{W} = 0. \tag{3·1}$$

The condition to be satisfied by the coefficients of an equation of the form

$$a_1\frac{d^2\overline{W}}{d\zeta^2}+b_1\frac{d\overline{W}}{d\zeta}+c_1\overline{W} = 0 \tag{3·2}$$

when $\overline{W} = 0$ at $\zeta = 0$ and $\zeta = 1$ is

$$\frac{b_1^2-4a_1c_1}{a_1^2} = -4\pi^2n^2 \quad (n = 1, 2, 3, \ldots). \tag{3·3}$$

Applying this result to (3·1) we obtain

$$\frac{m^2R_H^2}{f^2}+4a^2(1-f^2)(R_v-f^2) = -4\pi^2n^2(1-f^2)^2, \tag{3·4}$$

and this, of course, is a frequency equation, giving f when R_H, R_v and a are known. Interest centres principally upon small values of f, since with the long-wave patterns observed in the experiment the angular velocity relative to the rotating vessel, namely, $-2\Omega f/m$, is known to be small. Accordingly we can write (3·4) in the simplified form

$$\frac{m^2R_H^2}{f^2} = -4(a^2R_v+\pi^2n^2), \tag{3·5}$$

since R_v is of order unity. In this relation the quantity a is undefined, and in order to obtain a second relation between f, a, etc., we use the boundary condition at $r = r_0$ given in (2·21). Using (2·22), which in the present case may be written in the form

$$f\xi+\eta = 0, \tag{3·6}$$

together with (2·9), we have

$$2u = \xi(z)\left\{\frac{mC_m(\beta r)}{\beta r}+fC_m'(\beta r)\right\}. \tag{3·7}$$

Thus the boundary condition will be satisfied in the single-sided problem by choosing $C_m = J_m$ and by making β satisfy the equation

$$\frac{mJ_m(\beta r_0)}{\beta r_0}+fJ_m'(\beta r_0) = 0; \tag{3·8}$$

the annulus problem will not be considered here. Since $a = \beta h$, the parameter β can be eliminated between (3·5) and (3·8) to provide a relation between f, r_0, h, R_v and R_H which is the true frequency equation of the problem. It will be observed that if β is real and, accordingly, a real, then (3·5) will lead to a purely imaginary value for f so that there is no neutral progressive wave. On the other hand, when β is purely imaginary it is easily shown that progressive wave solutions are possible. If we solve for β from (3·5) we obtain

$$\beta^2h^2 = -\left\{\pi^2n^2+\frac{m^2R_H^2}{4f^2}\right\}\Big/R_v, \tag{3·9}$$

and thus

$$\beta r_0 = \mathrm{i}\lambda, \tag{3·10}$$

where

$$\lambda^2 = \left(\pi^2n^2+\frac{m^2R_H^2}{4f^2}\right)\frac{r_0^2}{h^2R_v}. \tag{3·11}$$

Substituting for β in (3·8) we have

$$\frac{mJ_m(\mathrm{i}\lambda)}{\mathrm{i}\lambda}+fJ_m'(\mathrm{i}\lambda) = 0,$$

where λ is real. Using the modified Bessel function I_m which is defined by the relation $I_m(z) = \mathrm{i}^{-m}J_m(\mathrm{i}z)$ (Whittaker & Watson, *Modern analysis*, p. 372), this relation can be written in the form

$$\frac{mI_m(\lambda)}{\lambda}+fI_m'(\lambda) = 0, \tag{3·12}$$

and for the particular barotropic flow which we have considered in this section this relation is exact. Equation (3·12) may be simplified as follows in the present case. For small values of f, λ is a large quantity, and it is permissible to use the asymptotic formulae for $I_m(\lambda)$ and $I_m'(\lambda)$, namely,

$$I_m(\lambda) \sim \frac{\mathrm{e}^\lambda}{(2\pi\lambda)^{\frac{1}{2}}}\left\{1-\frac{(4m^2-1)}{8\lambda}+o\left(\frac{1}{\lambda^2}\right)\right\},$$

$$I_m'(\lambda) \sim \frac{\mathrm{e}^\lambda}{(2\pi\lambda)^{\frac{1}{2}}}\left\{1-\frac{(4m^2+3)}{8\lambda}+o\left(\frac{1}{\lambda^2}\right)\right\}.$$

Accordingly (3·12) becomes approximately

$$\frac{m}{\lambda}\left\{1-\frac{4m^2-1}{\lambda}\right\}+f\left\{1-\frac{4m^2+3}{8\lambda}\right\} = 0,$$

and f is therefore given by

$$f = -\frac{m}{\lambda}\left\{1+\frac{1}{2\lambda}+o\left(\frac{1}{\lambda^2}\right)\right\}. \tag{3·13}$$

If only the first term is taken on the right-hand side of (3·13), so that $f = -m/\lambda$, it follows that the frequency equation is

$$f^2\left\{\pi^2n^2+\frac{m^2R_H^2}{4f^2}\right\}\frac{r_0^2}{h^2R_v} = m^2 \tag{3·14}$$

when we use (3·11), and the solution for f is given by

$$n^2\pi^2f^2 = m^2\left\{\frac{h^2}{r_0^2}R_v-\tfrac{1}{4}R_H^2\right\}. \tag{3·15}$$

This frequency equation will be valid provided the quantity in the brackets is sufficiently small. Evidently the condition for stability of the wave is

$$\frac{h^2}{r_0^2}R_v > \tfrac{1}{4}R_H^2, \tag{3·16}$$

since when this is satisfied a real value of f results. The quantity n in (3·15) is an integer, and in the most important case when W has no nodal surfaces in the region $0<\zeta<1$, which is the case usually observed in experiments, we can take $n=1$. With $n=1$ and (3·16) satisfied the formula for the angular velocity ω of propagation of the wave system becomes

$$\frac{\omega}{\Omega}=\frac{2f}{m}$$

$$=\pm\frac{2}{\pi}\left\{\frac{h^2}{r_0^2}R_v-\tfrac{1}{4}R_H^2\right\}^{\frac{1}{2}}, \tag{3·17}$$

the upper sign refers to a wave propagated in the E→W direction and the lower sign to one propagated in the W→E direction. The quantities R_v and R_H are independent of m, and thus the formula (3·17) is a non-dispersive propagation formula, which agrees with a statement due to Hide. Apart from this very minor qualitative agreement it is most difficult to compare (3·17) with any of Hide's empirical formulae, since he does not introduce the parameter R_v explicitly in his results. In the present theory R_H and R_v are introduced as two independent parameters, but in order to reproduce Hide's empirical formulae it seems to be necessary to postulate some relation between them. It is more useful at this stage of the theory, however, to investigate (3·16) in greater detail, since the result is quite decisive.

If we substitute for R_v and R_H in (3·16) it may be rearranged in the form

$$\Omega^2>g\alpha r_0^2\Theta_H^2/16\rho_0\Theta_V \tag{3·18}$$

for stability of the wave pattern, and we may state that according to barotropic theory no neutral progressive stable wave exists when

$$\Omega^2<g\alpha r_0^2\Theta_H^2/16\rho_0\Theta_V. \tag{3·19}$$

When this inequality (3·19) is satisfied, (3·15) does not indicate whether the corresponding wave is exponentially damped or exponentially increasing in amplitude, but it is likely that $\Omega=\Omega_{\text{crit.}}$, where

$$\Omega_{\text{crit.}}^2=g\alpha r_0^2\Theta_H^2/16\rho_0\Theta_V \tag{3·20}$$

represents an important and critical stage in the value of this parameter. It we take typical experimental values $\rho_0=1$, $r_0=15\,\text{cm}$, $\alpha=2{\cdot}5\times10^{-4}$, $g=10^3$, $\Theta_H=0{\cdot}16$, $\Theta_V=1{\cdot}45$, we obtain $\Omega_{\text{crit.}}=0{\cdot}25$, and this gives as the critical number of revolutions per minute ($=60\Omega_{\text{crit.}}/2\pi$) the value 2·4. The observed critical number of revolutions when spiral flow gives way to wave flow is a number near 3 for the above data, and, apparently, barotropic theory gives a quantitative result of the correct order of magnitude. Further agreement with experiment is certainly not forthcoming however, for, as stated in the introduction the theory must also explain why, for example, a three-wave pattern changes to a four-wave pattern and there is nothing in (3·18) to explain such a feature. In order to see how the above theory differs from Hide's empirical formulae it is useful at this stage to summarize his principal results.

Hide obtains a formula for the wave velocity in the form

$$R_0=-(0{\cdot}0288\pm0{\cdot}0008)\,\Theta\frac{(b-a)}{\frac{1}{2}(b+a)}, \tag{3·21}$$

where R_0, the Rossby number, is defined to be the ratio of the mean relative zonal angular speed of flow (this is identified by Hide with the angular velocity of propagation of the wave pattern) to the angular velocity of the cylinder, b is the outer cylinder radius, a the inner cylinder radius and Θ is defined by

$$\Theta = \frac{gh}{\frac{1}{2}\Omega^2(b^2-a^2)}\left|\frac{\Delta\rho}{\rho}\right|\left(\frac{1}{2}\frac{b+a}{b-a}\right), \tag{3·22}$$

where $\Delta\rho$ is the difference in density between the liquid at $r = a$ and $r = b$. We may, for the purpose of comparison, take $a = 0$, $b = r_0$ and $|\Delta\rho/\rho| = \alpha(\Delta T)/\rho$, and hence, in our notation,

$$\Theta = \frac{g\alpha h\Theta_H}{2\rho_0\Omega^2} = 2R_H. \tag{3·23}$$

Thus, assuming R_0 to be given by ω/Ω, we have, in our notation,

$$\frac{\omega}{\Omega} = -(0·0288\pm0·0008)\,4R_H = -0·13R_H. \tag{3·24}$$

This experimental result must be compared with (3·17), and, as has been stated earlier, no correspondence between the results is possible unless h^2R_v/r_0^2 is directly proportional to R_H^2. Hide states also that spiral flow changes to wave flow when $\Theta = \Theta_{\text{crit.}} = 1·58$; this corresponds to $R_H = 0·79$, and again no comparison is possible with (3·16).

It seems therefore that a barotropic type of solution is probably not adequate in explaining the principal features of the experiment, and a more elaborate theory will be established which will incorporate baroclinic features.

When viscosity and conductivity are retained and the simplifying assumption $R = K$ is made, the barotropic theory as expounded here is modified only in that $f - ia^2/2R$ replaces f everywhere in the analysis. It follows that the equation corresponding to (3·15) will be

$$\pi^2\left(f-\frac{ia^2}{2R}\right)^2 = m^2\left\{\frac{h^2}{r_0^2}R_v - \tfrac{1}{4}R_H^2\right\}.$$

The solutions for f are in general complex and no neutral waves can exist. Since $a^2<0$ the wave forms will in general be unstable.

4. The modified baroclinic solution

In this section it is proposed to obtain a solution of the equation (2·49) in which the singularities ζ_1 and ζ_2 of (2·50) and (2·51) are retained, ζ_3 and ζ_4 of (2·52) and (2·53) are ignored, and the conductivity and viscosity are made equal to zero. When R and K tend to infinity it will be noted that all the singularities ζ_s $(s = 1, 2, 3, 4)$ lie on the real axis, that in particular $\zeta_1 = \zeta_2 = -f/mR_H$, and these two will lie within the range $0<\zeta<1$ if f is negative and $|f|<mR_H$; this case is the important one, since we are concerned principally with progressive waves which are moving slowly in the west-east direction (i.e. in the same direction as the rotation). It is evident, therefore, that in any adequate theory of progressive east-west waves the singularities ζ_1 and ζ_2 must be taken into account in the solution of (2·49). The singularity ζ_3 always lies outside the range $0<\zeta<1$ even when R is infinite since $|f|\ll1$, so it would seem that ζ_3 is not as important a singularity as ζ_1 or ζ_2. The singularity ζ_4, on the other hand, will lie in the range $0<\zeta<1$ when R is infinite, $|f|\ll1$ and

$R_H(m-2)>1$. Taking R_H to be of magnitude 0·3 it follows that m must attain the value 6 before the singularity ζ_4 can lie in $0<\zeta<1$. Even though ζ_4 may be of importance for sufficiently large m we shall disregard it in the present section and will try to assess its influence in the next section. Accordingly, we shall make the following simplifying assumptions in equation (2·49):

(i) in the coefficient of $d^2\overline{W}/d\zeta^2$ the λ_1 term will be replaced by unity, which is its effective value at $\zeta = 0$,

(ii) the coefficient of $d\overline{W}/d\zeta$ is of the form

$$s\,imR_H\{-2-2R_H\zeta+R_H^2\zeta^2(4-m^2)+o(f)\},$$

and it will be assumed that this term takes the value $-2s\,imR_H$,

(iii) the coefficient of $\overline{W}$ will be taken in the form $-a^2s^2R_v$.

These three simplifying assumptions look after the singularity $s = 0$ effectively, and in all three cases it is assumed that the remaining terms take their surface values. Equation (2·49) then becomes

$$s^2\frac{d^2\overline{W}}{d\zeta^2}-2s\,imR_H\frac{d\overline{W}}{d\zeta}-a^2s^2R_v\overline{W} = 0, \tag{4·1}$$

where $s = i(f+mR_H\zeta)$, and we shall assume that f is a small negative quantity such that $-1<f/mR_H<0$.

It we take a new origin at the singular point and write

$$\zeta^* = \zeta+\frac{f}{mR_H} = \zeta-\zeta_0, \tag{4·2}$$

equation (4·1) becomes

$$\frac{d^2\overline{W}}{d\zeta^{*2}}-\frac{2}{\zeta^*}\frac{d\overline{W}}{d\zeta^*}-a^2R_v\overline{W} = 0, \tag{4·3}$$

and it is easily shown that the complete solution of (4·3) is

$$\overline{W} = \zeta^{*\frac{3}{2}}\{AJ_{\frac{3}{2}}(i\zeta^*\,aR_v^{\frac{1}{2}})+BJ_{-\frac{3}{2}}(i\zeta\,aR_v^{\frac{1}{2}})\}, \tag{4·4}$$

where A, B are two arbitrary constants and where $J_{\pm\frac{3}{2}}(\eta^*)$ are Bessel functions which are expressible in the closed form

$$J_{\frac{3}{2}}(\eta^*) = \left(\frac{2\eta^*}{\pi}\right)^{\frac{1}{2}}\left\{\frac{\sin\eta^*}{\eta^{*2}}-\frac{\cos\eta^*}{\eta^*}\right\},$$

$$J_{-\frac{3}{2}}(\eta^*) = -\left(\frac{2\eta^*}{\pi}\right)^{\frac{1}{2}}\left\{\frac{\sin\eta^*}{\eta^*}+\frac{\cos\eta^*}{\eta^{*2}}\right\}.$$

It will be noted that $J_{\frac{3}{2}}(\eta^*)$ tends to zero as $\eta^*\to 0$ and $J_{-\frac{3}{2}}(\eta^*)\to\infty$ as $\eta^*\to 0$, but the solution for $\overline{W}$ has no singularity at $\zeta^* = 0$, since the $\zeta^{*\frac{3}{2}}$ in (4·4) disposes of the singularity in $J_{-\frac{3}{2}}$ at $\zeta^* = 0$. Thus with a slight adjustment of the constants we can take

$$\overline{W} = A(\sin\eta^*-\eta^*\cos\eta^*)+B(\eta^*\sin\eta^*+\cos\eta^*), \tag{4·5}$$

where $\eta^* = i\zeta^*\,aR_v^{\frac{1}{2}}$. The boundary conditions upon $\overline{W}$ are $\overline{W} = 0$ at $\zeta = 0$ and $\zeta = 1$, thus if we write

$$\eta_0 = \frac{ifaR_v^{\frac{1}{2}}}{mR_H},\quad \eta_1 = i\left(1+\frac{f}{mR_H}\right)aR_v^{\frac{1}{2}}, \tag{4·6}$$

then

$$\left.\begin{aligned}A(\sin\eta_0-\eta_0\cos\eta_0)+B(\eta_0\sin\eta_0+\cos\eta_0) &= 0,\\ A(\sin\eta_1-\eta_1\cos\eta_1)+B(\eta_1\sin\eta_1+\cos\eta_1) &= 0.\end{aligned}\right\} \tag{4·7}$$

The consistency equation of the pair of equations (4·7) reduces to

$$(1+\eta_0\eta_1)\sin(\eta_0-\eta_1)-(\eta_0-\eta_1)\cos(\eta_0-\eta_1)=0, \tag{4·8}$$

and using (4·6) this becomes

$$\left\{1-\frac{fa^2R_v}{mR_H}\left(1+\frac{f}{mR_H}\right)\right\}\sin(\mathrm{i}aR_v^{\frac{1}{2}})-\mathrm{i}aR_v^{\frac{1}{2}}\cos(\mathrm{i}aR_v^{\frac{1}{2}})=0. \tag{4·9}$$

This represents the first relation between f, β, R_v and R_H. A second relation between these parameters is obtained by satisfying $u=0$ at $r=r_0$. This cannot be done exactly in the present case, since σ' and Ω' are now functions of z. If we again consider the case in which liquid occupies the whole region $0\leqslant r\leqslant r_0$, then the appropriate solution for u from (2·9) and (2·22), with $\mu=0$, is

$$2u=\left\{\frac{mJ_m(\beta r)}{\beta r}+\frac{\sigma'}{2\Omega'}J'_m(\beta r)\right\}\xi(z), \tag{4·10}$$

where $\sigma'=2\Omega(f+mR_H\zeta)$ and $\Omega'=\Omega(1+2R_H\zeta)$. If we disregard the ζ terms in the expressions of σ' and Ω' the second relation between the parameters is

$$\frac{mJ_m(\beta r_0)}{\beta r_0}+fJ'_m(\beta r_0)=0. \tag{4·11}$$

We first of all investigate the possibility of a solution of (4·9) and (4·11) in which f is purely real and small and β is a large imaginary value. Suppose we introduce λ as in (3·10), then with λ large (4·11) leads to

$$f+\frac{m}{\lambda}=0, \tag{4·12}$$

as in (3·13). Thus, since $a=\beta h=\mathrm{i}\lambda h/r_0$, (4·9) becomes

$$\left\{1+\frac{f\lambda^2h^2R_v}{mR_Hr_0^2}\left(1+\frac{f}{mR_H}\right)\right\}\sin\left(\frac{\lambda hR_v^{\frac{1}{2}}}{r_0}\right)-\frac{\lambda hR_v^{\frac{1}{2}}}{r_0}\cos\left(\frac{\lambda hR_v^{\frac{1}{2}}}{r_0}\right)=0, \tag{4·13}$$

and if we combine (4·12) and (4·13) and write, for simplicity,

$$E=\frac{hR_v^{\frac{1}{2}}}{r_0R_H},\quad x=\lambda R_HE, \tag{4·14}$$

then x has to be determined from

$$(1+E^2-xE)\sin x-x\cos x=0$$

or

$$\cot x=\frac{1+E^2}{x}-E. \tag{4·15}$$

It is evident that there are an infinite set of eigenvalues x_n which are the intersections of the two curves $y=\cot x$ and $y=(1+E^2)/x-E$. As in the previous section interest centres principally upon the first one. The curve $y=(1+E^2)/x-E$ crosses the axis of x at $x=E+E^{-1}>2$, and the first intersection of the two curves will therefore be near $x=2\pi$ so that $x_1=2\pi$, $x_n=n\pi$ $(n\geqslant 2)$. Thus the first eigenvalue of λ is $\lambda_1=2\pi/ER_H$, and thus the principal value of f is given by

$$f=-mER_H/2\pi; \tag{4·16}$$

the angular velocity ω of propagation of the wave system is given by

$$\frac{\omega}{\Omega} = \frac{2f}{m} = -\frac{R_H E}{\pi} = -\frac{hR_v^{\frac{1}{2}}}{\pi r_0}. \tag{4·17}$$

It was noted earlier that the boundary condition $u = 0$ at $r = r_0$ could not be exactly satisfied in this case, and it is of importance to determine how sensitive (4·17) is to this condition. Using (4·10) and satisfying $u = 0$ at $r = r_0$ at the height $\zeta = \frac{1}{2}$ leads to the relation

$$\frac{mJ_m(\beta r_0)}{\beta r_0} + \frac{f + \frac{1}{2}mR_H}{1+R_H} J'_m(\beta r_0) = 0$$

in place of (4·11). Thus the relation

$$\frac{f + \frac{1}{2}mR_H}{1+R_H} + \frac{m}{\lambda} = 0$$

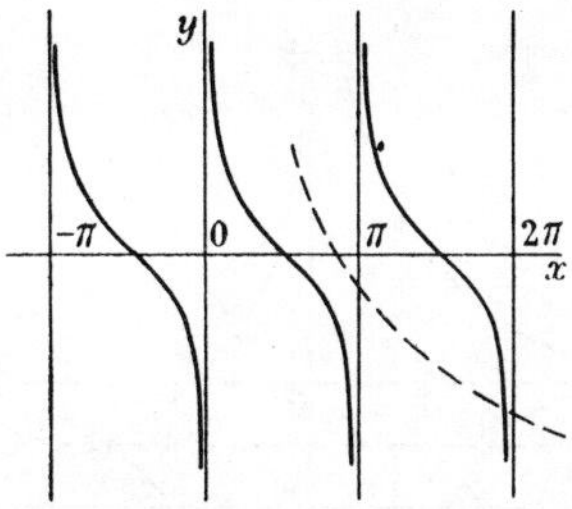

FIGURE 1. Graphs of $y = \cot x$, $y = (1+E^2)/x - E$.

replaces (4·12). Elimination of f between this equation and (4·13) leads to the relation

$$\cot x = \frac{1+E^2(1+R_H^2)}{x} - \tfrac{1}{4}x$$

in place of (4·15). The curve $y = \{1+E^2(1+R_H^2)\}/x - \frac{1}{4}x$ crosses the axis of x at

$$x = 2\{1+E^2(1+R_H^2)\}^{\frac{1}{2}},$$

and for the typical values of E and R_H in this problem this point is near the crossing point of the former curve. Thus the position of the first eigenvalue x_1 is little altered and x_1 is therefore near 2π, in fact, nearer 2π than the previous case. Thus the formulae (4·16) and (4·17) are not particularly sensitive to the boundary condition $u = 0$ at $r = r_0$.

So far we have demonstrated the existence of an infinite set of eigenvalues for f which correspond to purely imaginary values of β. The question now arises whether any other real eigenvalues of f exist or not. We deal now with the case in which f is real and β is real, and we shall assume that the second relation between f and β is (4·11). If f is small we can derive the analytical solution of (4·11) as follows. Let x_{sm} be the zeros of $J_m(x) = 0$ and assume that the solutions of

$$\frac{mJ_m(x)}{x} + fJ'_m(x) = 0\dagger$$

for small f are given by

$$x = x_{sm} + fy_{sm} + o(f^2),$$

† If we satisfy $u=0$, $r=r_0$ at a height $\zeta=\frac{1}{2}$, the same type of method may be applied, yielding a similar formulae for βr_0 as in (4·18) but with more complicated coefficients.

where y_{sm} is independent of f. Then by applying Taylor's theorem we get simply $y_{sm} = -x_{sm}/m$; thus the solutions of (4·11) are given by

$$\beta r_0 = x_{sm}\left(1-\frac{f}{m}\right), \tag{4·18}$$

ignoring terms of order f^2, where x_{sm} is a zero of $J_m(x) = 0$. Interest centres principally upon the first zero x_{1m} of $J_m(x) = 0$ and for future reference these are given in table 2; we make use later of the approximate result

$$x_{1m} = (\tfrac{3}{4}+\tfrac{1}{2}m)\,\pi.$$

TABLE 2

m	0	1	2	3	4	5	6
x_{1m}	2·4	3·8	5·1	6·4	7·6	8·8	9·9

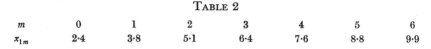

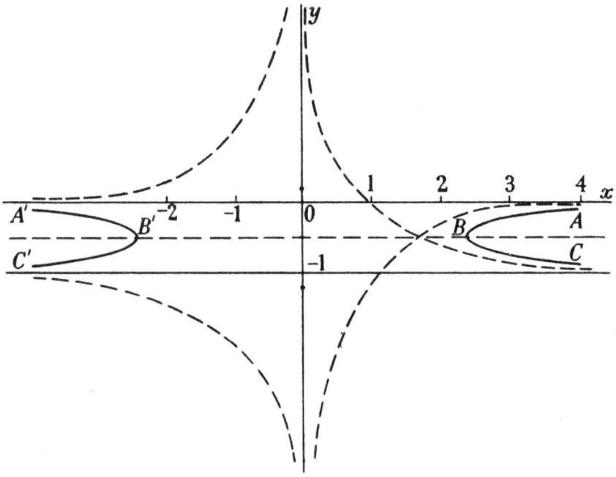

FIGURE 2

In the case of the first relation (4·9) we can now write

$$\left\{1-\frac{fa^2R_v}{mR_H}\left(1+\frac{f}{mR_H}\right)\right\} = aR_v^{\frac{1}{2}}\coth\,(aR_v^{\frac{1}{2}}). \tag{4·19}$$

If we write

$$y = f/mR_H, \quad x = aR_v^{\frac{1}{2}}, \tag{4·20}$$

equations (4·19) and (4·18) may be written more conveniently in the forms

$$1-yx^2(1+y) = x\coth x \tag{4·21}$$

and

$$x = \frac{hR_v^{\frac{1}{2}}x_{sm}}{r_0}(1-yR_H). \tag{4·22}$$

If the straight line (4·22) intersects the curve (4·21) a real eigen solution is possible in which both β and f are real. The curve defined by (4·21) is given in figure 2. It consists of two isolated points at (0, 0·26) and (0, −1·26), which are of no significance in the present problem, together with the two branches ABC, $A'B'C'$ which are asymptotic to $xy+1 = 0$ and $x(y+1) = 1$. The point B is (2·40, 0·5). The straight line (4·22) makes positive intercepts on the two axes, and it is evident that when the coefficients of x and y in this linear equation satisfy a particular relation the line will touch the branch ABC somewhere between B and C. The determination of this relation is of crucial importance for the stability problem; in general, this determination is quite a complicated procedure, but much of the difficulty can be avoided by using an approximate form of the curve (4·21) which is valid near the point B. If we take the origin of the curve ABC at B using the transformation $x = X+2{\cdot}40$, $y = Y-0{\cdot}5$, it is easily shown that the equation of the curve ABC in the neighbourhood of B is

$$Y^2 = a_1 X - b_1 X^2, \tag{4·23}$$

where $a_1 = 0{\cdot}0458$, $b_1 = 0{\cdot}0031$. The condition that $l_1 X + m_1 Y = n_1$ is tangent to this conic is

$$\tfrac{1}{4}a_1^2 m_1^2 = b_1 n_1^2 - a_1 l_1 n_1, \tag{4·24}$$

and in the present case the constants l_1, m_1 and n_1 are

$$\left.\begin{aligned} l_1 &= \frac{r_0}{hR_v^{\frac{1}{2}} x_{sm}}, \\ m_1 &= R_H, \\ n_1 &= 1+\tfrac{1}{2}R_H - \frac{2{\cdot}4 r_0}{hR_v^{\frac{1}{2}} x_{sm}}. \end{aligned}\right\} \tag{4·25}$$

It is easily shown that the tangent to the curve (4·23) which passes through the original O has an abscissa $X = 0{\cdot}3$ for the point of contact, and for the purposes of the present problem it is unnecessary to use the term $b_1 X^2$ in (4·23). Thus (4·24) can be simplified still further to

$$\tfrac{1}{4}a_1 m_1^2 + l_1 n_1 = 0, \tag{4·26}$$

and thus the desired criterion for contact of (4·21) and (4·22) is

$$0{\cdot}0115 \frac{h^2 R_v R_H^2 x_{sm}^2}{r_0^2} + \frac{hR_v^{\frac{1}{2}} x_{sm}}{r_0}(1+\tfrac{1}{2}R_H) - 2{\cdot}4 = 0. \tag{4·27}$$

The first term in the expression on the left-hand side is, in applications, considerably smaller than the others and can usually be ignored. As a general check upon this criterion it may be observed that when $R_H \to 0$ in (4·22) that the line becomes $x = hR_v^{\frac{1}{2}} x_{sm}/r_0$, and the condition for contact is then $hR_v^{\frac{1}{2}} x_{sm}/r_0 = 2{\cdot}4$. It follows from the above that no intersection of (4·22) and (4·21) will take place if

$$0{\cdot}0115 \frac{h^2 R_v R_H^2 x_{sm}^2}{r_0^2} + \frac{hR_v^{\frac{1}{2}} x_{sm}}{r_0}(1+\tfrac{1}{2}R_H) - 2{\cdot}4 < 0, \tag{4·28}$$

and this must be interpreted as the instability criterion for baroclinic flow, since, when the expression on the left-hand side of (4·28) is positive, real stable waves exist, and when negative the waves of this species have a complex value of f (see (4·33)). It is usually sufficient to deal with the instability criterion in the approximate form

$$\frac{hR_v^{\frac{1}{2}} x_{sm}}{r_0}(1+\tfrac{1}{2}R_H) < 2{\cdot}4. \tag{4·29}$$

This criterion differs very considerably from the barotropic criterion, namely,

$$\frac{hR_v^{\frac{1}{2}}}{r_0} < \tfrac{1}{2}R_H, \tag{4·30}$$

not only in the arrangement of its parameters h, r_0, R_v and R_H but also in an entirely new feature, namely, its dependence upon wave number through x_{sm}.

If we replace R_H and R_v in (4·29) by their original expressions in terms of Θ_H, Θ_V and Ω, etc., the instability criterion may be written in the form

$$\frac{h}{r_0}x_{sm}\left\{1+\frac{g\alpha h\Theta_H}{8\rho_0\Omega^2}\right\} < 2{\cdot}4\left(\frac{4\rho_0}{g\alpha\Theta_V}\right)^{\frac{1}{2}}\Omega, \tag{4·31}$$

and in this formula interest centres principally upon x_{1m}, which represents the major mode of the horizontal wave. It will be noted from the table of values of x_{1m} given earlier that x_{1m} increases steadily with m and, from (4·31), it will be noted that Ω increases with m. Alternatively, we can state that wave number $m = 0$ becomes unstable at $\Omega = \Omega_0$, wave number $m = 1$ becomes unstable at $\Omega = \Omega_1$, where $\Omega_1 > \Omega_0$, wave number $m = 2$ at $\Omega = \Omega_2 > \Omega_1 > \Omega_0$, and so on. This is similar to the behaviour in the Fultz experiment as described in the introduction to this paper. It may be noted also from (4·31) that if the heating constants $h\Theta_H$ and Θ_V can be maintained constant and Ω and r_0 are also kept constant, then, for variable h, stability will result if hx_{1m} is kept constant. Thus if h increases, x_{1m} must decrease, and hence m must decrease. In other words, if the depth alone is increased, smaller and smaller wave numbers can possibly appear. The demonstration of this particular feature has been given to the author by Hide, and this appears to strengthen the claim of the above baroclinic instability formula. It should be mentioned, however, that the relation hx_{1m} = constant used above is likely to be inexact, since Θ_V and $h\Theta_H$ are not under rigid control. In view of this qualitative agreement it is worth while to investigate (4·31) quantitatively, and if we use the typical values $h = 3$ cm, $r_0 = 15$ cm, $\Theta_H = 0{\cdot}16$, $\Theta_V = 1{\cdot}45$, $\rho_0 = 1$, $g = 10^3$, $\alpha = 2{\cdot}5\times10^{-4}$ and $\Omega = \Omega_c = 0{\cdot}3\,\mathrm{s}^{-1}$ (3 rev/min, approximately) we can write (4·31) in the form

TABLE 3

Ω/Ω_c	$\frac{5}{3}$	$\frac{3}{2}$	$\frac{4}{3}$	1	$\frac{2}{3}$	$\frac{1}{2}$
$\dfrac{12(\Omega/\Omega_c)}{1+0{\cdot}15(\Omega_c/\Omega)^2}$	18·6	17·5	14·5	10	6	3·6

$$\tfrac{1}{5}x_{1m}\left\{1+0{\cdot}15\left(\frac{\Omega_c}{\Omega}\right)^2\right\} < 2{\cdot}4\left(\frac{\Omega}{\Omega_c}\right). \tag{4·32}$$

From table 3 we deduce that $m = 0$ becomes unstable at approximately 1·3 rev/min, $m = 1$ becomes unstable at 1·5 rev/min, $m = 2$ at 1·9 rev/min, $m = 3$ at 2·1 rev/min, $m = 4$ at 2·4 rev/min, $m = 5$ at 2·6 rev/min, and so on. The experimental range is considerably wider than this, and thus the quantitative agreement is only fair.

We now investigate the formula for the wave velocity in the present case assuming that the wave exists and is stable. Suppose we use (4·23) in the approximate form

$$Y^2 = a_1X,$$

and we take the straight line to be $l_1 X + m_1 Y = n_1$, where l_1, m_1, n_1 are defined in (4·25). We then have

$$l_1 Y^2 + a_1 m_1 Y - a_1 n_1 = 0,$$

and solving this equation for Y $(= 0·5 + f/mR_H)$ we get the wave-velocity formula

$$\frac{f}{mR_H} + 0·5 = \frac{1}{2l_1}\{-a_1 m_1 \pm (a_1^2 m_1^2 + 4a_1 l_1 n_1)^{\frac{1}{2}}\}.$$

We have seen that the term $a_1^2 m_1^2$ is small compared with $4a_1 l_1 n_1$, and a sufficiently accurate formula is given by

$$\frac{f}{mR_H} + 0·5 = -\tfrac{1}{2}a_1 \frac{m_1}{l_1} \pm a_1^{\frac{1}{2}} \left(\frac{n_1}{l_1}\right)^{\frac{1}{2}},$$

or, written out in full,

$$\frac{f}{mR_H} + 0·5 = -0·0229 \frac{h}{r_0} R_v^{\frac{1}{2}} R_H x_{sm} \pm 0·2140 \left\{\frac{(1+\frac{1}{2}R_H)\, hR_v^{\frac{1}{2}} x_{sm}}{r_0} - 2·4\right\}^{\frac{1}{2}}. \tag{4·33}$$

It is not possible at this stage to discuss this formula in its relation to the experiment, since the parameter R_v is absent in Hide's work, but we shall return to this point in the next section.

The existence of two types of wave forms has been demonstrated, the first type possessing the wave-velocity formula (4·16), the second type possessing the wave-velocity formula (4·33). In the waves of the first type there is no suggestion of instability and this seems to be a feature of the second type only. It is possible that other wave types exist corresponding to complex values of β, but there is every likelihood that such wave types would always produce complex values of f, so that permanent waves of this species are unlikely.

The derivation of the velocity, pressure and temperature fields in the baroclinic case will be done only for the second type wave whose wave-velocity formula is (4·33). Using (4·5), (4·6) and (4·7) it follows that $\overline{W}$ can be expressed in the form

$$\overline{W} = \frac{A}{2R_H \Omega r_0 a}\left\{\left[1 - \frac{fa^2 R_v}{mR_H}(\zeta - \zeta_0)\right] \sinh(\zeta a R_v^{\frac{1}{2}}) - \zeta a R_v^{\frac{1}{2}} \cosh(\zeta a R_v^{\frac{1}{2}})\right\}, \tag{4·34}$$

and if A is treated as a real constant the solution for w can be taken in the form

$$w = A\left\{\left[1 - \frac{fa^2 R_v}{mR_H}(\zeta - \zeta_0)\right] \sinh(\zeta a R_v^{\frac{1}{2}}) - \zeta a R_v^{\frac{1}{2}} \cosh(\zeta a R_v^{\frac{1}{2}})\right\} J_m(\beta r)\cos(m\phi + \sigma t). \tag{4·35}$$

Using the relation $\eta = -\dfrac{2}{a}\dfrac{\mathrm{d}W}{\mathrm{d}\zeta}$ it then follows that

$$\eta = 2AaR_v(\zeta - \zeta_0)\left\{\frac{faR_v^{\frac{1}{2}}}{mR_H}\cosh(\zeta a R_v^{\frac{1}{2}}) + \sinh(\zeta a R_v^{\frac{1}{2}})\right\}, \tag{4·36}$$

and this function possesses a zero at $\zeta = \zeta_0$, so that ξ, which is defined in terms of η by the relation

$$\xi = -\frac{(1 + 2R_H \zeta)}{mR_H(\zeta - \zeta_0)}\eta, \tag{4·37}$$

is finite at all heights in the liquid. Using (2·9) and (2·10) it then follows that the solutions for u and v are

$$u = -\tfrac{1}{2}\eta \left\{\frac{1 + 2R_H \zeta}{f + mR_H \zeta}\frac{mJ_m(\beta r)}{\beta r} + J'_m(\beta r)\right\}\cos(m\phi + \sigma t) \tag{4·38}$$

and
$$v = \tfrac{1}{2}\eta\left\{\frac{1+2R_H\zeta}{f+mR_H\zeta}J'_m(\beta r)+\frac{mJ_m}{\beta r}\right\}\sin(m\phi+\sigma t). \tag{4·39}$$

It will be noted that $\eta>0$ in the main part of the liquid if $A>0$, and thus the velocity field is similar to that in the barotropic case apart from the zonal component v which has altered character near $r=r_0$. We have for P the formula

$$P=\frac{\rho_0\Omega i}{\beta mR_H}\{(f+mR_H\zeta)^2-(1+2R_H\zeta)^2\}\frac{\eta}{(\zeta-\zeta_0)},$$

and in order to be consistent with the assumption made concerning λ_1 early in this section, it is necessary to treat the term within the brackets as negative in sign. The complete formula for the pressure is then

$$p=-PJ_m(\beta r)\sin(m\phi+\sigma t), \tag{4·40}$$

so that $m\phi=\frac{1}{2}\pi$ is a line along which p is a maximum and $m\phi=-\frac{1}{2}\pi$ a line along which p is a minimum at $t=0$.

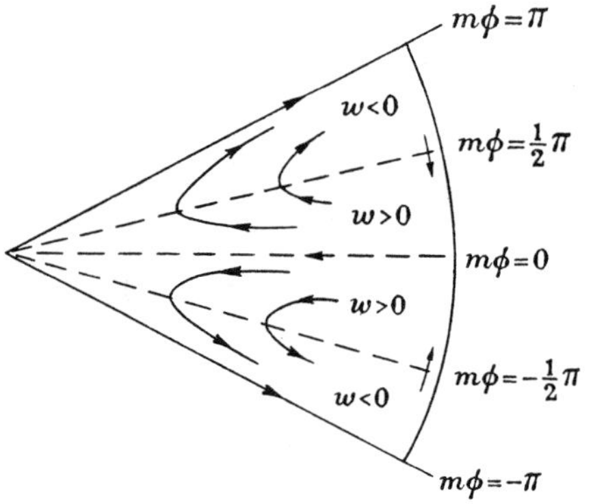

FIGURE 3

Since the temperature function τ is effectively given by $(1/g\alpha)\,(\mathrm{d}P/\mathrm{d}z)$ it follows that in the main body of the liquid the temperature distribution is such that $m\phi=\frac{1}{2}\pi$ is a line along which the temperature is at a maximum and $m\phi=-\frac{1}{2}\pi$ a line along which the temperature is a minimum. This distribution of temperature is more readily compared with W. H. Dines's statistical results (Brunt 1939) than the barotropic temperature results. The continued association of low pressure at $\zeta=0$ with high pressure in the main body of liquid above is still in disagreement with these statistical results, and it is unlikely therefore that this can be corrected by any theory which ignores the viscous stresses at the base of the liquid.

It is quite evident that the results which have emerged so far from the modified baroclinic theory are considerably closer to the experiment than the barotropic theory, but it is unlikely that good quantitative agreement can be attained until the singularity ζ_4 is retained in the discussion of the differential equation (2·49). The influence of viscosity and conductivity upon these results is a little obscure and this will be considered now. The differential equation (4·1) can be solved in the form (4·5) when s is given by (2·37) and s' is identically equal to s, that is if $K = R$. It is convenient to make this assumption $K = R$ in order to find out in which direction viscosity and conductivity influence the results. Hence the only change which need be made in (4·9) is to replace the term f/mR_H by

$$-\zeta_1 = \frac{f}{mR_H} - \frac{ia^2}{2RmR_H}.$$

Thus (4·9) becomes

$$\{1+\zeta_1 a^2 R_v(1-\zeta_1)\}\sin(iaR_v^{\frac{1}{2}}) - iaR_v^{\frac{1}{2}}\cos(iaR_v^{\frac{1}{2}}) = 0, \tag{4·41}$$

where ζ_1 is defined in (2·50). Equation (4·11), which is the second relation between β and f, is changed in the same way in this viscous case. It is now quite evident that the solution for f can be obtained by replacing f in (4·16) and (4·33) by $f - ia^2/2R$. When this is done the wave forms for which the frequency equation is (4·16) are unstable, since a^2 in this case is negative. On the other hand, those wave forms which have (4·33) as frequency equation are normally damped waves, since a^2 in this case is positive. In this latter case the detailed pattern is as follows:

(a) when $(1+\frac{1}{2}R_H)\frac{h}{r_0}R_v^{\frac{1}{2}}x_{sm} \geqslant 2·4$, all waves are damped;

(b) when $(1+\frac{1}{2}R_H)\frac{h}{r_0}R_v^{\frac{1}{2}}x_{sm} < 2·4$,

all waves will be damped
one wave is damped, other neutral
one wave is damped, other undamped

if $\frac{a^2}{2R} \gtreqless 0·214\left\{2·4 - \frac{h}{r_0}R_v^{\frac{1}{2}}x_{sm}(1+\frac{1}{2}R_H)\right\}$.

Interest centres principally upon the neutral wave, since the waves observed in the experiment can persist as long as the requisite steady conditions of temperature and rotation are maintained.

5. The relation between Θ_V and Θ_H

The basic temperature field introduced in (1·15) contains two parameters Θ_V and Θ_H which up to this point have been assumed to be quite independent of one another. In a recent paper Lorenz (1953) has considered this particular point and has shown that Θ_V and Θ_H are in fact linearly related, and it is proposed here to derive this relation by a method which is a slight modification of that due to Lorenz. If a uniqueness result were available for a problem of this type then one might expect such a relation to exist, since the mean horizontal gradient and mean vertical gradient of temperature would both be linearly related to the imposed mean horizontal temperature gradient on the boundary; however, since this approach is not possible we proceed as follows.

We introduce non-dimensional variables into equations (1·1) to (1·6) by writing

$$\left.\begin{aligned} t_1 = t/\Omega, \quad r_1 = r_0 r, \quad z_1 = hz, \quad \phi_1 = \Omega t + \phi, \\ u_1 = r_0\Omega u, \quad v_1 = r_0\Omega v, \quad w_1 = h\Omega w, \\ \rho_1 = \rho_0\rho, \quad T_1 = T_0 + (\Delta T_H)\,T, \quad p_1 = \rho_0 r_0^2\Omega^2 p, \end{aligned}\right\} \tag{5·1}$$

where the original variable has suffix 1 and the unsuffixed symbol is the non-dimensional variable. The equations (1·1) to (1·6) then become

$$\frac{du}{dt}-\frac{v^2}{r}=-\frac{1}{\rho}\frac{\partial p}{\partial r}+\frac{1}{\rho R}\left\{\frac{\partial^2 u}{\partial z^2}+\frac{h^2}{r_0^2}\left(\frac{\partial^2 u}{\partial r^2}+\frac{1}{r}\frac{\partial u}{\partial r}+\frac{1}{r^2}\frac{\partial^2 u}{\partial \theta^2}-\frac{2}{r^2}\frac{\partial v}{\partial \phi}\right)\right\}, \tag{5·2}$$

$$\frac{dv}{dt}+\frac{uv}{r}=-\frac{1}{\rho r}\frac{\partial p}{\partial \phi}+\frac{1}{\rho R}\left\{\frac{\partial^2 v}{\partial z^2}+\frac{h^2}{r_0^2}\left(\frac{\partial^2 v}{\partial r^2}+\frac{1}{r}\frac{\partial v}{\partial r}+\frac{1}{r^2}\frac{\partial^2 v}{\partial \theta^2}+\frac{2}{r^2}\frac{\partial u}{\partial \phi}\right)\right\}, \tag{5·3}$$

$$\frac{h^2}{r^2}\frac{dw}{dt}=-\frac{1}{\rho}\frac{\partial p}{\partial z}-\frac{gh}{r_0^2\Omega^2}+\frac{h^2}{\rho r_0^2 R}\left\{\frac{\partial^2 w}{\partial z^2}+\frac{h^2}{r_0^2}\left(\frac{\partial^2 w}{\partial r^2}+\frac{1}{r}\frac{\partial w}{\partial r}+\frac{1}{r^2}\frac{\partial^2 w}{\partial \theta^2}\right)\right\}, \tag{5·4}$$

$$\rho=1-\frac{\alpha\Delta T_H}{\rho_0}T, \tag{5·5}$$

$$-\frac{\alpha\Delta T_H}{\rho_0}\frac{dT}{dt}+\rho\,\mathrm{div}\,\mathbf{V}=0, \tag{5·6}$$

$$\rho\frac{dT}{dt}=\frac{1}{K}\left\{\frac{\partial^2 T}{\partial z^2}+\frac{h^2}{r_0^2}\left(\frac{\partial^2 T}{\partial r^2}+\frac{1}{r}\frac{\partial T}{\partial r}+\frac{1}{r^2}\frac{\partial^2 T}{\partial \theta^2}\right)\right\}, \tag{5·7}$$

where ΔT_H is the temperature difference between $z=0$, $r=0$ and $z=0$, $r=1$, and R and K are the Reynolds number and Péclet number already defined in (2·31). These six equations contain the four parameters h/r_0, R, K, $\epsilon=r_0^2\Omega^2/gh$ explicitly, and when the ϵ is combined with $\alpha\Delta T_H/\rho_0$ a fifth parameter enters, namely,

$$R_H^*=g\alpha h(\Delta T_H)/\rho_0 r_0^2\Omega^2. \tag{5·8}$$

From (2·31) it follows that $R_H^*=2R_H$, but it is more convenient to work with R_H^* in the present section. This parameter is the Rossby number of the problem. In the present problem, where h/r_0 is usually considerably less than unity, it may be noted that the neglect of the terms in (5·2) to (5·7) which involve h^2/r_0^2 leads to a consistent set of equations provided the exact viscous and conduction conditions at $r=1$ are suitably relaxed. The neglect of such terms in the equations is the same as saying that the solutions for the velocity, pressure, density and temperature fields are expanded in ascending powers of the parameter h^2/r_0^2, and we retain here only the leading terms of the expansions. This method of procedure exposes the important features of shallow systems, namely, that the vertical gradients of velocity are of considerably greater importance than the horizontal gradients, while the hydrostatic equation is satisfied in the first approximation. The equations (5·2) to (5·7) now become

$$\rho\left(\frac{du}{dt}-\frac{v^2}{r}\right)=-\frac{\partial p}{\partial r}+\frac{1}{R}\frac{\partial^2 u}{\partial z^2}, \tag{5·9}$$

$$\rho\left(\frac{dv}{dt}+\frac{uv}{r}\right)=-\frac{\partial p}{r\,\partial \phi}+\frac{1}{R}\frac{\partial^2 v}{\partial z^2}, \tag{5·10}$$

$$\frac{\partial p}{\partial z}=-\frac{gh}{r_0^2\Omega^2}+R_H^*T, \tag{5·11}$$

$$\rho=1-\left(\frac{r_0^2\Omega^2}{gh}\right)R_H^*T, \tag{5·12}$$

$$\left(\frac{r_0^2\Omega^2}{gh}\right)R_H^*\frac{dT}{dt}=\rho\,\mathrm{div}\,\mathbf{V}, \tag{5·13}$$

$$\rho\frac{dT}{dt}=\frac{1}{K}\frac{\partial^2 T}{\partial z^2}. \tag{5·14}$$

It is now evident that expansions of the velocity vector **V**, pressure p, density ρ and temperature T are permissible in ascending powers of the parameter R_H^*, since this parameter is not associated with the highest order derivatives. Accordingly, we assume that the complete solution of the above system of equations is expressible in the form

$$\left.\begin{aligned} u &= R_H^* u_1 + R_H^{*2} u_2 + \ldots, & \rho &= 1 + R_H^* \rho_1 + R_H^{*2} \rho_2 + \ldots, \\ v &= r + R_H^* v_1 + R_H^* v_2 + \ldots, & T &= \tau_0 + R_H^* \tau_1 + R_H^{*2} \tau_2 + \ldots, \\ w &= R_H^* w_1 + R_H^{*2} w_2 + \ldots, & p &= p_0 + R_H^* p_1 + R_H^{*2} p_2 + \ldots, \end{aligned}\right\} \tag{5·15}$$

where it is assumed that the terms with zero suffix represent the state of solid rotation, and where all the suffixed quantities are independent of the parameter R_H^*. We now substitute these expansions in the equations (5·9) to (5·14) and equate to zero the coefficients of successive powers of R_H^*.

We have then the following system of equations:

Terms independent of R_H^*:

$$r = \frac{\partial p_0}{\partial r}, \quad 0 = \frac{\partial p_0}{\partial \phi}, \quad -\frac{gh}{r_0^2 \Omega^2} = \frac{\partial p_0}{\partial z}, \quad 0 = \frac{\partial^2 \tau_0}{\partial z^2}. \tag{5·16}$$

These equations give the usual solution for p_0, namely,

$$p_0 = \tfrac{1}{2} r^2 - \frac{gh}{r_0^2 \Omega^2} z,$$

and τ_0 is evidently a linear function of z. If we impose upon T the condition that $\partial T/\partial z$ must vanish at $z = 1$ (see p. 35), which implies that there is no flow of heat across the free surface, then it follows that the only possible form of solution for τ_0 is

$$\tau_0 = \tau_0(r), \tag{5·17}$$

where the right-hand side is a function of r only. This implies that $\partial \tau_0/\partial z$ is zero everywhere in the liquid, and thus there is no heat transfer in the vertical direction associated with this term. A side condition of the form $d\tau_0/dr = 0$ at $r = 1$ can be imposed upon τ_0 in order to ensure that there is no heat flow across the side boundary into the liquid. It may be shown that for a solution of this kind $\partial \tau_2/\partial z$ does not vanish at $z = 0$, and thus the above temperature field will be related to the temperature distribution on $z = 0$. We impose upon $\tau_0(r)$ the condition

$$\tau_0(1) - \tau_0(0) = 1, \tag{5·18}$$

which ensures that the difference in temperature between $z = 0$, $r = 0$ and $z = 0$, $r = 1$ is ΔT_H.

Terms of the first order in R_H:

$$\frac{\partial u_1}{\partial t} - 2v_1 + \epsilon r \tau_0 = -\frac{\partial p_1}{\partial r} + \frac{1}{R} \frac{\partial^2 u_1}{\partial z^2}, \tag{5·19}$$

$$\frac{\partial v_1}{\partial t} + 2u_1 = -\frac{\partial p_1}{r \partial \phi} + \frac{1}{R} \frac{\partial^2 v_1}{\partial z^2}, \tag{5·20}$$

$$\frac{\partial p_1}{\partial z} = \tau_0(r), \tag{5·21}$$

$$\frac{1}{r} \frac{\partial}{\partial r}(r u_1) + \frac{\partial v_1}{r \partial \phi} + \frac{\partial w_1}{\partial z} = 0, \tag{5·22}$$

$$\frac{\partial \tau_1}{\partial t} + u_1 \tau_0'(r) = \frac{1}{K} \frac{\partial^2 \tau_1}{\partial z^2}. \tag{5·23}$$

In order to derive the relation between the mean gradients of temperature in the vertical and in the horizontal it is sufficient at this stage to consider the steady fields, and the terms in $\partial/\partial t$ and $\partial/\partial\phi$ can be ignored for our present purpose. Equation (5·21) can be solved immediately and gives

$$p_1 = z\tau_0(r) + p_1^*(r), \tag{5·24}$$

where $p_1^*(r)$ is a function of r only. We can now use equations (5·19) and (5·20) to determine u_1 and v_1 in terms of τ_0, $p_1^*(r)$, etc., and we obtain

$$2v_1 = \frac{\partial p_1}{\partial r} + \epsilon r\tau_0 - \frac{1}{R}\frac{\partial^2 u_1}{\partial z^2}; \tag{5·25}$$

hence

$$4u_1 = \frac{1}{R}\frac{\partial^2}{\partial z^2}\left\{\frac{\partial p_1}{\partial r} + \epsilon r\tau_0 - \frac{1}{R}\frac{\partial^2 u_1}{\partial z^2}\right\}$$

$$= -\frac{1}{R^2}\frac{\partial^4 u_1}{\partial z^4}. \tag{5·26}$$

The equation of continuity (5·22), in its symmetrical form with $\partial v_1/\partial\phi$ zero, shows that $\partial w_1/\partial z$ satisfies the same equation as u_1. The boundary conditions to be satisfied are $w = 0$ at $z = 0$ and $z = 1$, $u = 0$ at $z = 0$ and $\partial u/\partial z = 0$ at $z = 1$. This problem is precisely the same as that solved in Davies (1953, p. 101), where it is shown that

$$ru_1 = -\frac{\partial \psi_1}{\partial z}, \quad rw_1 = \frac{\partial \psi_1}{\partial r} \tag{5·27}$$

and

$$\psi_1 = F_0(r)\, G_0(z)$$

$$= F_0(r)\left\{1 - \frac{\sin\omega z \sinh\omega z}{s_1 S_1} - \frac{\sin\omega(1-z)\sinh\omega(1-z)}{s_1 S_1}\right.$$

$$- \frac{S_1^2 s_1 + S_1 C_1 c_1 + s_1 c_1 C_1}{S s_1(S_1 C_1 - s_1 c_1)}\sin\omega z \sinh\omega(1-z)$$

$$\left. - \frac{s_1^2 S_1 + c_1 S_1 C_1 + s_1 c_1 C_1}{S_1 s_1(S_1 C_1 - s_1 c_1)}\sin\omega(1-z)\sinh\omega(1-z)\right\}. \tag{5·28}$$

Here $\omega^2 = R$, $S_1 = \sinh\omega$, $C_1 = \cosh\omega$, $s_1 = \sin\omega$, $c_1 = \cos\omega$ and $F_0(r)$ is an arbitrary function of r. The solution for v_1 is then given by

$$2v_1 = z\tau_0'(r) + \frac{\mathrm{d}p_1^*}{\mathrm{d}r} + \epsilon r\tau_0 + \frac{1}{Rr}F_0(r)\, G_0'''(z). \tag{5·29}$$

If v_1 is to vanish at $z = 0$ then we must have

$$-\frac{1}{Rr}F_0(r)\, G_0'''(0) = \frac{\mathrm{d}p_1^*}{\mathrm{d}r} + \epsilon r\tau_0, \tag{5·30}$$

and if $\partial v_1/\partial z$ is to vanish at $z = 1$, then

$$-\tau_0'(r) = \frac{1}{Rr}F_0(r)\, G_0^{\text{iv}}(1). \tag{5·31}$$

These two equations determine p_1^* and $F_0(r)$ in terms of $\tau_0(r)$. Interest centres principally upon $F_0(r)$. It is shown in Davies (1953) that $G_0^{\text{iv}}(1) \sim 4\omega^4 = 4R^2$ when R is sufficiently large, and thus we have

$$F_0(r) = -\frac{1}{4R}r\tau_0'(r). \tag{5·32}$$

Thus when $\tau_0(r)$ is prescribed the stream function ψ_1 is uniquely determined, and we can now proceed to the solution of (5·23) which in the steady case can be written in the form

$$\frac{\partial^2\tau_1}{\partial z^2} = Ku_1\tau_0'(r)$$
$$= K\tau_0'(r)\left\{-\frac{1}{r}F_0(r)\,G_0'(z)\right\}. \tag{5·33}$$

The first integration of this with respect to z leads to

$$\frac{\partial\tau_1}{\partial z} = -\frac{K}{r}\tau_0'(r)\,F_0(r)\,G_0(z)+\Psi(r), \tag{5·34}$$

and, taking $\partial\tau_1/\partial z = 0$ at $z = 1$, it follows that $\Psi(r)\equiv 0$. The function $\partial\tau_1/\partial z$ then vanishes also at $z = 0$, but in the main portion of the liquid lying outside the boundary layers the function $G_0(z)$ has been shown in Davies (1953) to be $1+o(e^{-\omega z})$, hence in general

$$\frac{\partial\tau_1}{\partial z} = -\frac{K}{r}\tau_0'(r)\,F_0(r),$$

so that, using (5·32),
$$\frac{\partial\tau_1}{\partial z} = \frac{K}{4R}\tau_0'^2(r). \tag{5·35}$$

This result is in general agreement with that obtained by Lorenz. The vertical lapse rate of temperature is now given by

$$\frac{\partial T_1}{\partial z_1} = \frac{\Delta T_H}{h}R_H^*\frac{\partial\tau_1}{\partial z} = R_H^*\frac{\Delta T_H}{h}\left\{\frac{K}{4R}\tau_0'^2(r)\right\}, \tag{5·36}$$

and the horizontal lapse rate of temperature is given by

$$\frac{\partial T_1}{\partial r_1} = \frac{\Delta T_H}{r_0}\tau_0'(r). \tag{5·37}$$

In each of these expressions there will be further terms involving powers of the parameter R_H^* but, since this is small, it is unnecessary to take the investigation further.

Since the horizontal derivatives of velocity and temperature have been ignored with the h^2/r_0^2 terms it is not possible to define the function $\tau_0(r)$ precisely, and we may restate its qualitative properties, namely, $\tau_0'(1) = 0$, $\tau_0(1)-\tau_0(0) = 1$. When the first of these properties is satisfied it will be noted from (5·29) to (5·31) that $v_1(1) = 0$. Likewise $u_1(1) = 0$, and the only condition which cannot be satisfied is $w = 0$ at $r = 1$, although this one is evidently impossible to satisfy from the nature of our approach.

If we compare (5·35) and (5·37) with the assumed temperature distribution (1·15) we see that this assumed basic temperature field is not consistent with the above results, although it must be borne in mind that they refer to a mean state in the body of the liquid and well away from the boundaries. It is sufficient here to compare (5·36), (5·37) and (1·15) in their average values. Hence if we use a bar to denote an average value of a quantity over the range $r = 0$ to $r = 1$, so that

$$\bar{\phi} = \int_{r=0}^{r=1}\phi(r)\,r\,dr, \tag{5·38}$$

it then follows that
$$\frac{\Theta_V}{\frac{1}{2}r_0\,\Theta_H} = \frac{\partial T_1}{\partial z_1}\bigg/\frac{\partial T_1}{\partial r_1} = \frac{r_0}{h}R_H^*\frac{K}{4R}\frac{\overline{\tau_0'^2(r)}}{\overline{\tau_0'(r)}},$$

and hence
$$\frac{\Theta_V}{h\Theta_H} = \frac{1}{8}\frac{r_0^2}{h^2}R_H^*\frac{K}{R}\frac{\overline{\tau_0'^2(r)}}{\overline{\tau_0'(r)}}. \tag{5·39}$$

Using the definitions of R_H and R_v in (2·31) and noting that $R_H^* = 2R_H$, it now follows that
$$\frac{h^2R_v}{r_0^2} = \tfrac{1}{4}R_H^2\frac{K}{R}\frac{\overline{\tau_0'^2(r)}}{\overline{\tau_0'(r)}}, \tag{5·40}$$

and thus we see that the parameters $hR_v^{\frac{1}{2}}/r_0$ and R_H are on the average related linearly. This is the precise result which is needed to bring the present theory in line with the experiments. It remains now to make quantitative comparisons.

If we choose $\tau_0'(r) = 4(r-r^3)$ and $\tau_0(r) = 2r^2-r^4$, then it is easily shown that $\overline{\tau_0'(r)} = \frac{8}{15}$, $\overline{\tau_0'^2(r)} = \frac{2}{3}$, so that
$$\frac{h^2R_v}{r_0^2} = \tfrac{5}{16}R_H^2\frac{K}{R}. \tag{5·41}$$

A more precise choice of $\tau_0'(r)$ can be made by fitting a curve to the values of V_0 given in table 1, since V_0 is proportional to the radial temperature gradient, but this makes a negligible change in the result (5·41). Since $K/R = \mu c_v/k = \sigma =$ Prandtl number, we have, using the value $\sigma = 7$ which is valid for water at a temperature of about 18° C,
$$\frac{h^2R_v}{r_0^2} = 2{\cdot}2R_H^2,$$

and hence
$$\frac{hR_v^{\frac{1}{2}}}{r_0} = 1{\cdot}5R_H, \tag{5·42}$$

approximately.

It must be emphasized that the results (5·41) and (5·42) have been derived on the assumption that the flow is symmetrical about the axis. When there are waves present, it is most probable that the mean temperature fields will be altered; in the few experimental temperature distributions which are available to the author this is certainly true. Thus it is likely that the application of (5·42) to the stability formula (4·29) will produce results which are likely to be in increasing error as m, the wave number, increases. The determination of the modified formula which replaces (5·41) in the case of asymmetry is a difficult problem and one which will not be discussed any further here.

6. Comparison of theoretical and experimental results

If we substitute for $hR_v^{\frac{1}{2}}/r_0$ from (5·42) in (3·17) we obtain the following barotropic formula for the velocity of propagation of waves:
$$\frac{\omega}{\Omega} = 0{\cdot}9R_H \tag{6·1}$$

approximately, and this has to be compared with Hide's result (3·24). It is clear that this barotropic formula gives no indication of any instability and gives a result which is about seven times too large for the angular velocity of the waves.

If we use the baroclinic results we obtain, from (4·29),

$$x_{sm} R_H(1+\tfrac{1}{2}R_H) < 1\cdot 6 \tag{6·2}$$

as the criterion for instability. This criterion is then similar in form to that obtained from the experiments; the numerical results are given in table 4. No detailed experimental results are available to check table 4, but the results vary in the right direction and are substantially of the correct order of magnitude. These results refer expressly to the problem in which the liquid occupies the region $0 \leqslant r \leqslant r_0$. Experimental results for the annulus case in which the liquid occupies a region $r_i \leqslant r \leqslant r_0$, with $r_i = 2\cdot 45$ cm and $r_0 = 4\cdot 90$ cm, have been kindly supplied by Fultz in a private communication, and it is worth while at this stage to derive the theoretical results in this case.

TABLE 4

wave number, m	0	1	2	3	4	5	6
value of R_H when m-wave becomes unstable	0·56	0·40	0·29	0·24	0·20	0·17	0·15

It may easily be verified that all the analysis of § 4 applies to the annulus case provided the quantity x_{sm} in (4·18) which appears as the sth zero of $J_m(x) = 0$ is suitably modified. It is necessary to replace x_{sm} by $r_0 \beta_{sm}$, where $\beta = \beta_{sm}$ is the sth zero of the equation

$$J_m(\beta r_0)\, Y_m(\beta r_i) - J_m(\beta r_i)\, Y_m(\beta r_0) = 0, \tag{6·3}$$

and with this definition of β_{sm} the instability criterion (4·29) becomes

$$h\beta_{sm} R_v^{\frac{1}{2}}(1+\tfrac{1}{2}R_H) < 2\cdot 4. \tag{6·4}$$

As before, interest centres upon the first zero β_{1m}, and this can be determined with sufficient accuracy by substituting in (6·3) the asymptotic expansions of J_m and Y_m. This leads to the result

$$\beta_{1m} = \frac{\pi}{r_0 - r_i}\left\{1 + \frac{(4m^2-1)\,(r_0-r_i)^2}{8\pi^2 r_0 r_i} + \ldots\right\}. \tag{6·5}$$

The methods used in § 5 apply to the annulus case except that the averaging process given in (5·38) is now defined as follows:

$$\overline{\phi} = \int_{(r_i/r_0)}^{1} \phi(r)\, r\, \mathrm{d}r, \tag{6·6}$$

while $\tau_0(r)$ is a function satisfying $\tau_0'(1) = \tau_0'(r_i/r_0) = 0$ and $\tau_0(1) - \tau_0(r_i/r_0) = 1$. Writing $x = r_i/r_0$ and choosing $\tau_0'(r) = 12(r-x)\,(1-r^2)/(1-x)^3\,(3+x)$, it follows that the appropriate generalization of the result (5·41) is

$$\frac{h^2 R_v}{r_0^2} = \tfrac{3}{14} R_H^2 \frac{K}{R} \frac{(1-x)\,(35+47x+25x^2+5x^3)}{(3+x)\,(8-7x+3x^2+3x^3+3x^4)}. \tag{6·7}$$

Combining (6·4) and (6·7) we obtain the generalization of (6·2) to the annulus case.

When $r_i = \frac{1}{2}r_0 = 2\cdot 45$ cm, which is the case investigated by Fultz, (6·4) becomes

$$R_H(1+\tfrac{1}{2}R_H) < \frac{1\cdot 6}{\beta_{sm} r_0}, \tag{6·8}$$

taking $K/R = 7$ as for (5·42). Fultz uses the Rossby number Ro_T^* which is related to R_H by

$$Ro_T^* = (1+x)\, R_H, \tag{6·9}$$

and table 5 can then be constructed of the critical Ro_T^* values. It will be observed from table 5 that the agreement between the theoretical and experimental results is fairly satisfactory for small values of m but when $m \geqslant 3$ the divergence of the results is quite considerable. The wider divergence of the results when m increases can partly be explained by the neglect of the singularities ζ_3 and ζ_4 in building up the present baroclinic theory, and this will be enlarged upon shortly. Part of the discrepancy also is due to the approximate character of the relation (5·42), since the term on the right-hand side of this relation is merely the leading term of an infinite series. It is also necessary to note that the experimental values are obtained by keeping all the physical parameters fixed except the temperature difference $\Delta\theta$ between the two cylinders which is steadily increased from $\Delta\theta = 0$. Fultz states that the transition values will be different if $\Delta\theta$ is steadily decreased to zero; thus a given wave number can exist over a range of values of Ro_T^*. For example, in the experiment described, it is found that the upper limits of these ranges for wave numbers 4 and 5 are respectively 0·18 and 0·08 (cf. theoretical values 0·16 and 0·13), and it is possible that the theoretical values should be compared with this upper limit. The existence of this range, a phenomenon which has been called 'metastability' by Fultz, is not explained by any of the theory up to this point, and it is useful to conclude the present section with a brief discussion of the general stability characteristics of the flow.

TABLE 5. ANNULUS CASE $r_i = \frac{1}{2}r$

(Mean temperature 21° C, $\alpha = 2{\cdot}1 \times 10^{-4}$)

wave number, m	0	1	2	3	4	5
critical theoretical values of Ro_T^*	0·28	0·24	0·22	0·18	0·16	0·13
critical experimental values of Ro_T^*	0·26	0·22	0·20	0·11	0·07	0·04

The instability which is associated with the criterion (6·2) is linked with the appearance of a singular point $\zeta = \zeta_1$ within the range $0 < \zeta < 1$. At this point the function s, defined in (2·37), vanishes, and thus the angular velocity of the wave system equals the angular velocity of the liquid at some height within the liquid (it may be recalled that the effective angular velocity of the basic flow varies linearly with height). This type of instability accordingly is of the same type as that investigated by Heisenberg, Lin, Meksyn and others in the two-dimensional liquid motion between parallel planes, where the wave speed c becomes equal to the stream speed U at some intermediate point within the liquid.

The differential equation (2·49) has singular points also at the zeros $\zeta = \zeta_3$ and $\zeta = \zeta_4$ of λ_1, these being defined precisely in (2·52) and (2·53), and as stated earlier ζ_3 will lie outside the range $0 < \zeta < 1$, but ζ_4 may lie inside this range when R is effectively infinite. The function λ_1 is the determinant of the two equations of horizontal motion, and the vanishing of λ_1 implies that the horizontal velocity components are infinitely large. That this is so also follows from (2·49) when we investigate the solution in the neighbourhood of $\zeta = \zeta_4$. Making R infinite, we have

$$\zeta_4 = (1-f)/R_H(m-2),$$

and, bearing in mind that $f \ll 1$, it is evident that $m = 0$ and $m = 1$ make ζ_4 negative, so that there is no possibility of any resonance of the horizontal field in this case, likewise $m = 2$ makes ζ_4 infinite, and thus resonance of the horizontal velocity can occur only when $m > 2$. The effect of the ζ_4 singularity is discussed in the next section.

7. The variational method of solving the eigenvalue problem

The problem which is presented by equation (2·48) and the associated boundary conditions $\overline{W} = 0$ at $\zeta = 0$ and $\zeta = 1$ can be considered as a problem in the calculus of variations provided that the aim is merely to determine the wave-velocity formula and the stability criterion. In order to do this it is first of all necessary to write (2·48) in the Sturm–Liouville form, namely,

$$\frac{\mathrm{d}}{\mathrm{d}\zeta}\left\{k(\zeta)\frac{\mathrm{d}\overline{W}}{\mathrm{d}\zeta}\right\}+\{\lambda^* g(\zeta)-l(\zeta)\}\overline{W}=0, \tag{7·1}$$

and it is convenient, for the present purpose, to consider R_v to be the unknown eigenvalue in (2·48) so that

$$\lambda^* = R_v, \tag{7·2}$$

and $k(\zeta)$, $g(\zeta)$, $l(\zeta)$ are functions of ζ, not containing the parameter λ^*, which can be expressed in terms of s, s', λ_1, etc., in (2·48). When the transformation to the form (7·1) is effected it then follows Courant & Hilbert (1953) that the minimum value of the integral

$$I=\int_0^1\left\{k(\zeta)\left(\frac{\mathrm{d}\overline{W}}{\mathrm{d}\zeta}\right)^2+l(\zeta)\,\overline{W}^2(\zeta)\right\}\mathrm{d}\zeta, \tag{7·3}$$

subject to the normalizing condition

$$\int_0^1 g(\zeta)\,\overline{W}^2(\zeta)\,\mathrm{d}\zeta = 1 \tag{7·4}$$

is λ^*. This minimum is attained when $\overline{W}(\zeta)$ is the exact solution of (7·1) which satisfies $\overline{W} = 0$ at $\zeta = 0$ and $\zeta = 1$. An approximate value of λ^* can be obtained if a function $\overline{W}_A(\zeta)$ is taken which is an approximation to the exact $\overline{W}(\zeta)$.

We consider first the barotropic problem discussed in § 3 in order to assess the degree of error in this approach to the problem. In the barotropic problem, by comparing (7·1) and (3·1) with f^2 neglected compared with 1 or a^2R_v, it is easily shown that

$$k(\zeta) = -\frac{g(\zeta)}{a^2} = \exp-(mR_H\zeta/f), \quad l(\zeta) = 0. \tag{7·5}$$

In order to construct the approximate $\overline{W}$ function in this case it may be noted that $\zeta = 0$ and $\zeta = 1$ are simple zeros of $\overline{W}$. When $\overline{W}$ vanishes (3·1) indicates that the second differential at such a point becomes large when f is small; near $\zeta = 0$ it is easily shown that $\overline{W}$ is of the form $\zeta\exp(\zeta mR_H/2f)$, hence we assume that an approximation for $\overline{W}$ will be given by

$$\overline{W} = C\zeta(1-\zeta)\exp(mR_H\zeta/2f), \tag{7·6}$$

where C is a constant. Equation (7·4) then gives the following relation for C:

$$-a^2C^2\int_0^1 \zeta^2(1-\zeta)^2\,\mathrm{d}\zeta = 1, \tag{7·7}$$

and the approximate value of R_v will be given by

$$R_v = C^2\int_0^1\left\{1-2\zeta+\frac{mR_H}{2f}\zeta(1-\zeta)\right\}^2\mathrm{d}\zeta. \tag{7·8}$$

By eliminating C between (7·7) and (7·8) we obtain

$$a^2R_v\int_0^1 \zeta^2(1-\zeta)^2\,d\zeta+\int_0^1\left\{1-2\zeta+\frac{mR_H}{2f}\zeta(1-\zeta)\right\}^2 d\zeta = 0, \tag{7·9}$$

and upon integration this gives

$$a^2R_v+\frac{m^2R_H^2}{4f^2}+10 = 0. \tag{7·10}$$

This must be compared with (3·5), with $n = 1$, and it will be observed that the only departure is in the final term where 10 has replaced π^2 $(= 9{\cdot}8696)$. Thus the error is about $1\frac{1}{2}\,\%$. This method gives of course the first eigenvalue only, but in the present problem it is only the first eigenvalue which is of any interest.

We consider now the general case, and by comparing (7·1) and (2·49) we have

$$\left.\begin{aligned} k(\zeta) &= \lambda_1 s^{-1}(\zeta-\zeta_2)^{-a_2}(\zeta-\zeta_3)^{-a_3}(\zeta-\zeta_4)^{-a_4},\\ g(\zeta) &= -a^2\frac{sk(\zeta)}{\lambda_1 s'},\\ l(\zeta) &= a^2\frac{s^2}{\lambda_1}k(\zeta), \end{aligned}\right\} \tag{7·11}$$

where s, s' and λ_1 are defined in (2·37), (2·38) and (2·46) and a_2, a_3, a_4 are given by

$$a_2 = (1+2R_H\zeta_2)\bigg/\left\{\left(1-\frac{2f}{m}+\frac{ia^2}{Km}\right)^2-\left(\frac{a^2}{2R}-\frac{a^2}{2K}\right)^2\right\},$$

$$a_3 = m\bigg/\left\{m-2f-\tfrac{1}{2}ia^2\left(\frac{m}{R}-\frac{m+2}{K}\right)\right\},$$

$$a_4 = m\bigg/\left\{m-2f+\tfrac{1}{2}ia^2\left(\frac{m}{R}-\frac{m-2}{K}\right)\right\}.$$

We proceed upon the assumption that $K = R$, so that we have

$$a_2 = a_3 = a_4 = m\bigg/\left\{m-2f+\frac{ia^2}{R}\right\}; \tag{7·12}$$

hence in this case we have, apart from an arbitrary constant factor which is of no consequence here,

$$\left.\begin{aligned} k(\zeta) &= \lambda_1^{1-a_2}s^{-1-a_2},\\ g(\zeta) &= -a^2\lambda_1^{-a_2}s^{-1-a_2},\\ l(\zeta) &= a^2\lambda_1^{-a_2}s^{1-a_2}, \end{aligned}\right\} \tag{7·13}$$

since $s = s'$ when $K = R$. Ultimately, in order to obtain the wave-velocity formula, R will be made to tend to infinity in which case a_2 tends to $m/(m-2f)$, and thus for the west-east moving waves $(f<0)$, it follows that $0<a_2<1$; in this case s vanishes at $\zeta = \zeta_0 = -f/mR_H$, and it is evident that some difficulties are going to arise in the integration through $\zeta = \zeta_0$. The approximating function for $\overline{W}$ will be chosen to be simply

$$\overline{W} = C\zeta(1-\zeta), \tag{7·14}$$

since this satisfies the boundary conditions, and it is clear from the nature of the problem and also from the barotropic and baroclinic solutions already investigated that $\overline{W}$ has no singularities or zeros at any point of the range $0<\zeta<1$. From (7·3) it is clear that we now have the following integrals to evaluate:

$$I_1 = \int_0^1 \lambda_1^{1-a_2} s^{-1-a_2}(1-2\zeta)^2\,d\zeta, \tag{7·15}$$

$$I_2 = \int_0^1 \lambda_1^{-a_2} s^{1-a_2}\zeta^2(1-\zeta)^2\,d\zeta, \tag{7·16}$$

$$I_3 = \int_0^1 \lambda_1^{-a_2} s^{-1-a_2}\zeta^2(1-\zeta)^2\,d\zeta, \tag{7·17}$$

and it then follows that the required approximate eigenvalue for $\lambda^* = R_v$ is given by

$$a^2R_v I_3 + I_1 + a^2 I_2 = 0. \tag{7·18}$$

In order to clear up certain integration difficulties it is useful to repeat here the modified baroclinic problem which has been discussed in detail in § 4, and this will serve to indicate also to what extent (7·14) is a reasonable approximation to $\overline{W}$. In this case we take $\lambda_1 = 1$, $a_2 = 1$ and the I_2 term is completely ignored; this then arises from the following differential equation:

$$\frac{d}{d\zeta}\left\{s^{-2}\frac{d\overline{W}}{d\zeta}\right\} - a^2R_v s^{-2}\overline{W} = 0, \tag{7·19}$$

which is identical with (4·1). With the same assumptions the integrals to be evaluated are

$$I_1 = \int_0^1 s^{-2}(1-2\zeta)^2\,d\zeta, \quad I_3 = \int_0^1 s^{-2}\zeta^2(1-\zeta)^2\,d\zeta, \tag{7·20}$$

where s is given by
$$s = \mathrm{i}mR_H\left(\zeta + \frac{f}{mR_H} - \frac{\mathrm{i}a^2}{2R}\right) = \mathrm{i}mR_H\left(\zeta - \zeta_0 - \frac{\mathrm{i}a^2}{2R}\right), \tag{7·21}$$

and $0<\zeta_0<1$. Provided we retain the term $\mathrm{i}a^2/2R$ in s no difficulty arises in the integration, since the zero of s then lies outside the line of integration. When the integration is performed in this way and we subsequently make $R\to\infty$ we obtain

$$-m^2R_H^2 I_1 = 8 - \frac{1}{\zeta_0(1-\zeta_0)} + 4(2\zeta_0 - 1)\left\{\ln\left(\frac{1-\zeta_0}{\zeta_0}\right) + \mathrm{i}\pi\right\}, \tag{7·22}$$

$$-m^2R_H^2 I_3 = \tfrac{1}{3} - 4\zeta_0 + 4\zeta_0^2 + 2\zeta_0(1-\zeta_0)(1-2\zeta_0)\left\{\ln\left(\frac{1-\zeta_0}{\zeta_0}\right) + \mathrm{i}\pi\right\}. \tag{7·23}$$

If for the present we ignore the $\mathrm{i}\pi$ terms in (7·22) and (7·23), it follows from (7·18) that the required approximate relation between R_v and ζ_0 is then

$$a^2R_v\left\{\tfrac{1}{3} - 4\zeta_0 + 4\zeta_0^2 + 2\zeta_0(1-\zeta_0)(1-2\zeta_0)\ln\left(\frac{1-\zeta_0}{\zeta_0}\right)\right\} = \frac{1}{\zeta_0(1-\zeta_0)} - 8 - 4(2\zeta_0-1)\ln\left(\frac{1-\zeta_0}{\zeta_0}\right), \tag{7·24}$$

since I_2 is being ignored in this case. This relation has to be compared with (4·19) which we can write in the form

$$1 + a^2R_v\zeta_0(1-\zeta_0) = aR_v^{\frac{1}{2}}\coth aR_v^{\frac{1}{2}}. \tag{7·25}$$

It may be recalled that (7·25) is the exact relation arising from (7·19). The curve of $aR_v^{\frac{1}{2}}$ against ζ_0 has been given in figure 3, and the principal features of this curve are its symmetry about the line $\zeta_0 = \frac{1}{2}$, $aR_v^{\frac{1}{2}}$ tends to infinity as ζ_0 tends to 0 or 1, and $aR_v^{\frac{1}{2}} = 2{\cdot}40$ when $\zeta_0 = \frac{1}{2}$. The curve of $aR_v^{\frac{1}{2}}$ against ζ_0 given by (7·24) has similar features, but when

$\zeta_0 = \frac{1}{2}$ we now have $aR_v^{\frac{1}{2}} = 6^{\frac{1}{2}} = 2{\cdot}45$. Thus, provided the $i\pi$ terms occurring in (7·22) and (7·23) are ignored it is possible to achieve a similar result to the exact one, using (7·14), which gives an error of about 2 %.

It may be noted before proceeding any further that the results (7·21) and (7·22) for the integrals I_1 and I_3 could be obtained also by making R tend to infinity initially, and in the integration process we then avoid the singularity at $\zeta = \zeta_0$ by introducing a semi-circle $\Gamma_2 : \zeta = \zeta_0 + \epsilon\, e^{i\theta}$ $(\pi \leqslant \theta \leqslant 2\pi)$, which has its centre at $\zeta = \zeta_0$ and the path of integration from $\zeta_0 - \epsilon$ to $\zeta_0 + \epsilon$ is replaced by Γ_2. The $i\pi$ terms in (7·22) and (7·23) then arise from the integration around Γ_2 when ϵ tends to zero. As we have noted above, in order to achieve the same result as in § 4 it is necessary to discard the $i\pi$ terms; this is equivalent to taking the 'finite part' of the infinite integrals (7·20) so that we effectively take the *mean value* of two integrals to achieve the correct answer, and these integrals differ only in that the semicircle around the singularity at $\zeta = \zeta_0$ is above the line in one case and below the line in the other. A rigorous justification of this procedure is possible.

We are now in a position to extend the results of this paper beyond the baroclinic investigation of § 4, and this will be done by investigating the integrals (7·15), (7·16) and (7·17) in greater detail. The exact evaluation of these integrals is not possible in any simple form, and it is necessary to consider simplified forms of the integrands which will emphasize the different parameters of the problem. The modified baroclinic investigation of § 4 corresponds to $\lambda_1 = 1$, $a_2 = 1$ and I_2 being neglected. A case which is readily investigated is that when $\lambda_1 = 1$, $a_2 = m/(m-2f)$ and I_2 is retained. The retention of I_2 is equivalent to the retention of the term ss' in $(R_v + ss')\,\overline{W}$ in (2·49). The result is, however, not significantly different from that given in (7·24) and will therefore be omitted. It has been pointed out in § 6 that the presence of the singularity at $\zeta = \zeta_4$ may have an important bearing upon the results of § 4, and the remainder of this section will be devoted to an investigation of the case in which this singularity is retained. For simplicity we now choose $\lambda_1 = 1 - (\zeta/\zeta_4)$, where ζ_4 is given approximately by $\zeta_4 R_H(m-2) = 1$ (see (2·53)); we choose $a_2 = 1$ and I_2 will be neglected. We then have to evaluate

$$I_1 = \int_0^1 s^{-2}(1-2\zeta)^2\, d\zeta, \tag{7·26}$$

$$I_3 = \int_0^1 s^{-2}\zeta^2(1-\zeta)^2 \lambda_1^{-1}\, d\zeta, \tag{7·27}$$

where s, as before, is given by (7·21) in the general case. It will be noted that as ζ_4 tends to infinity this case becomes identical with that investigated in (7·20) et seq. The integral I_1 has been evaluated in (7·21) and we find that I_3 is given by

$$-m^2R_H^2 I_3 = \zeta_4\left\{P \ln\left(\frac{1-\zeta_0}{\zeta_0}\right) + Q \ln\frac{\zeta_4}{|\zeta_4 - 1|} + R\right\}, \tag{7·28}$$

where

$$P = \frac{\zeta_0^2(1-\zeta_0)^2}{(\zeta_4-\zeta_0)^2} + \frac{2\zeta_0(1-\zeta_0)(1-2\zeta_0)}{(\zeta_4-\zeta_0)}, \tag{7·29}$$

$$Q = \left\{\frac{\zeta_4(1-\zeta_4)}{\zeta_4-\zeta_0}\right\}^2, \tag{7·30}$$

$$R = \frac{1}{(\zeta_4-\zeta_0)}\{3\zeta_0^2 - \tfrac{5}{2}\zeta_0 + \tfrac{3}{2}\zeta_4 - \zeta_4\zeta_0 - \zeta_4^2\}, \tag{7·31}$$

and the 'finite part' has again been chosen. The approximate relation between R_v and the remaining parameters is $a^2R_vI_3+I_1 = 0$, where I_1 is taken in the form

$$-m^2R_H^2I_1 = -\frac{1}{\zeta_0(1-\zeta_0)}+8+4(2\zeta_0-1)\ln\left(\frac{1-\zeta_0}{\zeta_0}\right). \tag{7·32}$$

As in the previous case we see that as ζ_0 tends to zero or unity I_1 tends to ∞, while I_3 tends to a finite limit, thus $aR_v^{\frac{1}{2}}\to\infty$ as $\zeta_0\to 0$ or $\zeta_0\to 1$, just as in figure 3, while $aR_v^{\frac{1}{2}}$ attains a minimum value at an intermediate value of ζ_0. Since $\zeta_4 = 1/(m-2)\,R_H$ it follows that the experimental values of ζ_4 will be fairly large, and when ζ_4 is assumed to be large it may be shown that the minimum value of $aR_v^{\frac{1}{2}}$ is attained where $\zeta_0 = \frac{1}{2}-\frac{1}{12\zeta_4}$ and we have

$$(aR_v^{\frac{1}{2}})_{\text{min.}} = 2{\cdot}4\left(1-\frac{1}{4\zeta_4}\right). \tag{7·33}$$

It then follows that the criterion (6·2) becomes changed approximately to

$$x_{sm}R_H(1+\tfrac{1}{2}R_H)<1{\cdot}6\left(1-\frac{1}{4\zeta_4}\right),$$

and inserting the approximate value $\zeta_4 = 1/(m-2)\,R_H$ this becomes

$$x_{sm}R_H(1+\tfrac{1}{4}mR_H)<1{\cdot}6. \tag{7·34}$$

Thus for $m = 5$, $x_{1m} = 8{\cdot}8$ and the critical value of R_H for instability is $R_H = 0{\cdot}12$ compared with $R_H = 0{\cdot}13$ in table 4, and it is evident that the results which are derived from (7·34) are nearer the experimental figures quoted in this table (for $m\geqslant 2$), although it must be borne in mind that the latter refer to an experiment in which the liquid is bounded radially by two cylinders, while (7·34) applies to a liquid which is bounded externally by one cylinder only.

8. Conclusion

It is quite clear that the present theory establishes the inadequacy of barotropic theory in explaining stability phenomena in the dishpan experiment and shows that baroclinic theory, as yet in an approximate form, is capable of giving the main trend of the stability results. A more detailed investigation of equation (2·49) is essential to obtain more accurate quantitative results. However, even when this is accomplished the problem of incorporating the vertical acceleration term $w\,\partial V_0/\partial z$ remains, and it would seem that the phase changes of the long waves in the vertical direction (which do not appear in the present solution except when f is a complex quantity and the waves are growing or decreasing in amplitude) are intimately connected with this term. Much of the theory can be carried over into the corresponding atmospheric problem, and it throws some light upon the changes which occur in the long-wave patterns of the upper part of the troposphere.

References

Brunt, D. 1939 *Physical and dynamical meteorology.* Cambridge University Press.

Courant, R. & Hilbert, D. 1937 *Methoden der Mathematischen Physik,* vol. **1**, 2nd ed. Berlin: J. Springer.

Davies, T. V. 1953 *Phil. Trans.* A, **246**, 81–112.

Fultz, D. 1953 *Symposium on model experiments.* Department of Civil Engineering, Johns Hopkins University, Baltimore, Maryland.

Hide, R. 1953 Unpublished Thesis, University of Cambridge.

Kuo, H. L. 1954 *J. Met.* **4**, 399–411.

Lorenz, E. N. 1953 *Symposium on model experiments.* Department of Civil Engineering, Johns Hopkins University, Baltimore, Maryland.

Starr, V. P. & Long, R. R. 1953 *Geophys. Res. Pap.* no. 24, pp. 103–113.

Reprinted (with corrections) from *Journal of Fluid Mechanics*, Vol. 5, Part 4, 1959, published by the Cambridge University Press.

On the forced motion due to heating of a deep rotating liquid in an annulus

By T. V. DAVIES
King's College, London†

(Received 14 August 1958 and in revised form 7 November 1958)

In the laboratory experiments by Fultz & Riehl (1957) and by Hide (1958) on heated rotating liquids contained in the annulus between two cylinders, it has been observed that a strongly marked jet stream appears on the free surface of the liquid under certain conditions of rotating and heating. This jet stream meanders around the annulus in a regular wave-like pattern alternately approaching the outer and inner cylindrical boundaries. The present paper puts forward an analytical theory for this jet, or Rossby regime, in the course of which exact solutions are presented of certain fundamental non-linear partial differential equations. The assumption is made that the flow is geostrophic at the first approximation and that the heat transfer across the stream lines of geostrophic flow (that is, the isobars) is due to molecular conduction. From a calculation of the heat flow it appears that this leads to values of the heat transfer which are too small, so that the ageostrophic terms must be of importance in the actual heat transfer; nevertheless, the exact solution obtained here probably reveals the mechanism of the change from one wave pattern to another and certainly provides an explanation for the observed upper limit to the number of waves in a given geometrical configuration, as discussed by Hide. It has been established that the mean zonal flow and mean zonal temperature field are dependent upon the amplitude function of a finite amplitude wave solution. In this exact solution it is found that the amplitude and phase functions of the wave patterns are themselves interdependent and that the shape of the wave depends on the quantity of heat and angular momentum being transferred. It is shown that the wave pattern consisting of an integral number m lobes or petals can exist only in a restricted range of the Rossby number S—this is well-known from the experimental work of Fultz and Hide.

Introduction

In the laboratory experiments by Fultz & Riehl (1957) and Hide (1958), liquid contained in the annulus between two concentric circular cylinders (radii b and $a\,(<b)$: see figure 1) is bounded below by a horizontal smooth surface and bounded above by a free surface. The cylinders are constrained to rotate steadily about their common axis, the outer cylinder being maintained at a temperature T_b and the inner at a temperature $T_a\,(<T_b)$. Under certain circumstances of rotation and heating, the forced flow of the liquid relative to the cylinders consists of a well-marked wave pattern in which the fluid motion is principally horizontal and in

† Now at University College of Wales, Aberystwyth.

which a clearly defined jet stream can be observed on the free upper surface. The jet meanders regularly around the wave pattern, and the whole wave pattern plus the jet rotates relatively to the cylinders. A particular m-lobed wave pattern may be maintained indefinitely under constant conditions of rotation and temperature difference $T_b - T_a$, but can be changed by variation of either of these quantities. A discussion of the stability of the wave pattern has been made by the present author in an earlier paper (1956), and in this paper it was shown theoretically that the stability of the wave pattern is dependent principally upon one parameter known as the Rossby number S. In such stability analyses one is forced to assume that the wave amplitudes of the perturbation are infinitesimal compared, say, with the annulus radius $(b-a)$, and the results of such analyses will apply only to the initial stages of the wave growth under unstable conditions. The waves have an amplitude which is almost as large as the distance $(b-a)$, and this finiteness of amplitude can no longer be ignored in the investigation of the jet stream problem. This implies that the analytical investigation of the jet stream problem is necessarily one involving non-linear equations; until recently the only attempts which had been made to understand the jet stream structures mathematically were by numerical methods (Phillips 1956).

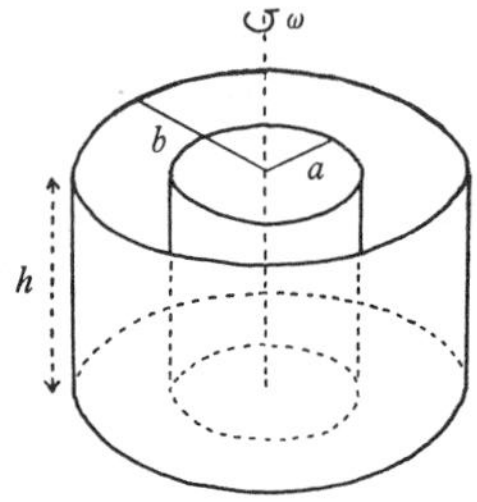

FIGURE 1. Definition sketch.

An analytical approach to the problem is possible, however, and the first step in this direction has been made by Miss Ruth Rogers (1959) who has investigated rectilinear jets using thermal boundary layer concepts in the heat transfer equation. The existence of such a rectilinear jet solution suggested to the present author that it might be profitable to investigate the corresponding jet problem in cylindrical co-ordinates and the present paper is a summary of the findings. It is interesting to note, however, that the boundary layer type of approximation made by Miss Rogers is not necessary in dealing with the present cylinder problem, and the solutions are correspondingly more valuable.

In the solution presented here it is found convenient to introduce amplitude and phase functions for the wave, and it then emerges that the zonal temperature field and the zonal flow can be expressed in terms of the amplitude and phase functions, which is something one would have expected from the many qualitative discussions of the corresponding meteorological problem (see, for instance, Lorenz 1957). It is found that the amplitude function and phase function are interdependent: one of these functions must be postulated before the complete solution can be obtained. Some guidance in postulating the nature of the phase function can be obtained from investigating the angular momentum and heat transfer associated with the wave. Particular examples illustrating different types of transfer have been included in this paper. One of the important results obtained is that the shape of the wave is dependent upon not only the amount of angular momentum transferred but also the amount of heat transferred; with an m-lobed wave pattern it is possible to transfer different amounts of heat and angular momentum within certain ranges. The m-lobed wave pattern is shown to exist only in certain ranges of the rotation and Rossby number, and when these ranges are combined with those obtained by the author in the earlier stability paper (1956) it is then possible to understand the complete stability diagram which has been obtained experimentally by Fultz (1956), and in particular to understand why there is a maximum number of waves possible in any given geometrical configuration. A result of secondary importance is that the steady solutions obtained here exist only if the ratio of the inner radius to the outer radius of the annulus is greater than a certain critical quantity. This implies that the steady wave regime cannot be maintained permanently in the open dishpan experiment.

A comparison of the theoretical absolute heat transport across either cylindrical boundary with that observed by Fultz indicates a variation with m in the correct sense, but the magnitude is considerably in error.

1. Statement of problem and method of solution

The dynamical equations of motion and the equation of heat transfer for a liquid contain terms which arise from the viscous stresses. One of the most striking features of the experiments conducted by Fultz & Riehl and by Hide is the negligible diffusion of the jet stream—a feature in which one might expect the viscous stresses to play a fundamental role. It is clear from order of magnitude arguments that the geostrophic approximation and the consequent 'thermal wind' together give results for the velocity field which are already good approximations (Davies 1953); and it would appear, although it is not possible to state this with precision, that there is probably a primary balance in the dynamical equations between the Coriolis acceleration terms and the pressure gradient (that is a geostrophic balance) and a separate but secondary balance between the viscous and inertia terms as in boundary-layer theory. Accordingly, in this non-viscous formulation of a theory of the experiments, molecular viscosity will be ignored completely.

In the absence of any heating the mean density of the liquid is taken to be ρ_0, and the small departure from this density due to a temperature increase τ above the mean is taken to be $-\alpha\tau$, where $\alpha = 2{\cdot}55 \times 10^{-4}\,\mathrm{g/cm^3}$ degree. Axes will be chosen which rotate steadily at an angular velocity ω about the fixed central z-axis, and the equations governing the motions will then be

$$\frac{du^*}{dt^*} - 2\omega v^* = -\frac{1}{\rho_0}\frac{\partial p^*}{\partial x^*}, \tag{1.1}$$

$$\frac{dv^*}{dt^*} + 2\omega u^* = -\frac{1}{\rho_0}\frac{\partial p^*}{\partial y^*}, \tag{1.2}$$

$$\rho_0\frac{dw^*}{dt^*} = -\frac{\partial p^*}{\partial z^*} + g\alpha\tau^*, \tag{1.3}$$

$$\frac{\partial u^*}{\partial x^*} + \frac{\partial v^*}{\partial y^*} + \frac{\partial w^*}{\partial z^*} = 0, \tag{1.4}$$

$$\frac{d\tau^*}{dt^*} = \kappa\nabla^2\tau^*, \tag{1.5}$$

where κ is the thermometric conductivity. Suppose that the typical temperature difference imposed externally in this problem is $(\Delta T)_H$, the suffix referring to a horizontal temperature contrast; then, if the liquid depth is h, we can introduce the non-dimensional symbols $x, y, \ldots, p$ defined by

$$\left.\begin{aligned} x^* = bx, \quad y^* = by, \quad z^* = hz; \\ u^* = 2\omega bSu, \quad v^* = 2\omega bSv, \quad w^* = 2\omega hSw; \\ t^* = t/2\omega S, \quad \tau^* = (\Delta T)_H\, \tau, \quad p^* = 4b^2\omega^2\rho_0 Sp; \end{aligned}\right\} \tag{1.6}$$

where the Rossby number S is defined by

$$S = \frac{gh}{4b^2\omega^2}\frac{\alpha(\Delta T)_H}{\rho_0}. \tag{1.7}$$

With these transformations the equations (1.1) to (1.5) become

$$S\frac{du}{dt} - v = -\frac{\partial p}{\partial x}, \tag{1.8}$$

$$S\frac{dv}{dt} + u = -\frac{\partial p}{\partial y}, \tag{1.9}$$

$$\frac{h^2}{b^2}S\frac{dw}{dt} = -\frac{\partial p}{\partial z} + \tau, \tag{1.10}$$

$$\frac{\partial u}{\partial x} + \frac{\partial v}{\partial y} + \frac{\partial w}{\partial z} = 0, \tag{1.11}$$

$$S\frac{d\tau}{dt} = \frac{\kappa}{2\omega}\left\{\frac{1}{b^2}\nabla_H^2\tau + \frac{1}{h^2}\frac{\partial^2\tau}{\partial z^2}\right\}, \tag{1.12}$$

where

$$\nabla_H^2 = \frac{\partial^2}{\partial x^2} + \frac{\partial^2}{\partial y^2}. \tag{1.13}$$

Now the Rossby number in jet flows is a small quantity of the order 0·1 to 0·01, and it is clear that the leading approximations to equations (1.8) to (1.12) will be as follows:

$$u_0 = -\frac{\partial p_0}{\partial y}, \quad v_0 = \frac{\partial p_0}{\partial x}, \quad w_0 = 0, \quad \tau_0 = \frac{\partial p_0}{\partial z}. \tag{1.14}$$

The first two equations represent the well-known geostrophic approximations for the horizontal motion, and combined with the fourth equation they lead to the equally well-known thermal wind equation of meteorology. The zero vertical velocity is a consequence of the vanishing of the horizontal divergence for the flow (u_0, v_0) coupled with (1.11). The heat transfer equation we treat in a more exact way, since if the conductivity is ignored it then follows that the isotherms and isobars everywhere coincide and there can be no heat transfer across the flow. We therefore retain the conductivity terms in (1.12) in order to ensure that there is a transfer of heat across the flow. On the left-hand side of (1.12), d/dt is an operator following the motion; but if we choose the angular velocity ω to be the angular velocity with which the wave system rotates relative to fixed axes in space, then the $\partial/\partial t$ term in d/dt can be omitted and the first approximation to (1.12) is

$$S\left\{u_0\frac{\partial\tau_0}{\partial x} + v_0\frac{\partial\tau_0}{\partial y}\right\} = \frac{\kappa}{2\omega}\left\{\frac{1}{b^2}\nabla_H^2\tau_0 + \frac{1}{h^2}\frac{\partial^2\tau_0}{\partial z^2}\right\}. \tag{1.15}$$

Equations (1.14) and (1.15) represent the equations of the first approximation, and the equations governing higher approximations will be developed later in this paper. When we substitute for u_0, v_0, τ_0 from (1.14) in (1.15), the resulting equation is a non-linear partial differential equation for p_0, namely

$$S\left\{\frac{\partial p_0}{\partial x}\frac{\partial \tau_0}{\partial y}-\frac{\partial p_0}{\partial y}\frac{\partial \tau_0}{\partial x}\right\}=\frac{\kappa}{2\omega}\left\{\frac{1}{b^2}\nabla_H^2\tau_0+\frac{1}{h_2}\frac{\partial^2\tau_0}{\partial z^2}\right\}\quad\left(\tau_0=\frac{\partial p_0}{\partial z}\right). \tag{1.16}$$

This is the equation derived originally by Miss Ruth Rogers (1959) in the investigation of the rectilinear jet.

One of the first points of interest concerning (1.16) is that to any solution found for τ_0 may be added an arbitrary linear function of z. Detailed measurements of the three-dimensional temperature field in the annulus experiment have been given by Fultz & Riehl (1957), and it is clear from these results that the mean vertical temperature field is approximately a linear function of z (except for an evaporation layer near the free surface). When this linear variation of temperature is subtracted from τ_0, the resulting temperature variation in the vertical is slow; hence if we introduce a new temperature function T_0 defined by

$$\tau_0 = cz+d+T_0, \tag{1.17}$$

and a corresponding new pressure function P_0 which differs from p_0 by a quadratic function of z, then T_0 and P_0 will have a slow variation in the vertical, and it will be sufficiently accurate, in the case of a liquid whose depth is large compared with the horizontal dimension, to simplify (1.16) to the form

$$\frac{\partial P_0}{\partial x}\frac{\partial T_0}{\partial y}-\frac{\partial P_0}{\partial y}\frac{\partial T_0}{\partial x}=\epsilon\left(\frac{\partial^2 T_0}{\partial x^2}+\frac{\partial^2 T_0}{\partial y^2}\right)\quad\left(T_0=\frac{\partial P_0}{\partial z}\right), \tag{1.18}$$

where

$$\epsilon = \kappa/2\omega b^2 S. \tag{1.19}$$

The non-dimensional constant ϵ is nothing more than a scaling constant, for if we write $P_0=\epsilon P_0'$, $T_0=\epsilon T_0'$, this constant cancels out in (1.17). It is a little more convenient, however, to write $P_0=\epsilon P_0'/m$, $T_0=\epsilon T_0'/m$, where m is the wave number (see (1.22)), and we shall consider (1.18) in the form

$$\frac{\partial P_0}{\partial x}\frac{\partial T_0}{\partial y}-\frac{\partial P_0}{\partial y}\frac{\partial T_0}{\partial x}=m\left(\frac{\partial^2 T_0}{\partial x^2}+\frac{\partial^2 T_0}{\partial y^2}\right)\quad\left(T_0=\frac{\partial P_0}{\partial z}\right). \tag{1.20}$$

(The dashes have not been retained in the dependent variables of this equation.) It may be noted that, using typical experimental values for all the constants, the value of the constant ϵ is about 10^{-3}.

We shall consider equation (1.20) in terms of polar co-ordinates (r,θ), where $x=r\cos\theta$, $y=r\sin\theta$. In this case (1.20) becomes

$$\frac{\partial P_0}{\partial r}\frac{\partial T_0}{\partial \theta}-\frac{\partial P_0}{\partial \theta}\frac{\partial T_0}{\partial r}=m\left\{r\frac{\partial^2 T_0}{\partial r^2}+\frac{\partial T_0}{\partial r}+\frac{1}{r}\frac{\partial^2 T_0}{\partial \theta^2}\right\}. \tag{1.21}$$

It may be observed that equation (1.20) is invariant with respect to a complex transformation

$$a+ib=f(x+iy),$$

since

$$\frac{\partial P_0}{\partial x}\frac{\partial T_0}{\partial y}-\frac{\partial P_0}{\partial y}\frac{\partial T_0}{\partial x}=\left|\frac{d(a+ib)}{d(x+iy)}\right|^2\left\{\frac{\partial P_0}{\partial a}\frac{\partial T_0}{\partial b}-\frac{\partial P_0}{\partial b}\frac{\partial T_0}{\partial a}\right\}$$

and

$$\frac{\partial^2 T_0}{\partial x^2}+\frac{\partial^2 T_0}{\partial y^2}=\left|\frac{d(a+ib)}{d(x+iy)}\right|^2\left\{\frac{\partial^2 T_0}{\partial a^2}+\frac{\partial^2 T_0}{\partial b^2}\right\}.$$

However, no use has been made of this interesting feature in this paper, although it can be used in extending the solutions obtained by Miss Rogers.

One of the most striking features of the experimental jet flows is the existence of a periodic structure in the θ-direction in which there is one regular well-marked stable wave pattern with a particular wave number m. This suggests that we investigate a solution of (1.21) of the form

$$P_0 = f + g\sin m\theta + h\cos m\theta, \tag{1.22}$$

$$T_0 = F + G\sin m\theta + H\cos m\theta, \tag{1.23}$$

where m is an integer and where $f, g, \ldots, H$ are functions of r, z only, although the z-variation of each of these functions is slow. When we substitute (1.22) and (1.23) in the left-hand side of (1.21), this side of the equation becomes

$$m\left\{\frac{1}{2}\left(G\frac{\partial h}{\partial r} - g\frac{\partial H}{\partial r} - H\frac{\partial g}{\partial r} + h\frac{\partial G}{\partial r}\right) + \cos m\theta\left(G\frac{\partial f}{\partial r} - g\frac{\partial F}{\partial r}\right)\right.$$
$$+\sin m\theta\left(h\frac{\partial F}{\partial r} - H\frac{\partial f}{\partial r}\right) + \tfrac{1}{2}\cos 2m\theta\left(G\frac{\partial h}{\partial r} - h\frac{\partial G}{\partial r} - g\frac{\partial H}{\partial r} + H\frac{\partial g}{\partial r}\right)$$
$$\left. + \tfrac{1}{2}\sin 2m\theta\left(G\frac{\partial g}{\partial r} - g\frac{\partial G}{\partial r} + h\frac{\partial H}{\partial r} - H\frac{\partial h}{\partial r}\right)\right\}. \tag{1.24}$$

When we substitute (1.23) in the right-hand side of (1.21), there will be no terms in $\cos 2m\theta$ or $\sin 2m\theta$; hence we must have

$$G\frac{\partial h}{\partial r} - h\frac{\partial G}{\partial r} - g\frac{\partial H}{\partial r} + H\frac{\partial g}{\partial r} = 0, \tag{1.25}$$

$$G\frac{\partial g}{\partial r} - g\frac{\partial G}{\partial r} + h\frac{\partial H}{\partial r} - H\frac{\partial h}{\partial r} = 0. \tag{1.26}$$

Comparing the remaining terms on the right-hand side with the corresponding ones in (1.24), we obtain the following three equations:

$$\frac{1}{2}\left(G\frac{\partial h}{\partial r} - g\frac{\partial H}{\partial r} - H\frac{\partial g}{\partial r} + h\frac{\partial G}{\partial r}\right) = r\frac{\partial^2 F}{\partial r^2} + \frac{\partial F}{\partial r}, \tag{1.27}$$

$$G\frac{\partial f}{\partial r} - g\frac{\partial F}{\partial r} = r\frac{\partial^2 H}{\partial r^2} + \frac{\partial H}{\partial r} - \frac{m^2}{r^2}H, \tag{1.28}$$

$$h\frac{\partial F}{\partial r} - H\frac{\partial f}{\partial r} = r\frac{\partial^2 G}{\partial r^2} + \frac{\partial G}{\partial r} - \frac{m^2}{r^2}G. \tag{1.29}$$

In addition to the five equations (1.25) to (1.29), it follows also from $T_0 = \partial P_0/\partial z$ that

$$F = \frac{\partial f}{\partial z}, \tag{1.30}$$

$$G = \frac{\partial g}{\partial z}, \tag{1.31}$$

$$H = \frac{\partial h}{\partial z}. \tag{1.32}$$

If we had retained the term $\partial^2 \tau_0/\partial z^2$, the only difference to the above equations would be the addition of terms $\partial^2 F/\partial z^2$, $\partial^2 H/\partial z^2$ and $\partial^2 G/\partial z^2$ on the right-hand sides of (1.27), (1.28) and (1.29) respectively. The equations (1.25) to (1.32) are still a non-linear set, and the principal aim now will be to obtain solutions which satisfy prescribed boundary conditions at the cylindrical boundaries.

Consider first of all equations (1.25) and (1.26). These are linear equations in h and g, and if, for example, g is eliminated between these two equations a second-order equation in r will be obtained for h. Hence, the general solution for h will contain two arbitrary functions of z. It is not necessary to perform this elimination, for it may be seen that the solutions for g and h will be

$$g = A(z)H + B(z)\,G, \tag{1.33}$$

$$h = -A(z)\,G + B(z)\,H, \tag{1.34}$$

where A and B are arbitrary functions of z. Using (1.31) and (1.32) it now follows that G and H must satisfy the equations

$$G = \frac{\partial}{\partial z}\{A(z)\,H + B(z)\,G\}, \tag{1.35}$$

$$H = \frac{\partial}{\partial z}\{-A(z)\,G + B(z)\,H\}, \tag{1.36}$$

and it is clear that the ultimate solutions for G and H will depend upon the nature of the variation of the functions $A(z)$ and $B(z)$.

Consider now equation (1.27) which we can write in the form

$$r\frac{\partial^2 F}{\partial r^2} + \frac{\partial F}{\partial r} = \frac{1}{2}\frac{\partial}{\partial r}\{Gh - gH\};$$

using (1.33) and (1.34) this becomes

$$r\frac{\partial^2 F}{\partial r^2} + \frac{\partial F}{\partial r} = -\tfrac{1}{2}A(z)\frac{\partial}{\partial r}(G^2 + H^2),$$

which has the first integral

$$r\frac{\partial F}{\partial r} = -\tfrac{1}{2}A(z)\,(G^2 + H^2) + \chi(z), \tag{1.37}$$

where χ is a function of z only. It is convenient at this stage to introduce local amplitude and local phase functions Φ and Ψ respectively, in place of H and G, and we shall define these functions as follows:

$$G = \Phi \sin \Psi, \quad H = \Phi \cos \Psi. \tag{1.38}$$

In terms of these new functions, (1.37) becomes

$$r\frac{\partial F}{\partial r} = -\tfrac{1}{2}A(z)\,\Phi^2 + \chi(z); \tag{1.39}$$

and if for convenience we use R in place of r as independent variable, where

$$R = \log_e r, \quad r = e^R, \quad r\frac{\partial}{\partial r} = \frac{\partial}{\partial R}, \tag{1.40}$$

then (1.39) may be written in the form

$$\frac{\partial F}{\partial R} = -\tfrac{1}{2}A(z)\,\Phi^2 + \chi(z). \tag{1.41}$$

In terms of R, equations (1.28) and (1.29) may be written as follows:

$$G\frac{\partial f}{\partial R} - g\frac{\partial F}{\partial R} = \frac{\partial^2 H}{\partial R^2} - m^2 H, \tag{1.42}$$

$$h\frac{\partial F}{\partial R} - H\frac{\partial f}{\partial R} = \frac{\partial^2 G}{\partial R^2} - m^2 G. \tag{1.43}$$

If we multiply (1.42) by H, (1.43) by G and add, we obtain

$$(hG - gH)\frac{\partial F}{\partial R} = H\left(\frac{\partial^2 H}{\partial R^2} - m^2 H\right) + G\left(\frac{\partial^2 G}{\partial R^2} - m^2 G\right).$$

It is easily shown from (1.38) that

$$H\frac{\partial^2 H}{\partial R^2} + G\frac{\partial^2 G}{\partial R^2} = \Phi\frac{\partial^2 \Phi}{\partial R^2} - \Phi^2\left(\frac{\partial \Psi}{\partial R}\right)^2,$$

and thus when we make use of (1.33) and (1.34) we obtain

$$-A\Phi^2\frac{\partial F}{\partial R} = \Phi\frac{\partial^2 \Phi}{\partial R^2} - \Phi^2\left(\frac{\partial \Psi}{\partial R}\right)^2 - m^2\Phi^2. \tag{1.44}$$

Comparing (1.41) and (1.44), it now follows that Φ and Ψ are related by the equation

$$\Phi\frac{\partial^2 \Phi}{\partial R^2} - \Phi^2\left(\frac{\partial \Psi}{\partial R}\right)^2 - m^2\Phi^2 = -A\Phi^2\{-\tfrac{1}{2}A\Phi^2 + \chi\}. \tag{1.45}$$

Using (1.42) and (1.43) once more, multiplying the former by h, the latter by g and adding, we obtain

$$(hG - gH)\frac{\partial f}{\partial R} = h\left(\frac{\partial^2 H}{\partial R^2} - m^2 H\right) + g\left(\frac{\partial^2 G}{\partial R^2} - m^2 G\right).$$

Substituting in this equation for h and g from (1.33) and (1.34), we obtain

$$\begin{aligned} -A\Phi^2\frac{\partial f}{\partial R} &= (BH - AG)\left(\frac{\partial^2 H}{\partial R^2} - m^2 H\right) + (AH + BG)\left(\frac{\partial^2 G}{\partial R^2} - m^2 G\right) \\ &= B\left\{H\frac{\partial^2 H}{\partial R^2} + G\frac{\partial^2 G}{\partial R^2} - m^2(H^2 + G^2)\right\} - A\left\{G\frac{\partial^2 H}{\partial R^2} - H\frac{\partial^2 G}{\partial R^2}\right\}; \end{aligned}$$

and from (1.38) it is easily shown that

$$H\frac{\partial^2 G}{\partial R^2} - G\frac{\partial^2 H}{\partial R^2} = \Phi^2\frac{\partial^2 \Psi}{\partial R^2} + 2\Phi\frac{\partial \Phi}{\partial R}\frac{\partial \Psi}{\partial R}.$$

Hence the equation for $\partial f/\partial R$ becomes

$$-A\Phi^2\frac{\partial f}{\partial R} = B\left\{\Phi\frac{\partial^2 \Phi}{\partial R^2} - \Phi^2\left(\frac{\partial \Psi}{\partial R}\right)^2 - m^2\Phi^2\right\} + A\left\{\Phi^2\frac{\partial^2 \Psi}{\partial R^2} + 2\Phi\frac{\partial \Phi}{\partial R}\frac{\partial \Psi}{\partial R}\right\}. \tag{1.46}$$

We may note at this stage that (1.41) or (1.44) is an equation which defines $\partial F/\partial R$ in terms of Φ and Ψ, and that (1.46) defines $\partial f/\partial R$ in terms of Φ and Ψ. Bearing in mind equation (1.30), which we can write alternatively in the form

$$\frac{\partial F}{\partial R} = \frac{\partial}{\partial z}\left(\frac{\partial f}{\partial R}\right), \tag{1.47}$$

it follows that when we substitute for $\partial F/\partial R$ and $\partial f/\partial R$ we obtain a second-order partial differential relation between Φ and Ψ which, coupled with (1.45), gives a complete solution of the problem. This second relation which follows from (1.47) is

$$-\tfrac{1}{2}A\Phi^2+\chi = \frac{\partial}{\partial z}\left\{B(-\tfrac{1}{2}A\Phi^2+\chi)-\left(\frac{\partial^2\Psi}{\partial R^2}+\frac{2}{\Phi}\frac{\partial\Phi}{\partial R}\frac{\partial\Psi}{\partial R}\right)\right\}. \tag{1.48}$$

In order to exploit equations (1.45) and (1.48) it is necessary to be able to separate the variables R and z. Without going into detail, it is sufficient to state that this is possible if, and only if,

$$\Phi = \frac{1}{A(z)}\phi(R), \tag{1.49}$$

$$\chi(z) = \frac{j}{A(z)}, \tag{1.50}$$

and $\partial\Psi/\partial R$ is independent of z, where $\phi(R)$ is a function of R only and j is a constant. If one uses the above formulae, it follows that $\partial F/\partial R$ is then given by

$$\frac{\partial F}{\partial R} = \frac{1}{A(z)}\{-\tfrac{1}{2}\phi^2(R)+j\}; \tag{1.51}$$

$\phi(R)$ satisfies the equation

$$\frac{d^2\phi}{dR^2}-\phi\left(\frac{d\Psi}{dR}\right)^2-m^2\phi = -\phi(-\tfrac{1}{2}\phi^2+j); \tag{1.52}$$

$\partial f/\partial R$ is given by

$$\begin{aligned} -\phi^2\frac{\partial f}{\partial R} &= \frac{B}{A}\phi\left\{\frac{d^2\phi}{dR^2}-\phi\left(\frac{d\Psi}{dR}\right)^2-m^2\phi\right\}+\frac{d}{dR}\left\{\phi^2\frac{d\Psi}{dR}\right\} \\ &= -\frac{B}{A}\phi^2(j-\tfrac{1}{2}\phi^2)+\frac{d}{dR}\left\{\phi^2\frac{d\Psi}{dR}\right\}; \end{aligned} \tag{1.53}$$

and finally, in order to satisfy (1.48) or (1.47), we must have

$$\frac{d}{dz}\left(\frac{B}{A}\right) = \frac{1}{A}. \tag{1.54}$$

Although the method of separating the variables is not along the lines of the well-known method used for linear partial differential equations, it is convenient to regard j as the separation constant.

Before proceeding further it is useful to express the temperature and pressure in terms of the amplitude and phase functions. If we substitute for G and H from (1.38) in (1.23), we obtain

$$T_0 = F+\Phi\cos(m\theta-\Psi), \tag{1.55}$$

hence

$$T_0 = F+\frac{1}{A}\phi(R)\cos(m\theta-\Psi). \tag{1.56}$$

Similarly, if we substitute for g and h from (1.33), (1.34) in (1.22), we obtain

$$P_0 = f + A(H\sin m\theta - G\cos m\theta) + B(G\sin m\theta + H\cos m\theta),$$

hence, using (1.38),

$$P_0 = f + A\Phi\sin(m\theta - \Psi) + B\Phi\cos(m\theta - \Psi). \tag{1.57}$$

Finally, making use of (1.49), we have

$$P_0 = f + \phi(R)\sin(m\theta - \Psi) + \frac{B}{A}\phi(R)\cos(m\theta - \Psi). \tag{1.58}$$

It is clear that $\phi(R)$ can be determined from (1.52) when $d\Psi/dR$ is known, and that B can be determined from (1.54) when A is known; hence, the knowledge of $d\Psi/dR$ as a function of R and of A as a function of z will be sufficient (together with the boundary conditions) to determine ϕ, B, F and f. The unknown constant j will, we shall find, be determined as an eigen-value similar to linear theory. It is important to point out that $\partial\Psi(R,z)/\partial R$ is a function of R only and the function Ψ is necessarily a function of R only, as may be verified from (1.35) or (1.36). This means that, with the present solution of the problem, that part of the temperature field which depends upon θ does not show variation in the vertical. This feature of the temperature field (not of the pressure field it may be noted) is contrary to the experiment where a phase change in the vertical is present in the temperature structure. This phase change will be discussed in greater detail in a future paper. To conclude this section we may note, from (1.51) and (1.53), that the fields of mean temperature F and mean pressure f satisfy the equation

$$\frac{\partial}{\partial R}\{f - BF\} = -\frac{1}{\phi^2}\frac{d}{dR}\left(\phi^2\frac{d\Psi}{dR}\right), \tag{1.59}$$

and thus they differ in profile as long as $\phi^2 d\Psi/dR$ is not constant. In the next section it will be shown that the horizontal transfer of westerly angular momentum is proportional to $\phi^2 d\Psi/dR$ at any level, and thus the mean temperature and mean pressure profiles will differ only when there is a transfer of westerly angular momentum.

2. The radial transfer of angular momentum and heat and the derivation of the vorticity field

In order to throw some light on the choice of the function $d\Psi/dR$ in (1.52), it is useful to calculate the transfer in the minus r direction of westerly (i.e. in the direction of θ increasing) angular momentum (M_H) across a circle of radius r at a height z. This is clearly the integral from $\theta = 0$ to $\theta = 2\pi$ of the product $-\rho_0 r^* u_\theta u_r$; hence

$$M_H = 4\rho_0 b^4\omega^4 S^2 \int_{\theta=0}^{2\pi} \frac{\partial p}{\partial R}\frac{\partial p}{\partial \theta}\,d\theta. \tag{2.1}$$

The leading terms in the angular momentum transfer will arise from the geostrophic flow discussed in the previous section, and, bearing in mind the transformation leading to (1.20), it follows that in terms of P_0 in (1.58) we have

$$M_H = \rho_0\kappa^2 m^{-2}\omega^2 \int_0^{2\pi} \frac{\partial P_0}{\partial R}\frac{\partial P_0}{\partial \theta}\,d\theta. \tag{2.2}$$

Using (1.58), we have

$$\frac{\partial P_0}{\partial \theta} = m\phi(R)\cos(m\theta - \Upsilon) - \frac{mB}{A}\phi(R)\sin(m\theta - \Upsilon), \tag{2.3}$$

$$\frac{\partial P_0}{\partial R} = \frac{\partial f}{\partial R} + \left(\frac{d\phi}{dR} + \frac{B}{A}\phi\frac{d\Upsilon}{dR}\right)\sin(m\theta - \Upsilon) + \left(\frac{B}{A}\frac{d\phi}{dR} - \phi\frac{d\Upsilon}{dR}\right)\cos(m\theta - \Upsilon), \tag{2.4}$$

and thus

$$M_H = -\rho_0 \kappa^2 m^{-1}\omega^2 \pi M, \tag{2.5}$$

where

$$M = \left(1 + \frac{B^2}{A^2}\right)\phi^2 \frac{d\Upsilon}{dR}. \tag{2.6}$$

We will now derive a general result concerning angular momentum transfer. The complete equation of motion in the direction of θ increasing relative to axes which are fixed in space is

$$\frac{\partial v}{\partial t} + u\frac{\partial v}{\partial r} + \frac{v}{r}\frac{\partial v}{\partial \theta} + w\frac{\partial v}{\partial z} + \frac{uv}{r} = \frac{1}{\rho}\left\{\frac{1}{r}\frac{\partial p_{\theta\theta}}{\partial \theta} + \frac{\partial p_{\theta z}}{\partial z} + \frac{1}{r^2}\frac{\partial}{\partial r}(r^2 p_{r\theta})\right\}, \tag{2.7}$$

where $p_{\theta\theta}$, $p_{\theta z}$, $p_{r\theta}$ are the viscous stresses. The appropriate continuity equation is

$$\frac{\partial p}{\partial t} + \frac{\partial}{\partial r}(\rho r u) + \frac{\partial}{\partial \theta}(\rho v) + \frac{\partial}{\partial z}(\rho r w) = 0, \tag{2.8}$$

and using these two equations we can deduce the Reynolds stress form of (2.7), namely

$$\frac{\partial}{\partial t}(\rho v r^2) + \frac{\partial}{\partial r}(\rho u v r^2) + \frac{\partial}{\partial \theta}(\rho v^2 r) + \frac{\partial}{\partial z}(\rho v w r^2) = r\frac{\partial p_{\theta\theta}}{\partial \theta} + r^2\frac{\partial p_{\theta z}}{\partial z} + \frac{\partial}{\partial r}(r^2 p_{r\theta}). \tag{2.9}$$

We shall write m_H and m_V for the horizontal ($-r$-direction) and vertical ($+z$-direction) transports of westerly angular momentum (about $r = 0$) across a circle of radius r at height z, so that

$$m_H = -\int_0^{2\pi} \rho u v r^2\, d\theta, \tag{2.10}$$

$$m_V = \int_0^{2\pi} \rho w v r^2\, d\theta. \tag{2.11}$$

We multiply (2.9) by $dr\,d\theta\,dz$ and integrate over an annular volume τ bounded by $z_0, z_1\,(> z_0)$, r_0 and $r_1\,(> r_0)$, and we then obtain after some reduction

$$\frac{\partial}{\partial t}\left\{\int_\tau \rho v r\, d\tau\right\} + \int_{z_0}^{z_1}(m_H|_{r_0} - m_H|_{r_1})\,dz + \int_{r_0}^{r_1}(m_V|_{z_1} - m_V|_{z_0})\,dr$$

$$= \int_{r_0}^{r_1} dr \int_0^{2\pi} r^2(p_{\theta z}|_{z_1} - p_{\theta z}|_{z_0})\,d\theta + \int_{z_0}^{z_1} dz \int_0^{2\pi} (r_1^2 p_{r\theta}|_{r_1} - r_0^2 p_{r\theta}|_{r_0})\,d\theta. \tag{2.12}$$

In the present problem the time average value of the first term is zero and henceforth this term will be ignored. In this case, equation (2.12) states that the total flow of westerly angular momentum outwards across the boundary S of a volume τ is equal to the moment about $r = 0$ of the viscous stresses acting on the complete surface S. Viscosity has been ignored in the formulation of the problem of the first section; but since the influence of viscosity in this angular momentum result is equivalent to an appropriate supply of angular momentum across S, it is clear that we can simulate the effect of viscosity by an appropriate distribution of sources and sinks of angular momentum over S. I shall assume therefore that there are distributions of sources and sinks: (a) on the surface $z = \delta$ which is the plane upper boundary of the 'boundary layer' in $0 < z \leqslant \delta$, and (b) on the surfaces $r = b-\delta$, $r = a+\delta$ which are the cylindrical boundaries on the inside of the 'boundary layers' in $b-\delta \leqslant r < b$, $a < r \leqslant a+\delta$. The details of this distribution of sources and sinks in any given case can be obtained only by solving the complete Navier-Stokes equations, but here we shall assume that the distribution can be prescribed. Away from the boundary layers it is a good approximation that the total flow of angular momentum across the boundary S is zero, and assuming this to be exactly true we obtain the following result from (2.12):

$$\int_{z_0}^{z_1} (m_H|_{r_0} - m_H|_{r_1})\, dz + \int_{r_0}^{r_1} (m_V|_{z_1} - m_V|_{z_0})\, dr = 0; \tag{2.13}$$

and if we take $z_1 = z_0 + \delta z$, $r_1 = r_0 + \delta r$, we deduce that

$$\frac{\partial m_H}{\partial r} = \frac{\partial m_V}{\partial z}. \tag{2.14}$$

This will be assumed to be valid in the range $\delta < z < h$, $a+\delta < r < b-\delta$. If we introduce now the quantities M_H, M_V to represent the horizontal and vertical transports of westerly angular momentum for the relative flow (i.e. relative to axes which are rotating with angular velocity ω as in § 1), then it easily follows that

$$\frac{\partial M_H}{\partial r} = \frac{\partial M_V}{\partial z}. \tag{2.15}$$

Hence with the M_H defined in (2.5) the corresponding M_V will be given by

$$M_V = \rho_0 \int_0^{2\pi} r^{*2}\, u_\theta u_z\, d\theta \tag{2.16}$$

$$= -\rho_0 \kappa^2 m^{-1} \omega^2 \pi \frac{d}{dr}\left(\phi^2 \frac{d\Psi}{dR}\right) \int^z \left(1 + \frac{B^2}{A^2}\right) dz. \tag{2.17}$$

It is clear now that if either M_H or M_V is prescribed on a plane $z =$ constant, then this is equivalent to postulating the behaviour of the unknown function Ψ.

If $\phi^2(d\Psi/dR) =$ constant, it follows that $M_V = 0$, and thus the source of angular momentum can be taken at the cylindrical wall $r = b$ with an equal sink at $r = a$. If, on the other hand, there is no source or sink of angular momentum at the side walls, the whole of the angular momentum which emanates from one part of the base must be assumed to return to a sink in the remaining part of the base, so that

$$\int_a^b M_V\, dr = 0. \tag{2.18}$$

This type of angular momentum flow is the one which is similar to that of the atmosphere, and this case can be satisfied here provided

$$\left(\phi^2 \frac{d\Psi}{dR}\right)\bigg|_b = \left(\phi^2 \frac{d\Psi}{dR}\right)\bigg|_a. \tag{2.19}$$

We shall discuss these results further in § 4, and we now turn our attention to the radially inward transport of heat.

The radially inward transport of heat (H.T.) across a circle of radius r^* at height z^* will be obtained by integrating the product $\kappa u_r(\partial\tau^*/\partial r^*)$, hence

$$\text{H.T.} = -4\kappa\rho_0 b\omega^2 S(\Delta T)_H \int_0^{2\pi} \frac{\partial p}{\partial\theta}\frac{\partial\tau}{\partial r}\,d\theta. \tag{2.20}$$

The leading terms in this heat transfer will be given by

$$\text{H.T.} = -4\kappa\rho_0 b\omega^2 S(\Delta T)_H\,\epsilon^2 m^{-2} \int_0^{2\pi} \frac{\partial P_0}{\partial\theta}\frac{\partial T_0}{\partial r}\,d\theta,$$

and since, from (1.56),

$$\frac{\partial T_0}{\partial r} = \frac{\partial F}{\partial r} + \frac{1}{A}\frac{d\phi}{\partial r}\cos(m\theta - \Psi) + \frac{1}{A}\phi\frac{d\Psi}{dR}\sin(m\theta - \Psi), \tag{2.21}$$

it follows that

$$\text{H.T.} = -4\kappa\rho_0 b\omega^2 S\epsilon^2 m^{-1}(\Delta T)_H\,\pi H, \tag{2.22}$$

where

$$H = \frac{1}{A}\left\{\phi\frac{d\phi}{d\tau} - \frac{B}{A}\phi^2\frac{d\Psi}{dr}\right\}. \tag{2.23}$$

It will be seen that there is an essential difference between the angular momentum and heat transport expressions, both in their z and r variations, in particular the heat transport can exist even when the momentum transport is zero.

A third quantity which will be required later in the paper is the vorticity of the two-dimensional flow of the previous section; if this is denoted by ζ_0 then we have, working with the non-dimensional symbols,

$$\zeta_0 = \frac{\partial v_0}{\partial x} - \frac{\partial u_0}{\partial y} = \frac{\partial^2 p_0}{\partial x^2} + \frac{\partial^2 p_0}{\partial y^2}, \tag{2.24}$$

hence

$$r^2\zeta_0 = r^2\frac{\partial^2 p_0}{\partial r^2} + r\frac{\partial p_0}{\partial r} + \frac{\partial^2 p_0}{\partial\theta^2}$$

$$= \epsilon^2 m^{-2}\left(\frac{\partial^2 P_0}{\partial R^2} + \frac{\partial^2 P_0}{\partial\theta^2}\right). \tag{2.25}$$

Using the expression (1.58) for P_0, we obtain after some reduction

$$r^2\zeta_0 = \epsilon^2 m^{-2}\left\{\frac{\partial^2 f}{\partial R^2} + X\sin(m\theta - \Psi) + Y\cos(m\theta - \Psi)\right\}, \tag{2.26}$$

where

$$X = \frac{d^2\phi}{dR^2} - \phi\left(\frac{d\Psi}{dR}\right)^2 - m^2\phi + \frac{B}{A}\left(\phi\frac{d^2\Psi}{dR^2} + 2\frac{d\phi}{dR}\frac{d\Psi}{dR}\right), \tag{2.27}$$

$$Y = \frac{B}{A}\left\{\frac{d^2\phi}{dR^2} - \phi\left(\frac{d\Psi}{dR}\right)^2 - m^2\phi\right\} - \left(\phi\frac{d^2\Psi}{dR^2} + 2\frac{d\phi}{dR}\frac{d\Psi}{dR}\right). \tag{2.28}$$

We shall satisfy the Helmholtz vorticity equation with the vorticity function (2.24) when we proceed to the higher approximations in the next section (see (3.13)).

3. Higher order approximations and the determination of the vertical velocity

It is possible to determine the higher order approximations in this problem by taking power series in S for the various dependent variables taking as the first approximation the equations (1.14). Thus we shall take

$$u = u_0 + Su_1 + S^2u_2 + \ldots, \tag{3.1}$$

$$v = v_0 + Sv_1 + S^2v_2 + \ldots, \tag{3.2}$$

$$w = Sw_1 + S^2w_2 + \ldots, \tag{3.3}$$

$$p = p_0 + Sp_1 + S^2p_2 + \ldots, \tag{3.4}$$

$$\tau = \tau_0 + S\tau_1 + S^2\tau_2 + \ldots, \tag{3.5}$$

where u_0, v_0, p_0, τ_0 are given by (1.14). If we substitute the above expressions in (1.8), (1.9), (1.10), (1.11) and (1.12) and equate the leading terms, (1.14) and (1.15) are obtained. Equating to zero the coefficients of the next power in S, we obtain the following equations:

$$\frac{du_0}{dt} - v_1 = -\frac{\partial p_1}{\partial x}, \tag{3.6}$$

$$\frac{dv_0}{dt} + u_1 = -\frac{\partial p_1}{\partial y}, \tag{3.7}$$

$$0 = -\frac{\partial p_1}{\partial z} + \tau_1, \tag{3.8}$$

$$\frac{\partial u_1}{\partial x} + \frac{\partial v_1}{\partial y} + \frac{\partial w_1}{\partial z} = 0, \tag{3.9}$$

$$u_0\frac{\partial \tau_1}{\partial x} + u_1\frac{\partial \tau_0}{\partial x} + v_0\frac{\partial \tau_1}{\partial y} + v_1\frac{\partial \tau_0}{\partial y} + w_1\frac{\partial \tau_0}{\partial z} = \epsilon\left(\frac{\partial^2 \tau_1}{\partial x^2} + \frac{\partial^2 \tau_1}{\partial y^2}\right), \tag{3.10}$$

where the term $\partial^2\tau_1/\partial z^2$ has been omitted in (3.10). From this set of five equations there are sufficient equations to solve for u_1, v_1, w_1, p_1 and τ_1. In order to determine w_1 however, it is necessary to use the three equations (3.6), (3.7) and (3.9).

The first equation (3.6) gives

$$\begin{aligned} v_1 &= \frac{\partial p_1}{\partial x} + u_0\frac{\partial u_0}{\partial x} + v_0\frac{\partial u_0}{\partial y} \\ &= \frac{\partial}{\partial x}\{p_1 + \tfrac{1}{2}u_0^2 + \tfrac{1}{2}v_0^2\} - v_0\zeta_0, \end{aligned} \tag{3.11}$$

where ζ_0 is defined in (2.24). Similarly (3.7) gives

$$\begin{aligned} u_1 &= -\frac{\partial p_1}{\partial y} - u_0\frac{\partial v_0}{\partial x} - v_0\frac{\partial v_0}{\partial y} \\ &= -\frac{\partial}{\partial y}(p_1 + \tfrac{1}{2}u_0^2 + \tfrac{1}{2}v_0^2) - u_0\zeta_0, \end{aligned} \tag{3.12}$$

and thus by substituting for u_1 and v_1 in (3.9) we obtain

$$\frac{\partial w_1}{\partial z} = \frac{\partial}{\partial x}(u_0\zeta_0) + \frac{\partial}{\partial y}(v_0\zeta_0),$$

so that, using (1.14), we have

$$\frac{\partial w_1}{\partial z} = u_0\frac{\partial \zeta_0}{\partial x} + v_0\frac{\partial \zeta_0}{\partial y};$$

hence the form of the Helmholtz vorticity equation is

$$\frac{\partial w_1}{\partial z} = \frac{\partial p_0}{\partial x}\frac{\partial \zeta_0}{\partial y} - \frac{\partial p_0}{\partial y}\frac{\partial \zeta_0}{\partial x}. \tag{3.13}$$

In polar co-ordinates this becomes

$$\frac{\partial w_1}{\partial z} = \frac{1}{r}\left\{\frac{\partial p_0}{\partial r}\frac{\partial \zeta_0}{\partial \theta} - \frac{\partial p_0}{\partial \theta}\frac{\partial \zeta_0}{\partial r}\right\},$$

and it may be verified that this equation can be written in the form

$$r^4\frac{\partial w_1}{\partial z} = \epsilon m^{-1}\left\{\frac{\partial P_0}{\partial R}\frac{\partial}{\partial \theta}(r^2\zeta_0) - \frac{\partial P_0}{\partial \theta}\frac{\partial}{\partial R}(r^2\zeta_0) + 2\frac{\partial P_0}{\partial \theta}(r^2\zeta_0)\right\},$$

so that by using (2.13) we have

$$\begin{aligned}\frac{r^4(\partial w_1/\partial z)}{\varepsilon m^{-1}} = &\left\{\frac{\partial f}{\partial R} + \left(\frac{d\phi}{dR} + \frac{B}{A}\phi\frac{d\Psi}{dR}\right)s_1 + \left(-\phi\frac{d\Psi}{dR} + \frac{B}{A}\frac{d\phi}{dR}\right)c_1\right\}\{Xc_1 - Ys_1\} \\ &- \left\{\frac{\partial^3 f}{\partial R^3} + \left(\frac{\partial X}{\partial R} + Y\frac{d\Psi}{dR}\right)s_1 + \left(\frac{\partial Y}{\partial R} - X\frac{d\Psi}{dR}\right)c_1\right\}\left\{\phi c_1 - \frac{B}{A}\phi s_1\right\} \\ &+ 2\left\{\frac{\partial^2 f}{\partial R^2} + Xs_1 + Yc_1\right\}\left\{\phi c_1 - \frac{B}{A}\phi s_1\right\},\end{aligned} \tag{3.14}$$

where we have written

$$s_r = \sin r(m\theta - \Psi), \quad c_r = \cos r(m\theta - \Psi). \tag{3.15}$$

In this expression for $\partial w_1/\partial z$ there will be terms independent of θ and it is clear that such terms will supply the first information concerning meridional cells in the general circulation pattern. These terms will arise from the c_1^2 and s_1^2 products and are as follows:

$$\begin{aligned}&-\tfrac{1}{2}Y\left(\frac{d\phi}{dR} + \frac{B}{A}\phi\frac{d\Psi}{dR}\right) + \tfrac{1}{2}X\left(-\phi\frac{d\Psi}{dR} + \frac{B}{A}\frac{d\phi}{dR}\right) - \tfrac{1}{2}\phi\left(\frac{\partial Y}{\partial R} - X\frac{d\Psi}{dR}\right) \\ &+\frac{1}{2}\frac{B}{A}\phi\left(\frac{\partial X}{\partial R} + Y\frac{d\Psi}{dR}\right) - \frac{B}{A}\phi X + \phi Y \\ &\equiv \frac{1}{2}\frac{\partial}{\partial R}\left\{\phi\left(-Y + \frac{B}{A}X\right)\right\} - \phi\left(-Y + \frac{B}{A}X\right).\end{aligned}$$

Using (2.14) and (2.15) we have

$$\frac{B}{A}X - Y = \left(1 + \frac{B^2}{A^2}\right)\left(\phi\frac{d^2\Psi}{dR^2} + 2\frac{d\phi}{dR}\frac{d\Psi}{dR}\right), \tag{3.16}$$

and thus if we denote by $\overline{w}_1$ that part of w_1 which is independent of θ when we have

$$\frac{r^4(\partial \overline{w}_1/\partial z)}{\varepsilon m^{-1}} = \frac{1}{2}\frac{\partial}{\partial R}\left\{\left(1 + \frac{B^2}{A^2}\right)\frac{d}{dR}\left(\phi^2\frac{d\Psi}{dR}\right)\right\} - \left(1 + \frac{B^2}{A^2}\right)\frac{d}{dR}\left(\phi^2\frac{d\Psi}{dR}\right). \tag{3.17}$$

It may be noted that the right-hand side of this expression can be written entirely in terms of M which is defined in (2.6), and in this case we have the interesting result

$$\frac{r^4(\partial \overline{w}_1/\partial z)}{\epsilon^2 m^{-4}} = \frac{1}{2}\frac{\partial^2 M}{\partial R^2} - \frac{\partial M}{\partial R}, \tag{3.18}$$

which relates the meridional part of the vertical velocity with the horizontal angular momentum transfer. Using (1.40), an alternative form of (3.18) is

$$\frac{2r^4(\partial \overline{w}_1/\partial z)}{\varepsilon m^{-1}} = r^2\frac{\partial^2 M}{\partial r^2} - r\frac{\partial M}{\partial r}. \tag{3.19}$$

We may note that the meridional part of the vertical velocity will be identically zero if M shows no variation with r or if M is proportional to r^2. The remaining terms in the expression for $\partial w_1/\partial z$ do not simplify in the same way as the above meridional part and in general we have from (3.14)

$$\begin{aligned}\frac{r^4(\partial w_1/\partial z)}{\varepsilon m^{-1}} &= \frac{1}{2}\frac{\partial^2 M}{\partial R^2} - \frac{\partial M}{\partial R} + \left\{X\frac{\partial f}{\partial R} - \phi\frac{\partial^3 f}{\partial R^3} + 2\phi\frac{\partial^2 f}{\partial R^2}\right\}\cos(m\theta - \Psi) \\ &- \left\{Y\frac{\partial f}{\partial R} - \frac{B}{A}\phi\frac{\partial^3 f}{\partial R^3} + \frac{2B}{A}\phi\frac{\partial^2 f}{\partial R^2}\right\}\sin(m\theta - \Psi) \\ &+ \frac{1}{2}\left\{\left(Y + \frac{B}{A}X\right)\frac{d\phi}{dR} - \phi\frac{\partial}{\partial R}\left(Y + \frac{B}{A}X\right) + 2\phi\left(Y + \frac{B}{A}X\right)\right\}\cos 2(m\theta - \Psi) \\ &+ \frac{1}{2}\left\{\left(X - \frac{B}{A}Y\right)\frac{d\phi}{dR} - \phi\frac{\partial}{\partial R}\left(X - \frac{B}{A}Y\right) + 2\phi\left(X - \frac{B}{A}Y\right)\right\}\sin 2(m\theta - \Psi).\end{aligned} \tag{3.20}$$

The terms which involve $\cos 2(m\theta - \Psi)$ and $\sin 2(m\theta - \Psi)$ are in general non-vanishing, thus w_1 will consist of a meridional part, a part which varies periodically with the wave and a part which varies periodically with half the fundamental wave length. To derive w_1 we can assume that $w_1 = 0$ at $z = 0$ then w_1 is the integral from 0 to z of the right-hand side of (3.20).

4. Particular examples of the foregoing theory

We consider first the boundary conditions. Since molecular viscosity is ignored, the condition of zero normal velocity has to be satisfied at each of the bounding solid surfaces. Therefore $\partial p/\partial \theta$ must vanish at the cylindrical walls, in other words the function ϕ in (1.58) must be zero at these boundaries. In the non-dimensional scheme in (1.6), the quantity b can be treated as the radius of the outer cylinder, and thus $r^* = b$ of $r = 1$ will represent the outer cylinder. If a is the radius of the inner cylinder, then $r = a/b$ will represent the inner cylinder. In terms of R introduced in (1.40) the outer and inner boundaries will be $R = 0$ and $R = -R_0$ respectively, where $R_0 = \log_e(b/a)$. Thus, the velocity conditions upon $\phi(R)$ reduce to the following:

$$\phi(0) = \phi(-R_0) = 0. \tag{4.1}$$

It is clear from (1.56) that the conditions of constancy of temperature will be satisfied on the two cylindrical boundaries due to (4.1). The only remaining condition upon the temperature field is that the difference in temperature from one cylinder to the other must be $(\Delta T)_H$ at some level. It follows therefore that

$$\tau\,|_{R=0} - \tau\,|_{R=-R_0} = 1. \tag{4.2}$$

In terms of F in (1.56) we must therefore have, at a particular z value,

$$F\,|_{R=0} - F\,|_{R=-R_0} = \frac{m}{\epsilon}. \tag{4.3}$$

Up to the present the function $A(z)$, introduced originally in (1.33), has been left arbitrary. It will be seen from (1.51) that $\partial F/\partial R$ is proportional to $1/A$ and that the heat flow at the cylindrical boundaries, namely $\partial F/\partial r$ is also proportional to $1/A$. In order to make the problem as simple as possible, it is proposed to take uniform heat flow over the cylindrical boundaries since there is no guidance from the experiment in this matter, thus with no loss of generality we shall take

$$A = 1, \tag{4.4}$$

in which case the constant j in (1.51) is a measure of the heat flow across a section of unit length of either cylinder. Accordingly, from (1.54), we have

$$B = z + \beta, \tag{4.5}$$

where β is an arbitrary constant. With this choice of A, the solutions (1.56) and (1.58) for T_0 and P_0 become

$$T_0 = F + \phi(R)\cos(m\theta - \Psi), \tag{4.6}$$

$$P_0 = f + \phi(R)\sin(m\theta - \Psi) + (\beta + z)\,\phi(R)\cos(m\theta - \Psi). \tag{4.7}$$

The third term of P_0 evidently becomes increasingly important as z increases, hence the phase difference of the temperature and pressure fields diminishes with increasing height. The constant β is a measure of the difference in phase of the temperature and pressure waves, and the value of β, here arbitrary, can be derived from the experiment; but whether β be positive or negative, the pressure wave will be ahead of the temperature wave at all levels, the departure of the two waves diminishing with increasing height. Thus, the pressure wave has a 'backward tilt', i.e. to the west as in the case of atmospheric troughs. We may also observe that the angular momentum transfer (2.6) will have a parabolic distribution in the vertical when (4.4) and (4.5) are true, and the maximum transfer will take place at the free surface.

It is worth while noting also that we may draw a parallel with the atmosphere where the heat source in the lowest layers (troposphere) is at the equator and in the upper layers (stratosphere) at high latitudes by taking

$$\frac{1}{A} = (z_0 - z)\,e^{-\lambda z}.$$

With this choice of A, equation (1.54) gives for B the value

$$B = -\frac{1}{\lambda} + \left(\beta e^{\lambda z} + \frac{1}{\lambda^2}\right)\Big/(z_0 - z).$$

We note that B has an infinity at the position where $1/A$ changes its sign, that is at the tropopause, and the pressure wave becomes 180° out of phase with the temperature wave in moving through this level. This will be avoided only if β is chosen appropriately.

Returning now to (4.3) and using (4.4), it then follows that the appropriate form of this condition is

$$\int_{R=-R_0}^{R=0} \frac{\partial F}{\partial R} dR = \int_{-R_0}^{0} \{j - \tfrac{1}{2}\phi^2(R)\} dR = \frac{m}{\epsilon}, \tag{4.8}$$

that is

$$jR_0 = \frac{m}{\epsilon} + \frac{1}{2}\int_{-R_0}^{0} \phi^2(R)\, dR. \tag{4.9}$$

Case I. Zero momentum transport; $d\Psi/dR = 0$.

This case may not have much practical significance, but so many of the technical difficulties encountered in general are also met in this simple case that it is worth while devoting considerable attention to it. The equation (1.52) now becomes

$$\frac{d^2\phi}{dR^2} = (m^2 - j)\,\phi + \tfrac{1}{2}\phi^3. \tag{4.10}$$

The first integral of (4.10) is

$$\left(\frac{d\phi}{dR}\right)^2 = (m^2 - j)\,\phi^2 + \tfrac{1}{4}\phi^4 + C, \tag{4.11}$$

where C is an arbitrary constant of integration. The function ϕ vanishes at the two end-points of the range $-R_0 \leqslant R \leqslant 0$; and, assuming that ϕ is a continuous function, it is necessary that $d\phi/dR$ should vanish within the R range. If we suppose that $d\phi/dR$ vanishes when $\phi = \phi_1$, then

$$0 = (m^2 - j)\,\phi_1^2 + \tfrac{1}{4}\phi_1^4 + C, \tag{4.12}$$

and thus

$$\left(\frac{d\phi}{dR}\right)^2 = \tfrac{1}{4}(\phi_1^2 - \phi^2)\,(4j - 4m^2 - \phi_1^2 - \phi^2). \tag{4.13}$$

Clearly it is necessary that

$$4j - 4m^2 - \phi_1^2 > 0 \tag{4.14}$$

in order for $(d\phi/dR)^2$ to be positive near $\phi = 0$; hence j is positive, or alternatively ϕ_1^2 possesses an upper bound $4(j - m^2)$. If we write

$$\phi_2^2 = 4j - 4m^2 - \phi_1^2, \tag{4.15}$$

then

$$\left(\frac{d\phi}{dR}\right)^2 = \tfrac{1}{4}(\phi_1^2 - \phi^2)\,(\phi_2^2 - \phi^2). \tag{4.16}$$

We shall take

$$\phi_2^2 > \phi_1^2, \quad k^2 = \frac{\phi_1^2}{\phi_2^2}, \tag{4.17}$$

since there is no loss of generality in doing this, and ϕ_1 will be taken to be positive. If we write

$$\phi = \phi_1 y, \quad x = \tfrac{1}{2}R\phi_2, \tag{4.18}$$

then (4.16) becomes

$$\left(\frac{dy}{dx}\right)^2 = (1 - y^2)\,(1 - k^2y^2), \tag{4.19}$$

where k^2 is defined in (4.17) and $0 < k^2 < 1$. The solution of (4.19) which vanishes when $R = 0$ or $x = 0$ is the Jacobian elliptic function $y = \operatorname{sn}(x, k)$, and hence the solution of (4.16) which vanishes at $R = 0$ is

$$\phi = \phi_1 \operatorname{sn}\{-\tfrac{1}{2}R\phi_2, k\}, \tag{4.20}$$

where a slight adjustment in sign has been made in order to make $\phi > 0$ when $-R_0 < R < 0$. This elliptic function has an infinite number of zeros since we have

$$\operatorname{sn}(u+2K, k) = -\operatorname{sn}(u, k),$$
$$\operatorname{sn}(u+4Kn, k) = \operatorname{sn}(u, k) \quad (n = 0, 1, 2 \ldots).$$

If that function $\phi(R)$ is chosen which vanishes at the points $R = 0$ and $R = -R_0$ and has one simple maximum in the range $-R_0 \leqslant R \leqslant 0$, then we must have

$$\tfrac{1}{2}R_0\phi_2 = 2K; \tag{4.21}$$

but there are an infinite set of solutions for ϕ, the one which possesses one maximum and one minimum being the case $\frac{1}{2}R_0\phi_2 = 4K$, and the general case is $\frac{1}{2}R_0\phi_2 = 2nK$. These different modes of solution are of course not superposable since the ϕ equation is non-linear and only one of them can exist at any one time. We shall concentrate here on the main mode which is given by (4.21). For this main mode of ϕ with a single maximum $\phi = \phi_1$ at $\frac{1}{2}R_1\phi_2 = K$ where $\operatorname{sn}(K, k) = 1$, it follows that the position of the maximum value is such that $R_1 = \frac{1}{2}R_0$; in terms of r, this indicates that the maximum is at r_1, where $r_1 = r_0^{\frac{1}{2}} = (a/b)^{\frac{1}{2}}$, and in terms of the original variables at $r_1^* = (ab)^{\frac{1}{2}}$, the geometric mean of the radii of the two cylinders.

The quantity K which appears in (4.21) is a function of k, and, when k is known, K can be found from tables. Since $k = \phi_1/\phi_2$ and ϕ_2 is a function of j (4.15), it follows that (4.21) is a relation between j and ϕ_1. We may observe that, since $\phi_1 < \phi_2$, then from (4.15) we obtain

$$\phi_1^2 < 2j - 2m^2 < \phi_2^2. \tag{4.22}$$

If we use (4.9), we obtain a second relation between j and ϕ_1, namely

$$jR_0 = \frac{m}{\epsilon} + \tfrac{1}{2}\phi_1^2 \int_{-R_0}^{0} \operatorname{sn}^2(-\tfrac{1}{2}R\phi_2, k)\, dR$$
$$= \frac{m}{\epsilon} + \frac{\phi_1^2}{\phi_2}\int_0^{2K} \operatorname{sn}^2(x, k)\, dx;$$

hence

$$jR_0 = \frac{m}{\epsilon} + 2k\phi_1 \int_0^{K} \operatorname{sn}^2(x, k)\, dx. \tag{4.23}$$

The complete elliptic integral E of the second kind is defined by

$$E = \int_0^K \operatorname{dn}^2(x, k)\, dx, \tag{4.24}$$

and since $\operatorname{dn}^2(x, k) = 1 - k^2 \operatorname{sn}^2(x, k)$, it follows

$$\int_0^K \operatorname{sn}^2(x, k)\, dx = \frac{K - E}{k^2}; \tag{4.25}$$

hence, from (4.23),

$$jR_0 = \frac{m}{\epsilon} + \frac{2\phi_1}{k}(K-E). \tag{4.26}$$

Equations (4.15), (4.17), (4.21) and (4.26) now represent four independent equations between ϕ_1, ϕ_2, k and j and ϵ. Hence, this can be regarded as a one-parameter problem in the sense that if one of these five quantities is defined then, in theory, the other four can be determined; the quantity ϵ is regarded as a parameter since the quantity ω is the angular velocity of the wave system (not the angular velocity of the apparatus) and is not therefore a prescribed quantity. It is probably most convenient to treat k as the parameter at our disposal in the range $0 < k < 1$. In terms of k we have

$$\phi_2 = \frac{4K}{R_0}, \quad \phi_1 = \frac{4kK}{R_0}, \tag{4.27}$$

$$j = m^2 + \frac{4K^2}{R_0^1}(1+k^2), \tag{4.28}$$

$$\frac{2\omega S b^2}{K} = \frac{1}{\epsilon} = mR_0 + \frac{4K\{2E-K(1-k^2)\}}{mR_0}. \tag{4.29}$$

Using these relations it is possible to throw some light on the conditions necessary for the existence of a particular wave number; their usefulness, however, is much reduced by the fact that the angular velocity ω in (4.29) is the angular velocity of the wave system with respect to fixed space axes and not the angular velocity ω_s of the apparatus as a whole. The difference between ω and ω_s is small and of the order S.

We consider first equation (4.29) which is of the form

$$\omega S = \frac{K}{2b^2}\left\{mR_0 + \frac{\mu^2}{mR_0}\right\}, \tag{4.30}$$

where $\mu^2 = 4K\{2E-K(1-k^2)\}$. For a given $R_0 (= \log b/a)$, a given m and a given k this relation between ω and S in the (ω, S)-plane is a rectangular hyperbola which we denote by Γ. As k varies from 0 to 1, it is easily shown that μ^2 moves from a minimum value of π^2 when $k = 0$ and increases monotonically to $+\infty$ as k tends to 1. Thus, if we let Γ_m denote the rectangular hyperbola

$$\omega S = \frac{K}{2b^2}\left\{mR_0 + \frac{\pi^2}{mR_0}\right\}, \tag{4.31}$$

it follows that as k moves from 0 to 1 the curve Γ in the (ω, S)-plane sweeps out that infinite area $\Gamma > \Gamma_m$ which lies on the side of the curve Γ_m remote from the origin. Since the minimum value of $mR_0 + (\pi^2/mR_0)$, considered as a function of mR_0, is attained when $mR_0 = \pi$ and its value is then 2π, it follows that the curves $\Gamma_1, \Gamma_2, \Gamma_3, \ldots$, corresponding to $m = 1, 2, 3, \ldots$, will move nearer to the origin until that integral value of $m = m^*$ is attained which makes $m^* R_0$ nearest π, and for m values greater than m^* the curves Γ_m will recede from the origin. For example, with $b = 2a$ ($R_0 = 0{\cdot}6931$), the successive curves Γ_s ($s = 1, 2, \ldots, 5$), approach the origin successively, but from $m = 6$ onwards the curves recede from the origin.

If we consider one of these curves, say Γ_1, then given a value of $\omega = \omega'$ and of $S = S'$ we can deduce that if the representative point (ω', S') is on the origin side of the curve Γ_1, then this particular wave number cannot exist with such a rotation and such a Rossby number. Alternatively, if the point (ω', S') is on the side of the curve Γ_1 remote from the origin, then there will be a unique k value in the range $0 < k < 1$ which will define the strength of the corresponding wave. A similar argument will apply to every curve $\Gamma_2, \Gamma_3, \ldots,$ of the family Γ_m, and we then have the following overall results:

(*a*) wave number $m = 1$ cannot exist if the point (ω, S) lies on the origin side of the curve Γ_1;

(*b*) wave numbers $m = 1$, $m = 2$ cannot exist if the point (ω, S) lies on the origin side of the curve Γ_2;

(*c*) wave numbers $m = 1$, $m = 2$, $m = 3$ cannot exist if the point (ω, S) lies on the origin side of the curve Γ_3;

and so on until that particular value of $m = m^*$ is attained which makes $m^* R_0$ nearest π; and for this case and beyond we have

(*d*) no wave numbers can exist if the point (ω, S) lies on the origin side of the curve Γ_{m^*}.

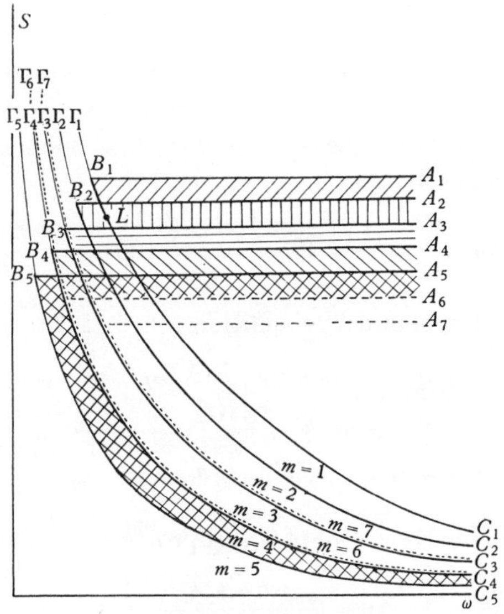

FIGURE 2. A schematic theoretical stability diagram.

In this final case (*d*) the theory does not give any indication of the particular flow pattern which will occur, but it may be inferred that the flow must be the spiral (or symmetric Hadley) type. The results stated in (*a*) to (*d*) above are summarized in diagrammatic form in figure 2.

It is of considerable interest to insert in figure 2 also the results concerning the existence of waves which were obtained by the present author in a stability investigation (1956). These results apply to infinitesimal waves, and the theory in that paper indicates that a wave number m can exist only if the Rossby number is less than a certain critical value. For convenience, table 5 of the earlier paper is reproduced below and expressed in terms of the parameters of this paper, the Rossby number Ro_T^* of the earlier paper being related† to the present S by the formula $S = \frac{1}{2}(1-a/b)\mathrm{Ro}_T^*$ and table 1 refers to the case $b = 2a$. This table is interpreted as follows: spiral flow will exist if $S > 0{\cdot}055$, wave number $m = 1$ can also exist if $S > 0{\cdot}05$, spiral flow and wave numbers $m = 1, 2$ can exist if $S > 0{\cdot}03$ and so on. When we insert the lines $S = 0{\cdot}055$, $S = 0{\cdot}05$; $S = 0{\cdot}03$, and so on, in figure 2 we can interpret the diagram in the following way. On the origin side of the curve $A_1B_1C_1$, the wave number $m = 1$ cannot exist; on the origin side of the curve $A_2B_2C_2$ the wave number $m = 2$ cannot exist, and so on. At such a point as L in this diagram it would then appear that any one of the wave patterns $m = 1$, $m = 2$ or $m = 3$ can exist; other factors must clearly enter into the discrimination between these possible wave patterns since only one wave is known to exist at any one time.

(Mean temperature 21 °C, $\alpha = 2{\cdot}1 \times 10^{-4}$)

Wave number m	0	1	2	3	4	5
Critical value of S	0·07	0·055	0·05	0·03	0·02	0·01

TABLE 1. Annulus case $b = 2a$

We now consider the heat transported by a particular wave pattern, this being equal to the heat flow across either of the cylindrical boundary walls. The heat flow per unit axial length across $r^* = b$ is given by

$$Q = \rho_0 c_p \kappa \int_0^{2\pi} \frac{\partial \tau^*}{\partial r^*} r^* \bigg|_{r^*=b} d\theta = \rho_0 c_p \kappa \frac{\epsilon}{m} (\Delta T)_H \int_0^{2\pi} \frac{\partial T}{\partial R}\bigg|_{R=0} d\theta.$$

Using (1.51) and also the boundary condition $\phi = 0$ at $R = 0$, we obtain

$$Q = Q(m,k) = \frac{2\pi\kappa\rho_0 c_p j \epsilon (\Delta T)_H}{mA(z)}$$

$$= 2\pi\kappa\rho_0 c_p m^{-1} (\Delta T)_H \epsilon \left\{ m^2 + \frac{4\kappa^2(1+k^2)}{R_0^2} \right\}.$$

The Nusselt number Nu (Hide 1958) for this problem may be defined by

$$\mathrm{Nu} = \frac{(b-a)Q}{2\pi b\kappa\rho_0 c_p (\Delta T)_H}; \tag{4.32}$$

and thus in the case $A = 1$ we have

$$\mathrm{Nu} = \frac{(1-a/b)}{R_0} \frac{m^2R_0^2 + 4K^2(1+k^2)}{m^2R_0^2 + 4K\{2E - K(1-k^2)\}}. \tag{4.33}$$

It is easily shown that $(1-a/b)/R_0$ is the Nusselt number for an annulus of solid but uniform material when the cylindrical boundaries are subject to a differential temperature; and if this basic Nusselt number is denoted by Nu*, it follows that

† The small error due to the angular velocity definitions being slightly different will be ignored here.

the presence of liquid in the annulus has the effect of increasing the effective Nusselt number in the ratio

$$\frac{\mathrm{Nu}}{\mathrm{Nu}^*} = \frac{m^2R_0^2+4K^2(1+k^2)}{m^2R_0^2+4K\{2E-K(1-k^2)\}}. \tag{4.34}$$

If k is near zero we have $\mathrm{Nu} \doteqdot \mathrm{Nu}^*$, but if k is near its upper limit of unity we have $K \sim \log(4/\sqrt{(1-k^2)})$, $E \sim 1$, so that

$$\frac{\mathrm{Nu}}{\mathrm{Nu}^*} \sim \frac{K}{E} = \log\left(\frac{4}{\sqrt{(1-k^2)}}\right). \tag{4.35}$$

Thus the heat flow can be increased indefinitely if k can be made to tend to unity.

It is possible to use this concept of heat transport in order to help discriminate between different regions in the (ω, S)-plane. Consider the point L in the (ω, S)-plane which lies on Γ_1, and which is in the zone between A_2B_2 and A_3B_3. At this point, waves $m = 1$ and $m = 2$ are possible. Reckoned relative to the curve Γ_1, the value of k at L is 0, and the associated Nu for this point will be

$$(\mathrm{Nu})_{L,m=1} = \mathrm{Nu}^*.$$

At this same point the value of k reckoned relative to the curve Γ_2 is k_2, where

$$\mu^2(k_2) = 2(\pi^2-R_0^2),$$

and the corresponding value of Nu is

$$(\mathrm{Nu})_{L,m=2} = \mathrm{Nu}^* \frac{4R_0^2+4K^2(k_2)(1+k_2^2)}{4R_0^2+4K(k_2)[2E(k_2)-K(k_2)(1-k_2^2)]} > \mathrm{Nu}^*.$$

Hence, the $m = 2$ wave at L is capable of transporting more heat than the $m = 1$ wave. If one then assumes that the preferred liquid motion is always that one which transports the greatest amount of heat, then the point L will correspond to the $m = 2$ wave. A similar argument will apply to any point in the restricted zone between A_2B_2 and A_3B_3, and consequently this zone will correspond to the $m = 2$ wave. Kuo (1957), in a stability investigation, discusses this same zone between A_2B_2 and A_3B_3 and arrives at a similar conclusion using a different method, namely that in moving across A_2B_2 into this zone the $m = 2$ wave is the one which has maximum growth rate.

On this basis the whole of the (ω, S)-plane can be subdivided into definite regions where one can expect symmetric flow, wave number 1, wave number 2 and so on, and the complete picture is shown in figure 2.† We can look upon the lines A_1B_1, A_2B_2, ... as lines of dynamical instability, that is where the infinitesimal amplitude waves successively become resonated, and upon the curves $\Gamma_1, \Gamma_2, \ldots$ as curves of heating instability where the liquid has to change its wave pattern due to the amount of heat available being excessive or insufficient to maintain a particular wave form.

If we apply the heat transport argument to a point in the (ω, S)-plane which lies on Γ_6 and is in the zone between A_6B_6 and A_7B_7 (we deal specifically here with the

† The scales used in the schematic diagram (figure 2) may be inferred from the fact that the right-hand side of (4.30) has the order of magnitude 10^{-5}.

case $b = 2a$), it follows that, since Γ_6 is on the side of Γ_5 remote from the origin, the heat transport associated with $m = 6$ is less than that associated with $m = 5$. Thus, in such a geometrical configuration the maximum possible amount of heat can be transported by the steady wave $m = 5$, and beyond this m value the steady waves become less efficient as transporters of heat. It is of course not possible by this argument to prove that wave numbers 6, 7, 8, ..., cannot occur, but they are certainly less efficient as transporters of heat than is wave number 5.

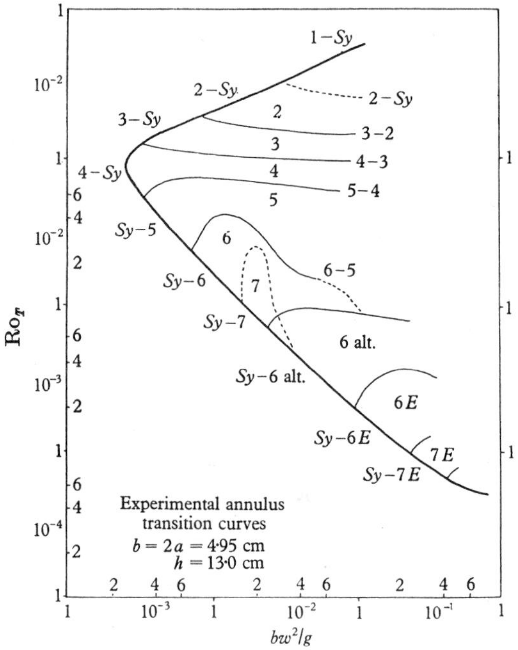

FIGURE 3. Experimental annulus transition curves obtained by Fultz.

We may compare figure 2 with one recently prepared by Fultz for the case $b = 2a$. The ordinate in the Fultz diagram, figure 3, is the Rossby number and the abscissa is a quantity proportional to ω_s^2; and it will be noted that there is a broad overall agreement between the two diagrams. There is a considerable complexity in the Fultz diagram for the lowest Rossby numbers where wave numbers 6 and 7 appear, and Fultz has described this region as containing types of instability which are inherently complicated. It is significant that this region of complicated wave features is associated in the theoretical investigation with the heat transport attaining its maximum value on Γ_5. Assuming that the value m^* gives an indication of the maximum number of steady waves in any given geometrical configuration, we have in general

$$m^* = \left[\frac{\pi}{R_0}\right] = \left[\frac{\pi}{\log(b/a)}\right], \tag{4.36}$$

where $[x]$ denotes that integral value which is closest to x. As b approaches a, $\log(b/a)$ tends to zero and m^* becomes large (this is observed experimentally; up to 15 waves have been produced in a sufficiently narrow annulus); as a tends to zero and lies in the range $0 < a < be^{-\pi}$, it would appear that no steady wave motion is then possible.

For moderate values of k the typical magnitude of Nu from (4.33) is 2 or 3; Fultz in a private communication gives values of Nu which are of order 30 and over. It is clear therefore that the process of molecular conduction as assumed here cannot be the correct one for the transfer of heat in this problem. It is possible of course to postulate the existence of an eddy conductivity in order to achieve the correct order of magnitude for the heat transfer, but the more correct conclusion is probably that the bulk of the heat transfer is effected by the ageostrophic flow. In this same communication, Fultz states that 'there is a faint indication of an increase of Nu with m or some possibility of a maximum for intermediate m; it is also probable that there might be local maxima in the regions of strong vacillation'. This is in qualitative agreement with the picture described above, and it is possible to accept the present theory in as much as it provides insight into the mechanism of the change-over from one wave pattern to another. In this respect also we may compare (4.36) with an experimental result due to Hide, namely

$$\frac{m^*}{\pi}\left(\frac{b-a}{b+a}\right) = 0{\cdot}67. \qquad (4.37)$$

Since
$$\log\left(\frac{b}{a}\right) = 2\left\{\left(\frac{b-a}{b+a}\right) + \frac{1}{3}\left(\frac{b-a}{b+a}\right)^3 + \dots\right\},$$

it follows from (4.36) that we have approximately

$$\frac{m^*}{\pi}\left(\frac{b-a}{b+a}\right)\left\{1 + \frac{1}{3}\left(\frac{b-a}{b+a}\right)^2 + \dots\right\} = 0{\cdot}5;$$

and thus this also provides some justification for accepting (4.36) as the upper limit of the wave number.

The function ϕ being known, the functions F and f can now be determined. Using (4.4) and (1.51), we have

$$F = jR - \tfrac{1}{2}\phi_1^2\int_{-R}^{0} \mathrm{sn}^2\{-\tfrac{1}{2}R\phi_2, k\}\,dR, \qquad (4.38)$$

there being no loss of generality in making $F = 0$ for $R = 0$. This gives the mean temperature field in the liquid. The mean pressure field f is given by (1.53); and in the present case $d\Psi/dR = 0$, we have

$$\frac{\partial f}{\partial R} = (\beta + z)(j - \tfrac{1}{2}\phi^2),$$

and
$$f = (\beta+z)\left\{jR - \tfrac{1}{2}\phi_1^2\int_{-R}^{0} \mathrm{sn}^2\{-\tfrac{1}{2}R\phi_2, k\}\,dR\right\} + \text{constant}. \qquad (4.39)$$

As mentioned earlier the profiles of mean temperature and mean pressure at any height z are identical.

Since
$$j - \tfrac{1}{2}\phi_1^2 = m^2 + \frac{4k'^2K^2}{R_0^2}$$

from (4.27) it follows that $\partial F/\partial R$ is always positive; and thus the mean temperature and mean pressure therefore increase monotonically with r. The minimum gradient will be encountered at $r^* = (ab)^{\frac{1}{2}}$ and the maxima of the gradient and therefore the maximum mean zonal velocity at the cylindrical walls. The action of viscosity in practice may invalidate this result near the bounding walls of the annulus.

Case II. Momentum transport proportional to $\phi^2(R)$; $d\Upsilon/dR$ = constant

In this case we shall assume that

$$\frac{d\Upsilon}{dR} = m\lambda, \tag{4.40}$$

where λ is a constant. This implies that $\Upsilon = m\lambda \log r$, and also, from (2.5) and (2.6), that the angular momentum transport is proportional to $\phi^2(R)$. Since ϕ vanishes at the bounding cylindrical walls and attains a maximum in the liquid between, it follows that the angular momentum shows a similar type of profile, and in order to produce such a horizontal transfer there will be in this case a mechanism supplying or withdrawing westerly angular momentum in the vertical direction. The equation (1.52) in this case becomes

$$\frac{dR^2}{d^2\phi} = (m^2 + m^2\lambda^2 - j)\,\phi + \tfrac{1}{2}\phi^3; \tag{4.41}$$

and, comparing (4.41) with (4.10), it is clear that the only difference between Case I and Case II lies in the coefficient of ϕ and that all the results pertaining to this case can be deduced from Case I provided m^2 is replaced by $m^2(1+\lambda^2)$. Thus, the formulae which replace (4.27) and which apply to this case will be

$$\left.\begin{aligned} \phi_2 = \frac{4K}{R_0}, \quad \phi_1 = \frac{4kK}{R_0}, \\ j = m^2(1+\lambda^2) + \frac{4K^2}{R_0^2}(1+k^2), \\ \frac{1}{\epsilon} = mR_0(1+\lambda^2) + \frac{4K}{mR_0}\{2E - K(1-k^2)\}. \end{aligned}\right\} \tag{4.42}$$

The formula for F, the mean zonal temperature, will be the same as (4.29), but the formula for $\partial f/\partial R$, given by (1.53), is in this case

$$\frac{\partial f}{\partial R} = (\beta + z)\,(j - \tfrac{1}{2}\phi^2) + 2m\lambda \frac{d}{dR}(\log \phi). \tag{4.43}$$

The solution for f, the mean zonal pressure, will be

$$f = (\beta + z)\left\{jR - \tfrac{1}{2}\phi_1^2 \int_{-R}^{0} \mathrm{sn}^2\,(-\tfrac{1}{2}R\phi_2, k)\,dR\right\} + 2m\lambda \log \phi, \tag{4.44}$$

and, since ϕ vanishes at the two bounding walls it will be seen that the mean zonal pressure and mean zonal velocity have singularities at the boundaries.

Case III. Momentum transfer proportional to ϕ^3; $d\Psi/dR = \gamma\phi(R)$

One of the objections to the previous case is that the mean zonal pressure and velocity fields have singularities at the cylindrical bounding walls. Here we investigate a solution which does not suffer from this disadvantage. The formula (1.53) for $\partial f/\partial R$ indicates that the singularity in the zonal velocity arises from the term $\dfrac{1}{\phi^2}\dfrac{d}{dR}\left(\phi^2\dfrac{d\Psi}{dR}\right)$ on the right-hand side; and provided $d\Psi/dR$ has a simple zero at each of the bounding walls, the singularity will not arise. If, for example, Ψ is such that

$$\frac{d\Psi}{dR} = \gamma\phi^s, \tag{4.45}$$

where $s \geqslant 1$, then the singularity of $\partial f/\partial R$ is avoided. We consider here the particular case $s = 1$, and shall take

$$\frac{d\Psi}{dR} = \gamma\phi \quad (\gamma = \text{constant}); \tag{4.46}$$

but the best possible value of s to choose must await a closer comparison with experiment. Whatever the deficiencies of this choice it has the great merit that the problem can be completely solved in this case and thus we can find what modifications are introduced into the solution by the presence of an angular momentum transfer.

Equation (1.52) for ϕ now becomes

$$\frac{d^2\phi}{dR^2} = (m^2-j)\,\phi + (\gamma^2+\tfrac{1}{2})\,\phi^3, \tag{4.47}$$

and this case can, as before, be solved in terms of elliptic functions. The first integral of (4.47) is

$$\left(\frac{d\phi}{dR}\right)^2 = (m^2-j)\,\phi^2 + (\tfrac{1}{4}+\tfrac{1}{2}\gamma^2)\,\phi^4 + \text{constant},$$

and if we suppose that $d\phi/dR$ vanishes when $\phi = \phi_1$, it follows that this equation can be expressed in the form

$$\left(\frac{d\phi}{dR}\right)^2 = \left(\frac{1+2\gamma^2}{4}\right)(\phi_1^2-\phi^2)(\phi_2^2-\phi^2), \tag{4.48}$$

where
$$\phi_2^2 = \frac{4(j-m^2)}{1+2\gamma^2} - \phi_1^2 > 0. \tag{4.49}$$

As before there is no loss of generality in taking $\phi_2 > \phi_1$, and we shall choose $k = \phi_1/\phi_2$, where $0 < k < 1$. The appropriate solution of (4.49) is

$$\phi = \phi_1\,\mathrm{sn}\{-\tfrac{1}{2}R\phi_2\sqrt{(1+2\gamma^2)}, k\}, \tag{4.50}$$

and this will satisfy both boundary conditions (4.1) provided

$$\tfrac{1}{2}R_0\phi_2\sqrt{(1+2\gamma^2)} = 2K. \tag{4.51}$$

The solution (4.50) has its maximum at the geometrical mean value $r^* = (ab)^{\frac{1}{2}}$; thus, this result is not influenced by momentum transport. The condition (4.9) becomes

$$jR_0 = \frac{m}{\epsilon} + \frac{2\phi_2}{\sqrt{(1+2\gamma^2)}}(K-E), \tag{4.52}$$

and thus the four equations which generalize the set (4.27) to (4.29) are as follows:

$$\phi_2 = \frac{4K}{R_0\sqrt{(1+2\gamma^2)}}, \quad \phi_1 = \frac{4Kk}{R_0\sqrt{(1+2\gamma^2)}}, \tag{4.53}$$

$$j = m^2 + \frac{4K^2(1+k^2)}{R_0^2}, \tag{4.54}$$

$$\frac{m}{\epsilon} = m^2 R_0 + \frac{\nu^2}{R_0}, \tag{4.55}$$

where
$$\nu^2 = \frac{4K}{1+2\gamma^2}\{2E - K[(1-k^2) - 2\gamma^2(1+k^2)]\}. \tag{4.56}$$

These equations can be interpreted as in the first case. It is easily shown that the quantity ν^2 defined in (4.56) increases monotonically from the value π^2 at $k = 0$ to infinity as k tends to unity, and thus it follows that all the detailed features of the stability diagram are not influenced by momentum transfer, in particular the result (4.36) for the maximum number of waves remains unchanged.

The formula for the mean temperature field is similar to the previous case, and is given by

$$F = jR - \tfrac{1}{2}\phi_1^2 \int_{-R}^{0} \mathrm{sn}^2\{-\tfrac{1}{2}R\phi_2\sqrt{(1+2\gamma^2)}, k\}\, dR. \tag{4.57}$$

The mean zonal velocity field $\partial f/\partial r$ can be deduced from $\partial f/\partial R$ using (1.53) and (4.37), which give

$$\frac{\partial f}{\partial R} = \frac{B}{A}(j - \tfrac{1}{2}\phi^2) - 3\gamma\frac{d\phi}{dR}; \tag{4.58}$$

and thus the solution for the mean zonal pressure function becomes

$$f = (\beta + z)\left\{jR - \tfrac{1}{2}\phi_1^2 \int_{-R}^{0} \mathrm{sn}^2(-\tfrac{1}{2}R\phi_2\sqrt{(1+2\gamma^2)}, k)\, dR\right\} - 3\gamma\phi(R) + \text{constant}. \tag{4.59}$$

In the case of zero momentum transfer ($\gamma = 0$), it was noted that $\partial f/\partial F$ maintains the same sign for all values of R in the range $-R_0 \leqslant R \leqslant 0$, but in (4.46) it will be observed that

$$\left(\frac{\partial f}{\partial R}\right)_{R=0} = (\beta + z)j + \tfrac{3}{2}\gamma\sqrt{(1+2\gamma^2)}\,\phi_1\phi_2, \tag{4.60}$$

$$\left(\frac{\partial f}{\partial R}\right)_{R=-R_0} = (\beta + z)j - \tfrac{3}{2}\gamma\sqrt{(1+2\gamma^2)}\,\phi_1\phi_2, \tag{4.61}$$

so that if γ is negative and sufficiently large (which ensures a transfer of westerly angular momentum towards $r = 0$) or if β is sufficiently small, then the possibility exists of a reversal in the direction of the mean zonal velocity. This suggests that the presence of easterlies embedded in a westerly zonal flow implies an angular momentum flow, as is well known to meteorologists. Using (4.48), we can say that if $\gamma < 0$ and

$$|\gamma \sqrt{(1+2\gamma^2)}\, \phi_1 \phi_2| > \tfrac{2}{3}\beta, \tag{4.62}$$

then easterlies will appear near the outer (hotter) cylinder.

It is of some interest in this case to determine the meridional part of the vertical velocity which is given by (3.18). We have

$$\frac{r^4(\partial \overline{w}_1/\partial z)}{\epsilon^3 m^{-4}(1+z^2)\gamma} = \frac{1}{2}\frac{d^2}{dR^2}(\phi^3) - \frac{d}{dR}(\phi^3)$$

$$= 3\phi\left\{\tfrac{1}{2}\phi\frac{d^2\phi}{dR^2} + \left(\frac{d\phi}{dR}\right)^2 - \phi\frac{d\phi}{dR}\right\}. \tag{4.63}$$

Near the boundary walls the right-hand side behaves like $3\phi(d\phi/dR)^2$; hence the mean vertical velocity will be upwards ($w_1 = 0$, $z = 0$). At the position of maximum ϕ, we have $d\phi/dR = 0$; hence the right-hand side is $\frac{3}{2}\phi^2 d^2\phi/dR^2$, which is necessarily negative. Hence, in the neighbourhood of the maximum value of ϕ, the mean vertical velocity is downwards. This velocity implies the existence of at least two cells, a direct cell near the outer cylinder and an indirect cell near the inner cylinder, and by considering the changes of sign of $\frac{1}{2}\phi\phi'' + \phi'^2 - \phi\phi'$ it may be verified that there are two and only two zeros of $\overline{w}_1$ between $R = 0$ and $R_1 = -R_0$, and hence there are only two cells in the meridional structure.

Case IV. The open dishpan problem. Non-existence of a continuous solution for ϕ

In this case we assume that the inner cylinder is removed and the liquid is enclosed by one cylinder of radius b. The boundary conditions to be satisfied by the function ϕ are now as follows. At the outer cylinder the normal velocity must vanish hence as before we must have $\phi(0) = 0$. At the central axis $r = 0$, or $R = -\infty$, since there is no source along the axis it is necessary that $\partial p/\partial\theta$ should vanish along the axis, hence $\phi(-\infty) = 0$. In addition, since u_θ must vanish at $r = 0$, it is necessary that $\phi'(-\infty) = 0$. Hence we must have

$$\phi(0) = 0, \quad \phi(-\infty) = \phi'(-\infty) = 0.$$

Since two derivatives vanish at $R = -\infty$, it follows from (4.38) that all the derivatives will vanish there, hence $\phi \equiv 0$. Thus, no continuous non-zero solution exists.

REFERENCES

Davies, T. V. 1953 *Rep. Aero. Res. Coun., Lond.*, no. 15876.

Davies, T. V. 1956 *Phil. Trans.* A, **249**, 27.

Fultz, D. 1956 Studies in experimental hydrodynamics applied to large scale meteorological phenomena. *Final Report Part I, Hydrodynamics Laboratory, Dept. of Meteorology, University of Chicago, Figure B.* 84.

Fultz, D. & Riehl, H. 1957 *Quart. J. Roy. Met. Soc.* **83**, 215.

Hide, R. 1958 *Phil. Trans.* A, **250**, 441.

Kuo, H. L. 1957 *Scientific Rep. No.* 7. *General Circulation Project, Massachusetts Inst. of Tech., Dept. of Meteorology.*

Lorenz, E. 1957 *Scientific Rep. No.* 9, *General Circulation Project, Massachusetts Inst. of Tech., Dept. of Meteorology.*

Phillips, N. 1956 *Quart. J. Roy. Met. Soc.* **82**, 125.

Rogers, R. H. 1959 *J. Fluid Mech.* **5**, 41.

82 JOURNAL OF METEOROLOGY VOLUME 13

Reprinted from *Journal of Meteorology*, Vol. 13, No. 1, Feb., 1956, published by the American Meteorological Society.

ENERGY-RELEASING PROCESSES AND STABILITY OF THERMALLY DRIVEN MOTIONS IN A ROTATING FLUID

By H.-L. Kuo

Massachusetts Institute of Technology [1]

(Manuscript received 3 January 1955)

ABSTRACT

The effects of the various physical factors on the motions produced by differential heating in a rotating fluid are examined by solving the simultaneous hydrodynamic and thermodynamic equations. It is shown that both the rotation Ω and static stability s tend to inhibit the motion by increasing the resistance of the fluid. These resistances are proportional, respectively, to $4\Omega^2 d^{-2}$ and gsa^{-2}, where d and a are the vertical and horizontal scales of the motion, and g is the acceleration due to gravity. Therefore, the type of the motion produced depends very much on the parameter $S = gsd^2(2\Omega a)^{-2}$. It is also shown that there are two different mechanisms through which the available potential energy produced by the heating is transformed into kinetic energy. One mechanism accomplishes this through the vertical motion associated with the meridional circulation ξ about the zonal axis; another mechanism acts through the circulation η about the north-south axis. The efficiency of the second mechanism is proportional to the rotation Ω and also proportional to the wave number l around the latitude circle, while the efficiency of the first mechanism is independent of these quantities.

The stability of the motion is studied first by expanding the complete solutions of the high-order partial differential equation governing the viscous flow into double Fourier series, and then also by obtaining analytic solutions of a simplified version of the differential equation. It is shown that, at lower rotation rates, symmetric convection is the most favored motion in the sense that its maintenance requires the lowest radial temperature contrast. However, the mean temperature contrast required to maintain the symmetric convection increases with Ω^2 at higher rotation rates, while that required to maintain a wave disturbance first decreases with increasing Ω, and then increases with Ω at very high rotation rates. The motion therefore breaks up into waves at the higher rotation rates. The critical radial temperature contrasts and the Rossby number R_{0T} obtained from the theory agree roughly with the measured values in experiments performed by Fultz.

These thermally driven disturbances produce a poleward and an upward transport of heat and a downward transport of zonal momentum in the zone of positive vertical shear. The maximum upward heat transfer occurs at the level $z = d/2$, and therefore has a cooling effect in the lower layers and a heating effect in the upper layers. This heat transfer is in the direction of producing and maintaining a stable stratification.

1. Introduction and summary of results

The present article is one of a series devoted to the study of the nature of the physical processes that take place in the general circulation of the atmosphere. Among these processes, the ones which maintain the global balance of energy and momentum are fundamental. In the past, the mechanism involved has by-and-large been looked upon as consisting of a large-scale convective process, with ascending motions near the equator and descending motions in higher latitudes, the development of a large zonal velocity being attributed to the deflecting force of the earth's rotation. This theory is very attractive, because it is simple and self-consistent in that it takes both the dynamic and the thermodynamic aspects of the problem into consideration. Serious doubts about the ability of this theory to explain the general circulation of the atmosphere have arisen only in relatively recent years, when observational data revealed that even the upper atmosphere is frequented by numerous large disturbances and does not follow any simple type of motion. The discovery of the strong jet streams in the upper atmosphere, flowing as a meandering river in a broad zonal current, lent more force to the supposition that the large-scale eddies in the atmosphere are not merely random disturbances superimposed on a system of zonal currents which is maintained by the simple convective process, but that they are rather organized disturbances and are integral parts of the general circulation. The statistical studies undertaken by Starr and his group at the Massachusetts Institute of Technology actually show that it is these large-scale disturbances which in reality perform the functions of transporting zonal momentum and energy. Thus, what we call the general circulation must include the secondary circulations such as the cyclones and anticyclones, and also small-scale disturbances even down to the scale of ordinary turbulence. The primary concern of our theoretical studies is to find the effects of

[1] The research reported in this article was sponsored by the Geophysics Research Directorate, Air Force Cambridge Research Center, under Contract No. AF 19(604)-1000.

the different physical factors that make the atmosphere behave as it does, and to explore the physical processes involved.

Previous investigations by the writer (see Kuo, 1953a, and references) show that the variation of the Coriolis parameter and of the mean zonal current with latitude, as manifested by the solutions of the barotropic or vertically-integrated baroclinic vorticity equation, tend to produce a "horizontal damping" effect on the disturbances and to make them tilt in such directions that zonal momentum is transported across latitude circles. The energy source of these disturbances is attributed to the baroclinicity of the atmosphere, as demonstrated by various theoretical studies of the instability of such systems for wave disturbances (see references cited in section 5, below).

However, although both the barotropic and the baroclinic aspects of atmospheric motions have been discussed by many meteorologists, the fundamental question as to what makes the atmosphere behave in this very complicated manner, and not in the simple manner depicted by the convective theory of Hadley, has not been answered by these particular studies. The possibility of having such a simple motion in a fluid under the influences of differential heating and rotation has been demonstrated by the dishpan experiments of Fultz (1951; 1953), which show that, when the rotation rate is low and the meridional temperature gradient is high, the motion actually sets in as symmetric meridional motion with zonal currents produced. The criterion for the onset of such a symmetric disturbance has been discussed by the writer in the previous papers (Kuo, 1954; 1955).

When the rotation rate is relatively high and the meridional temperature gradient small, the motion breaks up into waves; and the number of waves tends to increase with increasing rate of rotation, if the other factors are kept unchanged. The similarity between the flow patterns produced in the experiment at higher rotation rates and those in the atmosphere, even to the extent that a meandering jet stream is also produced in the experiment, indicates that the type of atmospheric motion must also be controlled primarily by the differential heating and rotation. The primary purpose of this article is to investigate how these different physical factors affect the mode of the energy release and the type of motion generated.

Since Fultz' experiments have shed much light on the physical nature of the general circulation of the atmosphere, and also have the desirable feature of having a simple intermediate regime besides the Hadley regime of symmetric convection and the ever-changing Rossby regime, characterized by regular waves, we shall formulate our problem according to the arrangement of the experiments, which may be considered as a simplified version of the atmosphere. The most important factors to be considered are differential heating and rotation. The primary function of the former is to produce and maintain a horizontal and a vertical temperature contrast in the fluid, thereby introducing a buoyancy force and a pressure force on the particles, which are displaced from their equilibrium positions, and creating motion if frictional effects are overcome. The vertical temperature distribution will be assumed as stable, since such a stratification will always be produced as a result of the upward transport of heat by the motion, unless the heating maintains an unstable stratification. In the experiment, especially for the high-rotation regime, these two temperature contrasts seem to be closely related; therefore, it may be possible to represent the thermal effect by a single parameter. However, as the relationship between these two temperature contrasts is still unknown, we may also take them as two separate factors.

As the motion of such a fluid system is ordinarily very complicated, we shall simplify the problem by linearization, assuming that at the initial moment the fluid is rotating at the rate Ω about the vertical axis, and that the differential heating has produced a purely zonal distribution of potential temperature which increases from the pole to the equator and also increases with height. A mean zonal current which increases upward is also assumed, to make the initial state an equilibrium state. A small random disturbance, consisting of all wave numbers, is then introduced, and our problem is to find out what type of motion will result from this initial disturbance. The type of motion that takes place in such a fluid system must depend upon the adjustment to the action of the different factors, for example, adjustment to the factors representing some kind of resistance and those representing the energy supply. The choice which the fluid makes in following a particular type of motion under given circumstances can best be understood if we assume that the motion tends to adopt a form in which the total resistance is made small and the kinetic energy converted from the thermal and potential energy is made large.[2] We shall call this the most favored motion. It is obvious that, if it is possible for a simple regular flow pattern to exist such as is found in the experiment when the fluid is contained between two concentric cylinders, it must be represented by a particular Fourier component of the initial disturbance which receives more energy from the energy-conversion process than is dissipated by friction. If the

[2] Another hypothesis, which may turn out to be of some use when dealing with the non-linear heat-transfer process, is that the motion should take such a form as to be most efficient in transporting heat from the heat source to the cold source. The existence of the strong meandering jet streams is to be expected from such a consideration, since it is a very efficient agent in transporting heat from the heat source to the cold source.

temperature contrast is raised gradually from below the critical value, this wave component will appear first as the critical temperature contrast is exceeded, and it will still be the dominating component even when more wave components are excited simultaneously. Thus, even at a later stage when the departure from the initial equilibrium state is no longer very small, the spectral distribution of the kinetic energy must be determined largely by the initial growth rates of the different wave components, on the assumption that the effects of the non-linear terms are merely to check the growth rate by adjusting the flow pattern. Thus it is reasonable to assume that both the mechanism which converts the available potential energy into kinetic energy and also the characteristic structure of the disturbance, particularly those features that manifest the effect of the temperature distribution, can be obtained by a study of the linearized equations. Our problem then becomes a boundary-value problem.

Since in this article we are interested in finding the lowest temperature contrast required to maintain the disturbances and the transition from one type of flow into another, we must let the rotation rate Ω vary from very small values to large values, and take into consideration the viscous effect. We shall, thus, first solve the eigenvalue problem by expanding the solution of the appropriate high-order viscous partial differential equation in a Fourier expansion, and then solve a more simplified form of the equation in closed mathematical form, the latter treatment also yielding the eigenfunctions, which are needed in discussing the various physical processes.

The computations from the Fourier series expansion show that, when the rotation rate is low, the most favored motion is actually represented by the symmetric convection. At moderately higher rotation rates, the mean temperature contrast required to maintain the symmetric convection continues to increase with increasing Ω, while that required to maintain the wave disturbances decreases with increasing Ω. The rate of decrease is higher with larger wave numbers. The number of waves must therefore tend to increase with increasing rotation rates, according to this study, if the heating is kept constant. At still higher rotation rates, the radial temperature contrast required to maintain the symmetric motion tends to increase according to Ω^2 or faster, while that required to maintain a wave disturbance with wave number $l \geqslant 1$ becomes proportional to Ω, and the most favored wave number seems to be determined almost entirely by the value of the parameter $S = gsd^2(2\Omega a)^{-2}$, where s is the static stability, and d and a are the vertical and the horizontal (radial) scales of the motion. Thus, S seems to be a convenient parameter in determining the dynamic similarity of model experiments for large-scale atmospheric motions. We observe that although the length ratio d/a is very small for the large-scale atmospheric motions, it is compensated by a very large value of the factor $gs/4\Omega^2$. Since this last factor is much smaller in the models than in the atmosphere, a much larger length ratio d/a is needed to produce similarity.

The physical meaning of the parameter S is discussed in section 7, below. It is shown that it represents a relative measure of the inhibiting effects of the stable stratification and of rotation. As has been discussed above, it is reasonable to expect the vertical temperature contrast to be roughly proportional to the mean meridional temperature contrast. The parameter S will then become proportional to the thermal Rossby number R_{0T}; therefore the type of the motion will be determined by the value of R_{0T}, which may be considered as a measure of the total effect of differential heating and rotation. The values of R_{0T} computed from the series expansion for a fixed static stability are in fairly good agreement with Fultz' experimental result.

A much more simplified form of the differential equation is discussed in sections 5 and 6 below, where the viscous effect is replaced by a frictional force proportional to the velocity, and certain other terms are omitted from the equation. The purpose is not so much to obtain a better quantitative result; it is rather to obtain a clearer insight into the physical processes involved. Here the parameter S enters in the analytic solution in the form $\beta^2 = \pi^2 S(1 + l^2\pi^{-2}a^2r_0^{-2})$, where r_0 is the mean distance from the axis of rotation. This solution shows that, to have a disturbance which does not decay, β^2 must be less than 5.7571. Therefore $\beta^2 \leqslant 5.7571$ constitutes a necessary condition for the wave disturbances. The most favored wave obtained from this solution corresponds roughly to $\beta^2 = 2.5792$. When this result is applied to the atmosphere at middle latitudes for disturbances extending to the tropopause level ($d = 10$ km), and we use a normal static stability factor $gs = 1.4 \times 10^{-4}$ sec^{-1}, it is found that the maximum number of non-decaying waves around the latitude circle is about ten; and the most favored wave number is about six, although the variation of the amplifying factor around this most favored wave number is usually slight. The form of β^2 also shows that, if s and d/a remain nearly constant, the number of baroclinically unstable waves decreases toward lower latitudes.

The inclusion of the frictional effect removes certain ambiguities of the theory and also enables us to fix the lowest limit of the mean meridional temperature contrast, or the vertical shear of the mean zonal wind, for maintaining baroclinically amplifying waves. The limiting vertical shear for middle latitude is about 1.2 (m/sec)/km, obtained by assuming a frictional coefficient $c = 0.25$ per day, corresponding to an eddy viscosity $\nu = 3 \times 10^5$ cm^2/sec. The solution gives proper westward tilts of the pressure and vertical-velocity fields and an eastward tilt of the temperature field, for the amplifying, the neutral, and also the slowly decaying disturbances, as distinguished from the results obtained in the previous studies where viscosity has been neglected entirely. From these solutions, we find that these thermally driven large-scale disturbances produce an upward and a poleward transfer of heat and a downward transfer of zonal momentum. The maximum of the upward heat transfer occurs at the level $z = d/2$, and therefore has the effect of heating the upper layers and cooling the lower layers, in the direction of producing and maintaining a stable stratification. The maximum transport is estimated to be about 0.44 cal cm^{-2} min^{-1}, which is quite appreciable, and seems to be of some importance in the heat-balance problem for the upper troposphere, where a radiational cooling is generally present. Such an upward heat transfer by the unstable waves has been suggested by Eady (1949).

The amount of thermal and potential energy converted into kinetic energy can be computed most conveniently from the volume integral of the upward heat transfer, $v_z\theta$. By substituting mean values of the various physical parameters representative for the atmosphere in the solutions, we find that the total energy released is about 2.4×10^{22} ergs/sec or 6.6×10^{-3} cal cm^{-2} min^{-1}, which is roughly equal to the estimated rate of dissipation of the kinetic energy of the atmosphere. The maximum downward transport of geostrophic zonal momentum obtained from these solutions is about 0.3 dyne/cm^2.

To understand the physical meaning of the mathematical results, we investigated the processes that convert thermal and potential energy into kinetic energy and the effects of the various physical factors, mainly through an examination of the governing partial differential equation. Such study reveals that there are two different processes which convert the available thermal and potential energy into kinetic energy. The first one, which is usually considered as the only process which can do this job, acts through the vertical motion associated with the circulation ξ about the x-axis. In this process, the potential energy associated with the undisturbed temperature distribution is released by the motion in the yz-plane at an angle smaller than the slope of the undisturbed isentropic surfaces. This process is independent of Ω and the number of waves, and therefore does not prefer any particular wave component. The other process which converts potential energy into kinetic energy operates through the vertical motion associated with the circulation η about the y-axis, *i.e.*, through the wave-like motion in the xz-plane[3]. The mechanism may be conceived as becoming active after the initial isentropic surface is deformed into a wavy form by the initial disturbance. This process is proportional to the wave number l around the latitude circle and also proportional to the rate of rotation, and therefore is more effective when the rotation rate is high. Thus, if the motion is determined by these factors alone, it must break up into waves at higher rotation rate.

The reason that the large-scale atmospheric motions are very nearly horizontal is explained by the constraining effect of the large static stability, which suppresses the vertical motion and sets up horizontal pressure forces in the fluid to convert the thermal and potential energy released into horizontal kinetic energy. Thus, although vertical motion is instrumental in releasing the available potential energy, vertical kinetic energy never develops to large amounts in the large-scale motions.

The examination of the governing partial differential equation also reveals that the effects of rotation and stable stratification are to increase the stability or resistance of the fluid. These effects are represented by $4\Omega^2\, \partial^2 V/\partial Z^2$ and $gs\, \Delta_h{}^2 V$, respectively, and therefore are inversely proportional to the squares of the vertical and the horizontal scales of motion. Thus, to diminish the rotational resistance, the motion must increase its vertical scale (Taylor effect); to diminish the effect of static stability, the horizontal scale must be increased. Therefore, the ratio of these two terms, as represented by S or β^2, must be a very important factor in determining the form of the motion. However, if the vertical temperature contrast remains roughly proportional to the horizontal temperature contrast, as is suggested in the experimental results, the motion can be specified by a single parameter alone, such as the Rossby number.

[3] A direct check of these different processes in the atmosphere can be obtained by a study of various correlations between the vertical velocity and the temperature fields. Such a study would be of paramount interest.

2. Equations of the problem

The equations of motion, continuity and heat conduction appropriate to the problem are, in cylinder polar co-ordinates (r, λ, z),

$$\frac{dv_r}{dt} - \left(2\Omega + \frac{v_\lambda}{r}\right) v_\lambda = -\frac{1}{\rho}\frac{\partial p}{\partial r} + r\Omega^2 + \nu\left(\nabla^2 v_r - \frac{v_r}{r^2} - \frac{2}{r^2}\frac{\partial v_\lambda}{\partial \lambda}\right), \quad (1)$$

$$\frac{dv_\lambda}{dt} + \left(2\Omega + \frac{v_\lambda}{r}\right) v_r = -\frac{1}{\rho}\frac{1}{r}\frac{\partial p}{\partial \lambda} + \nu\left(\nabla^2 v_\lambda - \frac{v_\lambda}{r^2} + \frac{2}{r^2}\frac{\partial v_r}{\partial \lambda}\right), \quad (2)$$

$$\frac{dv_z}{dt} = -\frac{1}{\rho}\frac{\partial p}{\partial z} - g + \nu\, \nabla^2 v_z, \quad (3)$$

$$\frac{d\rho}{dt} + \rho\left(\frac{\partial r v_r}{r\,\partial r} + \frac{1}{r}\frac{\partial v_\lambda}{\partial \lambda} + \frac{\partial v_z}{\partial z}\right) = 0, \qquad (4)$$

and

$$\rho J C_v \frac{d\theta}{dt} - \frac{p}{\rho}\frac{d\rho}{dt} = Jk\,\nabla^2\theta + q, \qquad (5)$$

where v_r, v_λ and v_Z denote the radial, zonal and vertical velocity-components relative to a system rotating with angular speed Ω; ρ, θ and p represent the density, temperature and pressure, g the gravity, ν and k the coefficients of kinematic viscosity and thermometric conductivity, q the heat added to the fluid other than through conduction, J the mechanical equivalent of heat, and $\nabla^2 = \partial^2/\partial r^2 + r^{-1}\,\partial/\partial r + r^{-2}\,\partial^2/\partial\lambda^2 + \partial^2/\partial z^2$ is the three-dimensional Laplacian operator. We shall assume a constant q, so forced motions produced by a variable heat source in the fluid are being excluded.

As has been discussed, we consider the motion as a superposition of a small disturbance on an equilibrium state of purely zonal flow v_0, which balances the basic meridional temperature contrast maintained by heat conduction alone. The vertical variation of v_0 is related to the basic radial temperature gradient by the thermal-gradient wind relation (Kuo, 1954),

$$\frac{\partial}{\partial z}\,(2\Omega v_0 + v_0^2/r) = g\alpha\,\frac{\partial \theta_0}{\partial r}, \qquad (6)$$

where α is the coefficient of volume expansion, equal to θ_0^{-1} for gases, and θ_0 is the basic temperature maintained by heating. The variation of density with temperature is assumed to be given by $\rho = \bar{\rho}_0(1 - \alpha\,\Delta\theta)$, where $\bar{\rho}_0$ is the density corresponding to a mean temperature $\bar{\theta}_0$, and $\Delta\theta$ is the deviation of the local temperature from $\bar{\theta}_0$.

According to the arrangement of the experiments, the mean temperature θ_0 may either increase at a rate $\partial\theta_0/\partial t = \epsilon$, or remain constant, corresponding to $\epsilon = 0$. Therefore, θ_0 satisfies the heat-conduction equation,

$$k\left(\frac{1}{r}\frac{\partial}{\partial r}\,r\,\frac{\partial \theta_0}{\partial r} + \frac{\partial^2 \theta_0}{\partial z^2}\right) = \frac{\partial \theta_0}{\partial t} = \epsilon, \qquad (7)$$

which has many different solutions. When ϵ differs from zero, the simplest solution is given by

$$\theta_0 = \theta_{00} + \frac{\partial \theta_0}{\partial z}\,z + \frac{\epsilon}{4k}\,r^2. \qquad (8)$$

When $\epsilon = 0$, (7) has the solution

$$\theta_0 = \theta_{00} + \frac{\partial \theta_0}{\partial z}\,z + C\log r, \qquad (9a)$$

and the more general solution

$$\theta_0 = \theta_{00} + \sum_a A_a\,J_0(ar)\cosh a(d - z), \qquad (9b)$$

where a may be either real or imaginary. We note that if only one term of (9b) is used, the mean temperature distribution is completely specified by a single parameter. However, since the observations are ordinarily not represented by such a solution, we shall assume θ_0 as being given by (8) or (9a). Further simplifications are to be introduced whenever desirable.

We note that if the angular velocity $\omega = v_0/r$ is used, the thermal-gradient wind relation (6) and the solution (8) give

$$2(\Omega + \omega)\frac{\partial \omega}{\partial z} = \frac{g\alpha}{r}\frac{\partial \theta_0}{\partial r} = \frac{g\alpha\epsilon}{2k}. \qquad (10)$$

Therefore, ω and $\partial\omega/\partial z$ are independent of r. This assumption excludes the effects of the meridional variation of the basic current from the present investigation.

In a manner similar to the previous treatment of the symmetric motion, we assume the fluid is nearly homogeneous and incompressible; so the effect of the variation of density may be neglected except when it is multiplied by g, where it introduces a "buoyancy force" given by $g\rho_0^{-1}(\rho_0 - \rho) = g\alpha\theta$, with θ now denoting the local temperature departure. This consideration is consistent with the assumption that the actual temperature at a given point is given by $\theta_0 + \theta$. The buoyancy force associated with the centrifugal force $r\Omega^2$ will be disregarded by limiting the discussion to the cases of not-very-high rotation rate, so that the free surface of the fluid is nearly horizontal and the change of depth (D) produced by the rotation is small ($\partial D/\partial r = r\Omega^2/g \ll 1$). Alternatively, we could also take the surfaces parallel to the free surface as the xy-plane, and the z-axis normal to the free surface; then the total force will be in the direction of $-z$.

Since the primary objective in this study is to find the instability criterion and the type of the most favored disturbance that will be produced in the fluid system, we shall restrict ourselves to the early stages of the motion during which the departures of the variables are still small, so that we may linearize the equations of motion and the energy equation. Thus, in the framework of these approximations, these equations are given by

$$\left(L + \frac{\nu}{r^2}\right)v_r - 2\Omega^* v_\lambda = -\frac{\partial \Pi}{\partial r}, \qquad (11)$$

$$\left(L + \frac{\nu}{r^2}\right)v_\lambda + 2\Omega^* v_r = -\,\partial\Pi/r\,\partial\lambda, \qquad (12)$$

$$L(v_Z) = g\alpha\theta - \partial\Pi/\partial z, \qquad (13)$$

$$\left(\frac{\partial}{\partial t} + \omega\frac{\partial}{\partial \lambda} - k\nabla^2\right)\theta + v_r\frac{\partial \theta_0}{\partial r} + v_Z\frac{\partial \theta_0}{\partial z} = 0, \qquad (14)$$

and

$$\frac{\partial r v_r}{\partial r} + \frac{\partial v_\lambda}{\partial \lambda} + r\frac{\partial v_Z}{\partial z} = 0, \qquad (15)$$

where v_r, v_λ and v_Z now denote the perturbation velocity components, Π is the ratio of the perturbation pressure p and the mean density $\bar{\rho}_0$, θ the perturbation temperature, and $L = \partial/\partial t + \omega(\partial/\partial\lambda) - \nu\nabla^2$. It may be noted that the "buoyancy force" $g\alpha\theta$, as it occurs in the vertical equation of motion, is accompanied by a pressure force $\partial\Pi/\partial z$; therefore, it does not necessarily produce vertical acceleration. In applications to the atmosphere, we should consider θ as representing the potential temperature.

Elimination of Π from the first two equations of motion gives the equation for the vertical component of vorticity $\zeta\ [= r^{-1}(\partial r v_\lambda/\partial r - \partial v_r/\partial\lambda)]$,

$$L(\zeta) - 2\Omega^* \frac{\partial v_Z}{\partial z} + \omega_Z \left(r \frac{\partial v_Z}{\partial r} + 2v_Z \right) = 0, \quad (16)$$

where $\Omega^* = \Omega + \omega$, and ω_Z is used for $\partial\omega/\partial z$. This equation indicates that the buoyancy force does not affect the vertical vorticity directly, but only indirectly through the changes it produces on the pressure distribution, the vertical velocity, and the other components of vorticity. Taking the divergence of the first two equations of motion, we obtain

$$L(D_h) - 2\Omega^*\zeta + \omega_Z\, \partial v_Z/\partial\lambda = -\nabla_h^2\Pi, \quad (17)$$

where

$$D_h = r^{-1}(\partial r v_r/\partial r + \partial v_\lambda/\partial\lambda),$$

and

$$\nabla_h^2 = \partial^2/\partial r^2 + r^{-1}\partial/\partial r + r^{-2}\partial^2/\partial\lambda^2$$

is the two-dimensional Laplacian operator. Eliminating Π from (17) and (13), we obtain

$$L\,\nabla^2 v_Z + 2\Omega^*\, \partial\zeta/\partial z + 2\omega_Z\zeta = g\alpha\,\nabla_h^2\theta. \quad (18)$$

It may be remarked that if hydrostatic equilibrium is assumed in (13), the first term of (18) will be $L\,\partial^2 v_Z/\partial z^2$ instead of $L\,\nabla^2 v_Z$. This approximation is valid if the horizontal scale of the motion is much larger than the vertical scale, so that $\partial^2/\partial z^2 \gg \nabla_h^2$. This condition is satisfied by almost all the large-scale disturbances in the atmosphere; therefore, the hydrostatic approximation is quite accurate for them. However, in the experiment the horizontal scale is not very large compared with the vertical scale; therefore, ∇_h^2 is not negligible against $\partial^2/\partial z^2$. Since the inclusion of ∇_h^2 in ∇^2 does not add any real mathematical difficulty to the problem, we shall not use the hydrostatic assumption.

The vorticity ζ can easily be eliminated from (16) and (18) to give

$$L^2\,\nabla^2 v_Z + 4(\Omega^*)^2 \frac{\partial^2 v_Z}{\partial z^2} - 2\Omega^* r\omega_Z \left(\frac{\partial^2 v_Z}{\partial r\,\partial z} - \frac{2}{r}\frac{\partial v_Z}{\partial z} \right) - 2\omega_Z^2 \left(r\frac{\partial v_Z}{\partial r} + 2v_Z \right) = 2\Omega^*\omega_Z \frac{\partial \zeta}{\partial\lambda} + g\alpha L\,\nabla_h^2\theta. \quad (19)$$

On the other hand, if we eliminate v_Z from (16) and (18), we obtain the following equation for ζ:

$$L^2\,\nabla^2\zeta + 4(\Omega^*)^2 \frac{\partial^2\zeta}{\partial z^2} - 2\Omega^* r\omega_Z \left(\frac{\partial^2\zeta}{\partial r\,\partial z} - \frac{2}{r}\frac{\partial\zeta}{\partial z} \right) - 2\omega_Z^2 \left(r\frac{\partial\zeta}{\partial r} + 2\zeta \right) = -2\Omega^*\omega_Z \frac{\partial}{\partial\lambda}\nabla^2 v_Z + g\alpha\left[2\Omega^* \frac{\partial}{\partial z}\nabla_h^2\theta - \omega_Z \left(r\frac{\partial}{\partial r} + 2 \right)\nabla_h^2\theta \right]. \quad (20)$$

It is seen that the buoyancy force represented by $g\alpha\theta$ is involved in this equation.

To obtain an equation in v_Z alone, we apply the operators $L_1 = \partial/\partial t + \omega\partial/\partial\lambda - k\nabla^2$ and L to (19),

TABLE 1. Coefficients of unknowns of (44).

Equation	B_{11}	B_{13}	B_{31}	B_{33}	B_{21}	B_{23}	CB_{22}	CB_{12}	CB_{32}
1–1:	ϕ_{11}	0	0	0	0	0	$\frac{8}{9}$	$-\frac{2}{9}q_{12}(7+\alpha_{12})$	0
1–3:	0	ϕ_{13}	0	0	0	0	$-\frac{8}{5}$	$\frac{6q_{12}}{25}(1-\alpha_{12})$	0
3–1:	0	0	ϕ_{31}	0	0	0	$-\frac{8}{15}$	0	$-\frac{2}{9}q_{32}(7+\alpha_{32})$
3–3:	0	0	0	ϕ_{33}	0	0	$\frac{24}{25}$	0	$\frac{6q_{32}}{25}(1+\alpha_{32})$
2–1:	0	0	0	0	ϕ_{21}	0	$-\frac{2}{9}q_{22}(7+\alpha_{22})$	$-\frac{2}{9}$	$\frac{6}{5}$
2–3:	0	0	0	0	0	ϕ_{23}	$\frac{6q_{22}}{25}(1+\alpha_{22})$	$\frac{2}{5}$	$-\frac{54}{25}$
2–2:	$\frac{2}{9}$	$-\frac{2}{5}$	$-\frac{6}{5}$	$\frac{54}{25}$	$\frac{2}{9}q_{21}(2-\alpha_{21})$	$-\frac{6q_{23}}{25}(14+\alpha_{23})$	$\phi_{22}x$	0	0
1–2:	$\frac{2}{9}q_{11}(2-\alpha_{11})$	$-\frac{6q_{13}}{25}(14+\alpha_{13})$	0	0	$-\frac{8}{9}$	$\frac{8}{5}$	0	$\phi_{12}x$	0
3–2:	0	0	$\frac{2}{9}q_{31}(2-\alpha_{31})$	$-\frac{6q_{33}}{25}(14+\alpha_{33})$	$\frac{8}{15}$	$-\frac{24}{25}$	0	0	$\phi_{32}x$

and combine it with (14) and (16). On making use of the identities

$$\nabla_h^2(rv_r) \equiv -\frac{\partial\zeta}{\partial\lambda} - \frac{1}{r}\frac{\partial^2}{\partial r\,\partial z}(r^2 v_Z), \tag{21}$$

and

$$L\frac{\partial}{\partial z} \equiv \frac{\partial}{\partial z}L - \omega_Z\frac{\partial}{\partial\lambda},$$

we finally obtain

$$L_1\left[L^2\,\nabla^2 v_Z + 4(\Omega^*)^2\frac{\partial^2 v_Z}{\partial z^2}\right] + gsL\,\nabla_h^2 v_Z$$
$$= \left(\frac{gs_r}{r} + 2\Omega^*\omega_Z\frac{L_1}{L}\right)\left[rL\frac{\partial^2 v_Z}{\partial r\,\partial z} + 2\Omega^*\frac{\partial^2 v_Z}{\partial\lambda\,\partial z} - \omega_Z\frac{\partial}{\partial\lambda}\left(r\frac{\partial v_Z}{\partial r} + 2v_Z\right)\right], \tag{22}$$

where $s = \alpha\,\partial\theta_0/\partial z$ and $s_r = \alpha\,\partial\theta_0/\partial r$. Here we have neglected a few rather small terms and have written L_1/L as a ratio in the terms arising from ω_Z, to simplify the form of this equation. If there is no basic current in the fluid, these terms disappear. In view of the fact that, for the case of marginal instability and symmetric motion, this ratio L_1/L is equal to k/ν, while for a non-viscous fluid and adiabatic motion it is equal to unity, it seems one may replace this ratio by a constant as an approximation even for the general cases. For the present problem it is convenient to take (22) as the governing equation and to derive the other quantities from the solution v_Z. Thus, the vorticity ζ can be obtained directly from (16). To obtain the horizontal velocity v_h, it is convenient to decompose it into an irrotational part $-\nabla\phi$ and a solenoidal part $\nabla \times \psi$ by the following substitutions:

$$v_r = -\frac{\partial\phi}{\partial r} - \frac{1}{r}\frac{\partial\psi}{\partial\lambda}, \quad v_\lambda = -\frac{1}{r}\frac{\partial\phi}{\partial\lambda} + \frac{\partial\psi}{\partial r}, \tag{23}$$
$$\partial v_Z/\partial z = \nabla_h^2\phi, \quad \text{and} \quad \zeta = \nabla_h^2\psi.$$

Equation (16) then gives

$$L\left(\frac{\partial\psi}{\partial z}\right) + \omega_Z\frac{\partial\psi}{\partial\lambda} = 2\Omega^*\frac{\partial\phi}{\partial z} - r\omega_Z\frac{\partial\phi}{\partial r}. \tag{24}$$

From this we find that v_r and v_λ are given by the following relations:

$$\frac{\partial}{\partial z}L(v_r) = -L\frac{\partial^2\phi}{\partial r\,\partial z} - \frac{2\Omega}{r}\frac{\partial^2\phi}{\partial\lambda\,\partial z},$$

and (25)

$$\frac{\partial}{\partial z}L(v_\lambda) = -L\frac{1}{r}\frac{\partial^2\phi}{\partial\lambda\,\partial z} + 2\Omega\frac{\partial^2\phi}{\partial r\,\partial z} - r\omega_Z\,\nabla_h^2\phi.$$

After finding v_Z and v_h, we may find the perturbation pressure p and the perturbation temperature θ from (17) and (14).

It may be remarked that (22) governs the motions produced by differential heating in a rotating fluid, including ordinary convection associated with an unstable vertical stratification. Since such convective motions are generally of rather short period, they will be excluded from the present study by the assumption of a stable vertical stratification ($\partial\theta_0/\partial z > 0$), which is generally the case when the heating does not sustain an unstable lapse rate. Thus, for our problem, the energy source is represented solely by the terms depending on the radial temperature gradient.

For the large-scale quasi-horizontal motions, it seems desirable to deal with an equation for the horizontal motion instead of v_Z. Thus, applying L_1 to (20) and making use of (14), (16), (18) and (21), we obtain

$$L_1\left[L^2\,\nabla^2\zeta + 4(\Omega^*)^2\frac{\partial^2\zeta}{\partial z^2}\right] + gs\,\nabla_h^2 L\zeta$$
$$- \left(\frac{gs_r}{r} + 2\Omega\omega_Z\frac{L_1}{L}\right)\left[rL\frac{\partial^2\zeta}{\partial r\,\partial z} + 2\Omega\frac{\partial^2\zeta}{\partial\lambda\,\partial z} - \omega_Z\frac{\partial}{\partial\lambda}\left(r\frac{\partial\zeta}{\partial r} + 2\zeta\right)\right]$$
$$= -2g\alpha\Omega\omega_Z\left(1 + \frac{L_1}{L}\right)\frac{\partial}{\partial\lambda}\nabla_h^2\theta. \tag{26}$$

It is seen that this equation has the same form as (22), except for the presence of the terms on the right-hand side. These terms disappear if there is no basic current, *i.e.*, if the motion is starting from relative rest. For this case, the equation for ψ is exactly the same as the equation for v_Z, and so are also the equations for v_r and v_λ. This is also true for the symmetrical motion; then all the terms involving $\partial/\partial\lambda$ disappear. To eliminate θ from (26) for the general case, we must apply other operators again, which will raise the order of this equation. This equation is simplified if we make the assumption that $L\,\nabla^2 v_Z$ is much smaller than the other terms in (18) and can therefore be neglected, which implies that we can also neglect $L(D_h)$ from (17). Thus, the approximate forms of these equations are

$$2\Omega^*\zeta - \omega_Z\,\partial v_Z/\partial\lambda = \nabla_h^2\Pi, \tag{27}$$

and

$$2\Omega^*\,\partial\zeta/\partial z + 2\omega_Z\zeta = g\alpha\,\nabla_h^2\theta. \tag{28}$$

These equations may be called the balance equations for the large-scale motions. Substituting (28) in (26), we obtain

$$L_1\left(L^2\nabla^2\psi + 4\Omega^2\frac{\partial^2\psi}{\partial z^2}\right) + gs\,\nabla_h^2\psi - (gs_rL + 2\Omega^*\omega_Z L_1)\frac{\partial^2\psi}{\partial r\,\partial z}$$
$$+ \omega_Z\left(\frac{gs_r}{r} + 2\Omega^*\omega_Z\frac{L_1}{L}\right)\frac{\partial}{\partial\lambda}\left(r\frac{\partial\psi}{\partial r} + 4\psi\right) = 0. \tag{29}$$

We can also solve this equation and derive other quantities from ψ.

3. Equations governing the stability criterion

In this study, the primary interest is to find the disturbance which grows fastest and the stability criterion that separates the developing disturbances from those that will be damped out. If we represent the rate of growth by the exponential time factor $\exp i\mu t$, this criterion is obtained by setting the imaginary part of μ to zero, while the real part of μ is proportional to the phase velocity of the disturbance and must be determined from the solution. Therefore, the concept of marginal instability is ordinarily not valid. However, in the framework of the approximations used in this study, in which the horizontal variation of the mean current ω and terms involving higher powers of ω are neglected, it can be shown that all the disturbances move with the constant mean angular speed $\bar{\omega}$. For this case, the time derivative can be eliminated by introducing a coordinate system moving with $\bar{\omega}$, which is equivalent to setting $\partial/\partial t$ equal to $-\bar{\omega}\,\partial/\partial\lambda$. We may then use the concept of marginal instability.

To simplify the differential equation, we use $w = r^{\frac{1}{2}}e^{-il\lambda}v_z$ as the dependent variable; then the Laplacian operator becomes

$$\nabla^2 v_z = r^{-\frac{1}{2}}\left(\frac{\partial^2 w}{\partial r^2} + \frac{\partial^2 w}{\partial z^2} - \frac{l^2 - \frac{1}{4}}{r^2}\,w\right)e^{il\lambda}.$$

We now approximate r^{-2} by r_0^{-2}, where $r_0 = (r_1 + r_2)/2$ is the mean radius. It may be remarked that this approximation is equivalent to replacing the Bessel function $Z_l(ar)$ by its asymptotic approximation. Neglecting the term $1/(4r_0^2)$ in the parentheses, and putting $\partial/\partial t + \omega\,\partial/\partial\lambda = il(\omega - \bar{\omega})$, we may write the approximated (22) in the non-dimensional form

$$\left[\nabla_1^6 + \left(\frac{\pi r_0}{d}\right)^2 T\frac{\partial^2}{\partial\zeta^2} + \left(\frac{\pi^2 r_0^2}{a^2}\frac{\partial^2}{\partial\xi^2} - l^2\right)R\right]\nabla_1^2 w$$

$$- \frac{k}{\nu}\left(2 + \frac{k}{\nu}\right)\frac{l^2}{\pi^2}M^2\left(\zeta - \frac{\pi}{2}\right)^2\nabla_1^4 w$$

$$- Q\left[\pi\nabla_1^2\frac{\partial^2 w}{\partial\xi\,\partial\zeta} - \frac{a}{r_0}liT^{\frac{1}{2}}\frac{\partial w}{\partial\zeta}\right.$$

$$\left. + \frac{k}{\nu}liM\left(\frac{\partial w}{\partial\xi} + \frac{2a}{\pi r_0}w\right)\right]$$

$$- \frac{liM}{\pi}\left(\zeta - \frac{\pi}{2}\right)\left[T\frac{\pi^2 r_0^2}{d^2}\frac{\partial^2 w}{\partial\zeta^2}\right.$$

$$+ \frac{k}{\nu}R\left(\frac{\pi^2 r_0^2}{a^2}\frac{\partial^2 w}{\partial\xi^2} - l^2 w\right)$$

$$\left. + \left(1 + \frac{2k}{\nu}\right)\nabla_1^6 w - \frac{k\pi}{\nu}Q\frac{\partial^2 w}{\partial\xi\,\partial\zeta}\right]$$

$$+ \frac{l^3 i}{\pi^3}\frac{k^2}{\nu^2}M^3\left(\zeta - \frac{\pi}{2}\right)^3\nabla_1^2 w = 0, \quad (30)$$

where $\xi = \pi r/a$, $\zeta = \pi z/d$, and $\nabla_1^2 = \pi^2 r_0^2(a^{-2}\,\partial^2/\partial\xi^2 + d^{-2}\,\partial^2/\partial\zeta^2) - l^2$. The origin of r, and therefore also that of ξ, is on the inner cylinder. The non-dimensional parameters T, Q, R and M are defined as follows:[4]

$$T = \frac{4\Omega^2}{\nu^2}r_0^4, \quad Q = \left(1 + \frac{k}{\nu}\right)\frac{\pi r_0^6}{ad}\frac{g\alpha}{k\nu}\frac{\partial\theta_0}{\partial r},$$

$$R = \frac{g\alpha}{k\nu}\frac{\partial\theta_0}{\partial z}r_0^4, \quad \text{and} \quad M = \frac{dr_0^2}{k}\omega_z. \tag{31}$$

Thus, T is a parameter which measures the effect of rotation, Q measures the effect of the mean meridional temperature contrast, R measures the effect of the static stability, and M measures the effect of the vertical shear of the basic current, which is proportional to Q. By considering M as an independent parameter, the result can also be applied to the case of a shearing current in a homogeneous fluid.

In seeking solutions of the differential equation (22) or the corresponding equations in v_r, v_λ or ψ, we must satisfy certain boundary conditions. For the

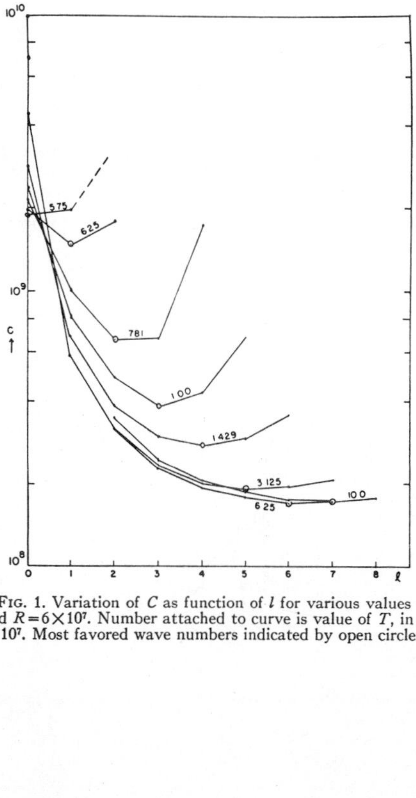

FIG. 1. Variation of C as function of l for various values of T and $R = 6\times10^7$. Number attached to curve is value of T, in unit of 10^7. Most favored wave numbers indicated by open circles.

[4] In application to the atmosphere, it is more convenient to use the depth of the equivalent homogeneous atmosphere as the length-scale instead of r_0.

present problem, we certainly must require the vanishing of the normal velocity components along the boundaries. If the boundary is rigid and rough, so that no slipping takes place along it, the tangential velocity components must also vanish; this, in turn, necessitates the vanishing of the normal gradient of the normal velocity v_n because of the continuity equation. On the other hand, the tangential stresses vanish on a free or perfectly smooth surface, which requires the vanishing of the normal gradient of the tangential velocities. Additional conditions depend upon the arrangement of the experiment. Thus, on the surfaces at which heat is supplied or removed, the temperature and also the temperature gradient may be kept constant. Expressed in terms of the velocity components, these conditions relate the higher derivatives. However, since the viscous terms become less important at higher rotation rates, and also since the conditions for the temperature distribution are less definite than the kinematic conditions, we shall pay less attention to the conditions relating the higher derivatives; we shall consider only the most important conditions on the two horizontal surfaces $z = 0$ and $z = d$, which can most readily be expressed in terms of v_Z. If the surface is rigid and rough, and the normal temperature gradient is kept constant, we have the following four conditions:

$$v_Z = 0, \quad Dv_Z = 0, \quad D^5 v_Z = 0$$

and

$$\nu^2 D^6 v_Z + 4\Omega^2 D^2 v_Z = 0, \tag{32}$$

where $D = \partial/\partial z$. The first two are the kinematic conditions, while the last two are deduced from (18) and (19).

On a free surface, the kinematic conditions are $v_Z = 0$ and $D^2 v_Z = 0$, while the third condition relates v_Z and ζ. This last condition is simplified if we assume that, at higher rotation rates, the balance condition (28) holds; we then obtain from (18) and (19) the conditions $D^4 v_Z = 0$ and $D^6 v_Z = 0$, respectively. Thus, on a free surface we have

$$v_Z = 0, \quad D^2 v_Z = 0, \quad D^4 v_Z = 0 \quad \text{and} \quad D^6 v_Z = 0. \tag{33}$$

In addition, we may either assume that all the variables are harmonic functions of r, or that $\partial v_Z/\partial r = 0$ on the vertical walls.

4. Solution by double Fourier series

The general eigenvalue problem represented by the differential equation (30) and the proper boundary conditions is very difficult to solve analytically, and especially so when there is a basic current in the fluid. Even when such solutions can be found, the frequency equation so derived is ordinarily complicated and the desired information can be obtained only through very tedious computations. Therefore, it is desirable to obtain approximate solutions that reveal the physical nature of the results more clearly. Such approximate solutions can be found by expanding the dependent variable in a double series of comparison functions, each satisfying the boundary conditions. The high degree of accuracy of this method has been demonstrated in the previous study of the purely symmetrical motion. We shall also limit ourselves to the simple boundary conditions given by (33) on the horizontal planes and to the vanishing of $\partial v_Z/\partial r$ on the vertical walls. These conditions are satisfied by the function $\sin s\zeta \cos t\xi$ for all integral values of s and t. Let us, therefore, put

$$w = \sum_t \sum_s A_{ts} \cos t\xi \sin s\zeta. \tag{34}$$

Substitute this in the differential equation (30) and make use of the following relations:

$$\begin{aligned} \sin t\xi &= \sum_m a_{mt} \cos m\xi, \\ a_{mt} &= -\frac{4t}{\pi(m^2 - t^2)} \quad \text{when } m - t \text{ is odd,} \\ &= 0 \quad \text{when } m - t \text{ is even or } m = t; \end{aligned} \tag{35}$$

$$\begin{aligned} \cos s\zeta &= \sum_n b_{ns} \sin n\zeta, \\ b_{ns} &= \frac{4n}{\pi(n^2 - s^2)} \quad \text{when } n - s \text{ is odd,} \\ &= 0 \quad \text{when } n - s \text{ is even or } n = s; \end{aligned} \tag{36}$$

$$\begin{aligned} \left(\zeta - \frac{\pi}{2}\right) \sin s\zeta &= \sum_n c_{ns} \sin n\zeta, \\ c_{ns} &= -\frac{8ns}{\pi(n^2 - s^2)^2} \quad \text{when } n - s \text{ is odd,} \\ &= 0 \quad \text{when } n - s \text{ is even or } n = s; \end{aligned} \tag{37}$$

$$\begin{aligned} \left(\zeta - \frac{\pi}{2}\right) \cos s\zeta &= \sum_n d_{ns} \sin n\zeta, \\ d_{ns} &= -2n/(n^2 - s^2) \quad \text{when } n - s \text{ is even,} \\ &= -1/2n \quad \text{when } n = s, \\ &= 0 \quad \text{when } n - s \text{ is odd;} \end{aligned} \tag{38}$$

$$\begin{aligned} \left(\zeta - \frac{\pi}{2}\right)^2 \sin s\zeta &= \sum_n e_{ns} \sin n\zeta, \\ e_{ns} &= \frac{8ns}{(n^2 - s^2)^2} \quad \text{when } n - s \text{ is even,} \\ &= \frac{\pi^2}{12} - \frac{1}{2n^2} \quad \text{when } n = s, \\ &= 0 \quad \text{when } n - s \text{ is odd;} \end{aligned} \tag{39}$$

and

$$\left(\zeta - \frac{\pi}{2}\right)^3 \sin s\zeta = \sum_n f_{ns} \sin n\zeta,$$

$$f_{ns} = -\frac{3ns}{n^2 - s^2}\left[\pi + \frac{16(n^2+s^2)}{(n^2-s^2)^2}\right] \qquad (40)$$

when $n - s$ is odd,

$= 0$ when $n - s$ is even or $n = s$.

Writing B_{mn} for $N_{mn}{}^2 A_{mn}$, and inverting the order of the repeated summations, we have (30) in the form

$$\sum_m \sum_n \lambda_{mn} \cos m\xi \sin n\zeta = 0, \qquad (41)$$

where

$$\begin{aligned}
\lambda_{mn} = \Bigg\{ & Q_{mn} - \frac{k}{\nu}\left(1 + \frac{k}{2\nu}\right) l^2 M^2 \left(\frac{1}{6} - \frac{1}{n^2\pi^2}\right) \\
& - \frac{k}{\nu}\frac{lia}{8\pi r_0}\frac{CM}{N_{mn}{}^2}\Bigg\} B_{mn} \\
& + C\Bigg\{\sum_t \sum_s \frac{t^2}{m^2 - t^2}\frac{ns}{n^2 - s^2} B_{ts} \\
& + \sum_s \frac{ns}{n^2 - s^2} q_{ms} B_{ms}\Bigg\} \\
& - \frac{8liM}{\pi^2}\sum_s \frac{ns}{(n^2 - s^2)^2}\Bigg\{s^2\pi^2 r_0{}^2 d^{-2} T \\
& + \frac{k}{\nu} R(m^2\pi^2 r_0{}^2 a^{-2} + l^2) + \left(1 + \frac{2k}{\nu}\right) N_{ms}{}^6\Bigg\} \frac{B_{ms}}{N_{ms}{}^2} \\
& - \frac{k}{\nu}\frac{li}{4} MC \sum_t \frac{t^2}{m^2 - t^2}\left[\sum_s \frac{2ns}{n^2 - s^2}\frac{B_{ts}}{N_{ts}{}^2} + \frac{B_{tn}}{N_{tn}{}^2}\right] \\
& - \frac{k}{\nu}\frac{l^2 M^2}{\pi^2}\sum_s \frac{ns}{(n^2 - s^2)^2} B_{ms}\Bigg\{8\left(2 + \frac{k}{\nu}\right) N_{ms}{}^2 \\
& \qquad - 3liM\frac{k}{\nu}\left[1 + \frac{16(n^2 + s^2)}{\pi(n^2 - s^2)^2}\right]\Bigg\}. \qquad (42)
\end{aligned}$$

In this expression, the various quantities are defined as follows:

$$Q_{mn} = n^2\pi^2 r_0{}^2 d^{-2} T + (m^2\pi^2 r_0{}^2 a^{-2} + l^2) R + N_{mn}{}^6,$$

$$N_{mn}{}^2 = l^2 + \pi^2 r_0{}^2 (m^2 a^{-2} + n^2 d^{-2}),$$

$$q_{mn} = \frac{li}{4}\frac{a}{r_0} T^{\frac{1}{2}} N_{mn}{}^{-2}, \qquad (43)$$

$$C = 16\frac{Q}{\pi} = 16\left(1 + \frac{k}{\nu}\right)\frac{g\alpha}{k\nu}\frac{\partial\theta_0}{\partial r}\frac{r_0{}^6}{ad},$$

and T, R, Q and M are as defined in (31).

Since (41) must be satisfied for all values of ξ and ζ, λ_{mn} must vanish identically, *i.e.*, $\lambda_{mn} \equiv 0$. This represents an infinite system of linear homogeneous equations for the infinite number of unknowns B_{mn}. The existence of the motion under consideration requires the vanishing of the determinant formed by the coefficients of B_{mn} in these equations. It may be remarked that, unlike the case of purely symmetric motion, the system with $l > 0$ does not fall into two mutually independent systems according to whether $m + n$ is odd or even. Therefore, we must take all combinations of m and n.

To simplify the computation, we shall at first neglect all terms involving higher powers of M in λ_{mn}. Corrections may be made later if desired. Since M is proportional to C, we may incorporate the terms in the third braces of (42) with those in the second. The simplified equation system is then given by

$$\begin{aligned}
\lambda_{mn} = \phi_{mn} B_{mn} & + \sum_t \sum_s \frac{t^2}{m^2 - t^2}\frac{ns}{n^2 - s^2} CB_{ts} \\
& + \sum_s \frac{ns}{n^2 - s^2} q_{ms}\left(1 - \frac{s^2 + \alpha_{ms}}{n^2 - s^2}\right) CB_{ms} = 0, \qquad (44)
\end{aligned}$$

where

$$\alpha_{mn} = \frac{m^2 gsd^2}{4\Omega^2 a^2}\left\{1 + \frac{l^2}{m^2\pi^2}\frac{a^2}{r_0{}^2} + \frac{\nu + 2k}{m^2\pi^2 k}\frac{a^2}{r_0{}^2}\frac{N_{mn}{}^6}{R}\right\}, \qquad (45)$$

and all the summations over t and s are for odd $m - t$ and odd $n - s$. In (44), C always occurs with the B with the subscript s; therefore, we may take CB_{ts} and CB_{ms} as the unknowns. Then C occurs in the form of C^{-2}. We shall compute the determinant of this system by using only the first nine equations, letting m and t, and also n and s, take the values of the three integers from 1 to 3. The coefficients of these equations are given in table 1, in which x is written for C^{-2}. It is seen that x occurs only in the last three diagonal elements, and therefore the determinant gives a cubic equation in x.

Since the sixth-order determinant Δ_6 formed by the first six coefficients of the first six equations is a diagonal determinant, the ninth-order determinant Δ_9 can be reduced to the product of Δ_6 and a third-order determinant Δ_3 by reducing all the first six elements of the last three rows of Δ_9 to zero. Since Δ_6 is always positive, the condition for the existence of the motion under consideration is given by

$$\Delta_3 = \begin{vmatrix} \dfrac{\phi_{22}x}{16} - g_{11} & g_{12} & g_{13} \\ g_{21} & \dfrac{\phi_{12}x}{16} - g_{22} & g_{23} \\ g_{31} & g_{32} & \dfrac{\phi_{32}x}{16} - g_{33} \end{vmatrix} = 0. \qquad (46)$$

A fairly close approximation to the lowest root of this equation may be obtained from the first element of Δ_3 alone, and is given by

$$C^2 = \phi_{22}/(16\, g_{11}), \qquad (47)$$

TABLE 2. Values of C (unit: 10^7) for various values of T and S.

		l							
log T	S	0	1	2	3	4	5	6	7
1.0	0	*.1972*		.2250	.2627	.3194	.3995		
3.0	0	*.2234*		.2453	.2818	.3334	.4151		
5.0	0	1.150		.8660	.7250	.6345	.5913		
	075	1.895		1.696	1.685	1.493			
7.0	0	74.48		7.647	6.482	5.134	4.382		
	.075	136.60		17.12	12.63	10.93	*10.33*	10.44	
	.15	184.27	50.32	27.66	21.33	20.10	*19.61*	22.25	28.51
	.25	238.50	81.10	48.28	*38.31*	42.90	68.82		
9.0	.075	13590.0		171.0	120.6	109.0	*103.1*	104.5	108.2
	.15	18130.0		278.9	213.8	*193.5*	193.6	221.1	285.0
	.25	23910.0		489.5	*377.3*	428.2	676.4		

where

$$g_{11} = \bar{g}_{11} + g_{11}^*,$$

$$\bar{g}_{11} = \frac{1}{81\,\phi_{11}} + \frac{1}{25\,\phi_{13}} + \frac{1}{25\,\phi_{31}} + \frac{81}{625\,\phi_{33}}, \quad (48)$$

and

$$g_{11}^* = -\frac{q_{21}q_{22}}{324\,\phi_{21}}(2 - \alpha_{21})(7 + \alpha_{22}) - \frac{9\,q_{22}q_{23}}{2500\,\phi_{23}}(1 - \alpha_{22})(14 + \alpha_{23}).$$

The various parameters involved are defined in (43) and (45). A slightly better approximation can be obtained by including more equations and more unknowns in the determinant.

It may be noted that the various ϕ's represent the resistance of the fluid system, $\bar{g}_{11}$ is a relative measure of the energy released by the meridional circulation ξ, and g_{11}^* is a relative measure of the energy released by the circulation η associated with the wave disturbances, as will be discussed in section 7, below. If $\bar{g}_{11}$ is the dominant part of g_{11}, we shall have symmetric motion; and if g_{11}^* dominates, we shall have wave motion. Since the factors $q_{21}q_{22}$ and $q_{22}q_{23}$ of g_{11}^* are proportional to T and also proportional to l^2, wave motions are favored at high rotation rates if the factors $(2 - \alpha_{21})$ and $(1 - \alpha_{22})$ are positive. We note that α_{2S} is proportional to the parameter $S = gsd^2(2\Omega a)^{-2}$, which represents the ratio between the inertia due to static stability and that due to rotation; therefore, this parameter is an important factor in determining the wave number. However, since the vertical temperature contrast is roughly proportional to the mean radial temperature contrast, S is roughly proportional to the Rossby number R_{0T} used below; therefore, it may not be necessary to consider it as another independent parameter.

In table 2, we have computed the eigenvalues C from (47) for different integral values of log T and a few selected values of S, to bring out the dependence of C and the most favorable wave number on S. For simplicity, we used a mean Prandtl number $\nu/k = 6$, and the length ratios $r_0 = a = 2d$. The calculation shows that, at low rotation rates ($T < 10^5$), the eigenvalue C is lowest for wave number zero; therefore, the symmetric motion is the most favored motion. If the static stability is kept very small, the motion changes directly to a large wave-number when the value of T is increased beyond 10^5. However, if a larger static stability is produced in the fluid, its large damping effect on the shorter waves will make the change gradual, with wave number 1 or 2 appearing first. The length ratios d/a and a/r_0 are also very effective factors in determining the number of waves; a decrease in the values of these ratios will increase the wave number, and conversely. Thus, if the ratios S and a/r_0 are kept constant as Ω increases, the most favored wave number will remain nearly unchanged, while an increase of the values of S or a/r_0 will shift it toward a smaller l. These calculations also show that, for $T > 10^7$, C increases with Ω^2 for $l = 0$, while for $l > 1$ it increases with Ω; therefore, the motion must break up into waves at high rotation rates, unless the mean radial and vertical temperature contrasts are increased

TABLE 3. Values of C (unit: 10^8) for various values of T and $R = 6 \times 10^7$.

	l								
$T \times 10^7$	0	1	2	3	4	5	6	7	8
0.5747	*19.40*	19.72							
0.6250	19.74	*14.785*	17.840						
0.78125	21.610	10.094	*6.641*	6.742	17.340				
1.0000	23.850	8.110	4.828	*3.831*	4.290	6.882			
1.4286	28.044	6.810	3.820	2.981	*2.767*	2.913	3.565		
3.1250	43.540	5.823	3.172	2.327	2.014	*1.912*	1.940	2.071	
6.2500	70.028	5.991	3.165	2.298	1.929	1.767	*1.718*	1.745	
10.0000	100.240	6.524	3.494	2.453	2.027	1.825	1.736	*1.726*	1.767

at a rate faster than Ω^2 by increasing the heating. Similarly, as the rotation rate increases, the temperature contrast required to maintain a fixed wave number $l > 1$ must increase at a rate faster than Ω, if the change of the vertical temperature contrast is slower than the change of the horizontal temperature contrast.

If, on the other hand, the rate of heating is kept constant as the rate of rotation increases, S will decrease since the vertical temperature contrast is roughly proportional to the radial temperature contrast at not-too-low rotation rates. The wave number must then increase. The intervals of T and S used in computing table 2 are too large; therefore, it is difficult to compare these results with observations. A more detailed computation is contained in table 3, corresponding to a fixed static stability factor $R = 6 \times 10^7$ and the same length ratios $r_0 = a = 2d$.

This computation shows that, for this value of R, symmetric motion is the most favored motion for all values of T less than 5.7×10^6. However, the most interesting result obtained in this computation is that the value of C for the symmetric motion ($l = 0$) increases while those for the wave disturbances ($l \geqslant 1$) decrease with increasing T, and the rate of decrease is larger for larger wave numbers. The number of waves therefore increases with increasing rotation rate. This computation also shows that the mean temperature contrast corresponding to the most favored wave decreases as the wave number increases, first rapidly and then slowly, finally remaining nearly constant.

The values of C in table 3 are plotted in fig. 1. It is seen that, for the rotation rates for which wave motions are preferable, the value of C decreases rapidly as l increases from zero to 2, while the variation of C around the most favored wave number $l = l_c$ is usually slight, indicating that l_c has only a statistical significance.

The total effect of rotation and differential heating is most conveniently described by a thermal Rossby number R_{0T}, which may be defined as a constant multiple of the ratio between C and T:

$$R_{0T} = \frac{gd\alpha\, \partial\theta_0/\partial r}{2\Omega^2 r_2} = \frac{1}{8[(\nu/k)+1]} \frac{a}{r_2} \frac{d^2}{r_0^2} \frac{C}{T}$$

$$= \frac{2[(\nu/k)+1]}{1} \frac{a}{r_2} K. \quad (49)$$

This is the thermal Rossby number used by Fultz, while K is the parameter used by the writer (Kuo, 1954; 1955). The values of R_{0T} corresponding to the most favored wave numbers in table 3 are plotted in fig 2. Also plotted in this figure are Fultz' experimental values of R_{0T} for the case of two concentric cylinders with radii 4.90 and 2.45 cm, and depth 13.2 cm. It is seen that the theoretical curves fit the observations well except for wave number zero, even though the length ratios used are different from those of the experiment. The large depth and small radii used in this series of experiment favor the symmetric motion, especially at lower rotation rate. The writer hopes to make another computation according to these length ratios at a later time.

At present, only one set of Fultz' experimental data with detailed temperature measurements is available. From these data, we find

$$\Omega = 0.303 \text{ sec}^{-1}, \quad r_0 = 10.3 \text{ cm}, \quad a = 8.2 \text{ cm},$$
$$d = 4.5 \text{ cm}, \bar{\theta}_0 = 20\text{C}, \quad \alpha = 2.05 \times 10^{-4} \text{ (C)}^{-1},$$
$$\partial\theta_0/\partial r = 0.60 \text{ c/cm}, \quad \partial\theta_0/\partial z = 1.60 \text{ c/cm},$$
$$\nu = 1.007 \times 10^{-2} \text{ cm}^2/\text{sec}, \quad K = 1.43 \times 10^{-3} \text{ cm}^2/\text{sec},$$
$$T = 4.1 \times 10^7, \quad R = 2.60 \times 10^8, \quad C = 5.1 \times 10^9$$
and $$S = 0.26.$$

The motion produced in this experiment is a fully developed, regular three-wave pattern. The values of C obtained from (47) are given in table 4. It is seen that the lowest value of C corresponds to $l = 3$. This

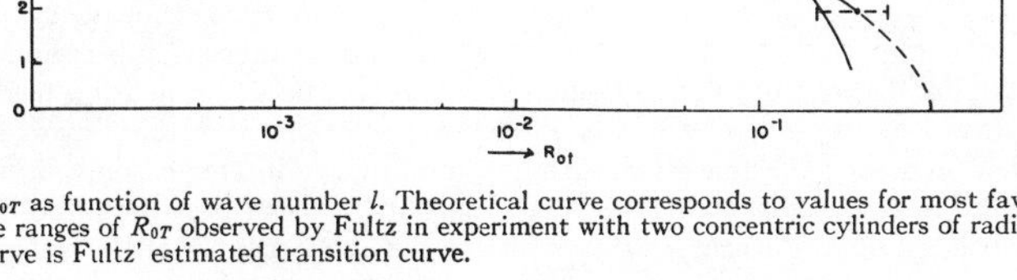

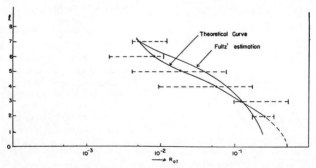

FIG. 2. Variation of R_{0T} as function of wave number l. Theoretical curve corresponds to values for most favored waves in table 3. Horizontal dash-lines are ranges of R_{0T} observed by Fultz in experiment with two concentric cylinders of radii 4.9 and 2.45 cm, and depth 13.2 cm. Other curve is Fultz' estimated transition curve.

TABLE 4. Values of C ($\times 10^9$) for data of Fultz, computed from (47).

l:	0	1	2	3	4	5
C:	16.25	5.60	3.50	2.82	2.91	4.73

value is somewhat less than the observed value, as is to be expected.

5. Analytic solutions for a semi-nonviscous fluid

Although the method used in the previous section is adequate for obtaining the critical mean temperature gradient needed in maintaining the different types of motions, the determination of the eigenfunctions by this method is very tedious. Since a discussion of the physical processes requires the distributions of various quantities, we shall solve a simplified version of the problem by assuming a frictional force proportional to the velocity, which is equivalent to replacing $-\nu\,\nabla^2 V$ and $-k\,\nabla^2\theta$ by cV and $c\theta$. Equations (22) and (29) then become second-order partial differential equations with regard to the space variables. The frictional coefficient c may either be considered as a function of the length scales of the velocity distribution or more simply as a constant. We also assume a harmonic variation with r for the various perturbation quantities, and we disregard the boundary conditions on the vertical walls. The boundary conditions on the two horizontal planes are simply $v_Z = 0$. Since the terms involving $\partial/\partial\lambda$ disappear for the symmetric motion, we shall discuss this case first.

Symmetric disturbance, $l = 0$.—As was shown in the previous paper (Kuo, 1955), oscillatory symmetric motions always decay; therefore, the lowest temperature contrast required to maintain such a motion is obtained by setting $\partial/\partial t$ equal to zero. For simplicity, we shall also take the frictional coefficient c to be zero. The operators L and L_1 are then identically zero. We put

$$v_Z = W(z) \exp \frac{i\pi}{a}\left(r + \frac{\omega_Z z}{2\Omega} r_0\right)$$

in (22), where a denotes the horizontal scale of the cell. Then W satisfies the equation

$$\frac{d^2W}{dz^2} + \frac{\pi^2}{a^2}\frac{r_0^2\omega_Z^2}{4\Omega^2}\left(1 - \frac{gs}{r_0^2\omega_Z^2}\right) W = 0. \qquad (50)$$

This equation has the solution

$$W = W_0 \sin \sigma z, \qquad (51)$$

where $\sigma = \pi r_0 \omega_Z (2\Omega a)^{-1}(1 - gs r_0^{-2}\omega_Z^{-2})^{\frac{1}{2}}$. The boundary conditions require $\sigma d = n\pi$, where n is any integer. It is seen that, with $s > 0$, the Richardson number $R_i = gs r_0^{-2}\omega_Z^{-2}$ must be less than 1 to have spontaneous symmetric motion. Putting $n = 1$, we find that the lowest temperature contrast is given by

$$|g\alpha\, \partial\theta_0/\partial r|_c = 2\Omega(4\Omega^2a^2d^{-2} + gs)^{\frac{1}{2}}, \qquad (52)$$

or

$$K_c = (gd/\Omega^2 a)\alpha\, \partial\theta_0/\partial r = 4(1 + S)^{\frac{1}{2}}. \qquad (53)$$

The asymptotic value of K_c obtained in the previous study (Kuo, 1954; 1955) for $s = 0$ is 4.8.

Unsymmetrical wave disturbances, $l \geqslant 1$.—Since the motion becomes unsymmetric only when the rotation rate is relatively high and when the mean meridional temperature gradient is not very large, the rate of development of the unsymmetric motions is generally not rapid. We can therefore neglect L^2 against $4\Omega^2$ and gs in (22) and (29), where L now stands for $\partial/\partial t + \omega\, \partial/\partial\lambda + c$. The motion is then quasi-geostrophic, and the simplified equations are roughly equivalent to the equations discussed by Charney (1947), Eady (1949), Fjörtoft (1950), Kuo (1952; 1953b; 1953c), Thompson (1953), and many others, except for the inclusion of friction and the effect of overturning in the meridional plane.

Neglecting L^2 and setting $L_1 = L$, and

$$\psi = \Psi(\zeta) \exp i\left(l\lambda - \mu t - \frac{\pi r}{a} + \frac{\pi}{a}\frac{r_0\omega_Z}{2\Omega} z\right)$$

in (29), we find Ψ satisfies the following differential equation:

$$\zeta_1(d^2\Psi/d\zeta^2 - \beta^2\Psi) + E_1\Psi = 0, \qquad (54)$$

where

$$\zeta = z/d, \quad \zeta_1 = \zeta - [(\mu + ic)/l\omega_Z d],$$

$$\beta^2 = \frac{\pi^2 d^2}{a^2}\frac{gs}{4\Omega^2}\left(1 + \frac{l^2a^2}{\pi^2 r_0^2} - \frac{r_0^2\omega_Z^2}{gs}\right), \qquad (55)$$

and

$$E_1 = 4\omega_Z d/\Omega.$$

The boundary conditions are

$$\zeta_1\, d\Psi/d\zeta = \Psi \quad \text{at} \quad \zeta = 0 \quad \text{and} \quad \zeta = 1. \qquad (56)$$

The corresponding differential equation for the amplitude function W of v_Z is

$$\frac{d^2W}{d\zeta^2} - \frac{2}{\zeta_1}\frac{dW}{d\zeta} - \beta^2 W + \frac{2\omega_Z d}{\Omega\zeta_1} W = 0. \qquad (57)$$

A comparison of (54) with (51) of Kuo (1952) shows that E_1 replaces the parameter $E_2 = gsdf^{-2}u_Z^{-1}(df/dy) - d\rho_0^{-1}(d\rho_0/dz)$; therefore it has the same effect as that of E_2, which is to add a negative phase velocity to the waves and to introduce a slight damping effect. The solution of (54) is of the type $\Psi = \eta e^{-\eta/2}F$, where F is the confluent hypergeometric function, and $\eta = 2\beta\zeta_1$. The determination of the eigenvalues from these solutions is rather involved (see Kuo, 1952). Since we are interested only in finding the most important physical processes, and since the value of E_1 for the experiment is of the order of 0.3 while that of

E_2 for the atmosphere is of the order of unity, we may neglect the last term of (54) and obtain a first approximation from the simplified equation. The results so obtained will then be more similar to those obtained by Eady (1949).

When the last term of (54) is omitted, it has the general solution

$$\Psi = Ae^{x} + Be^{-x}, \tag{58}$$

where $x = \beta\zeta_1$. Applying the boundary conditions to this solution, we obtain the frequency equation

$$1 - x_0 x_1 = \beta \coth \beta, \tag{59}$$

where

$$x_0 = \beta\zeta_1(0) = -\beta[\mu_r + i(\mu_i + c)]/l\omega_Z d, \quad x_1 = \beta + x_0, \tag{60}$$

and μ_r and μ_i are the real and imaginary parts of μ. Since β is real, the imaginary part of x_0x_1 must vanish identically, which gives

$$\mu_r = l\omega_Z d/2 = l\bar{\omega}. \tag{61}$$

Thus, according to this approximation, all the waves move with the angular speed of the mean current, in confirmation of the statement made in section 3, above. Equating the real part of (59) to zero, we obtain

$$\mu_i + c = +\,l d\omega_Z\left(\frac{\coth\beta}{\beta} - \frac{1}{\beta^2} - \frac{1}{4}\right)^{\frac{1}{2}} = \frac{l\omega_Z d}{\beta}\,\delta, \tag{62}$$

where δ is written for $+\,[\beta\coth\beta - 1 - (\beta^2/4)]^{\frac{1}{2}}$. It may be noted that the positive radical sign must be used for the amplifying, the neutral and the slowly decaying ($\mu_i > -c$) disturbances, since $\mu_i + c$ is positive for all these disturbances. Thus the inclusion of the frictional effect enables us to choose the proper sign for δ. This consideration also shows that the occurrence of these disturbances requires $\beta^2 < 5.7571$. This upper limit of β^2 gives an upper limit to the number of waves l, and is equivalent to the limit of α_{21} obtained in the previous section (multiplied by $\pi^2/4$). In the group of amplifying waves, there is in general a particular one which grows faster than the others. We can find this wave by finding the maximum value of μ_i. Thus, if c is assumed to be the same for all waves, the wave of maximum growth rate is given by

$$l^2\beta\frac{\partial\delta^2}{\partial\beta} + \frac{2\pi^2 r_0^2}{a^2}\delta^2\left(1 - \frac{1}{R_i}\right) = 0. \tag{63}$$

The root of $\partial\delta^2/\partial\beta = 0$ is $\beta^2 = 2.5792 = \beta_1^2$. For $R_i > 1$, the most unstable disturbance is on the short-wave side of that corresponding to $\beta = \beta_1$; when $R_i < 1$, the most unstable wave is on the long-wave side.

As a numerical example representative of atmospheric conditions at middle latitudes (45°N), let us take $2\Omega = 10^{-4}$ sec^{-1}, $r_0 = R\cos\phi = 4500$ km, $a = 1.5\,r_0$, $d = 10$ km, and the normal value of $gs = 1.4 \times 10^{-4}$ sec^{-2}. Assuming $R_i \gg 1$, we find that the maximum wave number[5] is about 10, and the most unstable wave is $l_c = 6$. When friction is neglected, the initial growth rate of this most unstable wave is roughly given by exp $(0.22\,u_Z t)$ per day, where u_Z is the vertical shear of the mean zonal wind, in meters per second per kilometer. This value is slightly higher than the maximum growth rate obtained in the previous studies (Kuo, 1952; 1953b; 1953c), largely because the stabilizing effect of the variation of the Coriolis parameter is neglected here. The values of the amplification factor $\mu_i + c$ for different wave numbers are plotted in fig. 3 (top). The unit is u_Z.

It may be noted that, if we take the friction coefficient c to be zero, all the waves which make β^2 less than 5.7571 will be amplified, no matter how small the vertical shear may be. To obtain a critical limit of the vertical shear or of the radial temperature gradient, we must take into consideration the frictional effect. For simplicity, we may put $c = -\nu\nabla^2 = \nu\pi^2(l^2\pi^{-2}r_0^{-2} + a^{-2} + d^{-2})$. Then the stability criterion (62) may be written as

$$\frac{g\alpha}{2\Omega r_0}\left|\frac{\partial\theta_0}{\partial r}\right| \begin{matrix} > \\ = \\ < \end{matrix} \frac{\nu\pi^2\beta}{l\delta a^2 d}\left(1 + \frac{a^2}{d^2} + \frac{\pi^2 r_0^2}{l^2 a^2}\right) \quad \begin{matrix}\text{amplified}\\ \text{neutral.}\\ \text{damped}\end{matrix} \tag{64}$$

[5] For the atmosphere, the vertical length-scale d usually varies with the horizontal scale, and the upper limit of β does not necessarily imply an upper limit of l. Therefore, we use $l(d_0/d)$ as the wave number in fig. 3.

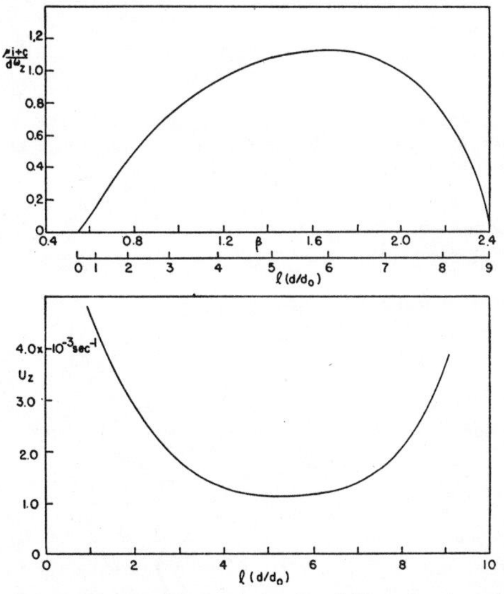

FIG. 3. Top: amplification factor $(\mu_i+c)/d\omega_z$ as function of β or l (for fixed values of s, a/r_0 and d/a). Bottom: critical vertical shear corresponding to $\mu_i=0$, $c=0.25$ per day and fixed s, a/r_0 and d/a.

For the atmosphere, we may take c as a constant, *e.g.*, $c = 0.25$ per day, corresponding to an eddy viscosity $\nu = 3 \times 10^5$ cm²/sec, and obtain the critical value of u_Z corresponding to $\mu_i = 0$ for different values of l. These values are plotted in fig. 3 (bottom). It is seen that the lowest value is about 1.2×10^{-3} sec⁻¹. When the stabilizing effect of the variation of the Coriolis parameter is included, this limiting value of the shear will be raised to about 1.6×10^{-3} sec⁻¹.

6. Transports of heat and zonal momentum

Eliminating B from the solution (58) by applying the boundary condition at $z = 0$ and replacing $e^{i\pi r/a}$ by $\cos(\pi y/a)$, where the origin of y is at $r = a/2$, we obtain

$$\psi = A' P(\zeta) \cos(\pi y/a) \times \exp\{i(\xi + \vartheta + \sigma_1 z) + \mu_i t\}, \quad (65)$$

where P and ϑ are functions of ζ, given by

$$P \cos \vartheta = \left[\delta^2 - \frac{\beta}{2}\left(1 - \frac{\beta}{2}\right)\right] \cosh \beta\zeta + \left(1 - \frac{\beta}{2}\right) \sinh \beta\zeta,$$

and

$$P \sin \vartheta = \delta(\sinh \beta\zeta - \cosh \beta\zeta), \quad (66)$$

and

$$\xi = l\lambda - \mu_r t - \delta, \quad \sigma_1 = \frac{\pi}{a}\frac{r_0 \omega_Z}{2\Omega}, \qquad A' = \frac{2A}{(1 - \frac{1}{2}\beta)^2 + \delta^2}, \quad (67)$$

and δ is given by the frequency equation (62). The vertical velocity is given by

$$v_Z = \frac{2\Omega}{gs} li\omega_Z \left\{\psi - \zeta_1 \left(\frac{d\psi}{d\zeta} - i\sigma_1\, d\psi\right)\right\}$$
$$= \frac{2\Omega}{gs} li\omega_Z A' G(\zeta) \times \exp\{\mu_i t + i(\xi + \alpha_1 + \sigma_1 z)\} \cos\frac{\pi y}{a}, \quad (68)$$

where G and α_1 are given by

$$G \cos \alpha_1 = \left\{1 - \frac{\beta}{2} + \delta^2 + \beta(\zeta - \tfrac{1}{2})\left[\frac{\beta}{2}\left(1 - \frac{\beta}{2}\right) - \delta^2\right]\right\} \times \sinh \beta\zeta - \left(1 - \frac{\beta}{2}\right) \beta\zeta \cosh \beta\zeta,$$

and

$$G \sin \alpha_1 = \delta \left\{\left[1 + \delta^2 + \frac{\beta^2}{4} + \beta(\zeta - 1)\right] \times \sinh \beta\zeta - \beta\zeta \cosh \beta\zeta\right\}. \quad (69)$$

From (66) and (69), it is found that the axes of the pressure field and the vertical-velocity field both incline westward and upward, and that the angle of inclination of the v_Z field is smaller than that of the pressure field. The distributions of the phase angles with height are represented in fig. 4 (top). It is seen that in the lower levels ascending motion takes place in the central and forward parts of the trough, while in the upper levels descending motion takes place in the center of the trough. The variations of the amplitudes of ψ and v_Z with height are given in Fig. 4 (bottom left).

The perturbation temperature θ can be obtained from the energy equation (14). Using the geostrophic radial velocity $v_{rg} = -r_0^{-1}\,\partial\psi/\partial\lambda$, and substituting v_Z from (68), and replacing the expansion coefficient α by θ_0^{-1}, we find

$$\theta = \frac{2\Omega\theta_0}{g}\left(\frac{\partial\psi}{\partial z} - i\sigma_1\psi\right)$$
$$= \frac{2\Omega\theta_0}{gd} \beta A' P' \cos\frac{\pi y}{a} \times \exp\{\mu_i t + i(\xi + \sigma_1 Z + \gamma)\}, \quad (70)$$

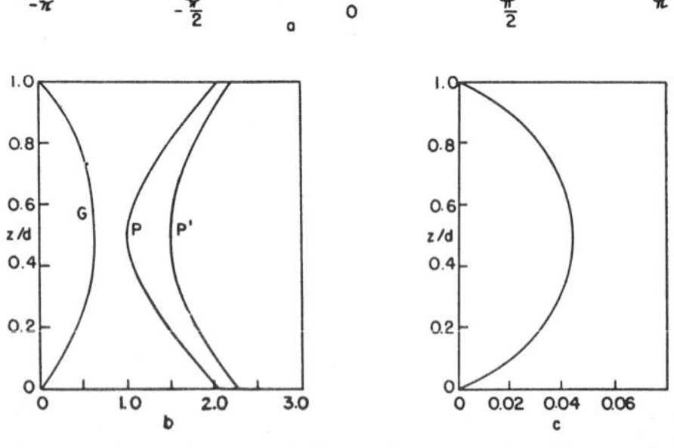

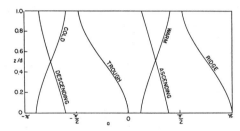

FIG. 4. Top: phase variations of p, v_z and θ. Bottom left: variations of amplitudes of $p(P)$, $v_z(G)$ and $\theta(P')$ with height. Bottom right: distribution of upward transport of heat $c_p\bar{\rho}\,\overline{\theta v_z}$ with height.

where P' and γ are given by

$$P' \cos \gamma = \left[\delta^2 - \frac{\beta}{2}\left(1 - \frac{\beta}{2}\right)\right] \sinh \beta\zeta + \left(1 - \frac{\beta}{2}\right) \cosh \beta\zeta,$$

and

$$P' \sin \gamma = \delta(\cosh \beta\zeta - \sinh \beta\zeta). \qquad (71)$$

The distributions of the phase angle γ and the amplitude P' are plotted in fig. 4 (top and left bottom). It is seen that the axis of the temperature field inclines eastward.

It may be noted that the angles of inclination ϑ, α_1 and γ are proportional to δ. Since δ is positive for the amplifying, neutral and slowly decaying disturbances when frictional effect is included, all these disturbances have the same characteristic inclinations.

The transport of heat by the vertical motion can be obtained from (68) and (70) and is given by

$$C_p\overline{\rho\theta v_Z} = \frac{4\Omega^2 r_0^2 \omega_Z \beta}{g^2 s l d} C_p \bar{\rho}\bar{\theta}_0 \bar{v}_{rg}^2 \times \cos^2 \frac{\pi y}{a} \frac{P'G}{P^2(\frac{1}{2})} \sin(\gamma - \alpha_1), \qquad (72)$$

where the bar denotes average over λ, $\bar{\rho}$ is mean density, and $\bar{v}_{rg}^2/2$ is the mean north-south geostrophic kinetic energy at $y = 0$, $z = d/2$, and is equal to $|v_{rg}|^2/4$, where $|v_{rg}|$ is the absolute maximum value of v_{rg} at the same level. This quantity is used as a measure of the intensity of the motion. This transport is upward at all levels, with the maximum occurring at the level $z = d/2$, as is indicated in fig. 4 (bottom right) which is computed from the solution corresponding to the most favored wave. The general feature holds also for the other disturbances. It is seen that this transport increases rapidly upward from the ground and decreases rapidly near the top, and therefore has a cooling effect in the lower layers and a warming effect in the upper layers, which is in the direction of producing and maintaining a stable stratification. If we take the average meridional velocity to be 10 m/sec, $r_0\omega_Z = 2 \times 10^{-3}$ sec^{-1}, $2\Omega = 10^{-4}$ sec^{-1}, and $gs = 1.4 \times 10^{-4}$ sec^{-2}, we find the maximum upward transport of heat is about 0.044 cal cm^{-2} min^{-1}, or 63 cal/cm^2 per day. This upward transport of heat produces a uniform heating of 0.5C per day of the upper half of the atmosphere, which is quite appreciable. Thus, it seems that such upward transport of heat by the large-scale disturbances may be of some importance in compensating the radiational cooling in the upper troposphere and lower stratosphere. This upward transport of heat may also explain the increase of temperature with height in the experiments.

In a similar manner, we find that the poleward transport of heat by the geostrophic meridional wind is given by

$$-C_p\overline{\rho\theta v_{rg}} = C_p\bar{\rho}\bar{\theta}_0 \frac{2\Omega}{g}\frac{l}{r_0}\frac{A'^2}{2} \cos^2 \frac{\pi y}{a} P^2 \frac{\partial \vartheta}{\partial z}$$

$$= C_p\bar{\rho}\bar{\theta}_0 \frac{2r_0\Omega}{gl} \bar{v}_{rg}^2 \cos^2 \frac{\pi y}{a} \frac{P^2}{P^2(\frac{1}{2})} \tan \Delta\vartheta, \qquad (73)$$

where $\Delta\vartheta$ is the inclination of the troughs and ridges with the vertical which is negative, therefore giving a poleward heat transfer. This expression also holds for the general geostrophic transport of heat and is the same as the one obtained by the writer in a previous study (Kuo, 1952). It is seen that this transport is proportional to the north-south kinetic energy and proportional to the inclination of the axis of the pressure field. Integrating over the depth d and the length of the latitude circle, and assuming a mean north-south velocity of 10 m sec, we find the total transport across 45 deg lat is about 1.0×10^{15} cal/sec, which is of the right order of magnitude when compared with the observed and also the required transport. If we put the origin of y at latitude 45 deg, the maximum transport will occur at this latitude, since the factor $f \cos \phi$ also has its maximum at this latitude. The latitudinal variation agrees roughly with the observed

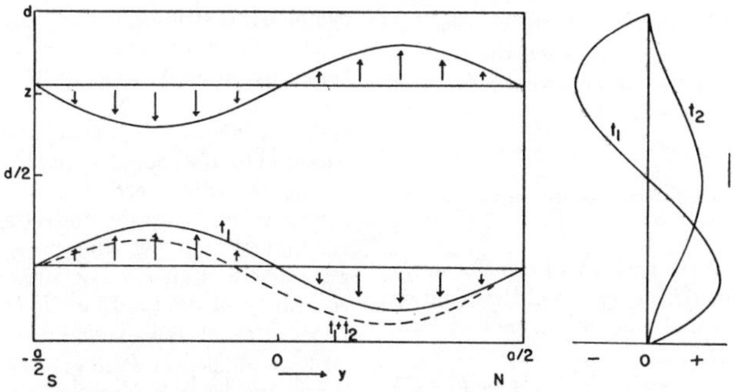

FIG. 5. Mean vertical transports of geostrophic and ageostrophic momentum and their vertical distributions.

and required variations. It may be remarked that a fraction R/C_p of this northward transport of heat represents the work done by the pressure force exerted by the air to the south on the air to the north of the latitude circle.

The geostrophic part of the zonal velocity is given by $v_{\lambda_g} = \partial\psi/\partial r = -\partial\psi/\partial y$. From this, it can readily be found that the mean vertical transport of the geostrophic zonal momentum by the large-scale eddies is given by

$$\tau_1 = \bar{\rho}\,\overline{v_{\lambda_g} v_Z} = -\frac{\Omega\omega_Z}{gs}\frac{\pi r_0^2}{la}\bar{\rho}\,\bar{v}_{r_g}^2 \times \sin\frac{2\pi y}{a}\frac{PG}{P^2(\frac{1}{2})}\sin(\alpha_1 - \vartheta). \quad (74)$$

This transport is downward north of $y = 0$ and upward in the more equatorial region, below the level $z = d/2$, and in the reverse directions at the upper levels. The distribution of this vertical transfer of momentum is schematically represented in fig. 5 (left), while the vertical variation of the function $PG \sin(\alpha_1 - \vartheta)$ is given by the right portion of this figure. The maximum value of this transport is about 0.3 dyne/cm^2, if we assume the mean velocity to be 15 m/sec. The vertical transport of the ageostrophic zonal momentum is given by

$$\tau_2 = \bar{\rho}\,\overline{v_{\lambda_a} v_Z} = -\frac{l r_0^2 \omega_Z^2}{gs}\frac{d}{r_0}\bar{\rho}\,\overline{v_{r_g}^2} \times \cos^2\frac{\pi y}{a}\frac{G}{P_{\frac{1}{2}}^2}(Q_1 \sin\alpha_1 - Q_2\cos\alpha_1), \quad (75)$$

where

$$Q_1 = (\zeta - \tfrac{1}{2})P\cos\vartheta + \frac{\delta}{\beta}P\sin\vartheta,$$

and

$$Q_2 = (\zeta - \tfrac{1}{2})P\sin\vartheta - \frac{\delta}{\beta}P\cos\vartheta. \quad (76)$$

This transport is downward in the whole region and at all levels, and has its maximum at the middle of the belt at the level $z = d/2$, which agrees qualitatively with the result obtained in the previous study (Kuo, 1952). The order of magnitude of τ_2 is the same as that of τ_1. When τ_1 and τ_2 are taken together, the region of downward transport in the lower layers will be extended to the south of $y = 0$, as is indicated by the dashed curve in fig. 5.

7. Energy transformation and some physical considerations

We shall now discuss the problem of transformation of heat energy into kinetic energy. From the equations of motion and the continuity equation, we find

$$\frac{\partial e}{\partial t} = -g\rho v_Z - \frac{p}{\rho}\frac{d\rho}{dt} - \mathrm{div}_3\,(e + p)\mathbf{c} - F, \quad (77)$$

where $e = \rho(v_x^2 + v_y^2 + v_Z^2)/2$, $\mathbf{c}$ is the three-dimensional velocity vector, and F is the loss of kinetic energy due to friction. In addition, we have the thermal energy equation. Since the kinetic-energy generating process is relatively rapid and more localized, we may visualize it as being nearly adiabatic and consider the slow symmetric heating as a static process.[6] Thus, adding (77) to the adiabatic thermal energy equation, integrating over the entire volume and making use of the relation

$$\int g\rho v_Z\,dV = (\gamma - 1)\int (\partial u/\partial t)\,dV,$$

which holds for the columns of the atmosphere, where $u = JC_v\rho T$, and $\gamma = C_p/C_v$, we find that the rate of increase of the total kinetic energy E is given by

$$\frac{\partial E}{\partial t} = -\frac{\gamma}{\gamma - 1}\int g\rho v_Z\,dV - D \approx \frac{\gamma}{\gamma - 1}g\int\frac{\rho_0}{\theta_0}v_Z\theta'\,dV - D, \quad (78)$$

where D is the total loss of kinetic energy through friction. Thus, the total kinetic energy generated is equal to the decrease of the available potential and internal energy, and is proportional to the volume integral of the upward transport of heat.

Besides the kinetic-energy generating process discussed above, we also have the non-adiabatic heating processes, such as radiation and conduction. We are here concerned only with the very slow non-adiabatic heating which may be considered as a static process and therefore may be represented by

$$q = \frac{C_pT}{\theta}\frac{d\theta}{dt} = \frac{C_pT}{\theta}\frac{\partial\theta}{\partial t},$$

where q is the non-adiabatic heating per unit mass. If q is a space function, this will lead to a differential heating and thereby increase the available potential and internal energy. For the systems we are considering, the temperature distribution so produced is a symmetric distribution.

The significance of these considerations can be tested by an application to the average conditions of the atmosphere. For a long-time average, the kinetic energy generated in the atmosphere as a whole is balanced by the frictional loss D. Taking the data used in the preceding section in computing the upward transport of heat, we find $\int g\rho_0\alpha\theta v_Z\,dV = 0.01$ cal cm^{-2} min^{-1} at 45°N. When integrated over the entire atmosphere, it gives 2.4×10^{22} ergs/sec as the rate of generation of the total kinetic energy, which is about 2 per cent of the average effective incoming solar

[6] This separation of the heating process into two parts is helpful in understanding its nature and also in avoiding the trivial conclusion $D = D$ when long-time averages are considered.

radiation and is roughly equal to the estimated rate of dissipation.

To understand the meaning of certain of the mathematical results, particularly the change of the flow patterns at different rotation rates, we shall discuss the effects of various physical factors. In our problem, heat energy is transformed into kinetic energy through a buoyancy force associated with the local temperature departure. However, since this buoyancy force is in the vertical direction, the question arises as to why the large-scale motions in the atmosphere are mainly horizontal. This seemingly difficult question is explained by the fact that the large-scale atmospheric motions are maintained by differential heating in horizontal directions, and not by the temperature contrast in the vertical direction. The atmosphere has a large stable stratification which acts as a constraint on the motion; it prevents the development of large vertical velocities, and builds up the motion in horizontal directions through the creation of horizontal pressure forces. To demonstrate this more clearly, let us consider the increase of kinetic energy through the release of thermal and potential energy associated with a given temperature distribution. Denoting the direction of the potential temperature gradient by n, whose horizontal component is in the direction of x_1, and denoting the angle between x_1 and n by $\gamma_0 - (\pi/2)$, $\tan\gamma_0 = -(\partial\theta_0/\partial x_1)(\partial\theta_0/\partial z)^{-1}$. According to whether $\partial\theta_0/\partial z$ is positive or negative, we have $0 \leqslant \gamma_0 \leqslant \pi/2$ or $\pi/2 \leqslant \gamma_0 \leqslant \pi$; and the sign of $\tan\gamma_0$ is that of $\partial\theta_0/\partial z$, since $\partial\theta_0/\partial x_1 < 0$ (see fig. 6). Suppose a particle at P is displaced a distance Δs in the x_1z-plane to Q, which makes an angle γ with x_1. The horizontal and vertical projections of Δs are Δx_1 and Δz, respectively. The excess of temperature of this particle at Q is given by

$$\theta = -\Delta x_1 \frac{\partial\theta_0}{\partial x_1} - \Delta z \frac{\partial\theta_0}{\partial z} = \frac{\partial\theta_0}{\partial z}(\Delta z_0 - \Delta z),$$

where Δz_0 is the increment of z along the isentropic surface through P corresponding to the same horizontal distance Δx_1. It is seen that when $|\Delta z| < |\Delta z_0|$, *i.e.*, $|\gamma| < |\gamma_0|$, the particle will be warmer than the surroundings if Δs has an upward component and colder if Δs has a downward component; therefore, the motion will be accelerated. Since this acceleration is produced by the component of the buoyancy force along s, it is given by

$$\frac{d^2s}{dt^2} = g\alpha\theta\sin\gamma$$

$$= \frac{\Delta s}{2} g\alpha \frac{\partial\theta_0}{\partial z}\sin 2\gamma(\tan\gamma_0 - \tan\gamma). \quad (79)$$

This equation shows that the motion will be accelerated only when the angle of displacement γ is smaller than γ_0, $\partial\theta_0/\partial z$ being positive. Since γ_0 is very small for the atmosphere, the motion must be nearly horizontal to have the available potential energy released and transformed into kinetic energy. This analysis demonstrates clearly that the large upward increase of potential temperature is the dominant factor which makes the large-scale motions in the atmosphere more horizontal. Because of the action of this factor, the vertical velocity is always much smaller than the horizontal velocity in the large-scale motions, and the vertical pressure distribution is very closely represented by the hydrostatic relation; therefore, this relation can be used for all practical purposes. However, this does not mean that the vertical velocity and vertical acceleration are exactly zero at all times. It merely means that the vertical acceleration is very small compared with the gravitational acceleration g, and also small compared with the horizontal acceleration. Thus, the total kinetic energy E is nearly equal to the horizontal kinetic energy E_h. If we find the rate of change of E_h from the two horizontal equations of motions alone (see Starr, 1949), it is evident that the direct mechanism that produces $\partial E_h/\partial t$ is through the work done by the horizontal pressure force. However, this horizontal pressure field may be considered as having been set up by the thermal effect, and the work done by this force is actually equivalent to the work done by the buoyancy force; this can easily be shown by a simple transformation of the energy equation, which takes the same form as (78), except E is replaced by E_h.

From (79) we find that the maximum acceleration is attained when $\gamma = \gamma_0/2$, *i.e.*, when the direction of displacement bisects the angle γ_0. Multiplying (79) by ds/dt, integrating over t, and putting $\gamma = \gamma_0/2$, we find that the maximum amount of kinetic energy attained by the particle at the end of the displacement is given by

$$\frac{1}{2}\left(\frac{ds}{dt}\right)_M^2 = \frac{(\Delta s)^2}{4} g\alpha \frac{\partial\theta_0}{\partial z}(\sec\gamma_0 - 1)$$

$$= -\tfrac{1}{4}(\Delta s)^2 g\alpha \frac{\partial\theta_0}{\partial x_1}(\csc\gamma_0 - \cot\gamma_0). \quad (80)$$

These equations show that, when the potential temperature is uniform in the horizontal directions but decreases upward ($\gamma_0 = \pi$), the maximum kinetic energy attainable is $-g\alpha(\partial\theta_0/\partial z)(\Delta s)^2/2$; while when it is uniform in the vertical but with horizontal variations ($\gamma_0 = \pi/2$), the maximum kinetic energy attainable is $g\alpha|\partial\theta_0/\partial x_1|(\Delta s)^2/4$. However, no energy can be released if the potential temperature increases upward and is uniform in the horizontal directions.

We are interested particularly in the case when θ_0 increases upward and γ_0 is a small acute angle. Then (80) reduces approximately to

$$\frac{1}{2}\left(\frac{ds}{dt}\right)_M^2 \approx \tfrac{1}{8}(\Delta s)^2 g\alpha \left(\frac{\partial\theta_0}{\partial x_1}\right)^2 \left(\frac{\partial\theta_0}{\partial z}\right)^{-1}. \quad (81)$$

The quantity on the right-hand side of this equation is a measure of the available potential energy of a stably stratified atmosphere, and is similar to the quantity discussed by Lorenz (1955).

Of course, not all the particles can take the path of optimum angle $\gamma = \gamma_0/2$. It seems reasonable to assume an equal distribution from zero to γ_0. Then, instead of (80) and (81), we obtain

$$\frac{1}{2}\left(\overline{\frac{ds}{dt}}\right)^2 = \tfrac{1}{4}(\Delta s)^2 g\alpha \frac{\partial\theta_0}{\partial z}\left(\frac{\tan\gamma_0}{\gamma_0} - 1\right)$$

$$\approx \tfrac{1}{12}(\Delta s)^2 g\alpha \left(\frac{\partial\theta_0}{\partial x_1}\right)^2 \left(\frac{\partial\theta_0}{\partial z}\right)^{-1}, \quad (82)$$

where the second line holds for very small γ_0.

However, although the above consideration demonstrates clearly the restraining effect of the stable stratification, it fails to explain the change of form of the motion under different conditions. Since the form of the motion is determined by the adjustment to the action of different factors, it can best be explained by an examination of the governing differential equation. For this purpose, it is more convenient to consider a simplified version of the problem by assuming a frictional force proportional to the velocity, replacing $-\nu\,\nabla^2 V$ and $-k\,\nabla^2\theta$ by CV and $C\theta$. For simplicity, we also assume that there is no basic current in the fluid, so that the equations for the horizontal velocity components are the same as the equation for v_Z. Under these assumptions, (22) may be written as

$$\left(\frac{\partial}{\partial t} + c\right)\left\{\left(\frac{\partial}{\partial t} + c\right)^2 \nabla^2 v + 4\Omega^2 \frac{\partial^2 V}{\partial z^2} + gs\nabla_h^2 V\right\}$$

$$= 2gs_r\left\{\left(\frac{\partial}{\partial t} + c\right)\frac{\partial^2 V}{\partial r\,\partial z} + \frac{2\Omega}{r}\frac{\partial^2 V}{\partial\lambda\,\partial z}\right\}, \quad (83)$$

where v may stand for any velocity component. The physical significance of the different terms of this equation can be more easily understood by considering first the purely symmetric motion alone. For this case, the terms involving $\partial/\partial\lambda$ disappear and the common factor $(\partial/\partial t + c)$ can be removed; therefore, (83) becomes

$$\left(\frac{\partial}{\partial t} + c\right)^2 \nabla^2 V + 4\Omega^2 \frac{\partial^2 V}{\partial z^2}$$

$$+ gs\,\nabla_h^2 V = 2gs_r \frac{\partial^2 V}{\partial r\,\partial z}. \quad (84)$$

It is evident that the three terms on the left-hand side of this equation represent a kind of resistance or inertia of the fluid system, which is composed of the resistance due to the development of the motion against friction, the inhibiting effects of rotation, and stable stratification (s assumed to be positive), respectively, while the term on the right represents the process that transforms the available potential and thermal energy into kinetic energy. The form of this right-hand term shows that this process is accomplished through the circulation ξ around the west-east axis and is proportional to the mean radial temperature gradient $\partial\theta_0/\partial r$.

This interpretation must also apply to the more general motions represented by (83). Just as for the symmetrical motion, the three terms in the braces on the left may be considered as representing the total resistance or inertia of the fluid system, while the two terms on the right represent two different ways of converting the thermal and potential energy into kinetic energy, each being proportional to $\partial\theta_0/\partial r$. As in the symmetric motion, the term $2gs_r(\partial/\partial t + c)\,\partial^2 V/\partial r\,\partial z$ represents an overturning process accomplished through the circulation ξ around the x-axis, while the second term $4\Omega gs_r r_0^{-1}\,\partial^2 V/\partial\lambda\,\partial z$ represents a converting process through the circulation η about the y-axis. The energy-releasing motion of the first process takes place in a direction which slopes upward toward the pole (the cold source) at an angle smaller than the slope of the undisturbed isentropic surface, with the returning branch of the motion occurring either at the same longitude or at another longitude and in the same sloping surface. This process is similar to the processes discussed by Mintz (1947) and Eady (1949; 1951). The efficiency of this process is independent of the wave number l, even when the motion consists of a wave motion. It is also independent of the rotation. On the other hand, the second energy-releasing process is accomplished mainly through the vertical motion associated with the circulation η in the xz-plane, and its efficiency is proportional both to the rate of rotation Ω and to the wave number l of the motion. This process of releasing the available potential energy can easily be understood if we consider that the initial isentropic surfaces are first

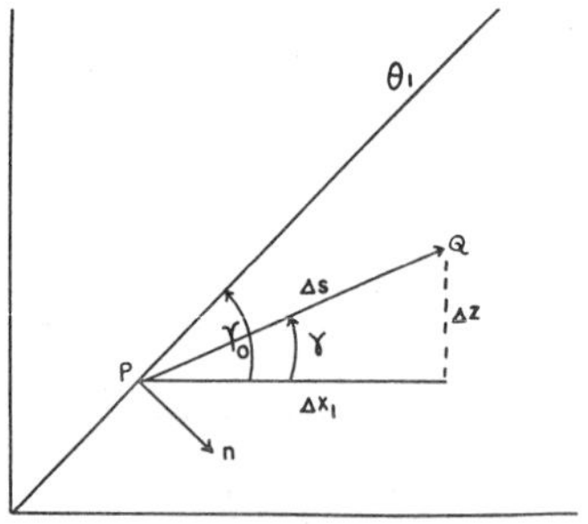

FIG. 6. Geometric relation between direction of displacement and isentropic surface.

deformed by the north-south motion of the wave-disturbance into a wavy form in the x-direction. The "eddy available potential energy" associated with this eddy temperature field is then released by the vertical motion of the circulation η of the wave motion.

Since the efficiency of the second energy-releasing process is proportional to Ω and also proportional to the wave number l, its importance increases with the rotation; it must become the dominant process when the rotation rate is high and the motion consists of a number of waves. Then the first process becomes of much less importance. The motion must therefore break up into a large number of waves at higher rotation rates, according to this consideration.

On the other hand, the motion must also adjust itself to the inhibiting effects represented by the left-hand terms of (83), so as to make the total resistance as small as possible. It may be remarked that, although both the rotation and the stable stratification tend to inhibit the motion, they actually work in different directions, so to speak, perpendicular to each other. To diminish the rotation effect represented by $4\Omega^2\, \partial^2 V/\partial z^2$, the motion must increase its vertical scale d, or stretch along the rotation axis; to diminish the effect of stable stratification represented by $gs\, \nabla_h^2 V$, it must increase its horizontal scale. Therefore, the ratio between these two terms must be an important parameter in determining the form of the flow, and the motion must decrease its horizontal scale and increase its vertical scale at higher rates of rotation, if the static stability remains the same. Thus, both from the point of view of increasing the efficiency of the energy-releasing process and from the point of view of diminishing the resistance, the number of waves must tend to increase with the rotation.

Acknowledgments.—The writer wishes to express his thanks to Prof. Victor P. Starr for many fruitful discussions, and to Mr. Paulo S. Castillo, Jr., for his assistance in the calculations.

REFERENCES

Charney, J. G., 1947: The dynamics of long waves in a baroclinic westerly current. *J. Meteor.*, **4**, 135–162.

Eady, E. T., 1949: Long waves and cyclone waves. *Tellus*, **1**, 33–52.

——, 1951: The quantitative theory of cyclone development. *Compendium Meteor.*, Boston, Amer. meteor. Soc., 464–469.

Fjörtoft, R., 1950: Application of integral theorems in deriving criteria of stability of laminar flows and of baroclinic circular vortex. *Geofys. Publ.*, **17**, No. 5, 1–52.

Fultz, D., 1951: Experimental analogies to atmospheric motion. *Compendium Meteor.*, Boston, Amer. meteor. Soc., 1235–1248.

——, 1953: *A survey of certain thermally- and mechanically driven fluid systems of meteorological interest.* Presented at "Symposium on model experiments," Dept. Civil Engr., Johns Hopkins Univ., Sept. 1953.

Hide, R., 1953: *Fluid motions in the earth's core; and some experiments on thermal convection in a rotating fluid.* Presented at "Symposium on model experiments," Dept. Civil Engr., Johns Hopkins Univ., Sept. 1953.

Kuo, H.-L., 1952: Three-dimensional disturbances in a baroclinic zonal current. *J. Meteor.*, **9**, 260–278.

——, 1953a: On the production of mean zonal currents in the atmosphere by large disturbances. *Tellus*, **5**, 475–493.

——, 1953b: The stability properties and structure of disturbances in a baroclinic atmosphere. *J. Meteor.*, **10**, 235–243.

——, 1953c: The development of quasi-geostrophic motions in the atmosphere. *Geophys. Res. Pap.*, No. 24, 27–52.

——, 1954: Symmetric disturbances in a thin layer of fluid subject to a horizontal temperature gradient and rotation. *J. Meteor.*, **11**, 399–411.

——, 1955: On convective instability of a rotating fluid with a horizontal temperature contrast. *J. mar. Res.*, **14**, 14–32.

Lorenz, E. N., 1955: Available potential energy in the atmosphere. Tellus, **7**, 157–167.

Mintz, Y., 1947: On the kinematics and thermodynamics of general circulation of the atmosphere in the higher latitudes. *Trans. Amer. geophys. Union*, **28**, 539–544.

Starr, V. P., 1951: Application of energy principles to the general circulation. *Compendium Meteor.*, Boston, Amer. meteor. Soc., 568–576.

Thompson, P. D., 1953: On the theory of large-scale disturbances in a two-dimensional baroclinic equivalent of the atmosphere. *Quart. J. r. meteor. Soc.*, **79**, 51–69.

DECEMBER 1956 H.-L. KUO 561

Reprinted from *Journal of Meteorology*, Vol. 13, No. 6, Dec., 1956, published by the American Meteorological Society.

FORCED AND FREE MERIDIONAL CIRCULATIONS IN THE ATMOSPHERE

By H.-L. Kuo

Massachusetts Institute of Technology

(Manuscript received 6 February 1956)

ABSTRACT

The meridional variation of the sum of the non-adiabatic heating and the eddy transfer of heat, and the vertical variation of the sum of the frictional dissipation and eddy transports of zonal momentum, are shown to act as two forcing functions which produce mean meridional circulations in the atmosphere. The form and intensity of these circulations are greatly influenced by the mean temperature distribution. When the meridional temperature contrast is higher than a certain limit, these forced motions change into a more violent free convection. The criterion of this transition is obtained by a simple method and expressed in terms of a Richardson number,

$$\mathrm{Ri} \equiv g \frac{\partial \log \theta}{\partial z}\left(\frac{\partial u_0}{\partial z}\right)^{-2} \leqslant f^2(fZ_0 + c^2)^{-1},$$

where Z_0 is the absolute vorticity of the mean zonal flow, and c is the coefficient of friction. This condition is generally not satisfied in the atmosphere, indicating that only weak, forced, mean meridional circulation can exist.

The form and intensity of the meridional circulation produced by sources of heat and momentum, and that produced by the mean non-adiabatic heating in an atmosphere at relative rest, are discussed. It is found that only a very weak, single, direct cell can be produced by the average non-adiabatic heating, with maximum meridional velocities of only a few centimeters per second. On the other hand, the effects of the horizontal eddy transport and frictional dissipation of zonal momentum tend to produce a three-cell meridional circulation in the troposphere, with a reverse cell in middle latitudes and direct cells in low and high latitudes. In the stratosphere, the circulations produced by this factor in low and middle latitudes are in the opposite sense as those in the troposphere.

1. Introduction and summary

In another article (Kuo, 1956b), the writer discussed the forced and free axially-symmetric meridional circulations in a deep layer of fluid contained between two rotating coaxial cylinders and heated from outside. It was shown that a single cell of very weak meridional circulation will be set up when heat is applied slowly. This cell may later change into a more violent free symmetric convection when the temperature contrast exceeds a certain limiting value which depends upon the rate of rotation, the static stability, the relative vorticity of the mean zonal current, and the Prandtl number. From the meteorological point of view, it is of great interest to discuss such circulations specifically for the atmosphere, in which effects of the compressibility and inhomogeneity of the air and the spherical shape of the earth are of importance. This latter factor introduces not only a different geometrical configuration, but also a different dynamical effect of the rotation, which is given by the variable Coriolis parameter $f = 2\Omega \sin \varphi$. In this article, we shall accordingly discuss (1) the various factors which may produce mean meridional circulations in the atmosphere, (2) the streamline patterns of the meridional circulations so produced, and (3) the conditions under which these motions may be amplified and thereby sustained as a more vigorous, free convection.

The nature of the mean meridional circulations in the atmosphere is greatly influenced by the presence of large eddy motions, which control the mean temperature and zonal velocity distributions through their transports of heat and momentum. Therefore, we must average the relevant equations over a complete latitude circle and obtain the equations for the averaged quantities, rather than assume that the physical quantities are exactly independent of longitude. In so doing, we find that the two factors $\partial H/a\,\partial\varphi$ and $\partial\chi/\partial p$ act as forcing functions which produce mean meridional circulations in the atmosphere. In the first expression,

$$H = Q/c_p - \frac{\partial(\overline{T'v'}\cos\varphi)}{a\cos\varphi\,\partial\varphi} - \frac{\partial\overline{T'\omega'}}{\partial p}$$

measures the net effect of the non-adiabatic heating Q (*e.g.*, radiation and turbulent heat conduction) and the convergence of eddy heat-transfer. In the second expression, χ measures the net effect of the convergence of the eddy transfer and the frictional dissipation of the zonal momentum, and is given by

$$\chi = g\frac{\partial\tau_x}{\partial p} + \frac{\partial(\overline{u'v'}\cos^2\varphi)}{a\cos^2\varphi\,\partial\varphi} + \frac{\partial\overline{u'\omega'}}{\partial p}.$$

The effect of the frictional dissipation, $\partial\tau_x/\partial p$, has been discussed by Kropatscheck (1935) and Prandtl (1936) on a hemispherical scale, while Eliassen (1952) discussed the effects of both $\partial\tau_x/\partial p$ and Q as point sources. Here we see that the meridional circulation in the atmosphere depends very much on the prevailing eddy motions, because these eddies are very efficient agents in transporting heat and momentum. Thus the meridional circulation in the atmosphere must be considered as a secondary process, its existence and form being controlled by the primary eddy process. The determination of such a secondary process can be sought only after a fairly accurate knowledge of the primary eddy process has been obtained.

During recent years, the question of the meridional transports of zonal momentum and heat by the large-scale atmospheric disturbances has been studied both statistically (Starr and White, 1954; Mintz, 1955) and theoretically (Kuo, 1949; 1951; 1952; 1953; 1956a). These studies show that the eddy process produces a horizontal convergence of zonal momentum in middle latitude, and divergences in low and high latitudes, with maximum transports occurring at the tropopause level. Since the dissipation of the zonal momentum takes place mainly through ground friction, the zonal momentum accumulated in the upper atmosphere by the horizontal eddy transports must be brought downward to compensate the low-level dissipation. Although the baroclinically unstable atmospheric disturbances are capable of transporting zonal momentum downward (Kuo, 1952; 1956a), it appears that this vertical eddy transport is somewhat smaller than that required. This gives an unbalanced χ-function, which acts as a forcing function to produce mean meridional circulation. It may also be remarked that, since the large-scale eddies in the stratosphere also produce a horizontal flux of zonal momentum, and since the eddies are unable to bring these accumulations of momentum downward because the mean zonal current decreases upward above the tropopause, a reverse horizontal transport by some mean meridional cell is needed in the stratosphere. Such circulations will also be produced through the forcing function $\partial\chi/\partial p$.

Since the magnitudes of the various terms in the functions H and χ vary from year to year, we shall discuss only the general effects of these forcing functions, and deduce the most probable form and intensity of the meridional circulation that may exist in the atmosphere. Thus, we shall discuss first the effects of point sources of heat and momentum, then the meridional circulation produced by an unbalanced χ-function, which we shall obtain from the statistical results of the eddy momentum-transports and frictional dissipation, and finally we shall discuss the circulation produced by the average radiational heating, assuming the motion to be starting from relative rest.

This study shows that the meridional circulation produced by the unbalanced momentum function, $\partial\chi/\partial p$, is a three-cell meridional circulation in the troposphere, with a reverse circulation (Ferrer cell) in middle latitudes and direct Hadley cells in low and high latitudes. The maximum north-south velocity is about 1 m/sec, and the corresponding maximum vertical velocity is of the order of 10^{-1} to 10^{-2} cm/sec. Although such vertical velocities are relatively small, they may have important climatological effects, especially if these mean motions are concentrated over certain sectors of the earth instead of being equally distributed over the zonal belt.

The meridional circulation produced by the average radiational heating is a very weak, direct cell, the maximum southward velocity on the earth's surface being less than 3 cm/sec; therefore, it is much weaker than that produced by the momentum function, $\partial\chi/\partial p$.

2. Governing equations for the mean meridional flow and the instability condition

Since the vertical dimension of the large-scale atmospheric motions is very small compared with the horizontal dimension, the vertical acceleration can be neglected in the third equation of motion (Kuo, 1956a), which means that hydrostatic equilibrium is preserved at all times. It is then more convenient to use the pressure p as the vertical coordinate and to measure the horizontal differentials along the isobaric surfaces, which simplifies the continuity equation into a form similar to that for a homogeneous and incompressible fluid. The pressure forces are then represented by the gradients of the geopotential, $\phi = gz$, of the isobaric surfaces, and the vertical velocity is replaced by $\omega \equiv dp/dt$.

Since in a rotating system the meridional pressure gradient is always nearly balanced by the Coriolis force associated with the mean zonal velocity, it is desirable to decompose the mean zonal velocity $\bar{u}$, the mean geopotential $\bar{\phi}$, and the mean temperature $\bar{T}$ into two parts, represented by u_0, ϕ_0 and T_0, and u_1, ϕ_1 and T_1. The quantities with the subscript zero then constitute a near-equilibrium state and change only very slowly with time. They are related by the following geostrophic and thermal wind relations:

$$\left(f + \frac{\tan\varphi}{a} u_0\right) u_0 = -\frac{\partial\phi_0}{a\,\partial\varphi}, \tag{1a}$$

and

$$\left(f + \frac{2\tan\varphi}{a} u_0\right) \frac{\partial u_0}{\partial p} = -\frac{\partial^2\phi_0}{a\,\partial\varphi\,\partial p} = \frac{R}{p}\frac{\partial T_0}{a\,\partial\varphi}. \tag{1b}$$

On the other hand, the second parts, u_1, ϕ_1 and T_1, together with the mean northward velocity v_1 and with ω_1, represent the axially-symmetric perturbation superimposed on the equilibrium state; they, therefore, constitute the active parts of the meridional circulation. For simplicity, we assume the frictional force associated with u_1 and v_1 to be proportional to u_1 and v_1, and the time variations to be represented by an exponential time factor. We may then represent the total effect of development and of work done against this part of friction, $\partial u_1/\partial t - \nu \nabla^2 u_1$ and $\partial v_1/\partial t - \nu \nabla^2 v_1$, by cu_1 and cv_1. It may be remarked that these frictional forces include the effects of genuine viscosity and of small-scale turbulence which are not included in the eddy-transport terms (eddy stresses, $\overline{u'v'}$ and $\overline{u'\omega'}$). We also note that the above mentioned assumption,

$$(\partial/\partial t - \nu \nabla^2)(u_1, v_1) = c(u_1, v_1),$$

is exactly correct if the motion is represented by a single eigenfunction. However, here we merely take it as an approximation for the purpose of simplifying the form of the differential equation. Similarly, we assume the effect of heat conduction, $k \nabla^2 T_1$, to be proportional to the perturbation temperature T_1, and replace $(\partial/\partial t - k \nabla^2)T_1$ by $c'T_1$. Since the Prandtl number of the air is nearly equal to 1, we may put $c' = c$. Thus, the zonally averaged equations of motion, the continuity equation, and the thermal energy equation may be written as follows:

$$cu_1 = Z_0 v_1 - \omega_1 \frac{\partial u_0}{\partial p} - g \frac{\partial \tau_x}{\partial p} - \frac{\partial(\overline{u'v'} \cos^2 \varphi)}{a \cos^2 \varphi \, \partial \varphi} - \frac{\partial \overline{u'\omega'}}{\partial p}, \quad (2)$$

$$cv_1 = -fu_1 - \partial \phi_1 / a\, \partial \varphi, \quad (3)$$

$$\partial \phi_1/\partial p = -RT_1/p, \quad (4)$$

$$\frac{\partial(v_1 \cos \varphi)}{a \cos \varphi \, \partial \varphi} + \frac{\partial \omega_1}{\partial p} = 0, \quad (5)$$

and

$$-c \frac{p}{R} \frac{\partial \phi_1}{\partial p} + \frac{1}{a} \frac{\partial T_0}{\partial \varphi} v_1 + \Gamma \omega_1 = \frac{1}{c_p} Q - \frac{\partial(\overline{T'v'} \cos \varphi)}{a \cos \varphi \, \partial \varphi} - \frac{\partial \overline{T'\omega'}}{\partial p}. \quad (6)$$

Here

$$Z_0 = f - \frac{\partial(u_0 \cos \varphi)}{a \cos \varphi \, \partial \varphi}$$

is the absolute vorticity of the mean zonal flow, $\tau_x = \rho\nu\, \partial u_0/\partial z$ is the eddy stress of the mean zonal velocity u_0, including that due to ground friction, a is the earth's radius, φ the latitude, $\Gamma = T \partial \log \theta/\partial p$, θ denoting the potential temperature, R is the gas constant, and Q is the mean heat added to a unit mass per unit time, such as that due to radiation, frictional dissipation, and turbulent heat conduction. The terms that are nonlinear in the perturbation quantities u_1, v_1, ω_1, T_1 and ϕ_1 have been omitted in these equations, as have some eddy terms in (3) which are ordinarily very small.

The continuity equation (5) indicates that the mean meridional velocity components can be represented by a stream function ψ, defined by

$$v_1 = \frac{1}{\cos \varphi} \frac{\partial \psi}{\partial p}, \quad \text{and} \quad \omega_1 = -\frac{1}{a \cos \varphi} \frac{\partial \psi}{\partial \varphi}. \quad (7)$$

Eliminating u_1 from (2) and (3), and making use of (7) and (1b), we obtain

$$A \frac{\partial \psi}{\partial p} + \frac{R}{a^2 p} \frac{\partial T_0}{\partial \eta} \frac{\partial \psi}{\partial \eta} = -\frac{c}{a} \frac{\partial \phi_1}{\partial \eta} + \frac{f}{\cos \varphi} \chi, \quad (8)$$

where $A = (fZ_0 + c^2)/\cos^2 \varphi$, and $\eta = \sin \varphi$. Eliminating ϕ_1 from (6) and (8), we finally obtain

$$\frac{\partial}{\partial p} A \frac{\partial \psi}{\partial p} + \frac{2R}{a^2 p} \frac{\partial T_0}{\partial \eta} \frac{\partial^2 \psi}{\partial \eta \, \partial p} + \frac{R}{a^2} \left(\frac{\partial}{\partial p} \frac{1}{p} \frac{\partial T_0}{\partial \eta} \right) \frac{\partial \psi}{\partial \eta} - \frac{R\Gamma}{a^2 p} \frac{\partial^2 \psi}{\partial \eta^2} = \frac{R}{ap} \frac{\partial H}{\partial \eta} + \frac{f}{\cos \varphi} \frac{\partial \chi}{\partial p}. \quad (9)$$

It may be remarked that the manner in which the effect of the conductive heating is taken into consideration differs from that of Oberbeck (1888) and that of Rogers (1954).

From this equation, we see that $\partial H/\partial \eta$ and $\partial \chi/\partial p$ appear as two forcing functions. Therefore the flow pattern and the intensity of the motion must be determined primarily by the magnitudes and distributions of these functions, unless mean meridional circulation can develop as a free convection resulting from instability of the mean-temperature and zonal-wind distributions with respect to axially symmetric perturbations. This free-convection case requires the existence of solutions of the homogeneous part of (9) which also satisfy the proper boundary requirements. For the present problem, the proper boundary condition is simply that ψ should remain constant along the boundary surfaces, that is, $\psi = 0$ for $\eta = 0$, $\eta = 1$, $p = 0$, and $p = p_0$.

Since the solution of an elliptic homogeneous partial differential equation has no extreme value inside a closed surface, the solution must be identically zero if it satisfies the above-mentioned boundary requirement. On the other hand, the solutions of the homogeneous equation of the hyperbolic type may vanish on the boundaries but are not identically zero. Therefore free mean meridional convection can exist only when (9) is of hyperbolic type, at least in part of the region inside the bounding surfaces. Thus the condition for the existence of free convection, or the resonance condition, is determined by the discriminant of the characteristics of (9) and is given by

$$\left(\frac{\partial \log T_0}{a\,\partial\varphi}\right)^2 - \frac{fZ_0 + c^2}{g}\frac{\partial \log\theta}{\partial z} \gtrless 0. \qquad (10)$$

The equal sign gives the lowest meridional temperature gradient that is able to maintain a free convection. In this case, (9) degenerates into parabolic type. On the other hand, if the meridional temperature gradient is less than this critical value in the whole region, the equation will be of elliptic type everywhere and only stable, forced convection can exist.

This instability or resonance condition can also be derived from the solution of the differential equation. A simple way of obtaining this criterion is to expand ψ into a double Fourier series, in the same manner as has been employed by the writer in the previous papers. This method has the advantage of being also applicable to equations of higher order, such as we would obtain if the Navier-Stokes equation of motion were being used instead of approximating $(\partial/\partial t - \nu\nabla^2)(u_1, v_1)$ by $c(u_1, v_1)$. Thus, we put

$$\psi = \sum_k \sum_l A_{kl} e^{i\pi[k(p/p_0)+l\eta]} = \sum\sum B_{kl} e^{ik\pi[(p/p_0)+\alpha_l\eta]}, \qquad (11)$$

where α_l is proportional to the inclination of the streamline. For simplicity, we shall assume α_l to be the same for all l harmonics. It may be remarked that the boundary conditions can always be satisfied by such a Fourier series. Substituting this stream function in the homogeneous part of (9), and disregarding the vertical variation of $\partial T_0/\partial\eta$, we obtain

$$2\frac{\partial T_0}{\partial\eta} = -\frac{p}{p_0}A\frac{a^2}{R\alpha} + p_0\Gamma\alpha. \qquad (12)$$

Since the critical value of $\partial T_0/\partial\eta$ is the minimum value that is able to maintain the free convection, the value of α must be chosen so as to make $\partial T_0/\partial\eta$ a minimum. This α is obtained by differentiating (12) with respect to α and putting $\partial^2 T_0/\partial\eta\,\partial\alpha = 0$, and is given by $\alpha^2 = a^2Ap(-Rp_0^2\Gamma)^{-1}$. Substituting this α in (12), we obtain the criterion

$$\left(\frac{\partial \log T_0}{a\,\partial\varphi}\right)^2 = \frac{fZ_0 + c^2}{g}\frac{\partial \log\theta}{\partial z}. \qquad (13a)$$

It is seen that this is the same as (10). This criterion may also be expressed in terms of a Richardson number Ri, by making use of the thermal wind relation (1b):

$$\mathrm{Ri} \equiv \frac{g\,\partial(\log\theta)/\partial z}{(\partial u_0/\partial z)^2} \leqslant \frac{f^2}{fZ_0 + c^2}. \qquad (13b)$$

When friction is neglected, we then have

$$\mathrm{Ri} \leqslant f\left[f - \frac{\partial(u_0\cos\phi)}{a\cos\phi\,\partial\phi}\right]^{-1}, \qquad (13c)$$

which can readily be shown to be the same as the well known criterion for inertial instability,

$$\left(\frac{\partial u_0\cos\varphi}{a\cos\varphi\,\partial\varphi}\right)_\theta \geqq f,$$

where the subscript θ denotes that the differentiation is to be taken along the isentropic surfaces.

3. Meridional circulations produced by sources of heat and momentum

In the atmosphere, the mean meridional temperature gradient is usually much smaller than the critical value given by (13a), except in very small regions near a front. Therefore only weak, forced meridional circulations can be produced by the existing forcing functions, $\partial H/\partial\eta$ and $\partial\chi/\partial p$. The intensity and form of such circulations, produced by point sources of heat and momentum, are given by the Green's function of the problem. To find the Green's function, we first specify the coefficients of (9). We assume the stratification factor Γ to be inversely proportional to p, *i.e.*, $\Gamma = -B/p$, where B is a constant. This is a good approximation for the mean conditions of the atmosphere, both for the troposphere and for the stratosphere. For simplicity, we take $\partial T_0/\partial\eta$ as constant and disregard the variation of the factor A. We may then introduce the following transformations:

$$\psi = (p/p_0)^{\frac{1}{2}}\Psi, \quad \text{and} \quad \zeta = 1/l \log p_0/p, \qquad (14)$$

where $l^2 = Aa^2/RB$. These substitutions transform (9) into the following:

$$\frac{\partial^2\Psi}{\partial\eta^2} + \frac{\partial^2\Psi}{\partial\zeta^2} - 2\gamma\frac{\partial^2\Psi}{\partial\eta\,\partial\zeta} - \frac{l^2}{4}\Psi = -E(\eta,\zeta), \qquad (15)$$

where $\gamma = (Bl)^{-1}\,\partial T_0/\partial\eta$ and

$$E = -(pp_0)^{\frac{1}{2}}\left[B^{-1}\frac{\partial H}{\partial\eta} - \left(\frac{RB}{fZ_0 + c^2}\right)^{\frac{1}{2}}\frac{f}{a}\frac{\partial\chi}{\partial\zeta}\right].$$

Equation (15) is an elliptic equation when γ^2 is smaller than 1. The Green's function of this equation can easily be obtained by making use of the substitution

$$y = (1 - \gamma^2)^{-\frac{1}{2}}(\eta + \gamma\zeta), \qquad (16)$$

which transforms (15) into the normal form,

$$\frac{\partial^2\Psi}{\partial y^2} + \frac{\partial^2\Psi}{\partial\zeta^2} - \frac{l^2}{4}\Psi = -E(\eta,\zeta). \qquad (17)$$

To construct the Green's function, let us first seek an elementary solution $V(r)$ of the homogeneous part of this equation, which is a function of the "distance" r between the source point (y', ζ') and the action point

(y, ζ) alone. Here r is defined by[1]

$$r^2 = (y - y')^2 + (\zeta - \zeta')^2$$
$$= \frac{1}{1-\gamma^2}\left[(\eta - \eta')^2 + \frac{1}{l^2}(\log p/p')^2 + \frac{2\gamma}{l}(\eta - \eta')\log\frac{p}{p'}\right]. \quad (18)$$

Thus, $V(r)$ satisfies the equation

$$\frac{d^2V}{dr^2} + \frac{1}{r}\frac{dV}{dr} - \frac{l^2}{4}V = 0. \quad (19)$$

One solution of this equation is the zero-order Hankel's function with imaginary argument, $iH_0^{(1)}(\frac{1}{2}ilr)$. This function behaves like $-(2/\pi)\log r$ as $r \rightarrow 0$, and like $r^{-\frac{1}{2}}e^{-\frac{1}{2}lr}$ as $r \rightarrow \infty$; therefore, it satisfies the requirements of a Green's function. To satisfy the lower boundary condition, $G = 0$, on the ground ($p = p_0$, $\zeta = 0$), we subtract a regular solution $iH_0^{(1)}(\frac{1}{2}ilr')$ from this principal solution and put

$$G(y, \zeta; y', \zeta') = \frac{i}{4(1-\gamma^2)^{\frac{1}{2}}}\left[H_0^{(1)}(\tfrac{1}{2}ilr) - H_0^{(1)}(\tfrac{1}{2}ilr')\right], \quad (20)$$

where

$$r'^2 = (y - y')^2 + (\zeta + \zeta')^2 = r^2 + \frac{4}{l^2}\log\frac{p_0}{p}\log\frac{p_0}{p'}. \quad (21)$$

The constant factor is chosen so as to make $-\oint(\partial G/\partial n)\,ds = 1$, where s is a small closed curve enclosing (y', ζ'). Since the two Hankel functions decrease exponentially with increasing r, and since $p = 0$ corresponds to $\zeta = \infty$ and l becomes infinity at the pole, G also satisfies the upper boundary condition and the condition at $\eta = 1$. The condition at $\eta = 0$ is satisfied by subtracting its image with respect to the equator. With this Green's function, we find that the solution of (15) is given by

$$\Psi(y, \zeta) = \iint G(y, \zeta; y', \zeta')\,E(y', \zeta')\,dy'\,d\zeta', \quad (22)$$

where the integration is to be taken over the whole region. Thus, the function $(p/p_0)^{\frac{1}{2}}G$ represents the stream function of the meridional circulation produced by a point source $\int E\,dx'\,d\zeta' = 1$ at (y', ζ') and $E = 0$ at all other points.

In fig. 1, the Green's function $4(p/p_0)^{\frac{1}{2}}G$ is plotted for a point source situated at $p' = 500$ mb and latitude 45 deg, and for a static stability factor $B = 45$ deg C and $\partial T_0/a\,\partial\varphi = -1.0 \times 10^{-7}$ (deg C)/cm, corresponding to $\gamma = -0.269$ and $l = 4.19$. The dashed line represents the isentropic surface through the source point. It is seen that the axis of the flow pattern slopes upward and northward, similar to the isentropic surface, but with a slightly smaller slope in regions far away from the source point. This indicates that the motion is drawing energy from the available energy associated with the horizontal temperature contrast in these regions. The asymmetry of the streamlines is due to the asymmetry of $\eta = \sin\varphi$.

From the distribution of the Green's function G it can readily be inferred that when H decreases with increasing φ it induces a direct circulation, since then

$$E = -(pp_0)^{\frac{1}{2}}\frac{1}{B}\,\partial H/\partial\eta$$

is positive. On the other hand, if χ decreases upward (so that it represents a sink of westerly momentum near the ground and a source at higher levels, giving a negative E), it will induce an indirect circulation; if χ increases upward, giving positive E, it will induce a direct circulation. These general results agree with the findings of Eliassen (1952) concerning the effects of the non-adiabatic heating and the frictional dissipation.

We shall now discuss the distribution of the forcing function. Statistical studies show that the large-scale atmospheric eddies produce a large convergence of zonal momentum in middle latitudes, and divergences in low and also in high latitudes, with maximum convergence and divergence occurring at the tropopause level. Thus, from Buch (1954), we find that $\partial^2(\overline{u'v'}\cos^2\varphi)/\partial\varphi\,\partial p$ is positive in middle latitudes and negative in low and high latitudes in the troposphere, with its magnitude decreasing downward. Since surface westerlies prevail in middle latitudes and surface easterlies prevail in low and also in high latitudes, and since the frictional dissipation decreases upward, $g\,\partial^2\tau_x/\partial p^2$ is also positive in middle latitudes and negative in low and high latitudes, but with its magnitude decreasing upward. Thus these two terms are generally of the same sign in the troposphere, and together they give a positive $\partial\chi/\partial p$ in middle latitudes and negative

[1] The effect of the variation of l with latitude can be taken into consideration by using the "local" values of l in ζ and ζ'.

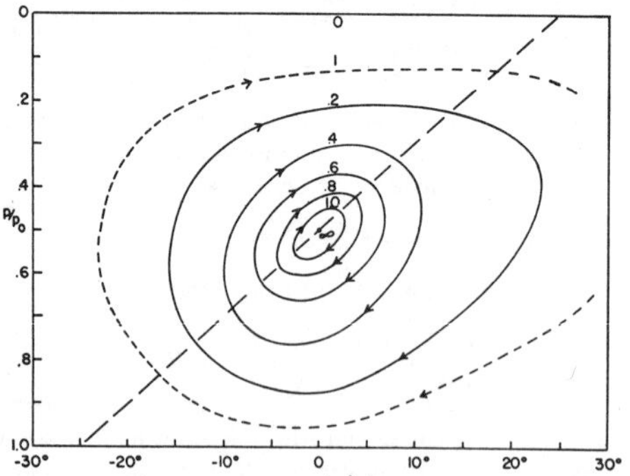

FIG. 1. Distribution of function $4(p/p_0)^{\frac{1}{2}}G$ for point source at latitude 45 deg and $p' = 500$ mb.

TABLE 1. Distribution of the forcing function in 10^{-8} m sec^{-2} mb^{-1}.

Lat (deg N):	65	60	55	50	45	40	35	30	25	20	15
15 cb:	2.6	3.1	−1.4	−9.3	−11.0	−16.7	−11.9	−3.0	10.0	13.3	2.5
20 cb:	2.3	2.4	2.7	0.8	−11.8	−8.7	−9.8	−1.2	7.1	6.0	3.4
30 cb:	3.1	2.9	4.1	5.2	4.4	0.4	1.7	0.9	−0.8	−4.6	−3.5
50 cb:	3.5	3.5	2.5	3.6	5.8	5.3	3.9	0.8	−2.0	−3.7	−4.5
70 cb:	2.6	4.0	4.2	4.0	3.3	3.1	1.2	−0.6	−0.5	−2.0	−2.5
85 cb:	0.5	3.2	4.5	5.2	4.0	1.8	−0.4	−1.6	−2.3	−3.0	−3.5
100 cb:	2.5	5.0	5.3	5.6	5.0	2.5	0	−1.8	−3.1	−3.8	−4.4
τ_0(dy/cm^2):	0.4	0.8	0.9	0.9	0.8	0.4	0	−0.2	−0.5	−0.6	−0.8

$\partial\chi/\partial p$ in low and high latitudes. For simplicity, we shall assume the vertical variation of the zonal stress, $\tau_x = \mu\, \partial u_0/\partial z$, to be represented by an exponential function of p,

$$\tau_x = \tau_0 \exp[\beta(p/p_0 - 1)],$$

and take $\beta = 2.5$. With this formula and the mean surface zonal stress τ_0 given by Priestley (1951) and Mintz (1955), and the $\overline{u'v'}$ statistics of Buch (1954) for the year 1950, we find the distribution of the unbalanced momentum function,

$$\partial\chi'/\partial p = g\frac{\partial^2\tau_x}{\partial p^2} + \frac{\partial^2(\overline{u'v'}\cos^2\varphi)}{a\cos^2\varphi\,\partial\varphi\,\partial p},$$

as given in table 1. From these values it is seen that the magnitude of the term $f\,\partial\chi'/\partial p$ is about 10^{-12} to 10^{-11} m sec^{-3} mb^{-1}, which is one order of magnitude larger than $(R/ap)\,\partial H/\partial\varphi$ in middle latitudes (see section 4, below).

Since the forcing function is given numerically at fixed grid points, (15) is most conveniently integrated by the relaxation method. However, since data are still lacking both in higher and in lower latitudes, and since the values given in table 1 may not be very representative, this equation is integrated only roughly, to give a probable pattern of the forced mean meridional circulation, which is represented schematically in fig. 2. It is seen that this distribution of the forcing function $\partial\chi/\partial p$ produces an indirect Ferrer cell in middle latitudes and two direct Hadley cells, one in low and one in high latitudes, in the troposphere. The maximum mean north-south velocity is about 1 m/sec, and the vertical velocity is of the order of 10^{-2} to 10^{-1} cm/sec. In the stratosphere, $\partial^2(\overline{u'v'}\cos^2\varphi)/\partial\varphi\,\partial p$ is positive in low latitudes and negative in middle latitudes; therefore the meridional circulations induced by this term are in the opposite sense as those of the troposphere. Most probably this upper circulation produced by the eddy stresses occupies the region from the tropopause up to about 35 km, and therefore may play some role in determining the latitudinal variation of the ozone concentration in the lower stratosphere.

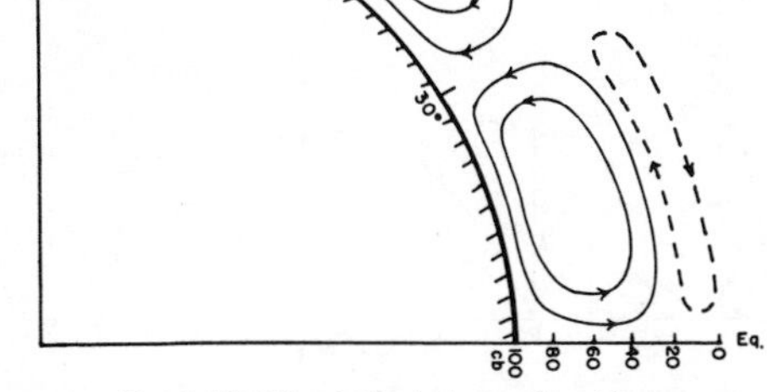

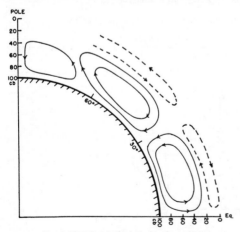

FIG. 2. Meridional circulation produced by momentum function $\partial\chi'/\partial p$.

4. Thermally-driven meridional circulation starting from relative rest

Although large eddy motions always prevail in the atmosphere and exert a controlling influence on the mean meridional circulation, a study of the purely symmetric meridional circulation produced by differential heating from a state of relative rest is of some theoretical interest. In this section, we shall be particularly concerned with the flow pattern and the intensity of such motions produced by the average radiational heating over the spherical earth. Since there is no motion to begin with, the temperature must be uniform on an isobaric surface. However, we shall assume a stable stratification to be present, represented by a constant $\Gamma = -B_0/p_0$. Thus, (9) simplifies to

$$\frac{4\Omega^2 + c^2}{1 - \eta^2}\,p\,\frac{\partial^2\psi}{\partial p^2} + \frac{RB_0}{a^2p_0}\frac{\partial^2\psi}{\partial\eta^2} = \frac{R}{c_p}\frac{\partial Q}{a\,\partial\eta}. \qquad (23)$$

For this stratification, it is convenient to use the variable q, defined by

$$q = 2(p/p_0)^{\frac{1}{2}}, \qquad (24)$$

as the vertical coordinate. This transforms (23) into

$$(1 - \eta^2)\frac{\partial^2\psi}{\partial\eta^2} + \frac{a^2}{RB_0}(4\Omega^2\eta^2 + c^2)\left(\frac{\partial^2\psi}{\partial q^2} - \frac{1}{q}\frac{\partial\psi}{\partial q}\right)$$
$$= \frac{ap_0}{c_pB_0}\cos\varphi\frac{\partial Q}{\partial\varphi}. \qquad (25)$$

We shall seek solutions of this equation which can be represented by the product of a function of q and another function of η. For simplicity, the non-adiabatic heating Q is supposed to be represented by[2]

$$Q = Dq\, J_1(\alpha q)\, (\cos^2 \varphi - \tfrac{2}{3}), \quad \alpha = 1.916, \tag{26}$$

which gives heating in the equatorial region ($|\varphi| < 35°\,16'$) and cooling at higher latitudes. The vertical variation of the stream function for this heating function may also be represented by $q\, J_1(\alpha q)$. Therefore, we put $\psi = q\, J_1(\alpha q)\, \Phi(\eta)$, where Φ is a function of η alone. The function Φ is required to be symmetric with respect to the equator, and to give zero mean north-south velocities at the equator and the poles ($\eta = 0$ and $\eta = \pm 1$). Therefore, we put

$$\Phi = \frac{2ap_0}{c_p B_0} D\eta(1 - \eta^2) \times [a_1 + a_3\eta^2 + \cdots + a_{2j+1}\eta^{2j} + \cdots]. \tag{27}$$

Substituting in (25), we find that the a's are connected by the following relations:

$$\begin{aligned} &2.3\, a_3 - (2.3 + \vartheta^2)a_1 = -1 \\ &\cdot \quad \cdot \quad \cdot \quad \cdot \quad \cdot \\ &\cdot \quad \cdot \quad \cdot \quad \cdot \quad \cdot \\ &2j(2j+1)a_{2j+1} \\ &\quad - [2j(2j+1) + \vartheta^2]a_{2j-1} - \beta^2 a_{2j-3} = 0, \end{aligned} \tag{28}$$

where $\vartheta^2 = a^2\alpha^2 c^2/RB_0$, and $\beta^2 = 4\Omega^2 a^2 \alpha^2/RB$. Writing $N_{j+1} = a_{2j+1}/a_{2j-1}$, and $N_j = a_{2j-1}/a_{2j-3}$, we then have

$$N_{j+1} = 1 + \frac{\vartheta^2}{2j(2j+1)} + \frac{\beta^2}{2j(2j+1)N_j}, \tag{29a}$$

and

$$N_j = -\frac{\beta^2}{2j(2j+1)} \Big/ \left[1 + \frac{\vartheta^2}{2j(2j+1) - N_{j+1}}\right]. \tag{29b}$$

The convergence of the series solution (27) at $\eta = \pm 1$ requires N_j to approach zero as j approaches infinity. Putting $j = m$ in (29a) and $j = m + 1$ in (29b), and equating the two expressions of N_{m+1}, we obtain the following continuous fraction:

$$N_m = \frac{-\dfrac{\beta^2}{2m(2m+1)}}{1 + \dfrac{\vartheta^2}{2m(2m+1)} + \cdots} \times \frac{\dfrac{\beta^2}{(2m+2)(2m+3)}}{1 + \dfrac{\vartheta^2}{(2m+2)(2m+3)} + \cdots}. \tag{30}$$

From (29a), we see that the condition for $N_{j+1} \to 0$ for very large j is

[2] More general vertical distributions can be represented by Fourier-Bessel series.

$$\lim_{j\to\infty} N_j = -\frac{\beta^2}{2j(2j+1) + \vartheta^2}. \tag{31a}$$

Thus, N_j is negative when β^2 and ϑ^2 are positive. The series is then an alternative series. Since (30) is valid for $j = 2$, we have

$$a_1 = \frac{1}{6 + \vartheta^2 - N_2}. \tag{31b}$$

This relation shows that no free non-oscillatory motion can exist, because for such motions ϑ^2 is positive and N_2 is negative; therefore a_1 is finite and Φ must be zero if D is zero. It is worth while, however, to mention that free oscillatory motions can exist in this atmosphere. This follows from the fact that c is imaginary for such motion, in which case ϑ^2 becomes negative and the denominator of (31b) may become zero. Such solutions are important for the theory of atmospheric tides (see Lamb, 1932).

It may be remarked that, although an exactly convergent series solution exists, this solution is difficult to obtain because the determination of the coefficients requires absolute accuracy. The most convenient plan for conducting the computation is to assume a rough approximation for one of the ratios N_j of large j, as suggested by (31a). Thence, N_{j-1}, N_{j-2}, $\cdots$, N_2 may be computed in succession by means of (30). Finally, a_1 may be determined by (31b).

For normal atmospheric conditions, we take $B_0 = 67$ deg C, corresponding to $\beta^2 = 160$ and $\vartheta^2 = 0.057 \approx 0$. We then find:

$$\begin{aligned} a_1 &= 0.04254, & a_9 &= 0.22365, & a_{17} &= 0.01238, \\ a_3 &= -0.12413, & a_{11} &= -0.14975, & a_{19} &= -0.00375, \\ a_5 &= 0.21616, & a_{13} &= 0.07965, & a_{21} &= 0.00097. \\ a_7 &= -0.25671, & a_{15} &= -0.03447, \end{aligned} \tag{32}$$

The meridional velocity, v_1, is given by

$$v_1 = \frac{1}{\cos\varphi}\frac{\partial\psi}{\partial p} = \frac{3.832\, a}{c_p B_0} D\, J_0(1.916\, q)\, V(\varphi), \tag{33}$$

where $V(\varphi) = \Phi/\cos\varphi$. This solution shows that the

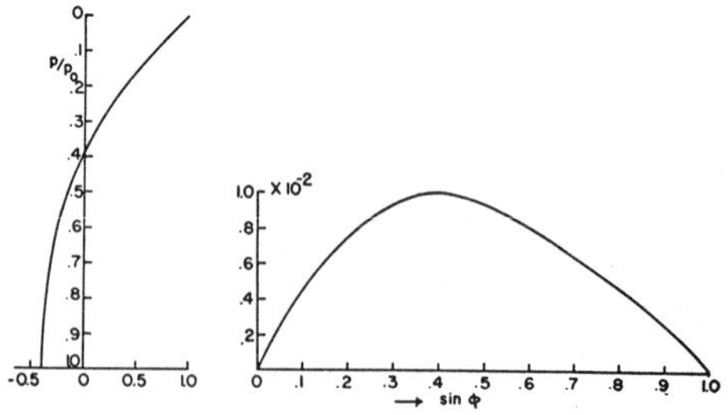

FIG. 3. Distribution of v_1; variation with pressure (left) and latitude (right).

meridional circulation so produced is a very weak, single direct cell covering the entire hemisphere. The variations of v_1 with height and latitude are represented in fig. 3. It is seen that the maxima of the north-south velocity occur at the top and bottom of the atmosphere and at latitude 23.5 deg ($\eta = 0.4$). To estimate the intensity of this motion, let us take $D = 4.8 \times 10^{-6}$ cal g^{-1} sec^{-1}, corresponding to a net gain of 0.05 cal cm^{-2} min^{-1} at the equator. If this heat is not carried away by motion, it will raise the mean temperature of the air at the equator by 0.3C per day. Using this value of D in (33), we find the maximum southward velocity on the earth's surface is 2.8 cm/sec, and the maximum northward velocity at the top of the atmosphere is 7 cm/sec. These meridional velocities are of the same order of magnitude as that obtained by Phillips (1956) through numerical integration.

A single cell of direct circulation will also occur in a two-layer atmosphere with a more stable stratosphere and a less stable troposphere.[3]

This direct circulation is so weak that it does not transport enough heat from low to high latitudes, and therefore cannot maintain a steady-state condition. As a result of the continued heating, a meridional temperature contrast will be built up, along with a stronger mean zonal current increasing upward. When the meridional temperature contrast reaches a certain limiting value, the situation will become unstable with respect to wave disturbances, and large eddies will develop. The appearance of these large eddies will greatly change the character of the mean meridional flow through their transfer of heat and zonal momentum.

[3] If a discontinuity of $\partial v_1/\partial p$ at the tropopause level is allowed, we may then use two Bessel functions with imaginary arguments to represent the vertical variation of v_1 or ψ in the two layers. The boundary conditions and the continuity requirements can be satisfied by choosing proper constants in these functions. These solutions lead to a negative α^2, and therefore negative values of β^2 and ϑ^2, and give rise to reverse cells at higher latitudes. However, the physical significance of such solutions seems somewhat dubious and therefore will not be given here.

REFERENCES

Buch, H. S., 1954: *Hemispheric wind conditions during the year 1950.* [Final Rep., Part 2, Contract AF19(122)–153], Cambridge, Mass. Inst. Tech., 126 pp.

Eliassen, A., 1952: Slow thermally or frictionally controlled meridional circulations in a circular vortex. *Astrophys. Norv.*, **5**, 19–60.

Kuo, H.-L., 1949: Dynamic instability of two-dimensional non-divergent flow in a barotropic atmosphere. *J. Meteor.*, **6**, 105–122.

——, 1951: A note on the kinetic energy balance of the zonal wind systems. *Tellus*, **3**, 205–207.

——, 1952: Three-dimensional disturbances in a baroclinic zonal current, *J. Meteor.*, **9**, 260–278.

——, 1953: On the production of mean zonal currents in the atmosphere by large disturbances. *Tellus*, **5**, 475–493.

——, 1956a: Energy releasing processes and stability of thermally driven motions in a rotating fluid. *J. Meteor.*, **13**, 82–101.

——, 1956b: Forced and free axially-symmetric convections produced by differential heating in a rotating fluid. *J. Meteor.*, **13**, 521–527.

Kropatscheck, F., 1935: Die Mechanik der gross Zirkulation der Atmosphäre. *Beitr. Physik fr. Atmos.*, **22**, 272.

Lamb, H., 1932: *Hydrodynamics.* London, Cambridge Univ. Press, 738 pp.

Mintz, Y., 1955: *Final computation of the mean geostropic poleward flux of angular momentum and of sensible heat in the winter and summer of 1949.* [Final Rep., Contract AF19(122)–48], Los Angeles, Univ. Calif., 14 pp.

Oberbeck, A., 1888: Über die Bewegungserscheinungen in der Atmosphäre. *Sitz.-Ber. Preuss. Akad. Wiss.*, p. 383.

Phillips, N. A., 1956: The general circulation of the atmosphere: A numerical experiment. *Quart. J. R. meteor. Soc.*, **82**, 123–164.

Prandtl, L., 1939: *Beiträge zur Mechanik der Atmosphäre.* Paris, P. Dupont, 32 pp.

Priestley, C. H. B., 1951: A survey of the stress between the ocean and atmosphere. *Union Géod. Géophys., Compte rendu du symposium sur la circulation general des oceans et de l'atmosphere*, p. 64.

Rogers, M. H., 1954: The forced flow of a thin layer of viscous fluid on a rotating sphere. *Proc. roy. Soc. London*, A., **224**, 192–208.

Starr, V. P., and R. White, 1956: Balance requirement of the general circulation. *Geophys. Res. Pap.*, No. 35, 57 pp.

Reprinted from *Journal of Meteorology*, Vol. 14, No. 6. Dec., 1957, published by the American Meteorological Society.

FURTHER STUDIES OF THERMALLY DRIVEN MOTIONS IN A ROTATING FLUID

By H.-L. Kuo

Massachusetts Institute of Technology

(Manuscript received 12 March 1957)

ABSTRACT

The transitions from the lower forced symmetric regime to the wave regime, within the wave regime itself and from the wave regime to the upper symmetric regime, are discussed by making use of the solution of a simplified version of the differential equation. It is found that the main features of these various transitions obtained by Fultz in some new experiments can be explained by the theories developed in this note and in the previous studies.

1. Introduction

In a previous paper (Kuo, 1956a, which we shall refer to as A hereafter) the writer discussed the nature of the motions produced by horizontal differential heating in a rotating fluid and determined the transitions from the wave regime to the high heating Hadley regime and from one wave number to another in the wave regime, by solving the partial differential equation for the vertical velocity

$$LL_1\left\{4\Omega'\Omega^*\frac{\partial^2 w}{\partial z^2}+L^2\nabla^2 w\right\}+gs_z L^2\nabla_h^2 w - gs_r(L_1+L)\left\{L\frac{\partial^2 w}{\partial r\partial z}+\frac{2\Omega'}{r}\frac{\partial^2 w}{\partial\lambda\partial z} - \omega_z\frac{\partial}{\partial\lambda}\left(\frac{\partial w}{\partial r}+\frac{2w}{r}\right)\right\} = g\alpha L^2\nabla_h^2 Q \quad (1)$$

which governs both the axially symmetric motion ($\partial/\partial\lambda = 0$) and the wave motion. In this equation, $L = \partial/\partial t + \omega(\partial/\partial\lambda) - \nu\nabla^2$, $L_1 = \partial/\partial t + \omega(\partial/\partial\lambda) - \kappa\nabla^2$, $\Omega' = \Omega + \omega$, $\Omega^* = \Omega + \zeta_0/2$, $\zeta_0(= r^{-1}\partial r v_0/\partial r)$ being the relative vorticity of the basic zonal current v_0, $\omega = v_0/r$, $\omega_z = \partial\omega/\partial z$, $s_z = \alpha\partial\theta_0/\partial z$, $s_r = \alpha\partial\theta_0/\partial r$ and $Q = \kappa\nabla^2\theta_0$ is the axially symmetric heating by conduction. This is equation (22) of A, except for the addition of the heating term on the right and the presence of ζ_0 in Ω^*. We also mention that a term $w\partial v_0/\partial z$ has been left out in the zonal equation of motion (12) of A.

This equation has been solved in A by Fourier series expansion. A much simplified version of this equation, obtained by replacing the operator ∇^2 by a constant multiple, has also been solved in analytic form in A. From these solutions it is found that wave motion cannot occur when the rotation rate is too low, and that it requires a finite limiting temperature gradient to bring it into existence. Within the Rossby wave regime itself, the characters of the motion are decisively influenced by the mean vertical temperature gradient; for example, the wave number seems to be determined completely by the parameter $S_z = (g\alpha d\Delta_z\theta)/4\Omega^2 a^2$, where $\Delta_z\theta$ is the mean vertical temperature contrast and $a = r_2 - r_1$. Since $\Delta_z\theta$ is not externally controlled in the experiment, but is determined internally by the non-linear convective upward heat transfer, this parameter is difficult to specify from the linear theory. Although it was suggested in A that one should expect the mean vertical temperature contrast to be roughly proportional to the mean horizontal temperature contrast $\Delta_r\theta$, no detailed measurement was available to enable us to determine the quantitative relationship between these two quantities. Therefore, only a few computations have been included in this paper which are mostly based on an assumed mean vertical temperature gradient. Although the computed transitions seem to be in qualitative agreement with the few observed transitions, it is difficult to obtain a more definite and clearer picture of the theoretical result from these computations because of the lack of a more systematic representation of this important parameter S_z.

More recently, detailed determinations of the transitions from the wave regime to the Hadley symmetric regime and from one wave number to another have been obtained by Fultz (1956) in a new set of experiments, in which a deep layer of fluid contained between two co-axial cylinders has been used. In this set of experiments, detailed measurement of the mean vertical temperature contrast $\Delta_z\bar{\theta}$ has also been obtained, and it is found that $\Delta_z\theta$ is usually roughly proportional to $\Delta_r\theta$, with a factor of proportionality of about 1.2 near the transition to the upper Hadley regime and about 1.8 near the lower transition to the wave regime. Thus a more detailed computation from the theory can now be made with this information of $\Delta_z\theta$. Because of the important meteorological, geophysical and astrophysical implications of these thermally driven motions, such a detailed computation is very desirable. The purpose of this note is to make such computations from the solutions obtained in A, and to compare them with these new experimental results. However, in order to make the results more comprehensible, part of the development of the theory will be repeated so that the present note can also be understood by itself. The computations show that the term $\partial^2 w/\partial r \partial z$, which is the only term that gives rise to instability for the symmetric disturbances, has little effect on the wave motions when the rotation rate is not very low. Therefore, this term may be neglected for the wave disturbances, and it is then convenient to treat the axially symmetric disturbances separately.

2. The lower Hadley symmetric regime

The nature of the forced and free axially symmetric disturbances has been discussed by the writer in a more recent paper (Kuo, 1956b, which we shall refer to as B) and many earlier papers. Here we shall obtain some more information from the solutions given in B, particularly those concerning the zonal velocity v_0 and the vertical temperature gradient. The equation that governs these disturbances may be obtained from (1) by setting $\partial/\partial\lambda = 0$. For a steady state it is given by

$$4\Omega_0^2 \frac{\partial^2\psi}{\partial z^2} + \nu^2 D^6 \psi + g\alpha r \frac{\partial}{\partial r}\left\{ \frac{\sigma}{r}\frac{\partial \theta_0}{\partial z}\frac{\partial \psi}{\partial r} - (\sigma+1)\frac{1}{r}\frac{\partial\theta_0}{\partial r}\frac{\partial\psi}{\partial z}\right\} = g\alpha\nu r A_1, \quad (2)$$

where

$$D^2 = r\frac{\partial}{\partial r}\frac{1}{r}\frac{\partial}{\partial r} + \partial^2/\partial z^2, \quad \Omega_0^2 = \Omega'\Omega^*,$$

ψ is the Stokes stream function for the meridional velocities u and w and σ is the Prandtl number. The heating, $\kappa\nabla^2\theta_0$, is assumed to increase linearly with r in order to provide a slowly increasing radial temperature contrast. Since the radius of the inner cylinder is relatively large and $d \gg r$, we may approximate D^2 by $\partial^2/\partial r^2 - (1/\bar{r})(\partial/\partial r)$, where $\bar{r}$ is the mean radius; or we may disregard the second term entirely.

For the lower Hadley regime, the terms involving $\partial\theta_0/\partial r$ and $\partial\theta_0/\partial z$ may be neglected. We then find the solution given by

$$\psi = \frac{4g\alpha r a^6 A}{\nu\pi^7}\sum_{n=D}^{\infty}\frac{\sin(2n+1)\eta}{(2n+1)^7} \times \left\{\frac{\sinh\lambda_n z + \sinh\lambda_n(d-z)}{\sinh\lambda_n d} - 1\right\} \quad (3)$$

$$\cong -\frac{g\alpha\nu A r}{2\pi\Omega_0^2} z(d-z)\sin\eta,$$

where $\eta = \pi y/a$, $y = r - r_1$, $a = \Delta r = r_2 - r_1$ and $\lambda_n \cong (2n+1)^3\pi^3\nu/2\Omega_0 a^3$. Because of the factor $(2n+1)^{-7}$, the higher order terms contribute very little to this solution.

Substituting $u = -\partial\psi/r\partial z$ into the thermodynamic equation

$$\kappa\nabla^2\theta' = u\frac{\partial\theta_0}{\partial r} = u\left\{\frac{A}{2}\left(y - \frac{a}{2}\right)^2 + \frac{\partial\tilde{\theta}_0}{\partial r}\right\}, \quad (4)$$

where $\tilde{\theta}_0$ represents the part of the mean temperature given by conductive equilibrium and the first term represents the differential heating, we find θ' is given by

$$\theta' = -\frac{a^3 A}{4\pi^3}\sum_{m=1}^{\infty}\frac{\sin 2m\eta}{m^3} + \frac{2g\alpha a^5 A}{\kappa\pi^6\Omega_0} \times \left(\frac{a^2 A}{8} + \frac{\partial\tilde{\theta}_0}{\partial r}\right)\sum_{n=0}^{\infty}\frac{\sin(2n+1)\eta}{(2n+1)^4}Z_n(z) + \frac{g\alpha a^7 A^2}{\kappa\pi^8\Omega_0}\sum_{n=0}^{\infty}\frac{Z_n(z)}{(2n+1)^4}\sum_{m=1}^{\infty}\frac{\delta_{mn}\sin m\eta}{m^3}, \quad (5)$$

where

$$\delta_{mn} = \frac{8mn}{(m^2-n^2)^2} \quad \text{when } m - n \text{ is even}, \quad m \neq n;$$

$$= -\left(\frac{\pi^2}{6} + \frac{1}{2m^2}\right) \quad \text{when } m = n;$$

$$= 0 \quad \text{when } m - n \text{ is odd};$$

and

$$Z_n(z) = \{\cosh\lambda_n z - \cosh\lambda_n(d-z)\}/\sinh\lambda_n d.$$

The first term is inadvertently left out in the solution (22) of B. Here again the high order terms in the second series contribute very little, likewise for the third series.

From this we find the average vertical temperature contrast $\Delta_z\bar{\theta}$, which is given by

$$\Delta_z\bar{\theta} = \frac{2\sigma g\alpha d a^3 A}{\pi^4 a^2 \Omega_0^2}\Delta_r\theta. \quad (6a)$$

This analysis shows that if the heating factor does not depend on the total radial temperature contrast, $\Delta_z\bar{\theta}$ will be roughly proportional to $\Delta_r\theta$. In addition, the upward heat transfer given by $\overline{w'\theta'}$ also tends to produce a positive $\Delta_z\theta$, therefore there is a tendency to have $\Delta_z\bar{\theta}$ proportional to the radial temperature gradient. On the other hand, if A is proportional to the radial temperature gradient, *i.e.*, if $a^3 A = \gamma\Delta_r\theta$, we then obtain

$$S_z = \frac{8\gamma\sigma}{\pi^4} R_{0T}^{*2}, \tag{6b}$$

where $R_{0T}^* = (g\alpha d\Delta_r\theta)/4\Omega_0^2 a^2$ is the thermal Rossby number and $S_z = (g\alpha d\Delta_z\theta)/4\Omega_0^2 a^2$.

We shall now analyze the zonal velocity produced by the meridional circulation. Since v' depends upon the equilibrium part of the zonal velocity v_0, which in turn depends upon the equilibrium temperature $\bar{\theta}_0$, we shall first obtain $\bar{\theta}_0$. According to the discussions in A, $\bar{\theta}_0$ may be represented by

$$\bar{\theta}_0 = c \log r/r_1 + \bar{\theta}_{r=r_1}. \tag{7}$$

From the thermal-gradient wind relation we then obtain

$$v_0 \cong \frac{g\alpha c}{2\Omega_0 r} z. \tag{8}$$

This is part of a solution discussed by the writer in an earlier paper (Kuo, 1954), and can explain a large part of the observed surface zonal current in the Hadley regime. We note that the vorticity of this mean current is zero and that it is not dissipating.

Substituting this v_0 and the stream function given by (3) in the zonal equation of motion (6) of B, with the nonlinear terms neglected, we then obtain,

$$v' \cong \frac{g\alpha d a^2 A}{\pi^3 \Omega_0}\left\{(2\zeta - 1)\sin\eta + \frac{\pi g\alpha d\Delta_r\bar{\theta}_0}{4\Omega_0^2 a^2}\zeta(1-\zeta)\cos\eta\right\}, \tag{9}$$

where $\zeta = 2/d$. Note that the first term gives a westerly current in the upper half and an easterly current in the lower half of the fluid, with a maximum velocity occurring midway between the cylinders. On the other hand, the second term gives a westerly current in the inner half and an easterly current in the outer half of the fluid. Thus, this solution gives a stronger westerly current near the top and near the inner cylinder and stronger easterlies in the lower and outer portion of the fluid.

It is interesting to note that the second term gives a negative mean vorticity while the first term does not contribute to the mean vorticity. This is to be expected, since in the upper branch of the meridional circulation there is a tendency to maintain a constant absolute angular momentum, while near the bottom this tendency is partly cancelled by friction.

3. The wave regime

The computations show that the analytic solution of the simplified version of the equation for wave disturbances, obtained by replacing the Laplacian operator ∇^2 by a constant multiple and other approximations, is valid for a large range of the wave disturbances. In order to demonstrate more clearly the precise meaning of this simplification and to establish its range of validity, we shall analyze the various approximations used in arriving at this simplified version.

When the terms $\partial^2 w/\partial r\partial z$ and $\partial^2 w/\partial\lambda\partial r$ are neglected, it can be seen that equation (1) permits solutions of the type

$$w = e^{i(l\lambda - \mu t)} C_l(br) \cdot W(z),$$

where $C_l(br)$ is the Bessel function of order l which has zeros at $r = r_1$ and $r = r_2$, and b is given by

$$b^2 \cong \frac{\pi^2}{a^2} + \frac{l^2 - \frac{1}{4}}{\bar{r}^2}. \tag{10}$$

This relation (10) can more easily be obtained from the asymptotic expansion of $C_l(br)$, as is used in A.

Even with these simplifications, the resulting equations in W are still too complicated for analytic discussion. We shall therefore limit ourselves in this note to the cases for which the thermal Rossby number R_{0T}^* and the static stability parameter S_z are relatively large and the effects of viscosity and heat conductivity are relatively small in the operators L and L_1, so that terms involving higher powers of νb^2 may be neglected. Other approximations that are valid for much lower Rossby numbers and higher rotation rates will be discussed in another paper. With these approximations, we find

$$\frac{1}{L} + \frac{1}{L_1} \cong \frac{2i}{\zeta}\frac{1}{dl\omega_z},$$

$$\frac{L}{L_1} \cong 1 - \frac{\sigma - 1}{\sigma + 1}\frac{(\nu + \kappa)b^2}{dl\omega_z}\frac{i}{\zeta} \cong 1.$$

Therefore equation (1) reduces to

$$\frac{d^2W}{d\zeta^2} - \frac{2}{\zeta}\frac{dW}{d\zeta} - \left(\beta^2 - \frac{F}{\zeta}\right)W = 0, \tag{11}$$

where

$$\zeta = \frac{z}{d} - \frac{\mu + ib^2(\nu + \kappa)}{dl\omega_z},$$

$$\beta^2 = b^2 a^2 S_z, \tag{12}$$

$$F \cong \frac{4a}{\bar{r}} R_{0T}^*.$$

This is equation (57) of A, where the quantity $(\nu + \kappa)b^2$ is denoted by c.

The solution of equation (11) can be expressed in terms of the Whitakers' functions,

$$W = A\eta V_1(\eta) + B\eta V_2(\eta), \tag{13}$$

where $\eta = 2\beta\zeta$. The asymptotic expansions of V_1 and V_2 are given by

$$V_1 = \eta^x e^{-\eta/2}\left\{1 + \frac{\frac{9}{4} - (x-\frac{1}{2})^2}{1\,!\eta} + \frac{\left[\frac{9}{4} - (x-\frac{1}{2})^2\right]\cdot x\cdot(3-x)}{2\,!\eta^2} + \cdots\right\} \quad (14a)$$

$$V_2 = \eta^{-x} e^{\eta/2}\left\{1 - \frac{\frac{9}{4} - (x+\frac{1}{2})^2}{1\,!\eta} + \frac{\left[\frac{9}{4} - (x+\frac{1}{2})^2\right]\cdot x\cdot(3-x)}{2\,!\eta\,!} - \cdots\right\} \quad (14b)$$

where $x = F/2\beta$. We note that all terms after the second contain the factor x, which is very small for this range of the experiment. Therefore, all these terms may be neglected in determining the phase relations. It will be shown that for small x the contribution from x to the phase velocity is so small that its effect can be disregarded completely. The solutions represented by the first two terms of (14a, b) are then exact solutions for the limiting case $x = 0$. Applying the boundary conditions $w = 0$ for $z = 0$ and $z = d$ to this limiting solution and eliminating the arbitrary constants from the two resulting equations, we obtain

$$4 - \eta_0\eta_1 - 2(2 - x^2)\beta\coth\beta - x(\eta_0 + \eta_1) - 5x^2 + x^4 = 0, \quad (15)$$

where

$$\eta_0 = -\frac{2\beta}{dl\omega_z}\{\mu_r + i\mu_i + ib^2(\nu + \kappa)\}$$

$$\eta_1 = 2\beta + \eta_0$$

μ_r and μ_i are the real and imaginary parts of μ.

Equating the imaginary and real parts of (15) to zero separately, and disregarding the terms involving x which are very small, we obtain

$$\frac{\mu_r}{l} = \tfrac{1}{2}d\omega_z, \quad (16)$$

$$\mu_i + (\nu + \kappa)b^2 = \frac{dl\omega_z}{\beta}\delta, \quad (17)$$

where $\delta^2 = \beta\coth\beta - 1 - \beta^2/4$. These are equivalent to the relations (59), (61) and (62) of A, which were obtained from the stream function ψ for the non-divergent part of the horizontal velocity, which is related to w by

$$g\alpha\frac{\partial\theta_0}{\partial z}w = 2\Omega l\omega_z i\left(\psi - \zeta\frac{\partial\psi}{\partial\zeta}\right).$$

Equation (17) expresses the condition for the existence of amplifying wave disturbances in terms β and ω_z. Since the left hand side must be positive, a first necessary condition for the wave disturbances is

$$\beta^2 \equiv b^2a^2S_z < 5.7571. \quad (18)$$

Because of the viscous term on the left, the limiting value of β^2 is slightly less than this value. Since β^2 contains the factor S_z which is proportional and nearly equal to $R_{0T}{}^*$, this upper limit of β^2 represents an upper limit of S_z or $R_{0T}{}^*$, beyond which the wave disturbances will be damped out.

Since the factor δ is always less than its maximum value which is finite, equation (17) shows that there is a minimum Rossby number below which wave disturbances will be damped out. As has been discussed in A, there exists a particular value of l or β for which the waves have the highest amplification rate. This value of β is obtained by differentiating (17) with respect to l and setting $(d/dl)[\mu_i + (\nu + \kappa)b^2]$ to zero, which gives

$$l^2\beta\frac{d\delta^2}{d\beta} + 2\left(\frac{\pi\bar{r}}{a}\delta\right)^2 = 0 \quad (19a)$$

and therefore

$$\beta^2 = \beta_c{}^2 = 2.5792. \quad (19b)$$

From this we find the maximum value of δ is

$$\delta_M = 0.31. \quad (19c)$$

Substituting this value of δ in (17) we then find the lowest radial temperature gradient required to excite the wave disturbances is given by

$$\frac{g\alpha}{2\Omega_0\bar{r}}\left|\frac{\partial\theta_0}{\partial r}\right| \geq \frac{(\nu + \kappa)b^2\beta}{dl\delta_M} \quad (20)$$

which is equivalent to equation (64) of A.

Substituting the definition of β given in (12) in this relation we then find the minimum radial temperature contrast which marks the transition from the lower Hadley symmetric regime to the wave regime is given by

$$(\Delta_r\theta_0)_{\min} = \frac{(\nu + \kappa)al^2}{0.31\bar{r}^2} \times\left\{1 + \left(\frac{\pi^2\bar{r}^2}{a^2} - \frac{1}{4}\right)\frac{1}{l^2}\right\}^{\frac{1}{2}}\cdot\left(\frac{\Delta_z\theta_0}{g\alpha d}\right)^{\frac{1}{2}}. \quad (21)$$

It is interesting to note that the rotation factor does not appear in this relation. Since $\Delta_z\theta_0$ is usually proportional to $\Delta_r\theta_0$, and since the factor on the right varies only slowly with the wave number, this minimum radial temperature contrast is nearly constant.

Using $r_2 = 4.95$ cm, $r_1 = 2.475$ cm and $d = 13$ cm, a mean temperature of 21.5C, as in Fultz's experiments, and using the observed values of $\Delta_z\theta_0$ on the lower transition, we may find $(\Delta_r\theta_0)_{\min}$ from (21). These values are given in table 1, and are also plotted in fig. 1, as the lower transition curve. It is seen that these computed values are only slightly less than the observed values which are nearly equal to 0.3C.

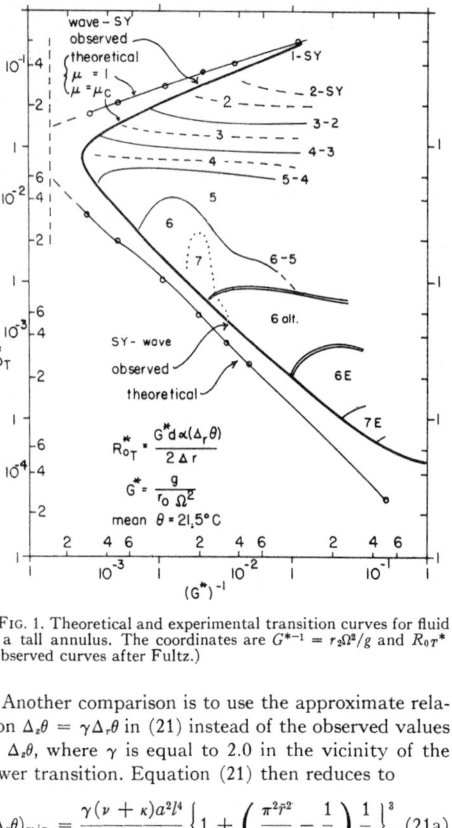

FIG. 1. Theoretical and experimental transition curves for fluid in a tall annulus. The coordinates are $G^{*-1} = r_2\Omega^2/g$ and R_{0T}^* (Observed curves after Fultz.)

Another comparison is to use the approximate relation $\Delta_z\theta = \gamma\Delta_r\theta$ in (21) instead of the observed values of $\Delta_z\theta$, where γ is equal to 2.0 in the vicinity of the lower transition. Equation (21) then reduces to

$$(\Delta_r\theta)_{\min} = \frac{\gamma(\nu+\kappa)a^2 l^4}{g\alpha d\bar{r}^4\delta_M{}^2}\left\{1+\left(\frac{\pi^2\bar{r}^2}{a^2}-\frac{1}{4}\right)\frac{1}{l^2}\right\}^3. \quad (21a)$$

Thus this equation expresses $(\Delta_r\theta)_{\min}$ as a function of the wave number l alone. The values of $(\Delta_r\theta)_{\min}$ obtained from this relation are given in table 1b. We note that $(\Delta_r\theta)_{\min}$ has an absolute minimum for the wave number 3 or 4, and increases rapidly toward $l = 1$. Therefore, wave numbers smaller than 3 will not appear at the lower transition. For wave numbers larger than 4, these values differ very little from those in table 1a.

TABLE 1. Minimum radial temperature contrast for wave disturbances.

a. Computed from (21) by making use of observed $\Delta_z\theta$

Ω (sec^{-1})	0.75	1.0	1.5	2.0	2.5	10.0
l	4	5	6	7	6	7
$(\Delta_r\theta_0)_{\min}$	0.16	0.19	0.24	0.25	0.20	0.23

b. Computed from (21a)

l	1	2	3	4	5	6	7
$(\Delta_r\theta_0)_{\min}$	0.37	0.14	0.12	0.12	0.15	0.21	0.28

From (18) and (19b) we find the upper limit and the most favorable values of the parameter S_{zc} for the wave disturbances, which are given in table 2, together with the observed average S_z for the different wave numbers. It is seen that the computed most favorable values of S_{zc} agree quite well with the observed values for the wave numbers 2, 3 and 4, but are somewhat too high for the larger wave numbers. Since the larger wave numbers are characterized by small Rossby numbers, it seems that a different approximation to equation (1) is required in order to obtain a better agreement with the experimental result.

Since S_z is about 1.2 to 1.8 times the value of R_{0T}^*, the corresponding values of R_{0T}^* can be obtained from the S_{zc} values given in table 2.

TABLE 2. Computed and observed S_{zc} and S_z.

Wave number l	1	2	3	4	5	6	7
$S_{z\,\max}$ cal.	0.555	0.485	0.404	0.325	0.260	0.210	0.170
S_{zc} cal.	0.249	0.218	0.181	0.145	0.115	0.094	0.076
S_{zc} obs.		0.250	0.180	0.110	0.060	0.040	0.020

It may be mentioned that in the observed values of S_z and R_{0T}^*, the actual rotation rate Ω is used instead of Ω_0. Since $\bar{\zeta}_0$ is negative at lower rotation rate because of the stronger influence of the symmetric motion, the factor $\mu_0 = \Omega_0{}^2/\Omega^2 \cong 1 + \bar{\zeta}_0/2\Omega$ is less than 1 at lower rotation rate and approaches 1 at higher rotation rate. Thus the use of Ω tends to give values of S_z smaller than the effective values at lower rates of rotation. This may explain the observed lower values of S_z at lower rotation rates for the same wave number.

4. The upper Hadley symmetric regime

The symmetric disturbances corresponding to larger mean temperature gradients and the instability condition have been investigated in the previous studies, particularly in B, where a simple criterion is obtained, which is given by

$$R_{0T}{}^* \geqq \frac{2}{\sigma+1}\left\{\mu_0\left(\sigma S_z + \frac{\nu^2 d^2\pi^4}{4\Omega^2 a^6}\right)\right\}^{\frac{1}{2}}, \quad (22)$$

where $\mu_0 \cong 1 + \bar{\zeta}_0/2\Omega$, $\bar{\zeta}_0$ being the mean relative vorticity of the mean zonal flow. Using the observed values of S_z and assuming $\bar{\zeta}_0 = 0$, we may compute the critical R_{0T}^* from this relation, which is given in table 3 and plotted in fig. 1 as the upper transition curve. However, since $\bar{\zeta}_0$ is negative according to the discussion in section 2, we have $\mu_0 < 1$ and therefore the critical values of R_{0T}^* must be somewhat smaller than these values. Therefore, the relation given by (22) should fit the observations better than these values given in table 3, if actual values of μ_0 are used.

TABLE 3. Critical values of S_{zc} and S_z for upper transition.

Ω, sec^{-1}	0.75	1.0	1.5	2.0	2.5	3.0	4.0
S_z, obs.	0.12	0.17	0.27	0.33	0.37	0.50	0.56
R_{0T}^*, obs.	0.11	0.15	0.22	0.28	0.32	0.43	0.52
R_{0T}^*, cal. ($\mu_0 = 1$)	0.22	0.27	0.33	0.37	0.40	0.46	0.52
critical μ_0	0.23	0.31	0.43	0.54	0.62	0.83	0.96

On the other hand, since μ_0 is not given, we may use both the observed R_{0T}^* and the observed S_z and compute the critical values of μ_0. These values are also given in table 3. It may be remarked that this variation of the value of μ_0 with rotation may also explain the increase of S_z with increasing rotation and given wave number, and the earlier damping out of the waves at lower rate of rotation.

5. Conclusion

From these computations, it is seen that the main features of the thermally driven motions in the rotating fluid and the transitions from the symmetric regime to the wave regime and that within the wave regime can be explained by the instability character of the flow. On the other hand, some features of the flow at much higher rotation rates seem to require a different approximation to the fundamental equation (1).

The convective transports of heat $\overline{u'\theta'}$ and $\overline{w'\theta'}$ and the upward transport of zonal momentum by the unstable waves have been discussed in a previous paper, A. The computations are based on atmospheric conditions. Since the general features are the same as in the experiments, they need not be repeated here.

REFERENCES

Davies, T. V., 1956: The forced flow due to heating of a rotating liquid. *Phil. Trans. A.*, **249**, 27–64.

Fultz, D., 1956: *Studies of thermal convection in a rotating cylinder with some implications for large-scale atmospheric motions.* Final report, part 1, Hydrodynamics Lab., University of Chicago.

Kuo, H.-L., 1954: Symmetric disturbances in a thin layer of fluid subject to a horizontal temperature gradient and rotation. *J. Meteor.*, **11**, 399–411.

——, 1956A: Energy releasing processes and instability of thermally driven motions in a rotating fluid. *J. Meteor*, **13**, 81–101.

——, 1956B: Forced and free axially symmetric convection produced by differential heating in a rotating fluid. *J. Meteor.*, **13**, 521–527.

Reprinted from *Quarterly Journal of the Royal Meteorological Society*, Vol. 82, No. 352, Apr., 1956.

The general circulation of the atmosphere : a numerical experiment

By NORMAN A. PHILLIPS
The Institute for Advanced Study, Princeton, U.S.A.

(Manuscript received 17 October 1955)

SUMMARY

A long-period numerical forecast is made with a two-level quasi-geostrophic model, starting with an atmosphere in relative rest. Both friction and non-adiabatic effects are included in the equations, the latter as a linear function of latitude. Principal empirical elements in the experiment are the intensity of the heating, the value of the vertical stability, and the type of frictional dissipation. The flow patterns which develop are quite realistic, including a jet and zonal surface westerlies in middle latitudes, and the growth of a large disturbance. The associated energy transformations are investigated, and demonstrate the important role of the disturbance in the development of the zonal currents. The meridional circulation is also studied, together with its contribution to the zonal momentum budgets of the lower and upper halves of the atmosphere. Truncation errors eventually put an end to the forecast by producing a large fictitious increase in energy.

1. Introduction

If directly reflected radiation is omitted from consideration, the atmospheric column above each square metre of the earth's surface receives on the average about 200 joules every second in the form of solar radiation. Estimates indicate that of this absorbed energy, only about five joules are transformed into kinetic energy before being re-radiated back to space (Brunt 1944). The ultimate explanation of this inefficiency is not a simple matter, depending as it does not only on the radiative and thermodynamic properties of the atmosphere, but also on the mechanism of frictional dissipation and the dynamics of the generation of kinetic energy on various scales.

Recent years have shown some progress in our understanding of all these aspects of the problem, but perhaps the greatest relative advance has occurred in the study of the hydrodynamics of the large-scale flow patterns which are presumably responsible for the generation of kinetic energy. Increased knowledge in this field is due primarily to the extension of the aerological network between 1935 and 1945. This has led not only to greater familiarity with the actual three-dimensional atmospheric motions, but has stimulated a great deal of theoretical work looking toward their explanation. In this way, for example, some success has been obtained in the forecasting of day-to-day changes by the numerical integration of simplified forms of the hydrodynamic equations.

The properties of a rotating fluid subjected to heating and cooling have also been studied experimentally, and the results to date have contributed significantly to our information. These laboratory experiments have been carried out with water in a rotating pan, the system being heated at the outer rim and cooled at the centre (Fultz 1951, Hide 1953). In spite of the obvious dissimilarities between the laboratory set-up and the atmosphere (one has but to consider, for example, the spherical shape of the earth and the presence of water vapour in the atmosphere with its profound effect on the distribution of heating and cooling), certain of the experimental flow patterns are remarkably like those encountered on weather maps. Thus one is almost forced to the conclusion that at least the gross features of the general circulation of the atmosphere can be predicted without having to specify the heating and cooling in great detail.

This paper presents the result of an attempt to do this by means of a numerical experiment based on recent experience in numerical forecasting.

Although the emphasis will be on the interpretation of the computations as shedding some light on the general circulation, the experiment is not without significance for the more practical problem of extending the range of numerical forecasts, since a highly desirable (if not absolutely necessary) requirement of a scheme for long-range forecasting is that it be able to predict the mean state of the atmosphere. From this aspect, the computation appeared to be a logical extension of recent work on short-range numerical weather prediction, not only providing some information on the validity of the physical assumptions, but also furnishing valuable experience in the numerical problems to be encountered in making long-range predictions.

The experiment contains empirical elements in that the representation of certain physical effects is based on meteorological experience with the actual atmosphere, rather than being predicted from the fundamental laws of physics. Thus, the vertical stability is assumed equal to that of the real atmosphere, the intensity of the heating and cooling is determined from measurements of the mean non-adiabatic processes in the atmosphere, and the values of the friction coefficients are also empirical. A more complete theory of the atmospheric motions will eventually explain these quantities also.

2. A summary of present knowledge of the general circulation

Let us begin by listing some of the most striking features of the atmosphere, calling for explanation, as known from observation. (In this initial attempt at a quantitative prediction of the general circulation it is obviously wise to omit from consideration phenomena which depend on longitudinal asymmetries in the surface of the earth or represent seasonal fluctuations, realizing, however, that these also belong to the problem of the general circulation).

1. The general increase of entropy (potential temperature) with height and the existence of the stratosphere.
2. The magnitude of the poleward decrease of temperature in the troposphere, this decrease being most rapid in middle latitudes. At the 500-mb level the equator-to-pole temperature difference is approximately 45°K in winter and 22°K in summer (Hess 1948).
3. The distribution of mean zonal wind. At the surface there are easterly trade winds in subtropical latitudes, westerlies in temperate latitudes, and weaker easterlies in polar regions. The westerly component increases with height to the tropopause level, in close agreement with the geostrophic requirement of the poleward temperature decrease. In the equatorward part of those latitudes with westerly surface winds (between 35° and 40°) this increase shows up in the presence of a 'jet' at the level of the tropopause. The zonal wind speed in the climatological jet seems to be about 50 m sec^{-1} in winter and 20 m sec^{-1} in summer (Mintz 1954), although individual jets may on occasion attain speeds twice as great (Palmén 1951).
4. The travelling cyclones and anticyclones which are a prominent feature of the flow pattern in extratropical latitudes. These are usually associated with 'fronts,' characterized by a cyclonic wind shift and sudden temperature change.
5. With the exception of an equatorward drift in the surface layers of the trade-wind regions, any organized meridional circulation seems to be too small (less than 1 m sec^{-1}) to appear clearly in the available wind statistics (Starr and White 1955).

The several estimates that have been made of the distribution of radiative heating and cooling in the atmosphere all agree that if the atmosphere were in radiative equilibrium, the temperature would decrease more rapidly with height in the troposphere, and the temperature difference between equator and pole would be larger than it is. It follows then that the atmospheric movements must on the average be such as to transport energy upward and poleward. In these elementary computations we shall not be able to predict a value of the vertical temperature gradient, the model being so crude as not even to recognize the existence of the stratosphere. However, the equations will permit a latitudinal transport of energy.

The frictional drag of the surface of the earth clearly gives rise to a positive torque (eastward acceleration) on the atmosphere in those latitudes with easterly surface winds, and a negative torque (westward acceleration) on the atmosphere in middle latitudes where westerly surface winds prevail. As was first pointed out by Jeffreys, there must therefore exist a net transfer of positive angular momentum into middle latitudes from polar and subtropical latitudes (Jeffreys 1926).

Early attempts to explain the observed distribution of surface zonal winds were based on extensions of Hadley's famous explanation of the trade winds (Hadley 1735). The motion was assumed to be independent of longitude, so that the generation of kinetic energy had to be accomplished by a direct meridional circulation. Bjerknes and collaborators have estimated the intensity of the (direct) meridional circulation of this type which would provide the required upward and poleward transport of heat on a yearly basis. The maximum meridional velocity in their calculation is about $2\frac{1}{2}$ m sec^{-1} (Bjerknes *et al.* 1933). It has long been realized that great difficulties are encountered in reconciling this simple picture with the existence of surface westerlies in middle latitudes, and that a more realistic picture can be obtained only by recognizing the contribution of the large-scale eddies to the meridional transports of energy and zonal momentum (Exner 1925).

However, the lack of aerological observations at that time precluded any quantitative examination of this process. Furthermore, a theoretical deduction of the properties of the large eddies was greatly hampered by the preoccupation of theoretical meteorologists with the difficult dynamics of the idealized polar-front discontinuity. The great increase in upper-air observations during and after the second world war not only made possible an observational verification of the important role the large disturbances play in the meridional transports of both energy and zonal momentum, but also provided the theoretician with more tractable (and realistic) equations by reducing the emphasis on the idealized polar front as a primary ingredient of extra-tropical models.

The meridional transport of zonal momentum by the eddies has been computed from observations (Widger 1949, Mintz 1955), with the result that Jeffreys' hypothesis has indeed been verified; the eddies account rather well for the total flux of zonal momentum into middle latitudes necessary to replace that lost by friction with the earth. Calculations of the poleward transport of sensible and latent heat by the eddies have also been made from observations (Starr and White 1955, Mintz 1955). In extra-tropical latitudes these transports are of the right order of magnitude to balance net radiational energy losses at high latitudes and gains at lower latitudes. (Unfortunately, the radiational gains and losses are not known well enough for a more exact comparison.)

It follows that the energetics of the large eddies must be considered together with that of the mean motion itself; the observed eddy-flux of zonal momentum into middle latitudes (where the zonal wind is a maximum) corresponding formally to a transformation of eddy kinetic energy into the kinetic energy of zonal motion (Starr 1953). However, the necessary generation of kinetic energy from potential energy (we use the term potential energy to include both gravitational energy and internal energy, since the latter is related uniquely to the former in a hydrostatic atmosphere) is difficult to study observationally, since it essentially requires a knowledge of the field of vertical motion, although some attempts have been made (Phillips 1949, Spar 1950, Palmén and Newton 1951). Here theory has been of great value, and the several theories of the instability of waves in a baroclinic zonal current (Charney 1947, Eady 1949, Fjørtoft 1950, Kuo 1952) have predicted that the large-scale disturbances of extratropical latitudes not only transport heat poleward and upward, but also generate kinetic energy, this energy coming primarily from the potential energy represented by the latitudinal temperature gradient.

In tropical latitudes on the other hand, the existence of the Hadley type of circulation seems to be borne out not only by direct observations (Riehl and Yeh 1950, Palmén 1955, Starr and White 1955), but also indirectly through the failure in low latitudes of the large-scale eddy mechanism to provide a sufficiently large poleward transport of energy (Starr and White 1955). The importance of the simple meridional type of circulation in low latitudes is also suggested by theory (Kuo 1954) and experiment (Hide 1953).

3. The equations

The vague outlines of a consistent theory of the general circulation have thus been gradually appearing during the last decade; in extra-tropical latitudes the large-scale turbulence is dominant (Eady 1950), while in low latitudes a more classical scheme seems to be indicated.

The large-scale motions in extra-tropical latitudes are quasi-geostrophic in character, and the geostrophic theory has been used with some success to forecast the flow-pattern changes from day to day. Although the equations used to date for this purpose have in general not included the effects of non-adiabatic heat changes and friction, it is possible to incorporate them in a crude manner. One can then test the extent to which the geostrophic theory is capable of explaining the observed general circulation as the result of a prescribed distribution of heat and cold sources, simply by making a ' forecast ' for a long period, starting, for example, with a resting atmosphere. Certain reservations are necessary in low latitudes, where the geostrophic theory is inadequate, but the results of all the perturbation studies of the last decade indicate that some success should attend a numerical experiment of this type (see especially Charney 1951).

The 2-level geostrophic model is perhaps the simplest model which would seem capable of incorporating the effects of both heating and friction. In deriving the equations for a simplified version of this model, we find it convenient to use the x, y, p, t-coordinate system (Eliassen 1949), and neglect the purely kinematic effects of the curvature of the earth. The following notation will be used :

x = distance coordinate to east
y = distance coordinate to north
p = pressure (the vertical coordinate)
t = time
(u, v, ω) = time rates of change of (x, y, p) following the motion
Φ = latitude
ϕ = geopotential (= gz where z is height)
$\mathbf{V}$ = horizontal velocity vector
f = Coriolis parameter = $2\Omega \sin \Phi$
A_v = lateral kinematic eddy-viscosity coefficient
A_T = lateral eddy-diffusion coefficient for heat
τ_x, τ_y = x and y components of the frictional (small-scale) stress acting across a horizontal surface
θ = potential temperature
dQ/dt = non-adiabatic rate of heating per unit mass

T = temperature
∇ = horizontal gradient operator on an isobaric surface
c_p, c_v = specific heats of air at constant pressure and volume
$R = c_p - c_v$
$\beta = df/dy$, Rossby's parameter $= 2\Omega a^{-1} \cos \Phi$
a = radius of the earth
Ω = rotation of the earth
g = acceleration of gravity
p_4 = pressure at the ground (assumed constant and equal to 1,000 mb)
ρ = density

The (approximate) equations of motion and continuity in this system are

$$\partial u/\partial t + \mathbf{V} \cdot \nabla u - fv = - \partial\phi/\partial x + A_v \nabla^2 u + g\, \partial\tau_x/\partial p \quad (1)$$

$$\partial v/\partial t + \mathbf{V} \cdot \nabla v + fu = - \partial\phi/\partial y + A_v \nabla^2 v + g\, \partial\tau_y/\partial p, \quad (2)$$

$$\nabla \cdot \mathbf{V} + \partial\omega/\partial p = 0, \quad (3)$$

and the thermodynamic energy equation is

$$\frac{1}{c_p T}\frac{dQ}{dt} = \frac{d \ln \theta}{dt} = \left(\frac{\partial}{\partial t} + \mathbf{V} \cdot \nabla + \omega \frac{\partial}{\partial p}\right) \ln \theta \quad (4)$$

In eqs. (1) and (2) we have neglected principally the terms $\omega\, \partial u/\partial p$ and $\omega\, \partial v/\partial p$.

The 2-level model we will use represents the flow pattern in the upper half of the atmosphere by that at the 250-mb level, and the flow pattern in the lower half of the atmosphere by that at the 750-mb level (Charney and Phillips 1953). For convenience we designate quantities measured at the 0-, 250-, 500-, 750-, and 1,000-mb levels by the subscripts 0, 1, 2, 3, and 4, respectively. As boundary conditions at the top and bottom we will take

$$\omega = 0 \text{ at } p = 0 \text{ and } p = p_4. \quad (5)$$

τ_x and τ_y necessarily vanish at $p = 0$, but unfortunately practically nothing is known about their value at 500 mb. We will therefore assume that they are much smaller at 500 mb than at 1,000 mb and set them equal to zero at level 2. At the ground level the stress is generally taken to be directed opposite to the surface wind C, and proportional to the square of the wind speed at anemometer height, according to the formula

$$|\tau_4| = \kappa\, \rho\, C^2$$

with a value of about 0·003 for the non-dimensional constant κ. For simplicity, however, we will assume that τ_4 is directed at a constant angle to the surface geostrophic wind, and is proportional to the first power of the speed. Assuming further that the anemometer wind speed is about 70 per cent of the geostrophic wind speed we can write

$$\frac{g}{p_2}\left(\frac{\partial\tau_y}{\partial x} - \frac{\partial\tau_x}{\partial y}\right)_4 = - k\, \zeta_4, \quad (6)$$

where the constant k is given by

$$k = 0{\cdot}98\, g\, \kappa\, \overline{C}_g\, (RT_4)^{-1}. \quad (7)$$

$\overline{C}_g$ is a characteristic value of the surface geostrophic wind speed, and ζ_4 is the surface geostrophic vorticity. k takes the value 4×10^{-6} sec^{-1} if we take $\overline{C}_g$ to be about 11 m sec^{-1}.

The quasi-geostrophic vorticity equations for our model will be obtained by cross differentiation of Eqs. (1) and (2) at levels 1 and 3, with the geostrophic assumption introduced in the result for all velocities except those in the term $f \nabla \cdot \mathbf{V}$. For this term we will substitute from the equation of continuity (3), with $\partial\omega/\partial p$ at levels 1 and 3 evaluated by taking centred finite differences, $(\partial\omega/\partial p)_1 \simeq (\omega_2 - \omega_0)/p_2$ and $(\partial\omega/\partial p)_3 \simeq (\omega_4 - \omega_2)/p_2$. Since ω_0 and ω_4 vanish, this gives us

$$\nabla \cdot \mathbf{V}_1 = -\nabla \cdot \mathbf{V}_3 = -\omega_2/p_2. \qquad (8)$$

The p derivatives of the stress τ will also be evaluated by finite differences. Since the stress vanishes at levels 0 and 2, we find that it does not appear in the vorticity equation at level 1, and only the curl of the surface stress, Eq. (6), appears in the vorticity equation for level 3.

$$(\partial/\partial t + \mathbf{V}_1 \cdot \nabla)(f + \zeta_1) - f\,\omega_2/p_2 = A_v\,\nabla^2\,\zeta_1 \qquad (9)$$

$$(\partial/\partial t + \mathbf{V}_3 \cdot \nabla)(f + \zeta_3) + f\,\omega_2/p_2 = A_v\,\nabla^2\,\zeta_3 - k\,\zeta_4. \qquad (10)$$

The thermodynamic energy equation will be written at level 2. Introducing finite differences of the form $(\phi_3 - \phi_1)/p_2 \sim (\partial\phi/\partial p)_2$ and using the relation

$$\theta = \partial\phi/\partial p \times \text{a function of pressure,}$$

and the hydrostatic equation

$$\partial\phi/\partial p = -RT/p \qquad (11)$$

we may write Eq. (4) in the form

$$\frac{\omega_2}{p_2}\left[\frac{\theta_1 - \theta_3}{\theta_2}\right](\phi_1 - \phi_3) = \left(\frac{\partial}{\partial t} + \mathbf{V} \cdot \nabla\right)(\phi_1 - \phi_3) - \frac{R}{c_p}\left(\frac{dQ}{dt}\right). \qquad (12)$$

The 2-level model is incapable of forecasting changes in the vertical stability parameter $(\theta_1 - \theta_3)/\theta_2$ and we must therefore take this to be a constant. Furthermore, since the percentage variation in $(\phi_1 - \phi_3)$ is far less than that of ω_2, we will also take $(\phi_1 - \phi_3)$ to be a constant on the *left* side of Eq. (12). ϕ_1 and ϕ_3 when they appear elsewhere in the equations, may then be considered as deviations from the standard atmosphere values.

Strictly speaking (dQ/dt) in Eq. (12) is the non-adiabatic rate of heating per unit mass at the 500-mb level. However, the crudeness of the 2-level model strongly suggests that this should be interpreted rather as the average non-adiabatic heating throughout an entire column of the atmosphere, and we can therefore neglect the contribution from the vertical transport of heat by small-scale turbulence. The remaining important physical processes determining dQ/dt are the release of latent heat, radiation, and lateral eddy diffusion on a scale smaller than that of the large disturbances (the latter being forecast in detail).

Evaporation and condensation have the effect of reducing the effective vertical stability $(\theta_1 - \theta_3)/\theta_2$ in regions of saturation. Furthermore, a net excess of condensation over evaporation in a given latitude belt corresponds to a non-adiabatic heating of the atmosphere in that latitude belt. Since we do not wish to encumber our model at this time with the details of the water budget, we will allow for the release of latent heat only qualitatively by reducing the stability factor $(\theta_1 - \theta_3)/\theta_2$ in Eq. (12) to 80 per cent of its value in the standard atmosphere, and at the same time reducing the latitudinal gradient of heating to allow roughly for the observed latitudinal transport of latent heat.

Fig. 1 summarizes several calculations of the latitudinal energy transports needed to balance the estimated annual gains and losses of energy by radiation. Although they all agree that the maximum transport should occur between 30° and 40°, the largest values (Houghton's and Simpson's) and the smallest values (Albrecht's and London's) differ by a factor of two. Fig. 2 summarizes various calculations of the *observed* latitudinal transports of energy in the form of sensible and latent heat. (The transport of potential energy is impossible to compute on a geostrophic basis since it can only be accomplished

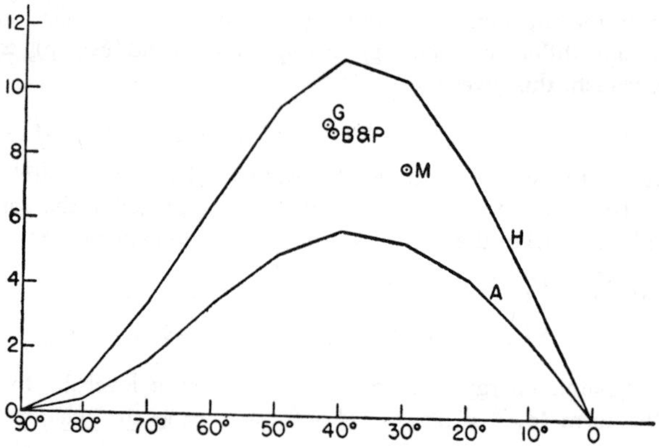

Figure 1. Poleward transport of energy across entire latitude circles required to balance radiational excesses and deficits in the annual mean. Units are 10^{19} cal day^{-1}. Curves H and A are the values obtained by Houghton (1954) and Albrecht (1931). The position of the maxima of the curves deduced by Gabites (1950), Baur and Philipps (1935), and Möller (1950) are indicated by the circles. The results of Simpson (1929) and London (1951) agree almost identically with those of Houghton and Albrecht, respectively.

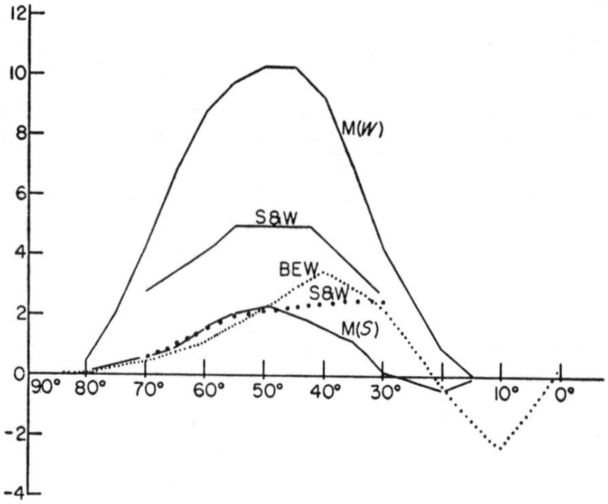

Figure 2. Observed poleward transports by eddies of sensible heat (full curves) and latent heat (dotted curves). Units are 10^{19} cal day^{-1}. M (W) and M (S) are Mintz's geostrophic measurements for winter and summer (Mintz 1955), the full curve S & W that of Starr and White (1955) for the annual mean. The dotted curve S & W is the measurement by Starr and White (*ibid.*) of the annual eddy transport of latent heat. The dotted curve BEW is the average of the estimate by Benson and Estoque and that of Wüst for the total transport of latent heat (Benson and Estoque 1954).

by a mean meridional circulation (Starr 1951), and the latitudinal transport of kinetic energy is negligible). A comparison of Figs. 1 and 2 shows that a considerable portion of the necessary transport is accomplished by eddies in middle and high latitudes, even if the larger 'radiative' values are accepted, while in lower latitudes some other mechanism seems to be necessary. (This may very well be accomplished by a direct meridional circulation at low latitudes. Palmén and Alaka (1952) have shown how such a cell fits in very well with the angular momentum budget at those latitudes, and Palmén has also demonstrated that it is quite consistent with the water budget of the doldrum belt).

Before determining the intensity of heating to use in our calculations, it is necessary to fix the geometry of the region containing our experimental 2-level atmosphere. We take the simplest conceivable arrangement, namely a rectangular region, limited by 'walls' at $y = \pm W$, but open at the western and eastern sides ($x = 0$ and L), where we impose the condition that the flow at $x = 0$ is identical with that at $x = L$ (cyclic continuity). The 'radiative' energy gains and losses will be specified as a *linear function of y*,

$$\left(\frac{dQ}{dt}\right)_{\text{rad}} = -2H(y/W). \qquad (13)$$

The constant H is the mean rate of heating per unit mass from $y = -W$ to $y = 0$ (or cooling from $y = 0$ to $y = W$). This heating will thus be independent of the motion. This condition is fulfilled neither in the dishpan experiments nor in the actual atmosphere but seems to be a reasonable first approximation.

The geometry of the sphere being different from that of our region, the determination of an appropriate value of H from curves of the type given in Figs. 1 and 2 is somewhat arbitrary. In the model the rate of energy transport across the line $y = 0$ from $x = 0$ to $x = L$ must be equal to $HWL\,p_4/g$ kj sec^{-1} if a steady state is to be attained. For every metre of this line, then, the rate of energy transport in a steady state must be $HW\,p_4/g$ kj m^{-1} sec^{-1}. The observed rate of eddy transport of sensible heat in the atmosphere at 45° latitude is about 6×10^{19} cal day^{-1}, or about 10^5 kj sec^{-1} per metre of length of the 45° latitude circle. Taking $W = 5 \times 10^6$ m (approximately half the pole-to-equator distance on the earth) we find by equating these values,

$$H \simeq 2 \times 10^{-3} \text{ kj ton}^{-1} \text{ sec}^{-1}. \qquad (14)$$

Since the total eddy transport of sensible and latent heat according to Fig. 2 is about equal to the mean of the radiation figures at 45°, this value of H also corresponds roughly to the observed radiation effects minus the observed convergence of latent heat transport.

The effect of lateral eddy diffusion on dQ/dt will be represented by

$$\left(\frac{dQ}{dt}\right)_{\text{diff}} = c_p\, A_T\, \nabla^2 T_2 = \frac{c_p}{R} A_T\, \nabla^2 (\phi_1 - \phi_3). \qquad (15)$$

We now make the assumption that f is a constant (equal to f_0) everywhere, except when it is differentiated with respect to y in Eqs. (9) and (10), where, following Rossby (1939) we assume that $df/dy \equiv \beta = $ constant.

Eqs. (9), (10) and (12) take a simpler form if we define a 'stream function' for the geostrophic wind,

$$\psi_1 = \phi_1/f_0, \qquad \psi_3 = \phi_3/f_0$$

and introduce the parameter

$$\lambda^2 = f_0^2\, \theta_2 [(\phi_1 - \phi_3)(\theta_1 - \theta_3)]^{-1} = \text{constant}. \qquad (16)$$

Eqs. (9), (10), and (12) may then be rewritten

$$(\partial/\partial t + \mathbf{V}_1 \cdot \nabla)(\beta y + \zeta_1) - f_0\, \omega_2/p_2 = A_v\, \nabla^2 \zeta_1, \qquad (17)$$

$$(\partial/\partial t + \mathbf{V}_3 \cdot \nabla)(\beta y + \zeta_3) + f_0\, \omega_2/p_2 = A_v\, \nabla^2 \zeta_3 - k\, \zeta_4, \qquad (18)$$

$$\frac{f_0\, \omega_2}{p_2} = \lambda^2 \left[\left(\frac{\partial}{\partial t} + \mathbf{V} \cdot \nabla\right)(\psi_1 - \psi_3) + \frac{2RH}{f_0\, c_p} \cdot \frac{y}{W} - A_T\, \nabla^2 (\psi_1 - \psi_3)\right]. \qquad (19)$$

Relatively little is known about the appropriate values for A_v and A_T. In our case they represent the effect of eddies smaller than the grid size used in the computations. Application of Richardson's empirical law $A \sim 0{\cdot}2\, l^{4/3}$ (Richardson 1926, Batchelor 1950), with l equal to $\Delta x \sim 3{\cdot}10^7$ cm (300 km) gives a value of about 10^5 m^2 sec^{-1} for A. In terms of the usual mixing length hypothesis, $A \sim \overline{v}l$, this corresponds to an effective (small-scale) eddy velocity of less than 1 m sec^{-1}. Machta has recently reported on a study of the lateral spread of radioactive dust from atomic explosions (Machta 1955), and deduced a value of A of about $\frac{1}{2}$ of this value (assuming Fickian diffusion of the dust cloud). Grimminger's computations of the lateral spread of mixing ratio lines on isentropic charts (Grimminger 1938) correspond to values of A from 10^4 to 10^6 m^2 sec^{-1}. Lacking any empirical or theoretical basis for a more definite choice for A_v and A_T, we shall set them both equal to

$$A_v = A_T = A = 10^5 \text{ m}^2 \text{ sec}^{-1}. \qquad (20)$$

We note in passing that this is about 1/40th of the value of A necessary to explain the heat transport required in Fig. 1 as a large-scale *austausch* process (Defant 1921), and it will therefore not balance the radiative heating by itself unless the latitudinal temperature gradient is 40 times as large as normal.

Eqs. (17), (18) and (19) are now in a form suitable for application of normal numerical forecasting techniques, if we assume that the vorticity at level 4, ζ_4, is defined by linear extrapolation from levels 1 and 3,

$$\zeta_4 = \tfrac{3}{2}\,\zeta_3 - \tfrac{1}{2}\,\zeta_1\,. \qquad (21)$$

and measure $\mathbf{V}$ and ζ by the geostrophic relation $u = -\,\partial\psi/\partial y,\ v = \partial\psi/\partial x$.

An efficient forecast scheme is obtained by defining the 'relative potential vorticities' at levels (1) and (3)

$$q_1 = \zeta_1 - \lambda^2\,(\psi_1 - \psi_3) = \nabla^2\,\psi_1 - \lambda^2\,(\psi_1 - \psi_3), \qquad (22)$$

$$q_3 = \zeta_3 + \lambda^2\,(\psi_1 - \psi_3) = \nabla^2\,\psi_3 + \lambda^2\,(\psi_1 - \psi_3), \qquad (23)$$

whereupon Eqs. (17)-(19) can be thrown into the forms :

$$\frac{\partial q_1}{\partial t} = -\,\mathbf{V}_1 \cdot \nabla\,(\beta y + q_1) + A\nabla^2 q_1 + \left(\frac{2RH\lambda^2}{f_0\,c_p}\right)\left(\frac{y}{W}\right) \qquad (24)$$

$$\frac{\partial q_3}{\partial t} = -\,\mathbf{V}_3 \cdot \nabla\,(\beta y + q_3) + A\nabla^2 q_3 - \left(\frac{2RH\lambda^2}{f_0\,c_p}\right)\left(\frac{y}{W}\right) - \frac{k}{2}[3q_3 - q_1 - 4\lambda^2\,(\psi_1 - \psi_3)]. \qquad (25)$$

Thus, if q and ψ are known at time t, Eqs. (24) and (25) give the values of $\partial q/\partial t$, so that values of q at $t + \Delta t$ may be obtained by extrapolation. Eqs. (22) and (23) then allow ψ_1 and ψ_3 to be determined at $t + \Delta t$ from the values of $q\,(t + \Delta t)$. Some caution must be used, however, in this scheme, and the actual numerical method is described in detail in the appendix.

The method of solution requires that certain boundary conditions are given at the boundaries of the rectangular region $0 \leqslant x \leqslant L,\ -W \leqslant y \leqslant W$. At $x = 0$ and $x = L$, as stated before, we merely require cyclic continuity – that is, we imagine that there is an infinite number of such rectangular regions along the x-axis, each undergoing the same motions.

At $y = \pm\,W$, the boundary conditions are not so obvious. In the usual method of making numerical forecasts, arbitrary conditions are specified on the lateral boundaries, and the portion of the region in which the forecast is valid shrinks with time because of these incorrect boundary conditions. In our case, where we intend to make a forecast for an extended period, it is obvious that this luxury cannot be enjoyed, and the boundary conditions at the walls ($y = \pm W$) must in some sense be stated correctly. Now the 'walls' are primarily a mathematical device to limit the motion, having no counterpart on the earth, and the geostrophic assumption seems to confuse the straightforward application of the physical conditions applying at real walls (Charney 1955), so that the boundary conditions we shall use there are somewhat heuristic in character. However, as will be seen in the next section, they lead to meaningful statements with regard to the energy and momentum integrals of the flow.

We first introduce the concept of the *mean* and *disturbed* flow, by defining

$$\bar{\psi}(y, t) \equiv \frac{1}{L}\int_0^L \psi(x, y, t)\, dx \quad . \quad . \quad . \quad . \quad (26)$$

as the *mean* value of ψ, and

$$\psi'(x, y, t) \equiv \psi(x, y, t) - \bar{\psi}(y, t) \quad . \quad . \quad . \quad (27)$$

as the *disturbance* value of ψ. This definition is, of course, readily extendable to other quantities such as q, ζ, u, v, ω, etc., as well as to their products.

An obvious first requirement is that

$$\psi' \equiv 0 \quad \text{at} \quad y = \pm W, \quad . \quad . \quad . \quad . \quad (28)$$

this corresponding to the statement that the normal geostrophic velocity vanishes at the wall. Another requirement we will impose somewhat arbitrarily is that

$$\zeta' \equiv 0 \quad \text{at} \quad y = \pm W. \quad . \quad . \quad . \quad . \quad (29)$$

Integration of Eq. (1) with respect to x at the walls, using cyclic continuity and the fact that v vanishes there, leads to the relations

$$\left.\begin{aligned} \partial\bar{u}_1/\partial t &= -\,\partial^2\bar{\psi}_1/\partial y\,\partial t = A\,\partial^2\bar{u}_1/\partial y^2 \\ \partial\bar{u}_3/\partial t &= -\,\partial^2\bar{\psi}_3/\partial y\,\partial t = A\,\partial^2\bar{u}_3/\partial y^2 - \tfrac{1}{2}k\,(3\bar{u}_3 - \bar{u}_1). \end{aligned}\right\} \quad . \quad . \quad (30)$$

We will assume that for all t,

$$\partial^2\bar{u}/\partial y^2 \equiv 0 \quad \text{at} \quad y = \pm W, \quad . \quad . \quad . \quad (31)$$

so that if $\bar{u}_1$ and $\bar{u}_3$ are initially zero at the walls, they must then remain zero, according to Eq. (30). The final boundary condition at the walls is therefore

$$\partial\bar{\psi}/\partial y \equiv 0 \quad \text{at} \quad y = \pm W. \quad . \quad . \quad . \quad (32)$$

Because of the linearizing assumption concerning $(\phi_1 - \phi_3)$ which was made on the left side of Eq. (12), the dependent variables ψ_1 and ψ_3 in Eqs. (17)-(32) appear only in differentiated form or in the combination $(\psi_1 - \psi_3)$. We are therefore at liberty to fix the value of (for example) $\bar{\psi}_3$ at $y = -W$. This, together with Eqs. (22)-(25) and the boundary conditions Eqs. (28)-(32), is sufficient to determine the motion completely.

It will be noticed that this set of equations and boundary conditions possesses a certain symmetry. If ψ at the initial time has the symmetry $\psi(x, y, t_0) \equiv -\psi(x - L/2, -y, t_0)$, then this symmetry will be preserved. Thus, for example, $\bar{u}(y, t) = -\partial\bar{\psi}/\partial y$ would be an *even* function of y and $(\bar{\psi}_1 - \bar{\psi}_3)(y, t)$ would be an *odd* function of y for all t. Any deviations of the actual forecast $\bar{u}$ and $(\bar{\psi}_1 - \bar{\psi}_3)$ (mean temperature) from this symmetry therefore depend completely on the deviation of the *initial* flow pattern from the symmetrical one (or on round-off errors), and do not necessarily represent anything real. This property was not used explicitly in the computation; the approximate symmetry maintained during its course served as a crude check on the calculations.

4. Equations for the meridional circulation and energy transformations

The writer has recently shown how the simple quasi-geostrophic Eqs. (22)-(25) and the boundary conditions Eqs. (28)-(32), without friction and heating, may be used to form the energy equations for this model, and how the implied meridional circulation may be computed (Phillips 1954). We shall now derive these results for the non-adiabatic case with friction of the type included in Eqs. (24) and (25).

We first write Eqs. (17)-(19) in their averaged form,

$$\partial^2 (\partial\bar{\psi}_1/\partial t)/\partial y^2 - \bar{\omega}_2 f_0/p_2 = A\, \partial^2 \bar{\zeta}_1/\partial y^2 - \overline{\mathbf{V}_1' \cdot \nabla\zeta_1'}, \qquad (33)$$

$$\partial^2 (\partial\bar{\psi}_3/\partial t)/\partial y^2 + \bar{\omega}_2 f_0/p_2 = A\, \partial^2 \bar{\zeta}_3/\partial y^2 - \overline{\mathbf{V}_3' \cdot \nabla\zeta_3'} - k\, \bar{\zeta}_4, \qquad (34)$$

$$\frac{\bar{\omega}_2 f_0}{p_2} = \lambda^2 \left[\frac{\partial(\bar{\psi}_1 - \bar{\psi}_3)}{\partial t} + \overline{\mathbf{V}_1' \cdot \nabla(\psi_1' - \psi_3')} + \frac{2RH}{f_0 c_p} \cdot \frac{y}{W} - A\, \frac{\partial^2(\bar{\psi}_1 - \bar{\psi}_3)}{\partial y^2}\right], \qquad (35)$$

and then subtract these from Eqs. (17)-(19) to get the deviation form :

$$\nabla^2\, \partial\psi_1'/\partial t - \omega_2' f_0/p_2 = A\, \nabla^2 \zeta_1' - [\mathbf{V}_1 \cdot \nabla(\beta y + \zeta_1)]', \qquad (36)$$

$$\nabla^2\, \partial\psi_3'/\partial t + \omega_2' f_0/p_2 = A\, \nabla^2 \zeta_3' - [\mathbf{V}_3 \cdot \nabla(\beta y + \zeta_3)]' - k\, \zeta_4', \qquad (37)$$

$$\frac{\omega_2' f_0}{p_2} = \lambda^2 \left\{\frac{\partial(\psi_1' - \psi_3')}{\partial t} + [\mathbf{V}_1 \cdot \nabla(\psi_1 - \psi_3)]' - A\, \nabla^2(\psi_1' - \psi_3')\right\}. \qquad (38)$$

We obtain four energy equations in the following way. First multiply Eq. (33) by $-\bar{\psi}_1$ and Eq. (34) by $-\bar{\psi}_3$, and integrate the sum of the two resulting equations over the entire region, invoking the boundary conditions as needed. This gives an equation for the time rate of change of the *kinetic energy of the mean zonal flow*, $\bar{K}$:

$$\left.\begin{aligned} \partial\bar{K}/\partial t &\equiv \partial/\partial t \int \tfrac{1}{2}(\bar{u}_1^2 + \bar{u}_3^2)\, d\sigma = \\ &= -(f_0/p_2)\int \bar{\omega}_2(\bar{\psi}_1 - \bar{\psi}_3)\, d\sigma - A\int(\bar{\zeta}_1^2 + \bar{\zeta}_3^2)\, d\sigma - \\ &\quad - k\int \bar{u}_3\, \bar{u}_4\, d\sigma - \int\left[\bar{u}_1 \frac{\partial(\overline{u_1' v_1'})}{\partial y} + \bar{u}_3 \frac{\partial(\overline{u_3' v_3'})}{\partial y}\right] d\sigma. \end{aligned}\right\} \qquad (39)$$

($d\sigma$ is the area element $dx\, dy$). We then follow a similar procedure with Eq. (36) and Eq. (37), multiplying them by $-\psi_1'$ and $-\psi_3'$, adding and integrating. This results in an equation for the time rate of change of the *kinetic energy of the disturbed flow*, K'. After some manipulation we find :

$$\left.\begin{aligned} \partial K'/\partial t &\equiv \partial/\partial t \int \tfrac{1}{2}[(\nabla\psi_1')^2 + (\nabla\psi_3')^2]\, d\sigma = \\ &= -(f_0/p_2)\int \omega_2'(\psi_1' - \psi_3')\, d\sigma - A\int[(\zeta_1')^2 + (\zeta_3')^2]\, d\sigma - \\ &\quad - k\int \mathbf{V}_3' \cdot \mathbf{V}_4'\, d\sigma + \int\left[\bar{u}_1 \frac{\partial(\overline{u_1' v_1'})}{\partial y} + \bar{u}_3 \frac{\partial(\overline{u_3' v_3'})}{\partial y}\right] d\sigma. \end{aligned}\right\} \qquad (40)$$

Equations for the time rate of change of potential energy are obtained from Eq. (35) and Eq. (38) by multiplying these with $(\bar{\psi}_1 - \bar{\psi}_3)$ and $(\psi_1' - \psi_3')$, respectively, before integrating over the region. Eq. (35) gives the following equation for the rate of change of the *potential energy of the mean flow*, $\bar{P}$:

$$\left.\begin{aligned} \partial \bar{P}/\partial t &\equiv \tfrac{1}{2}\lambda^2 \,\partial/\partial t \int (\bar{\psi}_1 - \bar{\psi}_3)^2 \, d\sigma = \\ &= (f_0/p_2)\int \bar{\omega}_2 (\bar{\psi}_1 - \bar{\psi}_3)\, d\sigma + \lambda^2 \int \overline{v_1'(\psi_1' - \psi_3')}\, \partial (\bar{\psi}_1 - \bar{\psi}_3)/\partial y \, d\sigma - \\ &- (2RH\lambda^2/f_0 c_p)\int \left(\frac{y}{W}\right)(\bar{\psi}_1 - \bar{\psi}_3)\, d\sigma - \lambda^2 A \int \left[\frac{\partial(\bar{\psi}_1 - \bar{\psi}_3)}{\partial y}\right]^2 d\sigma. \end{aligned}\right\} \tag{41}$$

Eq. (38) gives an equation for the time rate of change of the *potential energy of the disturbed motion*, P' :

$$\left.\begin{aligned} \partial P'/\partial t &\equiv \tfrac{1}{2}\lambda^2 \,\partial/\partial t \int (\psi_1' - \psi_3')^2 \, d\sigma = \\ &= (f_0/p_2)\int \omega_2' (\psi_1' - \psi_3')\, d\sigma - \lambda^2 \int \overline{v_1'(\psi_1' - \psi_3')}\, \partial (\bar{\psi}_1 - \bar{\psi}_3)/\partial y \, d\sigma - \\ &\qquad - \lambda^2 A \int [\nabla (\psi_1' - \psi_3')]^2 \, d\sigma. \end{aligned}\right\} \tag{42}$$

The combined energy equation is obtained by adding Eqs. (39)-(42) :

$$\left.\begin{aligned} \partial (\bar{P} + P' + \bar{K} + K')/\partial t &= -A \int (\zeta_1^2 + \zeta_3^2)\, d\sigma - \\ - A \int [\nabla (\psi_1 - \psi_3)]^2 \, d\sigma - k \int \mathbf{V}_3 \cdot \mathbf{V}_4 \, d\sigma &- \frac{2RH\lambda^2}{f_0 c_p} \int \left(\frac{y}{W}\right)(\bar{\psi}_1 - \bar{\psi}_3)\, d\sigma. \end{aligned}\right\} \tag{43}$$

According to this, the total change in energy in our model is given by

(a) A loss of energy due to the lateral eddy viscosity A. This is always a loss.

(b) A change due to the effect of surface friction, k. This is usually a loss since $\mathbf{V}_4$ and $\mathbf{V}_3$ tend to have the same direction.

(c) A change due to the non-adiabatic heating, H. This is an increase in energy when the heating is positively correlated with the temperature (the latter being proportional to $\psi_1 - \psi_3$).

It will be recalled from Eq. (13) that the total amount of heat energy added is zero. However, this can result in an increase of *available* potential energy in the model if the heat is added at high temperature and taken away at low temperatures – formally a *decrease* in the entropy of the system.

A more instructive breakdown of the energy transformations is given, however, by the four individual Eqs. (39)-(42). We notice that there are four terms which appear twice in the four equations, once with a positive sign and once with a negative sign. These terms can be considered as representing a transformation of energy from one form to another. To bring this out more clearly we first introduce symbolic notation of the form $\{\bar{P} \cdot \bar{K}\}$ to represent the various quantities on the right sides of Eqs. (39)-(42), the notation signifying a transformation of energy from one form – the first in the bracket – to the second form (Blackadar 1955).

$$\left.\begin{aligned}
\{\bar{Q}\cdot\bar{P}\} &\equiv -\frac{2RH\lambda^2}{f_0\,c_p}\int\frac{y}{W}(\bar{\psi}_1-\bar{\psi}_3)\,d\sigma\\
\{\bar{P}\cdot P'\} &\equiv -\lambda^2\int\overline{[v_1'(\psi_1'-\psi_3')]}\,\frac{\partial(\bar{\psi}_1-\bar{\psi}_3)}{\partial y}\,d\sigma\\
\{P'\cdot K'\} &\equiv -\frac{f_0}{p_2}\int\overline{\omega_2'(\psi_1'-\psi_3')}\,d\sigma\\
\{K'\cdot\bar{K}\} &\equiv -\int\left[\bar{u}_1\frac{\partial(\overline{u_1'v_1'})}{\partial y}+\bar{u}_3\frac{\partial(\overline{u_3'v_3'})}{\partial y}\right]d\sigma\\
\{\bar{P}\cdot\bar{K}\} &\equiv -\frac{f_0}{p_2}\int\bar{\omega}_2(\bar{\psi}_1-\bar{\psi}_3)\,d\sigma.\\
\{\bar{K}\cdot A\} &\equiv A\int(\bar{\zeta}_1^2+\bar{\zeta}_3^2)\,d\sigma\\
\{K'\cdot A\} &\equiv A\int\overline{[(\zeta_1')^2+(\zeta_3')^2]}\,d\sigma\\
\{\bar{P}\cdot A\} &\equiv \lambda^2A\int\left[\frac{\partial(\bar{\psi}_1-\bar{\psi}_3)}{\partial y}\right]^2d\sigma\\
\{P'\cdot A\} &\equiv \lambda^2A\int\overline{[\nabla(\psi_1'-\psi_3')]^2}\,d\sigma\\
\{\bar{K}\cdot k\} &\equiv k\int\bar{u}_3\,\bar{u}_4\,d\sigma\\
\{K'\cdot k\} &\equiv k\int\overline{\mathbf{V}_3'\cdot\mathbf{V}_4'}\,d\sigma
\end{aligned}\right\}. \qquad (44)$$

The physical interpretation of these expressions is quite clear. First we note that the expression for the potential energy of the model consists essentially of the integral of the square of the temperature deviations (at 500 mb) from the standard atmosphere value. Lorentz, in a beautiful attempt to reconcile the synoptic meteorologist's intuitive association of *available* potential energy with temperature *gradients*, has recently shown how a similar expression can be approximated from the usual definition of the potential plus internal energy of the atmosphere as the volume integral of $\rho\,(\phi + c_v\,T)$ (Lorentz 1955).

$\{\bar{P}\cdot P'\}$ represents a transformation of mean potential energy into the disturbance potential energy. This is accomplished by the horizontal transport of sensible heat by the disturbance velocity v_1' [or v_3', since $\mathbf{V}_1'\cdot\nabla(\psi_1'-\psi'_3)\equiv\mathbf{V}_3'\cdot\nabla(\psi_1'-\psi_3')$] from warmer to colder regions. The transformations of potential into kinetic energy, $\{\bar{P}\cdot\bar{K}\}$ and $\{P'\cdot K'\}$, represent the effect of vertical circulations in *meridional* and *zonal* planes, respectively. The transformation of disturbance kinetic energy into the kinetic energy of the mean zonal flow, $\{K'\cdot\bar{K}\}$, is positive when large values of $\bar{u}$ are correlated with latitudinal convergence of the mean eddy momentum transport, $\overline{u'v'}$.

The loss of kinetic energy by lateral eddy-viscosity, $\{\bar{K}\cdot A\}$ and $\{K'\cdot A\}$, is of the same form as that for an incompressible viscous fluid (Lamb 1932). The loss of potential energy by lateral eddy diffusivity, $\{\bar{P}\cdot A\}$ and $\{P'\cdot A\}$, represents the tendency of the diffusion process to smoothe out the temperature gradients. Finally, we note that the loss of kinetic energy by skin friction, $\{\bar{K}\cdot k\}$ and $\{K'\cdot k\}$, can also be written in the form $-k\int\psi_3\,\zeta_4\,d\sigma$. As Charney and Eliassen have shown (1949), this can be interpreted

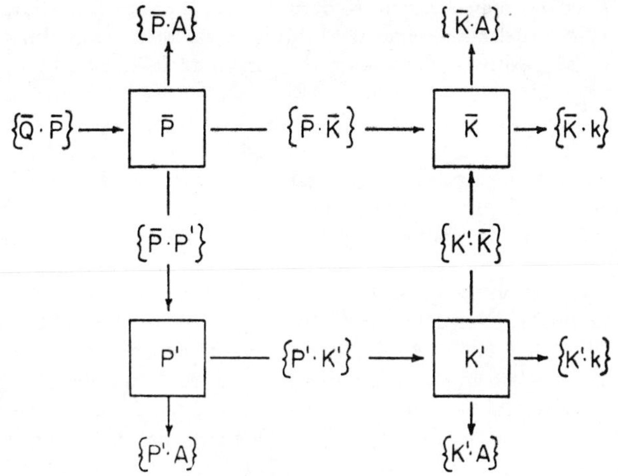

Figure 3. Energy flow diagram. The flow of energy is in the direction of the arrow if the associated transformation { · } is positive. The numerical computations give positive values for all the transformations except $\{\overline{P} \cdot \overline{K}\}$.

as an implied reaction of the air above the friction layer to frictionally produced convergence and divergence in the friction layer; the reaction producing horizontal divergence aloft above surface lows and convergence aloft above surface highs. If the flow patterns do not change phase drastically with height, this means a net flow aloft from low to high pressure, with a consequent loss of kinetic energy at those levels.

An interesting way of considering these various energy transformations now is in the form of an energy flow diagram. In this diagram (Fig. 3) each of the four boxes represents a type of energy. The bracketed quantities then represent the 'flow' of energy, their form being given by the above expressions. (The arrows are drawn as if the transformation integrals were all positive – so far merely a matter of definition.)

In a steady state the energy level in each of the boxes must be fixed, and the 'flow' into and out of each box must add up to zero. The old classical theories of the general circulation, since they disregarded the effect of the large eddies in maintaining the mean motion, would imply that the transformation $\{\overline{P} \cdot \overline{K}\}$ is positive, supplying sufficient energy to maintain $\overline{K}$ against friction. This would be accomplished by a direct meridional circulation, $\overline{\omega}_2$ being negative at high temperatures (low latitudes) and positive at low temperatures (high latitudes).

However, the available wind statistics suggest that $\{\overline{P} \cdot \overline{K}\}$ is actually slightly negative (Starr 1954). Since the only other source of energy in our scheme for $\overline{K}$ is K', measurements of $\{K' \cdot \overline{K}\}$ are of great importance in deciding the path of the energy flow. Observations show that $\{K' \cdot \overline{K}\}$ is positive and sufficiently large to account for the frictional losses of $\overline{K}$ (Arakawa 1953, Starr 1953). (Note, however, that in a more complete formulation, $\{K' \cdot \overline{K}\}$ would also include a term $\int \overline{u}\, \partial\, (\overline{u' \omega'})/\partial p\, d\sigma$.) If K' loses energy by $\{K' \cdot \overline{K}\}$, it must therefore gain energy from P', i.e., *as we progress along a latitude circle*, there must be a tendency for cold air to sink and warm air to rise. The difficulty of observing vertical motion, however, has so far prevented any objective measurement of this process.

Finally, if P' is to supply energy to K', it must receive energy from $\bar{P}$ by the transformation $\{\bar{P} \cdot P'\}$. No actual measurements of this have yet been made, although it is easy to see that it must be positive. Examining the integrand in the formula for $\{\bar{P} \cdot P'\}$ in Eq. (44), we note that the first term, $\overline{v_1'(\psi_1' - \psi_3')}$, is proportional to the poleward transport of sensible heat by eddies, and is known to be positive (Fig. 2). The second term, $\partial(\bar{\psi}_1 - \bar{\psi}_3)/\partial y$ is proportional to $\partial\bar{T}_2/\partial y$ and is therefore negative. This, together with the negative sign in front of the integral, shows that $\{\bar{P} \cdot P'\}$ is positive.

The scheme of energy transformations pictured in Fig. 3 (except for the questionable direction of $\{\bar{P} \cdot \bar{K}\}$) thus seems to be a plausible one, in so far as it agrees with what is known at present from observations. It is by no means a new concept, being implicit in most recent writings on the general circulation (e.g. van Mieghem 1952), and has also been independently formulated in the same manner by Lorentz (1955). However, it provides an excellent means for examining the extent to which our simple model contains the physical processes known to be important in the real atmosphere.

The meridional circulation in our model is calculated from the continuity Eq. (3) with the boundary conditions Eq. (5) on ω. Defining the mean meridional velocities, $\bar{V}_1$ and $\bar{V}_3$, by

$$\bar{V}_1 = \frac{1}{Lp_2}\int_0^{p_2} dp \int_0^L v\,dx, \qquad (45)$$

and

$$\bar{V}_3 = \frac{1}{Lp_2}\int_{p_2}^{p_4} dp \int_0^L v\,dx, \qquad (46)$$

we find by integration of Eq. (3) that

$$\frac{\partial\bar{V}_1}{\partial y} = -\frac{\partial\bar{V}_3}{\partial y} = -\frac{\bar{\omega}_2}{p_2}. \qquad (47)$$

$\bar{\omega}_2/p_2$ can then be evaluated either from Eqs. (33), (34), or (35), if ψ_1 and ψ_3 and their time derivatives are known.

We naturally take $\bar{V}_1$ and $\bar{V}_3$ to be equal to zero at $y = -W$. It is then simple to show that the form of Eqs. (17), (18) and (19) is such that $\int_{-W}^{W} \bar{\omega}_2\,dy$ vanishes, so that $\bar{V}_1$ and $\bar{V}_3$ will also vanish at $y = W$. Since $\bar{V}_1 \equiv -\bar{V}_3$, we need then fix our attention on only $\bar{V}_1$, $\bar{V}_3$ always being the negative of $\bar{V}_1$.

The meridional circulation $\bar{V}$ appears (implicitly) only in the divergence term in the vorticity equation Eqs. (17) and (18) (or Eqs. (33) and (34)), since the remaining terms, e.g., $\mathbf{V} \cdot \nabla\zeta$, were evaluated geostrophically. We must therefore expect that the motions we find in our quasi-geostrophic model, although they contain an implicit mean meridional circulation, do not include the possibility of gravitational-inertia instability of the Høiland-Solberg type (Høiland 1939). That type of instability would, in fact, be retained only if we replaced f_0 by $f + \zeta$ in the divergence term, and also included the non-geostrophic velocities together with the omitted terms $\omega\,\partial u/\partial p$ and $\omega\,\partial v/\partial p$.

By introducing the geostrophic approximation only for the zonal velocity $\bar{u}$, Eliassen (1952) has derived equations for an axially symmetric vortex which to some extent recognize these effects. However, it does not seem possible to retain this feature in a completely quasi-geostrophic model and still keep the internal consistency of Eqs. (17)-(19). The $\bar{V}$ calculated from our model will therefore be only partially applicable to the atmosphere in regions of very large horizontal gradients in $\bar{T}$ and $\bar{u}$ or in equatorial latitudes where f is small.

From the averaged forms Eqs. (33)-(35) of the equations, it is clear that the meridional circulation in a hypothetical steady state depends not only on the ' external ' factors of heat and skin friction, but also on the distribution of $\overline{\mathbf{V}' \cdot \nabla \zeta'}$ and $\overline{\mathbf{V}' \cdot \nabla T'}$. As mentioned earlier in the introduction, the latter quantities are observed to be of the same order of magnitude as the former ones, at least in extratropical latitudes, and must be considered just as much as the ' external ' factors in any discussion of a mean meridional circulation.

5. Final design of the experiment

A deduction of the atmospheric general circulation from physical principles seems to be most satisfying if it begins with a resting atmosphere, and then demonstrates how the observed motions appear as a natural consequence of the laws of physics. We will follow this approach to some extent, the physical laws in our case being represented by the equations for our simplified quasi-geostrophic model. They are admittedly based on a judicious mixture of empirical fact with physical theory, and therefore have only limited application, but, as we shall see, they go surprisingly far toward providing a partial explanation of the gross features of the general circulation.

The ideal form of our numerical experiment would therefore be to start with an atmosphere at rest, except for some small irregular motions, and simply make a numerical forecast for a long time. At first the latitudinal heating and cooling will begin to create a mean latitudinal temperature gradient. After this has reached a certain critical value, large-scale eddies will presumably develop, having a certain characteristic wavelength (Eady 1949), and modifying the mean zonal flow in turn by non-linear interactions. One would hope that ultimately some sort of quasi-steady state would be reached, in which the input of energy would be balanced by frictional losses, and the typical flow patterns would have some resemblance to those in the actual atmosphere.

By means of linearized perturbation theory, it is possible to estimate both the intensity of the latitudinal temperature gradient which must exist before the initial small irregular motions will begin to amplify, and the dimensions of the dominant wave which will appear. If W is taken as 5,000 km (so that the total ' latitudinal ' extent of our region from $y = -W$ to $y = W$ is approximately equal to the equator-to-pole distance on the surface of the earth), one finds that in the two-level model the critical temperature difference between $y = W$ and $y = -W$ is about 56°C, and the most unstable wavelength is about 6,000 km (Phillips 1954).

These values are somewhat unrealistic when compared with the yearly mean temperature difference in the troposphere from pole to equator (about 34°C at 500 mb) and the predominant wavelength of actual extratropical disturbances. The discrepancy seems most likely to be a partial failure of the two-layer model to represent accurately the degree of baroclinic instability in the atmosphere. This has been shown theoretically by Kuo (1953), and is also suggested by differences in numerical forecasts obtained with two- and three-level geostrophic models (Charney 1954). Further calculations with more sophisticated equations will presumably eliminate this difficulty; for the present, however, we can merely recognize its existence.

The size of the electronic computer available for the computations determines the maximum number of grid points we can use to describe the motion in our rectangular region $-W \leqslant y \leqslant W$, $0 \leqslant x \leqslant L$. The computer used was that at the Institute for Advanced Study. It had an ' internal ' rapid-access memory of 1024 40-binary digit ' words,' together with a magnetic drum (of slower access time) with a capacity of 2048 such words. Much of this space must be used for the code, however, and this, together with various other considerations (for example, partial duplication of stored information so as to allow rapid recovery after recognized errors) resulted in a choice of a 17 × 16 lattice of grid points, 17 in the y-direction, and 16 in the x-direction. Δy was set equal to 625 km, so that the distance $2W$ was equal to 10,000 km. A large value for Δx would presumably allow several eddies to form in the distance $L = 16\Delta x$, but would produce relatively large truncation errors. A smaller value of Δx, on the other hand, would result in the formation of only one large eddy, of wavelength L, but with less truncation error. The latter alternative was taken. Setting L equal to 6,000 km then gave a Δx of 375 km.

In the absence of eddies, the rate of heating we have chosen, Eq. (14), results in a rate of heating and cooling at $y = \pm W$ of about $\pm$ 0·23°C per day, so that about four months are necessary to create a latitudinal temperature gradient strong enough to give rise to unstable waves. (This is slower than the equivalent mean radiative effects in the actual atmosphere because of the allowances made for latent heat transport and the difference in geometry.) To save time, therefore, a forecast for 130 days was first made with the motion independent of x, i.e. no eddies. This could be done with time steps of one day without violating the computational stability criterion, and resulted in the distributions of mean temperature anomaly and zonal wind shown in Table 1. At this point a small random disturbance ψ' was introduced, varying with x and y but identical at both levels. The forecast from then on was made with the complete equations using time steps of two hours or less, as determined by the computation stability criterion. The initial ψ' values at successive grid points were generated by a random number generating process based on repeated squaring of an initially given generating number. (A discussion of this method is given in 'Monte Carlo Method', *Appl. Math. Series*, **12**, Nat. Bur. Standards, Washington.)

TABLE 1. DISTRIBUTION OF $\bar{T}_2$, $\bar{u}$, $\bar{V}_1$, AND $\bar{\zeta}_1$ AT THE END OF THE PRELIMINARY FORECAST WITHOUT EDDIES

j	$\bar{T}_2$ (°C)	$\bar{u}_1$ (m sec^{-1})	$\bar{u}_2$ (m sec^{-1})	$\bar{u}_4$ (m sec)$^{-1}$	$\bar{V}_1$ (mm sec^{-1})	$\bar{\zeta}_1$ (10^{-4} sec^{-1})
15	− 30·1	6·1	4·0	− 0·3	11	0·184
14	− 28·2	16·9	11·0	− 0·6	25	0·152
13	− 25·0	24·9	16·3	− 0·9	30	0·104
12	− 20·8	30·1	19·8	− 1·0	28	0·064
11	− 15·9	33·3	21·8	− 1·0	27	0·038
10	− 10·8	35·1	23·0	− 1·1	29	0·020
9	− 5·4	36·0	23·6	− 1·1	28	0·008
8	0	36·3	23·8	− 1·1	29	0
7	5·4	36·0	23·6	− 1·1	28	− 0·008
6	10·8	35·1	23·0	− 1·1	29	− 0·020
5	15·9	33·3	21·8	− 1·0	27	− 0·038
4	20·8	30·1	19·8	− 1·0	28	− 0·064
3	25·0	24·9	16·3	− 0·9	30	− 0·104
2	28·2	16·9	11·0	− 0·6	25	− 0·152
1	30·1	6·1	4·0	− 0·3	11	− 0·184

During the numerical forecasts with the complete equations, a record of the flow patterns was obtained periodically at intervals of one day, so that the development of the motion could be examined in detail. By recording at these times the ψ values at two successive time steps, ω_2 could be computed from Eq. (19), making it possible to calculate all of the different energy transformations, Eq. (44), and the meridional circulation, Eq. (47), every 24 hr. The results are described in the following sections.

6. Development of zonal flow in the absence of eddies

Before discussing the results of the complete forecast containing the eddies, we will examine briefly the results of the preliminary forecast which was made without allowing the motions to vary with x. As mentioned in the previous section, this forecast was made merely to save time, since the large-scale eddies in the two-level model cannot develop until a suitable mean temperature gradient exists.

This forecast started with the 'atmosphere' at rest, i.e. ψ_1 and ψ_3 were identically equal to zero. The heating then caused $\bar{q}_1$ and $\bar{q}_3$ to change according to Eqs. (24) and (25), producing the changes in $\bar{\psi}_1$ and $\bar{\psi}_3$ prescribed by Eqs. (22) and (23). After $\bar{\psi}$ and $\bar{q}$ were no longer identically zero, the motion was affected by the frictional terms $A\,\partial^2\bar{q}/\partial y^2$ and $-k\,\bar{\zeta}_4$ in addition to the heating.

The distribution of mean temperature, $\bar{T}_2$, zonal velocity $\bar{u}$ and the mean meridional circulation, $\bar{V}_1$, at the end (130 days) of this preliminary forecast is shown in Table 1. Here j, the latitudinal coordinate, is equal to $8(y + W)/W$. The temperature distribution is very simple, consisting of an almost linear temperature increase from $-30{\cdot}1$°C at $y = W$ to $+30{\cdot}1$°C at $y = -W$. The zonal wind distribution is also very regular, consisting of a very broad west wind at level 1, with a maximum velocity of 36 m sec^{-1}, and uniform weak easterlies everywhere at the ground. As might be expected, the meridional circulation $\bar{V}$ consists of a single weak direct cell, with a maximum velocity of 3 cm sec^{-1}. The mean zonal momentum of the atmosphere [as indicated by the values for $\bar{u}_2 \equiv \frac{1}{2}(\bar{u}_1 + \bar{u}_3)$] is positive, the result of surface friction acting on the weak surface easterlies.

A forecast of this type (no variation with x) using more exact equations (e.g. including the advection of relative zonal momentum $\bar{u}$ by $\bar{V}$) would probably have resulted in weak surface westerlies in high latitudes. Therefore, as has been said earlier in section 3, the meaned form of our present equations furnishes only an incomplete description of the processes in a true Hadley-type circulation, and the results shown in Table 1 cannot be interpreted as a complete picture of that type of circulation. They were obtained only to get an initial zonal wind field to use in making a forecast with the large-scale eddies present.

The zonal kinetic energy $\bar{K}$ and the mean potential energy $\bar{P}$ at the end of the preliminary forecast are given in Table 2, together with the values of the five energy transformation functions associated with the mean flow at that time. The units of $\bar{K}$ are such that a velocity of 1 m sec^{-1} at both level 1 and 3 at every grid point would correspond to a value of 10 for $\bar{K}$. $\bar{P}$ is in the same units. The units for the energy transformations are such that one unit of them corresponds to a change of one unit in $\bar{K}$ (or $\bar{P}$) in 24 hr.

TABLE 2. Energy parameters at end of preliminary forecast

$\bar{K}$	4265
$\bar{P}$	24368
$\{Q \cdot \bar{P}\}$	440
$\{\bar{P} \cdot \bar{K}\}$	41
$\{\bar{K} \cdot A\}$	9
$\{\bar{K} \cdot k\}$	− 27
$\{\bar{P} \cdot A\}$	48

The energy-transformation functions show that energy in this process is going from $\bar{P}$ to $\bar{K}$, through the agency of the small direct meridional circulation. The *negative* value of $\{\bar{K} \cdot k\}$, signifying an *increase* of zonal kinetic energy at levels 1 and 3 because of skin friction at the ground, is somewhat surprising at first. It is negative because the weak surface easterlies give rise to an (implicit) equatorward flow in the friction layer, which must be balanced by a net poleward flow aloft. Since the mean zonal wind above the friction layer is westerly, this increases the kinetic energy at those levels. We shall see later that as the surface zonal wind distribution becomes more realistic, $\{\bar{K} \cdot k\}$ does become positive.

Before passing on to more interesting results, we note that the jet-like character of the actual atmospheric zonal wind is not present in $\bar{u}_1$ in Table 1. The mean relative vorticity $\bar{\zeta}_1 = -\partial\bar{u}_1/\partial y$ is completely monotonic in character, without the maximum and minimum to the north and south of the maximum value of $\bar{u}$ that is characteristic of a true jet.

7. Development of the flow with eddies present

Following the completion of the preliminary forecast, during which the motion was independent of x, an initial flow pattern was defined by adding a small 'random' disturbance to the mean flow existing at the end of the preliminary forecast. This initial disturbance had a kinetic energy value, K', of 768 units, corresponding to a root mean square velocity of 8·8 m sec^{-1}. Since it was identical at level 1 and 3 $[\psi_1'(x, y, 0) \equiv \psi_3'(x, y, 0)]$, P' was initially zero.

The development of this composite flow pattern with time was then forecast with the complete Eqs. (22)-(25) (including the heating) as described in the appendix. In discussing the results, which in general were obtained at intervals of one day, we shall find it convenient to refer to the results for '3 days,' '18 days,' etc., with '0 days' referring to the time at which the variation with x was introduced.

Table 7 contains a listing of the energy parameters at daily intervals from 0 to 31 days, using the same units as those in Table 2. Looking first at the successive values of K' we see that, following an initial decrease during the first five days, K' showed a steady increase up to 25 days (except for a temporary decrease from 13 to 16 days). After 25 days, the changes in K' are at first irregular and then show a very pronounced increase with time from 28 to 31 days. (These latter changes are highly influenced by truncation errors, and are discussed separately in section 9).

The initial decrease in K' was due to small-scale lateral eddy-viscosity and surface skin friction, as shown by the relatively large initial values for $\{K' \cdot A\}$ and $\{K' \cdot k\}$. The former process was important because of the highly irregular nature of the initial ψ' distribution, while the latter effect was large because ψ_1' and ψ_3' were initially identical (so that the Charney-Eliassen frictional mechanism was very efficient).

During the period from five days to about 23-27 days, a very regular wave developed having many of the features of the large-scale eddies seen on actual weather charts. Figs. 4 to 9 contain the 1,000-mb flow pattern (defined by $\psi_4 = \frac{3}{2}\psi_3 - \frac{1}{2}\psi_1$) and the 500-mb temperature pattern (proportional to the values of $\psi_1 - \psi_3$) at intervals of three days during part of this period. The following points may be noted:

(a) The wave moves eastward at a speed of about 1,800 km/day, the apparent slow westward motion on the charts appearing only because they are shown at three-day intervals. The regularity of this, as well as that of other features present in the figures, is borne out by the intermediate charts which are not shown.

(b) The wave begins as a 'warm low' (e.g., at eleven days), but the tongue of cold air gradually catches up with the deepening surface low centre, and the tongue of warm air moves over the surface high centre, so that the final stages (e.g. 23 and 26 days) look very much like those of an *occluded cyclone*.

(c) The main surface troughs and ridges (and also those at the upper levels) are orientated so as to lean back towards the north-west in the northern half of the region, and toward the south-west in the southern half of the region.

(d) Definite indications of something similar to cold and warm fronts are to be seen in the 1,000-mb contours, with the main temperature gradient occurring on the cold side of the ' frontal ' troughs. On some charts (e.g. 17 days) these are so pronounced

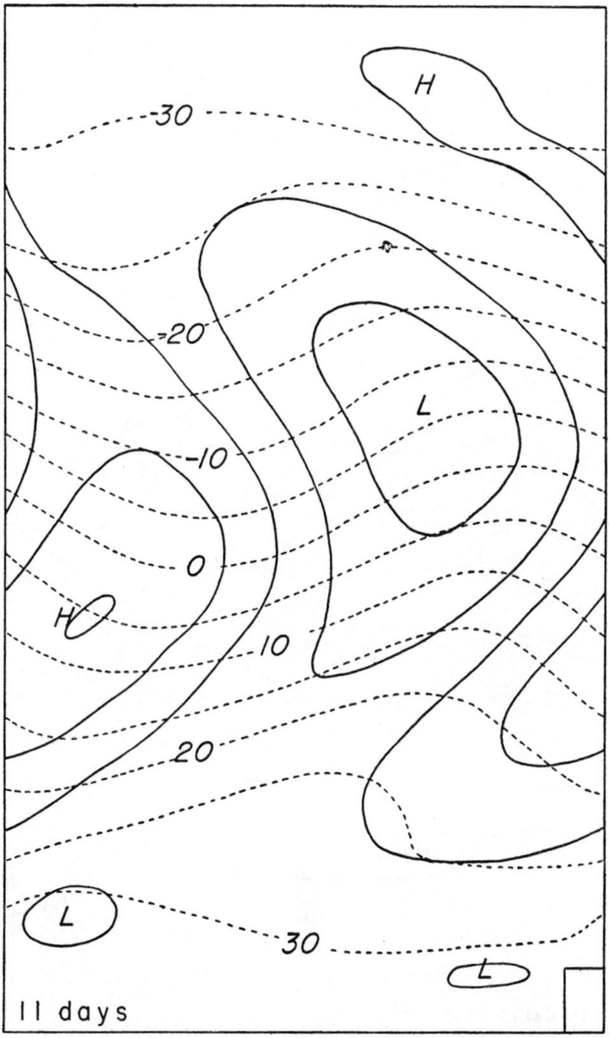

Figure 4. Distribution of 1,000-mb contour height at 200-foot intervals (solid lines) and 500-mb temperature at 5°C intervals (dashed lines) at 11 days. The small rectangle in the lower right corner shows the size of the finite-difference grid intervals Δx and Δy.

as almost to force a kinking of the contour lines. (Because of the symmetry of the equations, equally sharp ridges are also formed. This symmetry would be removed if $f + \zeta$ replaced f_0 as the coefficient of the horizontal divergence in the vorticity equation).

The field of vertical motion at 500 mb at 20 days is shown in Fig. 10. Here the vertical velocities w_2 were obtained from ω_2, using the relationship $w_2 \simeq -\omega_2 (z_1 - z_3)/p_2$ The overall aspect is quite realistic, especially the rapid changes from ascending to descending motion in the vicinity of the frontal troughs, together with the general ascent

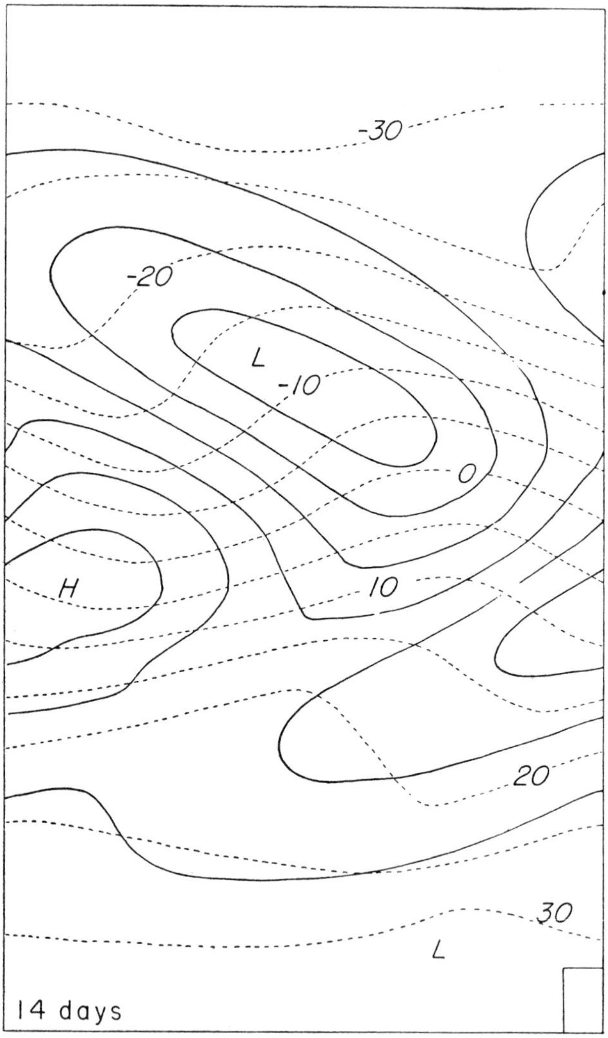

Figure 5. Distribution of 1,000-mb contour height at 200-foot intervals (solid lines) and 500-mb temperature at 5°C intervals (dashed lines) at 14 days. The small rectangle in the lower right corner shows the size of the finite-difference grid intervals Δx and Δy.

in the region of the main low and the descent associated with the high pressure centre.

In Fig. 11 the meridional circulation $\overline{V}_1$ is shown. According to Eq. (45), this is the mean meridional motion in the upper half of the atmosphere, the circulation in the lower half being equal and opposite. Initially we find only the very weak and broad direct cell characteristic of the preliminary forecast without eddies. As the eddy develops, however, we see the appearance of a definite three-celled circulation, with an indirect cell in middle latitudes and two somewhat weaker direct cells to the north and south. This is a characteristic feature of the unstable baroclinic waves in the two-level model, as has

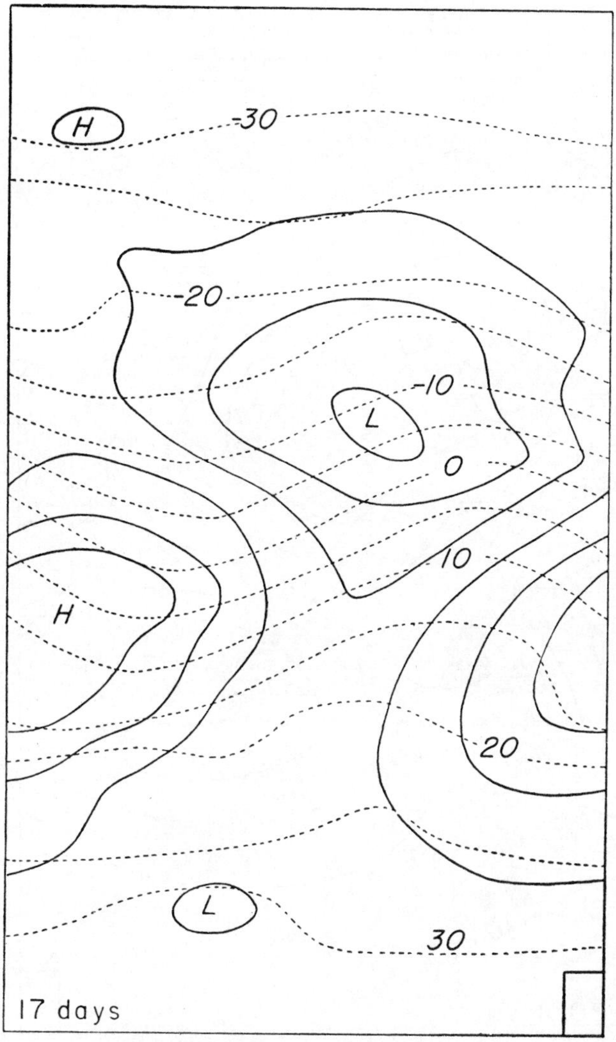

Figure 6. Distribution of 1,000-mb contour height at 200-foot intervals (solid lines) and 500-mb temperature at 5°C intervals (dashed lines) at 17 days. The small rectangle in the lower right corner shows the size of the finite-difference grid intervals Δx and Δy.

been shown previously by the writer (Phillips 1954). After 26 days, the field of $\overline{V}$ became very irregular owing to large truncation errors, and is therefore not shown.

The variation with time of the mean temperature at 500 mb, $\overline{T}_2$, is illustrated in Fig. 12, in the form of the accumulated temperature change since zero days. In the first five days, the temperature difference between $y = -W (j = 0)$ and $y = W (j = 16)$ continued to increase at the same rate (about 0·4°C per day) as that which prevailed during the preliminary forecast without eddies. As the disturbance developed, it transported sensible heat poleward because of the correlation between v' and T_2' (Figs. 4-9). This

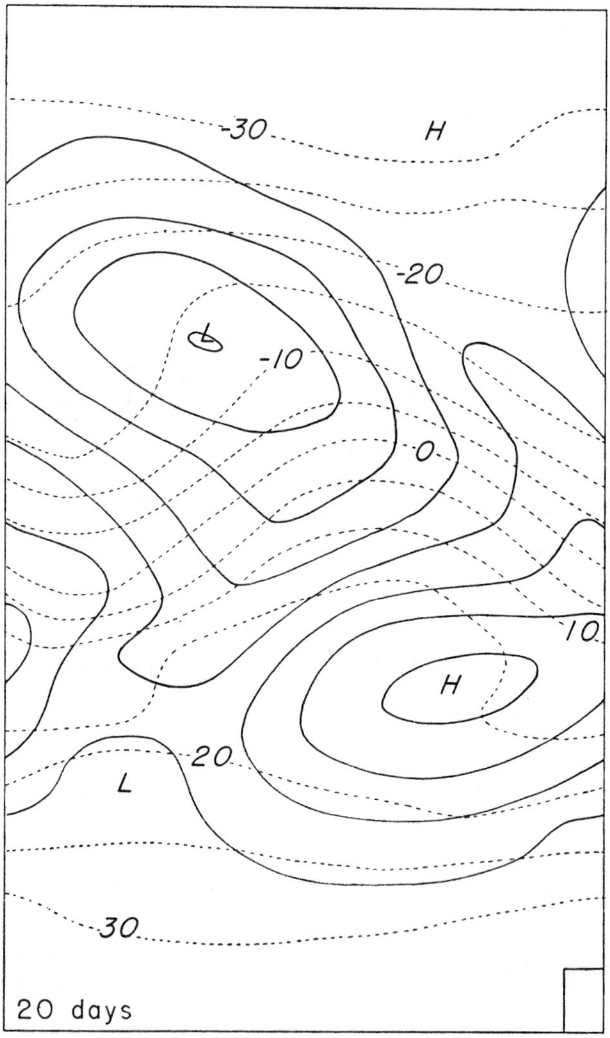

Figure 7. Distribution of 1,000-mb contour height at 200-foot intervals (solid lines) and 500-mb temperature at 5°C intervals (dashed lines) at 20 days. The small rectangle in the lower right corner shows the size of the finite-difference grid intervals Δx and Δy.

stopped the increase in the total mean temperature difference and eventually reduced it at the end of the period to a value below that existing at 0 days. In the later stages of the process (23-28 days) we find a marked concentration of the temperature gradient in central latitudes, while to the north and south the temperature gradient is very weak. By this time the exchange process had produced a relatively warm region at $j = 13$ and a relatively cool region at $j = 3$, reminiscent of the cut-off warm highs and cold lows frequently observed to the north and south of the main westerly current on actual atmospheric charts (Fig. 9).

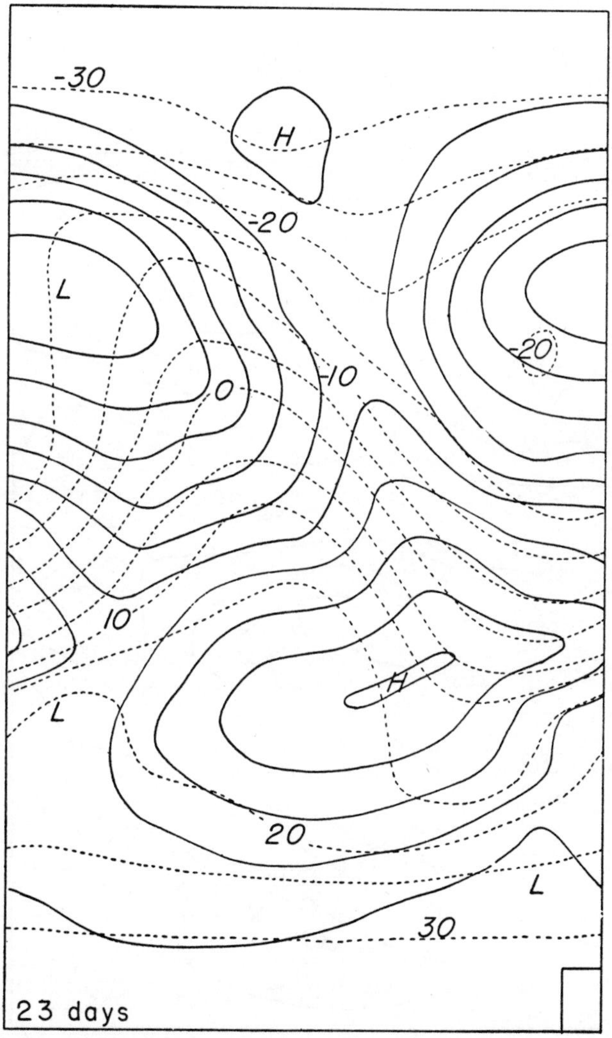

Figure 8. Distribution of 1,000-mb contour height at 200-foot intervals (solid lines) and 500-mb temperature at 5°C intervals (dashed lines) at 23 days. The small rectangle in the lower right corner shows the size of the finite-difference grid intervals Δx and Δy.

The thermodynamic energy equation for the model, Eq. (19), can be written in its x-averaged form as

$$\frac{\partial \bar{T}_2}{\partial t} = - \frac{\partial \overline{v_1' T_2'}}{\partial y} - \frac{2H}{c_p} \frac{y}{W} + \frac{f_0^2}{R\lambda^2 p_2} \bar{\omega}_2 + A \frac{\partial^2 \bar{T}_2}{\partial y^2}. \quad . \quad . \quad (48)$$

The average size and distribution with y of the five terms in this equation during the period 10-20 days are show in Table 3, with $y = (j - 8)\,\Delta y$. The contribution from the non-adiabatic heating, given by $-2Hy/c_p W$, is of course a warming at low latitudes

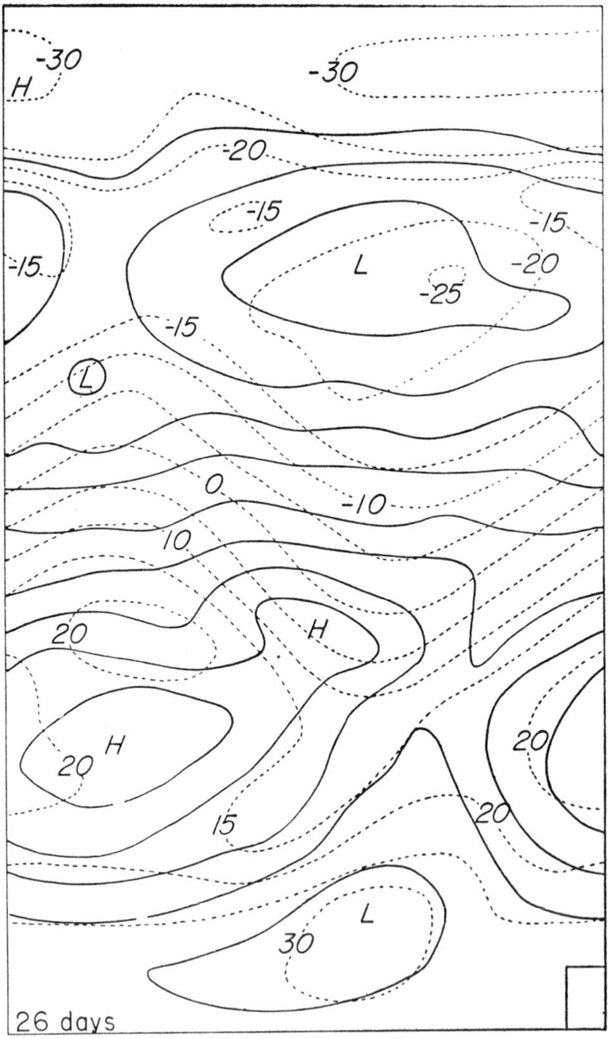

Figure 9. Distribution of 1,000-mb contour height at 200-foot intervals (solid lines) and 500-mb temperature at 5°C intervals (dashed lines) at 26 days. The small rectangle in the lower right corner shows the size of the finite-difference grid intervals Δx and Δy.

($j < 8$) and a cooling at high latitudes ($j > 8$). The convergence of the eddy transport $-\partial(\overline{v_1' T_2'})/\partial y$ opposes this, tending to destroy the latitudinal temperature gradient, especially in the centre of the region. On the other hand, the temperature change produced by the mean meridional circulation, $(f^2/R\lambda^2 p_2) \cdot \overline{\omega}_2$ cancels the non-adiabatic

Figure 10. Distribution of vertical velocity at 500 mb in cm sec^{-1} (solid lines) and 1,000-mb contour height at 200-ft intervals (dashed lines) at 20 days. The small rectangle in the lower right corner shows the size of the finite-difference grid intervals Δx and Δy.

effect near the walls, but, because of the indirect circulation in middle latitudes, contributes greatly to an *increase* in $-\partial \overline{T}_2/\partial y$ in the centre of the region. The resulting temperature changes, $\partial \overline{T}_2/\partial t$, show a tendency to a decrease of the temperature gradient in the outer regions, $0 < j < 6$ and $10 < j < 16$, and a tendency towards an increase in the centre $6 < j < 10$. (We note that the contribution from the lateral diffusion is generally negligible.)

Although the numbers in Table 3 do not represent a completely steady state, they

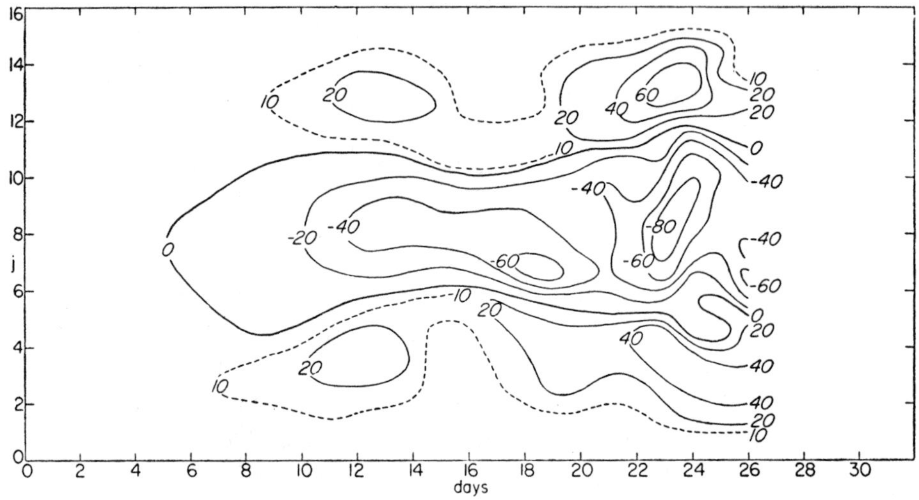

Figure 11. Variation with latitude (j) and time of the mean meridional velocity, $\overline{V}_1$, in the upper half of the atmosphere. Units are cm sec^{-1}.

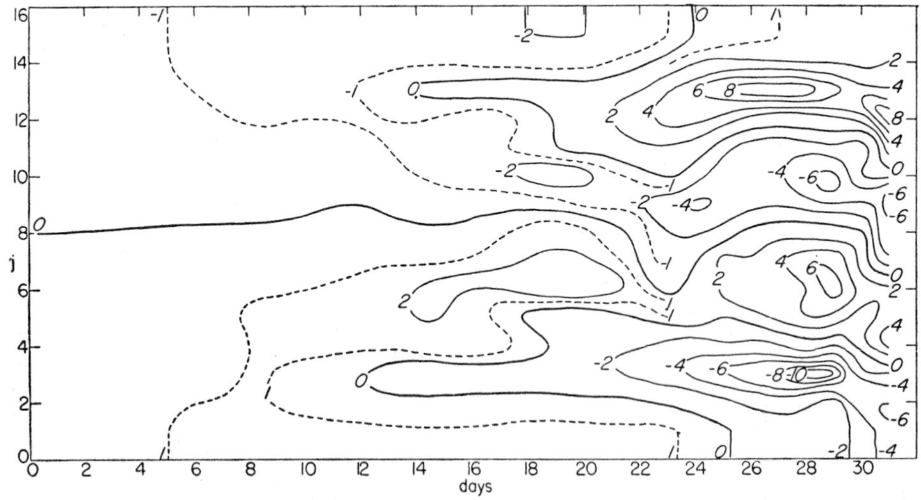

Figure 12. Variation of 500 mb mean temperature, $\overline{T}_2$, with latitude (j) and time, shown as the accumulated change from the temperature distribution at the end of the preliminary forecast (Table 1). Units are °C.

suggest that the latitude of maximum $\partial \overline{T}/\partial y$ in the atmosphere may be determined to some extent dynamically, and not merely by the latitudinal gradient in radiation.

The changes with time of $\bar{u}_1$ and $\bar{u}_4$, the mean zonal velocities at 250 and 1,000 mb, are shown in Figs. 13 and 14. The interesting phenomena here are (*a*) the formation of a strong jet in the centre of the region, and (*b*) the change in $\bar{u}_4$ from uniform weak easterlies to a pattern with westerlies in middle latitudes and easterlies to the north and south. The processes which create these changes can be seen by studying the zonal momentum budgets of the upper and lower halves of the atmosphere.

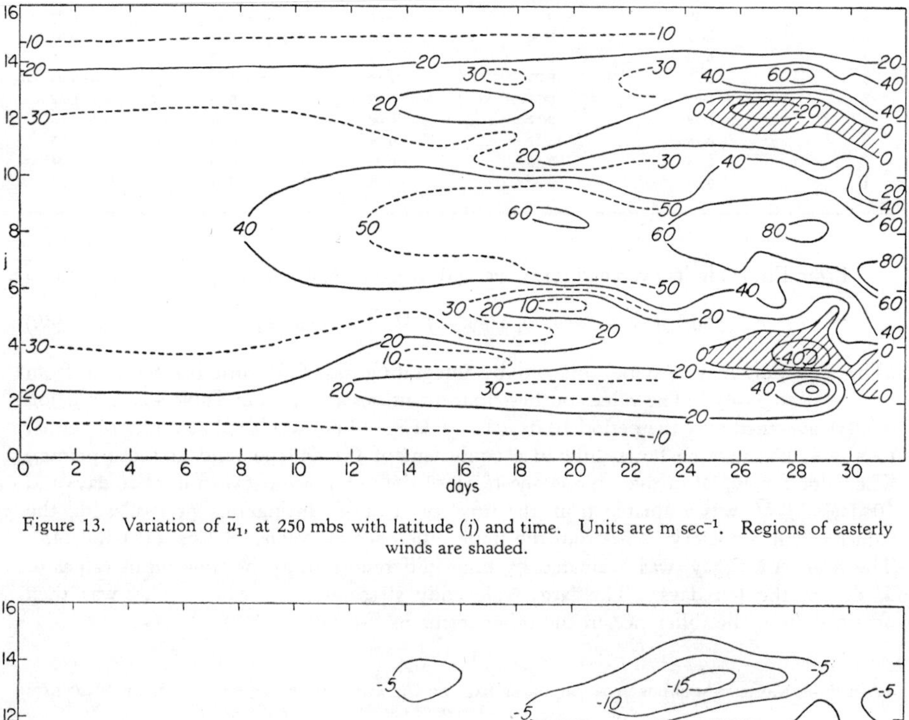

Figure 13. Variation of $\bar{u}_1$, at 250 mbs with latitude (j) and time. Units are m sec^{-1}. Regions of easterly winds are shaded.

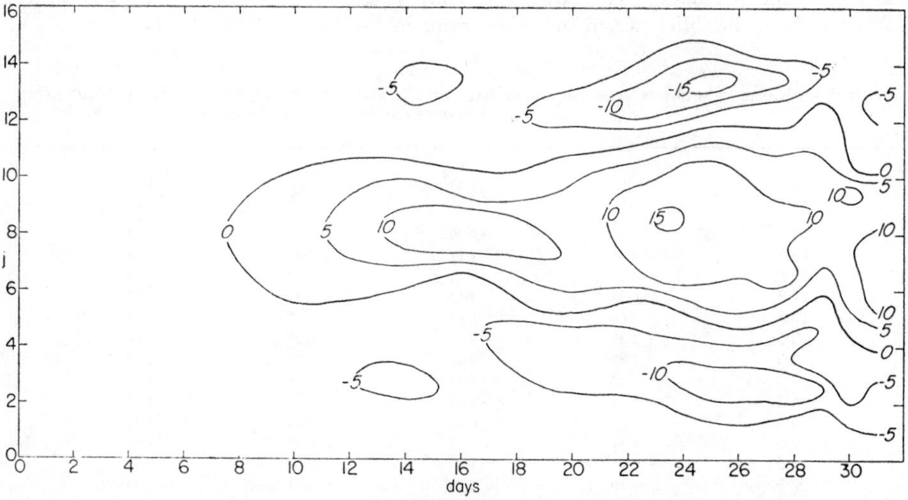

Figure 14. Variation of $\bar{u}_4$, at 1,000 mb with latitude (j) and time. Units are m sec^{-1}.

TABLE 3. EVALUATION OF THE TERMS IN THE THERMODYNAMIC ENERGY EQUATION DURING THE PERIOD 10-20 DAYS. UNITS ARE DEG DAY^{-1}.

j	$\frac{\partial \bar{T}_2}{\partial t}$	$-\frac{2H}{c_p}\frac{y}{W}$	$\frac{f_0^2}{R\lambda^2}\frac{\bar{\omega}_2}{p_2}$	$-\frac{\partial(\overline{v_1' T_2'})}{\partial y}$	$A\frac{\partial^2 \bar{T}_2}{\partial y^2}$
15	− 0·01	− 0·30	0·23	0·01	0·05
14	0·06	− 0·26	0·22	0·06	0·04
13	0·16	− 0·22	0·08	0·32	− 0·02
12	0·21	− 0·17	− 0·08	0·43	0·03
11	0·10	− 0·13	− 0·38	0·61	− 0·00
10	− 0·20	− 0·09	− 0·97	0·82	0·04
9	− 0·10	− 0·04	− 0·36	0·30	0·00
8	0·12	0·00	− 0·05	0·18	− 0·01
7	0·16	0·04	0·39	− 0·28	0·01
6	0·29	0·09	1·16	− 1·01	− 0·05
5	− 0·25	0·13	0·29	− 0·69	0·02
4	− 0·22	0·17	0·08	− 0·41	− 0·06
3	− 0·26	0·22	− 0·14	− 0·39	0·05
2	− 0·05	0·26	− 0·22	− 0·05	− 0·04
1	0·00	0·30	− 0·25	0·01	− 0·06

From Eq. (1) in its averaged form, we find that the change in $\bar{u}_1$ with time is given by

$$\partial \bar{u}_1/\partial t = -\partial(\overline{u_1' v_1'})/\partial y + f_0 \bar{V}_1 + A\,\partial^2 \bar{u}_1/\partial y^2. \qquad (49)$$

(This equation may also be obtained by integrating Eq. (33) with respect to y from $y = -W$ to $y = y$.) The values of these four quantities are listed in Table 4 as a function of $y\,(j)$, averaged over the period 10 days to 20 days. (They are listed at values of j equal to $n + \frac{1}{2}$, because the finite-difference equivalent of Eq. (49) is valid at those points.) The value for $\partial \bar{u}_1/\partial t$ in the table is one-tenth of the difference between $\bar{u}_1$ at 20 days and 10 days. $f_0 \bar{V}_1$ was evaluated from the time mean of $\bar{V}_1$ during this period, using the values calculated every 24 hr from the finite-difference analogues of Eqs. (19) and (45). The term $A\,\partial^2 \bar{u}_1/\partial y^2$ was evaluated by finite differences from the time mean values of $\bar{u}_1$ during the ten days. The large-scale eddy stress term $-\partial(\overline{u_1' v_1'})/\partial y$ was then obtained from the difference in the other terms in Eq. (49).

TABLE 4. MOMENTUM BUDGET FOR THE UPPER HALF OF THE ATMOSPHERE DURING THE PERIOD 10-20 DAYS (Units are m sec^{-1} day^{-1}).

j	$\frac{\partial \bar{u}_1}{\partial t}$	$f_0 \bar{V}_1$	$A\frac{\partial^2 \bar{u}_1}{\partial y^2}$	$-\frac{\partial(\overline{u_1' v_1'})}{\partial y}$
14·5	0·35	0·59	− 0·07	− 0·17
13·5	0·54	1·17	− 0·43	− 0·20
12·5	− 0·26	1·39	0·40	− 2·05
11·5	− 0·93	1·19	− 0·17	− 1·95
10·5	− 1·66	0·16	0·31	− 2·13
9·5	1·29	− 2·43	− 0·27	3·99
8·5	1·82	− 3·40	− 0·16	5·38
7·5	1·12	− 3·54	− 0·04	4·70
6·5	1·73	− 2·48	− 0·31	4·52
5·5	− 3·31	0·65	0·48	− 4·44
4·5	− 0·49	1·42	− 0·45	− 1·46
3·5	− 0·84	1·64	0·69	− 3·17
2·5	1·19	1·26	− 0·55	0·48
1·5	0·34	0·67	− 0·10	− 0·23

During this time the changes in $\bar{u}_1$ – an increase in middle latitudes with decreases to the north and south – are evidently determined mainly by the Coriolis term $f_0 \bar{V}_1$ and the large-scale eddy stress term $-\partial(\overline{u_1' v_1'})/\partial y$, the latter of these two being the larger. The contribution from the meridional circulation is in general opposite to the *observed* changes in $\bar{u}_1$, *so as to reduce the effect of the eddy term at level 1.* The resulting picture in central latitudes is thus very much like that postulated by Rossby as existing during the building up of a zonal wind maximum (Staff members 1947).

The momentum budget for the lower half of the atmosphere may be studied by means of the equation

$$\partial \bar{u}_3/\partial t = -\partial(\overline{u_3' v_3'})/\partial y + f_0 \bar{V}_3 + A\,\partial^2 \bar{u}_3/\partial y^2 - k\,\bar{u}_4 \quad . \quad . \quad (50)$$

Table 5 lists the values of these quantities in a fashion analogous to those in Table 4. Here we find that the principal terms are the Coriolis term $f_0 \bar{V}_3$ and the surface skin-friction term $-k\,\bar{u}_4$, these two being usually of the same magnitude but opposite in sign.

The importance for the zonal momentum balance in our model of the implicit meridional circulation characteristic of the amplifying baroclinic wave is thus quite clear : it tends to balance both the large values of $-\partial(\overline{u' v'})/\partial y$ in the upper atmosphere and the effect of surface friction on the lower atmosphere. The simultaneous development of middle-latitude surface westerlies and a jet is thus a combined result of the large-scale eddy momentum transport $\overline{u' v'}$ and the meridional circulation $\bar{V}$.

The meridional circulation, as is clear from Tables 4 and 5, is such as to *reduce* the large change in zonal wind shear with height, $\partial(\bar{u}_1 - \bar{u}_3)/\partial t$, which would otherwise result from the large-scale eddy-stress terms and skin friction alone. This result has previously been derived by Fjørtoft (1951).

TABLE 5. Momentum budget for the lower half of the troposphere during the period 10-20 days (Units are m sec^{-1} day^{-1}).

j	$\frac{\partial \bar{u}_3}{\partial t}$	$f_0 \bar{V}_3$	$A\frac{\partial^2 \bar{u}_3}{\partial y^2}$	$-\frac{\partial(\overline{u_3' v_3'})}{\partial y}$	$-k\bar{u}_4$
14·5	0·03	− 0·59	− 0·02	− 0·06	0·70
13·5	0·06	− 1·17	− 0·12	− 0·02	1·37
12·5	− 0·46	− 1·39	0·14	− 0·68	1·47
11·5	− 0·46	− 1·19	− 0·02	− 0·53	1·28
10·5	− 0·40	− 0·16	0·12	− 0·46	0·10
9·5	0·75	2·43	− 0·09	− 0·02	− 1·57
8·5	0·88	3·40	− 0·13	0·91	− 3·30
7·5	0·87	3·54	− 0·09	0·48	− 3·06
6·5	1·14	2·48	− 0·06	− 0·33	− 0·95
5·5	− 0·89	− 0·65	0·15	− 0·64	0·25
4·5	− 0·60	− 1·42	− 0·09	− 0·79	1·70
3·5	− 0·68	− 1·64	0·24	− 1·02	1·74
2·5	0·25	− 1·26	− 0·15	0·07	1·59
1·5	0·09	− 0·67	− 0·03	0·00	0·79

Eqs. (49) and (50) are at most only approximate statements of the real atmospheric momentum budget (although they are exact for our simplified model). The same equations for the atmosphere should also include the following additional types of terms on the right side of, say, Eq. (49) :

$$-\partial(\bar{u}_3 \bar{V}_3)/\partial y + \bar{\omega}_2 \bar{u}_2/p_2 + \overline{\omega_2' u_2'}/p_2 \quad . \quad . \quad . \quad (51)$$

In order to obtain some idea of the importance of these terms, whose effect is not included in our model, they have been evaluated from the fields of u and ω at 23 days, and are shown in Table 6. (Some ambiguity arises from their finite-difference evaluation because $\bar{u}_3$ and $\bar{V}_3$ are logically measured at values of $j = n + \frac{1}{2}$ while ω is defined at integral values of j. This was resolved by using simple interpolation where necessary.) For comparison, Table 6 also contains the values of $f_0 \bar{V}_3$ and $-k\bar{u}_4$ at 23 days. Each of the three terms in Eq. (51) are as large at *some* latitudes as the surface skin-friction term or the Coriolis term, but in general they are smaller than the latter two. Their sum, it is interesting to note, would act to increase the 'subtropical' surface easterlies and to diminish the 'polar' easterlies. This suggests that a model incorporating these terms might predict this feature of the real zonal circulation at the surface, i.e. that the trade winds are much more pronounced than the polar easterlies. Our simple equations, because of their symmetry, are deficient in this respect.

Implicit in all of these results is the initial assumption that the small-scale vertical stress, τ_x and τ_y, can be neglected at the 500-mb level. If this assumption is not valid, i.e. if τ at that level is an appreciable fraction of the stress at the ground, the computations here must be viewed with some scepticism. For example, Sheppard (1953), in discussing qualitatively the importance for the momentum budget of an appreciable vertical small-scale eddy stress in the free atmosphere, reached quite different conclusions concerning the meridional circulation in middle latitudes. The intensity of the Ferrel-type cell would of course be diminished by a net downward-directed τ at 500 mb, but this stress would have to be comparable with that at the ground before it would alter appreciably the results shown in Table 4. Although there is some recent evidence suggesting that τ does not decrease as rapidly with height as has hitherto been supposed (Sheppard, Charnock and Francis 1952), there is as yet no clear indication that τ at 5 km is very large.

TABLE 6. ADDITIONAL MOMENTUM TERMS FOR THE LOWER HALF OF THE ATMOSPHERE AT 23 DAYS (Units are m sec^{-1} day^{-1}).

j	A $\frac{\overline{\omega}_2 \bar{u}_2}{p_2}$	B $-\frac{\partial(\bar{u}_3 \bar{V}_3)}{\partial y}$	C $\frac{\overline{\omega_2' u_2'}}{p_2}$	Sum of $A + B + C$	$f_0 \bar{V}_3$	$-k\bar{u}_4$
15	0·40	− 0·14	0·06	0·32	− 1·36	0·88
14	1·16	− 0·23	0·06	0·99	− 4·25	2·77
13	− 0·24	0·40	1·49	1·65	− 5·46	4·06
12	− 1·28	− 0·02	3·92	2·62	− 2·33	2·49
11	− 0·48	0·40	1·60	1·52	1·16	− 0·78
10	− 1·37	0·77	1·40	0·80	3·00	− 3·15
9	− 2·70	2·21	0·85	0·36	5·75	− 4·68
8	− 0·73	− 0·03	0·88	0·12	7·69	− 4·80
7	1·78	− 0·84	1·19	2·13	7·15	− 4·04
6	4·37	− 2·28	0·65	2·74	3·70	− 1·57
5	2·27	− 0·13	− 2·82	− 0·68	− 1·81	1·13
4	− 0·04	− 0·02	− 3·17	− 3·23	− 4·57	2·42
3	− 0·68	− 0·39	− 0·78	− 1·85	− 3·42	2·80
2	− 0·59	0·21	0·05	− 0·33	− 1·75	1·70
1	− 0·16	0·08	− 0·00	− 0·08	− 0·56	0·49

8. Energy transformations during the forecast

One of the main purposes of this numerical experiment was the investigation of the energetics of the atmosphere. Table 7 contains values of the various energy parameters obtained during the course of the general forecast at 24-hourly intervals. The units are the same as those given for Table 2 in section 5. We will consider in this section only the values from about 5 to 26 days, the later values requiring a separate discussion since they contain large truncation errors, and the earlier values being of no special interest. The mean values of the energy parameters during the period 5-26 days are also included in the table.

Looking first at the energy input values, $\{\overline{Q}\cdot\overline{P}\}$, we see that this is uniformly positive, as is to be expected from the positive correlation between the heating and $\overline{T}_2$. The mean value of $\{\overline{Q}\cdot\overline{P}\}$ over the period 5-26 days is 448 units, while the *calculated* dissipation of energy during this period is almost as large, the sum of the 6 dissipation terms being 423 units.

The average $\{\overline{Q}\cdot\overline{P}\}$ value of 448 units corresponds to a rate of energy input of about 2·6 joules sec^{-1} m^{-2}, about half of the estimated rate of energy dissipation in the real atmosphere (Brunt 1944). Although it is possible to assign part of this discrepancy to the smallish value we chose for H (H having been determined so as to get ' similarity ' only in the latitudinal eddy transport of sensible heat), the model itself is undoubtedly too simple for us to expect any closer agreement.

In Section 4 a scheme was outlined for the energy transformations occurring in the atmosphere, where the kinetic energy $\overline{K}$ of the zonal motion was maintained by a flow of energy from the eddies, which received their energy in turn from the mean potential energy $\overline{P}$ (see also Lorentz 1955). The mean values of $\{\overline{P}\cdot P'\}$, $\{P'\cdot K'\}$, and $\{K'\cdot\overline{K}\}$ in Table 7 agree with this picture (Fig. 3), all three values being positive.

The direct exchange of energy between $\overline{P}$ and $\overline{K}$, given by $\{\overline{P}\cdot\overline{K}\}$, is predominantly *negative* in Table 7, especially after the appearance of surface westerlies in middle latitudes. This is a result of the greater intensity of the central indirect cell compared to the weaker direct cells to the north and south (Fig. 11), and to the relatively large mean temperature gradient in middle latitudes. However, the magnitude of $\{\overline{P}\cdot\overline{K}\}$ is small, and it is conceivable that a true Hadley-type circulation in low latitudes (for which our present theory is to some extent inadequate) might contribute enough to make $\{\overline{P}\cdot\overline{K}\}$ positive, although it would undoubtedly still be small in comparison to $\{K'\cdot\overline{K}\}$.

The pictorialisation of the direction of the energy transformations in Fig. 3 is thus borne out by the computations, except that $\{\overline{P}\cdot\overline{K}\}$ is negative. It is of course not possible to state definitely that this diagram is a complete representation of the principal energy changes occurring in the atmosphere, since our equations are so simplified, but the verisimilitude of the forecast flow patterns suggests quite strongly that it contains a fair element of truth. Further computations with more exact equations will presumably refine the picture considerably, as will an extension of observational studies using real data.

Of the amount of energy dissipated by friction during the period 5-26 days, somewhat more than half was done through the agency of the lateral eddy-vicosity A, whose value is perhaps one of the least satisfactorily known parameters in the experiment. As a check on the importance of this parameter, the experiment was re-run with $A = 0$. The development of the flow pattern was in general quite similar to that with $A = 10^5$ m^2 sec^{-1}, except that large truncation errors appeared earlier in the forecast period, so that the check computation with $A = 0$ could not be carried as far as the one containing the lateral viscosity. The direction of the energy transformation was, however, the same.

9. Finite-difference (truncation) errors

An exact detailed analysis of the truncation errors introduced by the employment of finite differences is of course possible only when the continuous solution of the differential equation is known. In our case this is not possible (if it were, there would be no need to use finite differences), and we must therefore use some cruder technique.

TABLE 7. ENERGY AND ENERGY-TRANSFORMATION VALUES

Days	K'	$\overline{K}$	P'	$\overline{P}$	E	$\{\overline{Q}\cdot\overline{P}\}$	$\{\overline{P}\cdot P'\}$	$\{P'\cdot K'\}$	$\{K'\cdot\overline{K}\}$	$\{\overline{P}\cdot\overline{K}\}$	$\{\overline{K}\cdot k\}$	$\{K'\cdot k\}$	$\{\overline{K}\cdot A\}$	$\{K'\cdot A\}$	$\{\overline{P}\cdot A\}$	$\{P'\cdot A\}$
0	768	4265	0	24368	29401	440	0	0	− 11	41	− 27	266	9	330	48	0
1	357	4328	24	24698	29407	443	3	18	− 27	41	− 27	102	9	139	48	8
2	215	4389	20	25044	29668	446	5	4	− 6	41	− 27	26	9	73	49	5
3	161	4450	19	25380	30010	449	20	12	− 7	35	− 28	8	10	45	50	3
4	139	4513	29	25708	30389	452	38	22	− 0	34	− 28	5	10	30	50	2
5	137	4578	46	26016	30777	455	65	44	11	32	− 27	4	10	21	51	2
6	159	4649	68	26300	31176	457	101	80	28	41	− 26	7	10	17	52	3
7	198	4723	94	26554	31569	460	150	132	53	36	− 23	12	10	16	52	3
8	260	4806	130	26756	31952	461	229	203	81	14	− 19	21	10	17	52	4
9	356	4890	182	26873	32301	462	335	306	122	7	− 12	34	10	20	53	6
10	493	4988	251	26891	32623	462	464	431	193	− 28	− 0	49	11	26	53	8
11	678	5113	333	26786	32910	461	614	592	291	− 37	21	67	12	36	53	11
12	867	5279	409	26562	33117	460	719	766	441	− 43	55	84	15	49	52	14
13	968	5530	407	26335	33240	457	636	831	625	− 72	99	92	23	62	53	15
14	909	5770	298	26289	33266	457	411	666	577	− 72	128	84	33	71	53	14
15	813	5848	204	26403	33268	458	313	438	352	− 99	128	61	42	75	54	11
16	795	5819	217	26483	33314	458	433	403	212	− 119	115	45	51	75	55	11
17	875	5826	312	26386	33399	458	646	548	235	− 128	110	50	59	75	55	13
18	1004	5994	419	26125	33542	455	783	719	381	− 192	114	66	75	75	57	16
19	1171	6265	495	25798	33729	452	832	770	324	− 151	125	80	99	77	59	18
20	1542	6278	616	25368	33804	449	981	813	74	− 72	143	89	94	90	59	21
21	2171	6021	851	24704	33747	443	1269	964	− 83	− 60	166	103	65	109	55	28
22	3046	5830	1201	23697	33774	435	1626	1282	103	− 52	196	130	53	132	53	37
23	3654	6219	1462	22459	33794	423	1703	1698	898	− 113	264	157	78	155	55	45
24	3890	6879	1332	21521	33622	412	990	1315	514	− 54	353	181	90	211	57	47
25	4044	7510	1132	21280	33966	408	545	730	340	− 166	357	152	137	268	62	45
26	3809	8664	1077	21409	34959	407	402	391	237	− 256	342	63	237	302	73	46
27	4259	8950	1158	21573	35940	407	247	259	− 324	− 15	327	7	263	357	75	54
28	4216	10921	932	22267	38336	410	− 273	117	− 1137	− 180	231	27	485	407	103	53
29	6613	10099	1040	22600	40352	412	635	− 457	− 6574	462	146	79	395	713	96	78
30	11339	6722	2182	21403	41646	408	2409	857	373	− 287	174	124	151	1613	57	147
31	12395	9422	2070	20734	44621	395	363	− 1182	539	801	321	55	251	2707	76	188
5-26 (mean)	1447	5795	524	25318	33084	448	648	642	273	− 72	119	74	56	90	55	19

One approach which suggests itself is a comparison between the forecast changes of energy forms, K', $\overline{K}$, P', $\overline{P}$, and the changes in these quantities implied by the finite-difference evaluation of the various energy transformations. Although the continuous equations Eqs. (17)-(19) have the exact energy integrals, Eqs. (39)-(42), the finite-difference equations (see the appendix) do not, and the disagreement between the 'observed' changes in energy and those computed from the energy-transformation functions may then be taken as a partial measure of the importance of truncation error. Such a comparison is also of immediate interest concerning the validity of the energy transformations themselves.

In Table 8 are listed the 24-hr changes in the 'observed' total energy $\Delta E = \Delta(K' + \overline{K} + P' + \overline{P})$, together with the corresponding changes computed from the finite-difference form of the energy budget Eq. (43). Each of the latter values was obtained by adding up the energy transformations concerned at n days and at $n + 1$ days, and then dividing by two to get the 'computed' change in E from n to $n + 1$ days. If we look at the differences, we see that they are rather less than the typical value of $\{\overline{Q} \cdot \overline{P}\}$ (448 units) until about 23-24 days. In the early days, when the disturbance was small and the motion therefore rather linear in character, the agreement is remarkably good. As the disturbance increases in size and K' begins to approach $\overline{K}$ in magnitude, the disagreement increases.

TABLE 8. 24-HR CHANGES IN TOTAL ENERGY OBSERVED (ΔE) AND COMPUTED FROM EQ. (43).

Period (days)	ΔE	E Budget	Difference
0- 1	6	− 10	16
1- 2	261	238	23
2- 3	342	336	6
3- 4	379	372	7
4- 5	388	388	0
5- 6	399	395	4
6- 7	393	392	1
7- 8	383	383	0
8- 9	349	364	− 15
9-10	322	334	− 12
10-11	287	290	− 3
11-12	207	227	− 20
12-13	123	153	− 30
13-14	26	94	− 68
14-15	2	80	− 78
15-16	46	96	− 50
16-17	85	101	− 16
17-18	143	74	69
18-19	187	23	164
19-20	75	− 26	101
20-21	− 57	− 65	8
21-22	27	− 125	152
22-23	20	− 249	269
23-24	− 172	− 429	257
24-25	344	− 570	914
25-26	993	− 635	1628
26-27	981	− 666	1647
27-28	2396	− 786	3182
28-29	2016	− 995	3011
29-30	1294	− 1476	2770
30-31	2975	− 2531	5506

The sign of the disagreement shows a surprisingly slow variation with time, but no explanation for this phenomenon has yet been found. A similar examination of the *individual* energy budgets for K', $\overline{K}$, P' and $\overline{P}$ showed that most of the fictitious energy increase in the last ten days occurred in $\overline{K}$, except in the last three days, where it occurred mainly in K'. After about 25 days, the field of $\bar{u}_1$ contains several places where minimum and maximum values of $\bar{u}_1$ occur at neighbouring grid points (Fig. 13), so that the breakdown of the finite-difference scheme is not surprising.

This breakdown of the computations can presumably be postponed by taking smaller values of Δx and Δy, but this will not eliminate the difficulty completely, and at the same time will require smaller time steps to satisfy the computational stability criterion. Somewhat the same type of disadvantage also appears if higher-order differences are introduced in an attempt to obtain more accurate derivatives. It was thought initially that the introduction of a lateral eddy-viscosity into the equations would eliminate some of the bad effects of truncation errors, by smoothing out the small-scale motions. To some extent this was true, since the computation incorporating A could be carried farther than the check computation with $A = 0$, but evidently a still more fundamental modification of the equations is required.

10. Conclusions

The experiment has succeeded in several aspects; it has predicted the easterly-westerly-easterly distribution of surface zonal wind, the existence of a jet, and the required net poleward transport of energy. Furthermore, the energy-transformation processes which produced these phenomena agree qualitatively with what little is known of the principal energy transformations in the atmosphere. Considering the simplicity of the model, these modest successes are quite gratifying.

There are failures in some of the details; the relative strength of the sub-tropical easterlies compared to those in polar latitudes was not predicted, and the mean latitudinal temperature gradient was too large. Certain features of the disturbance were also not very realistic. However, there is good reason to believe that these failures are merely results of the extreme simplicity of the equations that were used, and will be corrected when more accurate equations are employed.

Certain of the assumptions in this particular numerical experiment can be eliminated in a rather straightforward manner, e.g. the geostrophic assumption and the simplified geometry. However, a further refinement of the model will soon run into the more difficult physical problems of small-scale turbulence and convection, the release of latent heat, and the dependence of radiation on temperature, moisture, and cloud. Progress in the past in developing an adequate theory of the general circulation has had as its main obstacle the difficulty of solving the non-linear hydrodynamical equations. High-speed computing machines have to some extent eliminated this problem, and further progress in understanding the large-scale behaviour of the atmosphere should come to depend more and more on a fuller understanding of the physical processes mentioned above.

Acknowledgments

The research carried out was sponsored by the Office of Naval Research and the Geophysics Research Directorate.

The writer also wishes to acknowledge the invaluable assistance of the staff of the Electronic Computer Project at the Institute for Advanced Study, especially Dr. H. H. Goldstine for his contribution to the solution of some of the numerical problems, and Mr. Glenn Lewis for his help in the design of an efficient code. The experiment is a natural extension of the work by Dr. J. Charney on numerical prediction, and has benefited greatly from his interest and encouragement.

APPENDIX

1. THE NUMERICAL FORECASTING PROCEDURE

The forecasting procedure replaces the continuous independent variables by the discrete variables i, j, τ, according to the scheme

$$x = i\,\Delta x \quad (i = 0, 1, 2, \ldots, I-1)$$

$$y = j\,\Delta y \quad (j = 0, 1, 2, \ldots, J)$$

$$t = \tau\,\Delta t \quad (\tau = 0, 1, 2, \ldots)$$

$i = 0$ corresponds to $x = 0$ and $i = I$ corresponds to $x = L$. $j = 0$ corresponds to $y = -W$, and $j = J$ to $y = +W$.

To describe the numerical process we first define the finite difference operators $\mathcal{L}$ and $\mathcal{J}$ as follows (ϵ is the ratio $\Delta x/\Delta y$) :

$$\Delta x^2\,\nabla^2 S \simeq \mathcal{L}_{ij}\,S = S_{i+1\,j} + S_{i-1\,j} - 2\,S_{ij} + \epsilon^2\,(S_{i\,j+1} + S_{i\,j-1} - 2\,S_{ij})$$

$$4\Delta x\,\Delta y\,\mathcal{J}\left(\frac{R, S}{x, y}\right) \simeq \mathcal{J}_{ij}(R, S) = (R_{i+1\,j} - R_{i-1\,j})\,(S_{i\,j+1} - S_{i\,j-1}) - (R_{i\,j+1} - R_{i\,j-1})\cdot$$
$$\cdot(S_{i+1\,j} - S_{i-1\,j}).$$

It is convenient to introduce also the non-dimensional constant

$$\gamma = \lambda^2\,\Delta x^2$$

and to replace the potential vorticities q by

$$\eta_{ij} = q_{ij}\,\Delta x^2.$$

If we then form the finite-difference equivalent of our definition of the x-mean, Eq. (26),

$$\overline{\psi}_{j\tau} = I^{-1} \sum_{i=0}^{I-1} \psi_{ij\,\tau} \qquad \text{(A1)}$$

$$\psi'_{ij\tau} = \psi_{ij\tau} - \overline{\psi}_{j\tau}, \qquad \text{(A2)}$$

Eqs. (22) and (23) can be written as the following four equations (for convenience we suppress here the τ subscript) :

$$\mathcal{L}_{ij}\,\psi_1' - \gamma\,(\psi_1' - \psi_3')_{ij} - \eta'_{1ij} = 0, \qquad \text{(A3)}$$

$$\mathcal{L}_{ij}\,\psi_3' + \gamma\,(\psi_1' - \psi_3')_{ij} - \eta'_{3ij} = 0, \qquad \text{(A4)}$$

$$\epsilon^2\,(\overline{\psi}_{1\,j+1} + \overline{\psi}_{1\,j-1} - 2\overline{\psi}_{1j}) - \gamma\,(\overline{\psi}_{1j} - \overline{\psi}_{3j}) - \overline{\eta}_{1j} = 0, \qquad \text{(A5)}$$

$$\epsilon^2\,(\overline{\psi}_{3\,j+1} + \overline{\psi}_{3\,j-1} - 2\overline{\psi}_{3j}) + \gamma\,(\overline{\psi}_{1j} - \overline{\psi}_{3j}) - \overline{\eta}_{3j} = 0. \qquad \text{(A6)}$$

Given η_1' and η_3', Eqs. (A3) and (A4) determine ψ_1' and ψ_3' in the interior $(0 \leqslant i \leqslant (I-1),\ 1 \leqslant j \leqslant (J-1))$ if we use the boundary conditions

$$\psi'(i, j) = 0 \quad \text{at} \quad j = 0 \quad \text{and} \quad J, \qquad \text{(A7)}$$

$$\psi'(0, j) = \psi'(I, j), \qquad \psi'(-1, j) = \psi'(I-1, j). \qquad \text{(A8)}$$

These are equivalent to Eq. (28) and the cyclic boundary condition. The two equations, (A3) and (A4), are then easily solved for ψ' by relaxation techniques (Charney and Phillips 1953).

The solution of the *ordinary* difference equations (A5) and (A6) for $\bar{\psi}_j$, when $\bar{\eta}_j$ is known, uses the boundary conditions

$$\left.\begin{aligned} \bar{\psi}(j=J) &= \bar{\psi}(j=J-1), \\ \bar{\psi}(j=0) &= \bar{\psi}(j=1), \end{aligned}\right\} \qquad \text{(A9)}$$

together with one extra condition; for example,

$$\bar{\psi}_3(j=0) = 0. \qquad \text{(A10)}$$

Solution of Eqs. (A5) and (A6) by conventional relaxation methods is not very satisfactory; their one-dimensional character and the boundary conditions (A9) do not make for very rapid convergence of the iterative process. Furthermore, a rather accurate solution is required, if the computation of $\bar{\omega}_{2j}$ from Eq. (A18) is to be at all accurate. They can be solved ' exactly ' by using a finite-difference analogue of a Green's function, but this involves either (a) a tabulation of a rather large number of Green's function values (of the order of $\frac{1}{2}J^2$), or, (b) the computation of the Green's function as needed from products of the form a^j and a^{-j}, whose scaling becomes awkward. Dr. H. Goldstine of the Institute for Advanced Study suggested a method to the writer which was free from these objections, and which proved to be extremely satisfactory with respect to accuracy, speed of computation, and size of the code needed. The method is applicable to a somewhat wider class of ordinary difference equations, and will be described by Goldstine and von Neumann at a later time.

The usual technique employed in numerical forecasting in forming a finite difference equivalent of (24)-(25) is to evaluate the right side of those equations at time τ and express the left side as a centred difference $(q_{ij\,\tau+1} - q_{ij\,\tau-1})/2\Delta t$ (after a single uncentred step at the very beginning). However, it can be shown that in our case this procedure is not stable because of the frictional terms involving A and k; if they are evaluated at τ, they give rise to both exponentially amplified and damped solutions, whereas only the damped solution is real. This difficulty can be overcome either by evaluating the frictional terms (explicitly and uncentred) at $\tau - 1$, or (implicitly and centred) as an average at $\tau - 1$ and $\tau + 1$. The latter method is slightly more accurate and formed the basis of the scheme employed in the calculations.

The actual finite-difference forms used for Eqs. (24) and (25) were the following :

$$\left.\begin{aligned} \left[-\alpha\mathscr{L}+1\right]\eta_{1ij\,\tau+1} = x_{1ij} = \eta_{1ij\,\tau-1} &+ c\mathscr{J}_{ij}(bj+\eta_1,\psi_1)_\tau + \\ &+ \alpha\mathscr{L}\eta_{1ij\,\tau-1} + h(2j-J)/J, \end{aligned}\right\} \qquad \text{(A11)}$$

$$\left.\begin{aligned} \left[-\alpha\mathscr{L}+1+\frac{3k\Delta t}{2}\right]\eta_{3ij\,\tau+1} = x_{3ij} = \eta_{3ij\,\tau-1} &+ c\mathscr{J}_{ij}(bj+\eta_3,\psi_3)_\tau + \\ &+ \alpha\mathscr{L}\eta_{3ij\,\tau-1} - h(2j-J)/J + \\ &+ k\Delta t\left[\tfrac{3}{2}\eta_{3\,\tau-1} - \eta_{1\tau} - 4\gamma(\psi_1-\psi_3)_\tau\right]_{ij}, \end{aligned}\right\} \qquad \text{(A12)}$$

where $\alpha = A\,\Delta t/(\Delta x)^2, \quad b = \beta\,\Delta x^2\,\Delta y, \quad c = \Delta t/2\,\Delta x\,\Delta y,$

and $h = 4RH\,\gamma\,\Delta t/f_0\,c_p.$

The lateral diffusion terms $A\,\nabla^2\eta$ were thus evaluated completely implicitly while the surface friction term $-k\zeta_4$ was evaluated partly implicitly and partly explicitly.

The computation stability criterion, which sets an upper limit to the allowable time step Δt, in the absence of the frictional terms can be written

$$c\,(|\psi_{i+1\,j} - \psi_{i-1\,j}| + |\psi_{i\,j+1} - \psi_{i\,j-1}|) < 1. \qquad \text{A13)}$$

The frictional term makes this restriction more severe, but for the small values of A and k we are using (for $\Delta t = 1$ hr and $\Delta x = 375$ km, $\alpha = 0{\cdot}00256$ and $k\Delta t = 0{\cdot}0144$) this is only a small effect, and the computations remain stable if we replace 1 in (A13) by, say, 0·95. The code was then designed to apply the test (A13) at every point, and to stop if the criterion was exceeded. (This is easily done during the computation of x in Eqs. (A11) and (A12).) The largest value of the left side of (A13) that had been reached so far in the computation was also periodically printed out every 24 hr, making it possible to shorten the time step before (A13) was violated.

The solution of the implicit Eqs. (A11) and (A12) for $\eta_{ij\,\tau+1}$ proceeds in two steps: first, the straightforward computation of x_{ij}, and second, the inversion of the two equations (s taking on the values 1 and 3)

$$\left[\alpha\mathcal{L}_{ij} - \mu_s\right] \eta_{sij\,\tau+1} = -\, x_{sij} \qquad \text{(A14)}$$

for $\eta_{sij\,\tau+1}$, where $\mu_s = 1$ for $s = 1$ and $\mu_s = 1 + \frac{3}{2}\,k\Delta t$ for $s = 3$. This last process was in turn divided up into two steps,

$$\left[\alpha\mathcal{L}_{ij} - \mu_s\right] \eta'_{sij\,\tau+1} = -\, x'_{sij}, \qquad \text{(A15)}$$

$$\alpha\epsilon^2\,(\bar{\eta}_{j+1} + \bar{\eta}_{j-1} - 2\bar{\eta}_j)_{s\,\tau+1} - \mu_s\,\bar{\eta}_{sj\,\tau+1} = -\,\bar{x}_{sj}, \qquad \text{(A16)}$$

by again introducing the finite-difference means analogous to Eqs. (A1) and (A2). Eq. (A15) was solved by relaxation with $\eta' = 0$ at $j = 0$ and $j = J$ and the cyclic boundary condition

$$\eta'\,(i = 0) = \eta'\,(i = I).$$

Eq. (A16) was solved 'exactly,' by the same technique as was used for Eqs. (A5) and (A6), with the boundary conditions,

$$\left.\begin{aligned} \bar{\eta}\,(j = 0) &= \bar{\eta}\,(j = 1), \\ \bar{\eta}\,(j = J) &= \bar{\eta}\,(j = J - 1). \end{aligned}\right\} \qquad \text{(A17)}$$

Finally $\eta_{ij\,\tau+1}$ was obtained by adding η' and $\bar{\eta}$.

The general computational scheme, then, proceeded very much as described by Charney and Phillips (1953), the 'history' of the motion being carried by the η's, with the ψ's being determined from (A3)-(A6) at each time step after the η's had been extrapolated forward in time by (A11)-(A12). The only variation from conventional schemes was the partially implicit character of Eqs. (A11) and (A12), necessitating an additional inversion of an elliptic partial difference equation.

The extrapolated Liebman process (Charney and Phillips 1953) was used in the relaxation solution of Eqs. (A3), (A4) and (A15). The initial guess, $<\psi'_{ij\,\tau+1}>$, for $\psi'_{ij\,\tau+1}$ in Eqs. (A3) and (A4) was obtained by the formula

$$<\psi'_{ij\,\tau+1}> = 2\,\psi'_{ij\tau} - \psi'_{ij\,\tau-1}.$$

In order to do this, it was necessary to store the otherwise unused values of $\psi'_{\tau-1}$, but the resulting increase in the speed of the computation through the decrease in the required number of iterations in the Liebman process made this very worth while. The relaxation process for ψ' was carried out until the quantity $|\psi'_{\nu+1} - \psi'_{\nu}|_{1ij} + |\psi'_{\nu+1} - \psi'_{\nu}|_{3ij}$ was everywhere less than $\frac{3}{8} \times 10^5$ m^2 sec^{-1}, about $\frac{3}{8}$ m in units of isobaric height (the subscript ν indicates successive iterative guesses). This took between 3 and 6 iterations, depending on the size of the time step.

The solution of Eq. (A15) by relaxation was very rapid because of the small value of the ratio α/μ. (The optimum over-relaxation process has an eigenvalue of about 10^{-3}.) Here the first guess was $< \eta' > = \mu^{-1} x'$, and very few iterations (< 5) were necessary to reduce the error in η' to less than 600 m^2 sec^{-1} (corresponding to an error in $q = \Delta x^{-2} \eta$ of less than 4×10^{-9} sec^{-1}).

The complete set of computations for one time step took about 50 sec. About 18 sec were spent in the computation of $x_{\tau+1}$, 2 sec in the solution of (A16), 8 sec in (A15), 2 sec in the solution of (A5) and (A6), and 20 sec in the solution of (A3) and (A4).

The η's and the ψ's were both stored as 20 binary-digit numbers; the scaling being such that the round-off error in storing η corresponded to an error of about $\pm 2 \times 10^{-9}$ sec^{-1} in q, and that incurred in storing ψ corresponding to an error in isobaric height of about $\pm$ 0·006 m. As far as is known, round-off errors of this type did not influence the computations to any significant degree.

A time step of 2 hr was used until $t = 8$ days, one of $1\frac{1}{2}$ hr until $t = 12$ days, one of 1 hr until $t = 23$ days, and the forecast was finished using a time step of $\frac{1}{2}$ hr. The 31-day forecast thus required a total of 812 time steps. Whenever the time step was shortened at time t from Δt to $\Delta t'$, values of $\eta_{\tau-1} = \eta\,(t - \Delta t')$ for the first computation of Eqs. (A11) and (A12) with the new time step were obtained by interpolation from the values of $\eta\,(t)$ and $\eta\,(t - \Delta t)$.

The forecasting code proper, which solved (A3)-(A6) and (A11)-(A12) required almost 2,000 separate instructions and constants. The computation of the energy terms, meridional circulation, $\bar{u}$, $\overline{T}_2$, etc., required about 1,700 separate instructions, almost as much as the forecast code itself. An additional 3,000 instructions were used to perform miscellaneous tasks, e.g., the formation of the initial ψ and η fields at $t = 0$, the interpolation necessary when the time step was changed, and the computation of the preliminary forecast without eddies.

2. Numerical evaluation of the energy parameters and the meridional circulation

In general, the finite-difference evaluation of the energy functions is somewhat arbitrary, since the finite-difference forecast equations (A3)-(A6) and (A11)-(A12) do not possess exact energy integrals, and therefore do not lead automatically to a specification of the proper way to evaluate the functions using ψ values at only two time steps. (This is true even of the simplest barotropic vorticity equation $\nabla^2 \partial\psi/\partial t = -\mathbf{V} \cdot \nabla\nabla^2 \psi$ in the finite-difference form by which it has hitherto been solved, (e.g., Charney, Fjørtoft, and von Neumann 1950).) Therefore, the following formulae will be for the most part simply listed, with little or no justification being given for the particular form employed.

For simplicity we introduce the abbreviated notation for the sums

$$X\,S_{ij} = I^{-1} \sum_{i=0}^{I-1} S_{ij},$$

$$Y\,S_{ij} = J^{-1} \sum_{j=1}^{J-1} S_{ij}.$$

At 24-hourly intervals, a record was made of the two latest ψ-fields, $\psi_{ij\tau}$ and $\psi_{ij\,\tau-1}$, at levels 1 and 3. These were then averaged and differenced to form

$$\delta\,\psi_{ij} = \psi_{ij\tau} - \psi_{ij\,\tau-1},$$
$$\psi_{ij}{}^* = \tfrac{1}{2}\,(\psi_{ij\tau} + \psi_{ij\,\tau-1}),$$

and these new quantities were used throughout in the computation of the energy parameters and the meridional circulation. For convenience, the asterisk will be dropped from now on, ψ_{ij} always implying $\psi_{ij}{}^*$.

ω_2 was determined from the finite-difference form of Eq. (19):

$$\omega_{2ij} = \frac{\lambda^2 p_2}{f_0}\left[\frac{(\delta\psi_1 - \delta\psi_3)_{ij}}{\Delta t} - \frac{\mathcal{J}_{ij}(\psi_1, \psi_3)}{4\,\Delta x\,\Delta y} + \frac{2RH\,(2j-J)}{f_0\,c_p\,J} - \frac{A}{\Delta x^2}\mathcal{L}(\psi_1 - \psi_3)\right] \quad . \quad (A18)$$

The meridional circulation was determined by the equation

$$\overline{V}_{1\,j+\frac{1}{2}} = \overline{V}_{1\,j-\frac{1}{2}} - \frac{\Delta y}{p_2}\,\overline{\omega}_{2j}, \qquad j = 1, 2, \ldots, J-1, \quad . \quad . \quad (A19)$$

with $\overline{V}_1 = 0$ at $j = \frac{1}{2}$, and $\overline{\omega}_{2j}$ being given by X ω_{2ij}. The smallness of $\overline{V}_1$ at $j = J - \frac{1}{2}$ is a fairly severe test of the effect of round-off error in the computations, the exact *finite-difference* solution leading to a zero value for $\overline{V}_1$ and $\overline{V}_3$ at $j = J - \frac{1}{2}$. The average value of $|\overline{V}_{1\,J-\frac{1}{2}}|$ was about 5 mm sec^{-1} during the 31-day forecast, i.e., about 1 per cent of the maximum values of $\overline{V}_1$ away from the walls.

The kinetic energies were computed from the formulae

$$K' = \frac{10}{2J\,\Delta x^2}\sum_{j=0}^{J-1} \mathrm{X}\{[(\psi'_{i+1} - \psi'_i)^2_{1j} + (\psi'_{i+1} - \psi'_i)^2_{3j}] + \epsilon^2[(\psi'_{j+1} - \psi'_j)^2_{1i} + (\psi'_{j+1} - \psi'_j)^2_{3i}]\},$$

$$\overline{K} = \frac{10}{2\,\Delta y^2}\,\mathrm{Y}\,[(\overline{\psi}_{j+1} - \overline{\psi}_j)_1{}^2 + (\overline{\psi}_{j+1} - \overline{\psi}_j)_3{}^2], \quad . \quad . \quad . \quad . \quad . \quad (A20)$$

and the potential energies from

$$\left.\begin{aligned} P' &= \frac{10\,\lambda^2}{2}\,\mathrm{Y\,X}\,(\psi_1' - \psi_3')^2{}_{ij}, \\ \overline{P} &= \frac{10\,\lambda^2}{2}\,\mathrm{Y}\,(\overline{\psi}_1 - \overline{\psi}_3)^2{}_j. \end{aligned}\right\} \quad . \quad . \quad . \quad (A21)$$

The eleven energy transformations had the formulae :

$$\{\overline{Q}\cdot\overline{P}\} = -\frac{2RH\,\lambda^2 l}{f_0\,c_p}\,\mathrm{Y}\,\frac{2j-J}{J}\,(\overline{\psi}_1 - \overline{\psi}_3)_j$$

$$\{\overline{P}\cdot P'\} = -\frac{\lambda^2 l}{4\,\Delta x\,\Delta y}\,\mathrm{Y}\,[(\overline{\psi}_1 - \overline{\psi}_3)_j\,\mathrm{X}\,\mathcal{J}(\psi_1', \psi_3')_{ij}]$$

$$\{P'\cdot K'\} = -\frac{f_0 l}{p_2}\,\mathrm{Y\,X}\,\omega'_{2ij}\,(\psi_1' - \psi_3')_{ij}$$

$$\{K'\cdot\overline{K}\} = \frac{l}{4\,\Delta x^3\,\Delta y}\,\mathrm{Y}\,\{[(\overline{\psi}_{j-1} - \overline{\psi}_{j+1})\,\mathrm{X}\,(\psi'_{i+1} - \psi'_{i-1})_j\,\mathcal{L}\,\psi'_{ij}]_1 + $$
$$+ [(\overline{\psi}_{j-1} - \overline{\psi}_{j+1})\,\mathrm{X}\,(\psi'_{i+1} - \psi'_{i-1})_j\,\mathcal{L}\,\psi'_{ij}]_3\}$$

$$\{\overline{P}\cdot\overline{K}\} = -\frac{f_0 l}{p_2}\,\mathrm{Y}\,\overline{\omega}_{2j}\,(\overline{\psi}_1 - \overline{\psi}_3)_j$$

$$\{\overline{K}\cdot A\} = Al\,\mathrm{Y}\,(\overline{\zeta}_1{}^2 + \overline{\zeta}_3{}^2)_j$$

$$\{K'\cdot A\} = Al\,\mathrm{Y\,X}\,[(\zeta'_{1ij})^2 + (\zeta'_{3ij})^2]$$

$$\{\overline{P} \cdot A\} = \frac{\lambda^2 Al}{\Delta y^2} \mathrm{Y} \, [(\overline{\psi}_1 - \overline{\psi}_3)_{j+1} - (\overline{\psi}_1 - \overline{\psi}_3)_j]^2$$

$$\{P' \cdot A\} = \frac{\lambda^2 Al}{J \, \Delta x^2} \sum_{j=0}^{J-1} \mathrm{X} \{[(\psi_1' - \psi_3')_{i+1} - (\psi'_1 - \psi_3')_i]_j^2 + \epsilon^2 [(\psi_1' - \psi_3')_{j+1} - (\psi_1' - \psi_3')_j]_i^2\}$$

$$\{\overline{K} \cdot k\} = - kl \, \mathrm{Y} \, \overline{\zeta}_{4j} \, \overline{\psi}_{3j}$$

$$\{K' \cdot k\} = - kl \, \mathrm{Y} \, \mathrm{X} \, \zeta'_{4ij} \, \psi'_{3ij}$$

Here $l = 10$ days $= 8{\cdot}64 \times 10^5$ sec and $\zeta_{ij} = \Delta x^{-2} \mathcal{L}_{ij} \psi$. The units for the four energies and the eleven energy transformations will then be the same as those in the tables in the text if the dimensional quantities in the above formulae are measured in the metre-ton-second system. (The formula for $\{K' \cdot \overline{K}\}$ uses the relationship $\overline{v\zeta} = - \partial \, (\overline{uv})/\partial y$ which is valid when u and v are given by a stream function.)

3. Numerical values of the physical constants

The constants appearing in the equations had the following values :

$H = 2 \times 10^{-3}$ kj ton^{-1} sec^{-1} (2×10^{-6} j g^{-1} sec^{-1})

$\lambda^2 = f_0^2 \, \theta_2 \, [(\theta_1 - \theta_3)\,(\phi_1 - \phi_3)]^{-1} = 1{\cdot}5 \times 10^{-12}$ m^{-2}

$\Delta x = 375$ km

$\Delta y = 625$ km

$R = 287$ kj ton^{-1} deg^{-1}

$c_p = 1004$ kj ton^{-1} deg^{-1}

$A = 10^5$ m^2 sec^{-1} (zero in check computation)

$k = 4 \times 10^{-6}$ sec^{-1}

$\beta = 1{\cdot}6 \times 10^{-11}$ sec^{-1} m^{-1}

$p_2 = \frac{1}{2} \, p_4 = 500$ mb

$I = J = 16$

The value for λ^2 comes from values of

$f_0 = 10^{-4}$ sec^{-1}

$\phi_1 - \phi_3 = 77{,}499$ m^2 sec^{-2}

$\theta_2/(\theta_1 - \theta_3) = 11{\cdot}625$

(The last value is slightly larger than that occurring in the standard atmosphere, to allow qualitatively for the destabilizing effect of the release of latent heat.)

References

Albrecht, F. 1931 *Met. Z.*, **48**, p. 57.

Arakawa, H. 1953 *J. Met.*, **10**, p. 392.

Batchelor, G. K. 1950 *Quart. J. R. Met. Soc.*, **76**, p. 133.

Baur, F. and Philipps, H. 1935 *Beitr. Geophys.*, **45**, p. 82.

Benson, G. S. and Estoque, M. A.	1954	*J. Met.*, **11**, p. 462.
Bjerknes, V., Bjerknes, J., Solberg, H. and Bergeron, T.	1933	*Physikalische Hydrodynamik*, Berlin (J. Springer).
Blackadar, A. K.	1955	*J. Met.*, **12**, p. 165.
Brunt, D.	1944	*Physical and dynamical meteorology*, Cambridge University Press.
Charney, J.	1947	*J. Met.*, **4**, p. 135.
	1951	*U.G.G.I. Ass. Met. Compte Rendu*, Brussels, p. 47.
	1954	*Proc. Nat. Acad. Sci.*, **40**, p. 99.
	1955	Unpublished.
Charney, J. and Eliassen, A.	1949	*Tellus*, **1**, No. 2, p. 38.
Charney, J., Fjørtoft, R. and von Neumann, J.	1950	*Ibid.*, **2**, p. 237.
Charney, J. and Phillips, N.	1953	*J. Met.*, **10**, p. 71.
Defant, A.	1921	*Geog. Ann.*, Stockholm, **3**, p. 209.
Eady, E. T.	1949	*Tellus*, **1**, No. 3, p. 33.
	1950	*Cent. Proc. R. Met. Soc.*, p. 156.
Eliassen, A.	1949	*Geofys. Publ.*, Oslo, **17**, No. 3.
	1952	*Astrophys. Norveg.*, Oslo, **5**, No. 2.
Exner, F.	1925	*Dynamische meteorologie*, Vienna (J. Springer).
Fjørtoft, R.	1950	*Geofys. Publ.*, Oslo, **17**, No. 6.
	1951	*Compendium Met., Amer. Met. Soc.*, p. 454.
Fultz, D.	1951	*Ibid.*, p. 1235.
Gabites, J. F.	1950	Doctoral thesis, M.I.T.
Grimminger, G.	1938	*Trans. Amer. Geophys. Un.*, **19**, p. 163.
Hadley, G.	1735	*Phil. Trans. Roy. Soc.*
Hess, S.	1948	*J. Met.*, **5**, p. 293.
Hide, R.	1953	*Quart. J. R. Met. Soc.*, **79**, p. 161.
Houghton, H.	1954	*J. Met.*, **11**, p. 1.
Høiland, E.	1939	*Arch. Math. Naturv.*, **42**, No. 5.
Jeffreys, H.	1926	*Quart. J. R. Met. Soc.*, **52**, p. 85.
Kuo, H. L.	1952	*J. Met.*, **9**, p. 260.
	1953	*Ibid.*, **10**, p. 235.
	1954	*Ibid.*, **11**, p. 399.
Lamb, H.	1932	*Hydrodynamics*, 6th Ed., Cambridge University Press.
London, J.	1951	*Progr. Rep. Dept. Met., New York Univ.*, No. 131.07.
Lorentz, E. N.	1955	*Tellus*, **7**, p. 157.
Machta, L.	1955	Paper presented at 135th national meeting Amer. Met. Soc., New York (Abstract in *Bull. Amer. Met. Soc.*, **35**, p. 493).
Mintz, Y.	1954	*Bull. Amer. Met. Soc.*, **35**, p. 208.
	1955	'Investigations of the general circulation of the atmosphere,' final report, Dept. Met., Calif. Univ., Los Angeles.
Möller, F.	1950	*Experientia*, **6**, p. 361.
Palmén, E.	1951	*Compendium Met., Amer. Met. Soc.*, p. 599.
	1955	'Investigations of the general circulation of the atmosphere,' final report, Dept. Met., Calif. Univ., Los Angeles.
Palmén, E. and Alaka, M. A.	1952	*Tellus*, **4**, p. 324.
Palmén, E. and Newton, C.	1951	*J. Met.*, **8**, p. 25.
Phillips, N.	1949	*Ibid.*, **6**, p. 193.
	1954	*Tellus*, **6**, p. 273.
Richardson, L. F.	1926	*Proc. Roy. Soc.*, A, **110**, p. 709.
Riehl, H. and Yeh, T. C.	1950	*Quart. J. R. Met. Soc.*, **76**, p. 182.
Rossby, C.-G. and collaborators	1939	*J. Mar. Res.*, New Haven, **2**, p. 38.
Sheppard, P. A.	1953	*Proc. Toronto Met. Conf., R. Met. Soc.*, p. 103.
Sheppard, P. A., Charnock, H. and Francis, J. R. D.	1952	*Quart. J. R. Met. Soc.*, **78**, p. 563.
Simpson, G. C.	1929	*Mem. R. Met. Soc.*, **3**, No. 23, p. 53.
Spar, J.	1950	*J. Met.*, **7**, p. 48.
Staff members, Dept. Met., Chicago Univ.	1947	*Bull. Amer. Met. Soc.*, **28**, p. 255.
Starr, V. P.	1951	*Compendium Met., Amer. Met. Soc.*, p. 568.
	1953	*Tellus*, **5**, p. 494.
	1954	*Ibid.*, **6**, p. 268.
Starr, V. P. and White, R.	1955	'Studies of the atmospheric general circulation,' final report, Dept. Met., M.I.T., p. 186.
van Mieghem, J.	1952	*Tellus*, **4**, p. 334.
Widger, W.	1949	*J. Met.*, **6**, p. 291.

CATALOG OF DOVER BOOKS

Relativity, quantum theory, nuclear physics

THE PRINCIPLE OF RELATIVITY, A. Einstein, H. Lorentz, M. Minkowski, H. Weyl. These are the 11 basic papers that founded the general and special theories of relativity, all translated into English. Two papers by Lorentz on the Michelson experiment, electromagnetic phenomena. Minkowski's SPACE & TIME, and Weyl's GRAVITATION & ELECTRICITY. 7 epoch-making papers by Einstein: ELECTROMAGNETICS OF MOVING BODIES, INFLUENCE OF GRAVITATION IN PROPAGATION OF LIGHT, COSMOLOGICAL CONSIDERATIONS, GENERAL THEORY, and 3 others. 7 diagrams. Special notes by A. Sommerfeld. 224pp. 5⅜ x 8.
S81 Paperbound **$1.75**

SPACE TIME MATTER, Hermann Weyl. "The standard treatise on the general theory of relativity," (Nature), written by a world-renowned scientist, provides a deep clear discussion of the logical coherence of the general theory, with introduction to all the mathematical tools needed: Maxwell, analytical geometry, non-Euclidean geometry, tensor calculus, etc. Basis is classical space-time, before absorption of relativity. Partial contents: Euclidean space, mathematical form, metrical continuum, relativity of time and space, general theory. 15 diagrams. Bibliography. New preface for this edition. xviii + 330pp. 5⅜ x 8.
S267 Paperbound **$1.85**

PRINCIPLES OF QUANTUM MECHANICS, W. V. Houston. Enables student with working knowledge of elementary mathematical physics to develop facility in use of quantum mechanics, understand published work in field. Formulates quantum mechanics in terms of Schroedinger's wave mechanics. Studies evidence for quantum theory, for inadequacy of classical mechanics, 2 postulates of quantum mechanics; numerous important, fruitful applications of quantum mechanics in spectroscopy, collision problems, electrons in solids; other topics. "One of the most rewarding features . . . is the interlacing of problems with text," Amer. J. of Physics. Corrected edition. 21 illus. Index. 296pp. 5⅜ x 8. S524 Paperbound **$1.85**

PHYSICAL PRINCIPLES OF THE QUANTUM THEORY, Werner Heisenberg. A Nobel laureate discusses quantum theory; Heisenberg's own work, Compton, Schroedinger, Wilson, Einstein, many others. Written for physicists, chemists who are not specialists in quantum theory, only elementary formulae are considered in the text; there is a mathematical appendix for specialists. Profound without sacrifice of clarity. Translated by C. Eckart, F. Hoyt. 18 figures. 192pp. 5⅜ x 8. S113 Paperbound **$1.25**

SELECTED PAPERS ON QUANTUM ELECTRODYNAMICS, edited by **J. Schwinger.** Facsimiles of papers which established quantum electrodynamics, from initial successes through today's position as part of the larger theory of elementary particles. First book publication in any language of these collected papers of Bethe, Bloch, Dirac, Dyson, Fermi, Feynman, Heisenberg, Kusch, Lamb, Oppenheimer, Pauli, Schwinger, Tomonoga, Weisskopf, Wigner, etc. 34 papers in all, 29 in English, 1 in French, 3 in German, 1 in Italian. Preface and historical commentary by the editor. xvii + 423pp. 6⅛ x 9¼. S444 Paperbound **$2.45**

THE FUNDAMENTAL PRINCIPLES OF QUANTUM MECHANICS, WITH ELEMENTARY APPLICATIONS, E. C. Kemble. An inductive presentation, for the graduate student or specialist in some other branch of physics. Assumes some acquaintance with advanced math; apparatus necessary beyond differential equations and advanced calculus is developed as needed. Although a general exposition of principles, hundreds of individual problems are fully treated, with applications of theory being interwoven with development of the mathematical structure. The author is the Professor of Physics at Harvard Univ. "This excellent book would be of great value to every student . . . a rigorous and detailed mathematical discussion of all of the principal quantum-mechanical methods . . . has succeeded in keeping his presentations clear and understandable," Dr. Linus Pauling, J. of the American Chemical Society. Appendices: calculus of variations, math. notes, etc. Indexes. 611pp. 5⅜ x 8.
S472 Paperbound **$2.95**

ATOMIC SPECTRA AND ATOMIC STRUCTURE, G. Herzberg. Excellent general survey for chemists, physicists specializing in other fields. Partial contents: simplest line spectra and elements of atomic theory, building-up principle and periodic system of elements, hyperfine structure of spectral lines, some experiments and applications. Bibilography. 80 figures. Index. xii + 257pp. 5⅜ x 8. S115 Paperbound **$1.95**

THE THEORY AND THE PROPERTIES OF METALS AND ALLOYS, N. F. Mott, H. Jones. Quantum methods used to develop mathematical models which show interrelationship of basic chemical phenomena with crystal structure, magnetic susceptibility, electrical, optical properties. Examines thermal properties of crystal lattice, electron motion in applied field, cohesion, electrical resistance, noble metals, para-, dia-, and ferromagnetism, etc. "Exposition . . . clear . . . mathematical treatment . . . simple," Nature. 138 figures. Bibliography. Index. xiii + 320pp. 5⅜ x 8. S456 Paperbound **$1.85**

FOUNDATIONS OF NUCLEAR PHYSICS, edited by **R. T. Beyer.** 13 of the most important papers on nuclear physics reproduced in facsimile in the original languages of their authors: the papers most often cited in footnotes, bibliographies. Anderson, Curie, Joliot, Chadwick, Fermi, Lawrence, Cockcroft, Hahn, Yukawa. UNPARALLELED BIBLIOGRAPHY. 122 double-columned pages, over 4,000 articles, books classified. 57 figures. 288pp. 6⅛ x 9¼.
S19 Paperbound **$1.75**

MESON PHYSICS, R. E. Marshak. Traces the basic theory, and explicity presents results of experiments with particular emphasis on theoretical significance. Phenomena involving mesons as virtual transitions are avoided, eliminating some of the least satisfactory predictions of meson theory. Includes production and study of π mesons at nonrelativistic nucleon energies, contrasts between π and μ mesons, phenomena associated with nuclear interaction of π mesons, etc. Presents early evidence for new classes of particles and indicates theoretical difficulties created by discovery of heavy mesons and hyperons. Name and subject indices. Unabridged reprint. viii + 378pp. 5⅜ x 8. S500 Paperbound **$1.95**

MICROWAVE TRANSMISSION, J. S. Slater. First text dealing exclusively with microwaves, brings together points of view of field, circuit theory, for graduate student in physics, electrical engineering, microwave technician. Offers valuable point of view not in most later studies. Uses Maxwell's equations to study electromagnetic field, important in this area. Partial contents: infinite line with distributed parameters, impedance of terminated line, plane waves, reflections, wave guides, coaxial line, composite transmission lines, impedance matching, etc. Introduction. Index. 76 illus. 319pp. 5⅜ x 8.
S564 Paperbound **$1.50**

THE ANALYSIS OF SENSATIONS, Ernst Mach. Great study of physiology, psychology of perception, shows Mach's ability to see material freshly, his "incorruptible skepticism and independence." (Einstein). Relation of problems of psychological perception to classical physics, supposed dualism of physical and mental, principle of continuity, evolution of senses, will as organic manifestation, scores of experiments, observations in optics, acoustics, music, graphics, etc. New introduction by T. S. Szasz, M. D. 58 illus. 300-item bibliography. Index. 404pp. 5⅜ x 8. S525 Paperbound **$1.75**

APPLIED OPTICS AND OPTICAL DESIGN, A. E. Conrady. With publication of vol. 2, standard work for designers in optics is now complete for first time. Only work of its kind in English; only detailed work for practical designer and self-taught. Requires, for bulk of work, no math above trig. Step-by-step exposition, from fundamental concepts of geometrical, physical optics, to systematic study, design, of almost all types of optical systems. Vol. 1: all ordinary ray-tracing methods; primary aberrations; necessary higher aberration for design of telescopes, low-power microscopes, photographic equipment. Vol. 2: (Completed from author's notes by R. Kingslake, Dir. Optical Design, Eastman Kodak.) Special attention to high-power microscope, anastigmatic photographic objectives. "An indispensable work," J., Optical Soc. of Amer. "As a practical guide this book has no rival," Transactions, Optical Soc. Index. Bibliography. 193 diagrams. 852pp. 6⅛ x 9¼. Vol. 1 T611 Paperbound **$2.95**
Vol. 2 T612 Paperbound **$2.95**

THE THEORY OF OPTICS, Paul Drude. One of finest fundamental texts in physical optics, classic offers thorough coverage, complete mathematical treatment of basic ideas. Includes fullest treatment of application of thermodynamics to optics; sine law in formation of images, transparent crystals, magnetically active substances, velocity of light, apertures, effects depending upon them, polarization, optical instruments, etc. Introduction by A. A. Michelson. Index. 110 illus. 567pp. 5⅜ x 8. S532 Paperbound **$2.45**

OPTICKS, Sir Isaac Newton. In its discussions of light, reflection, color, refraction, theories of wave and corpuscular theories of light, this work is packed with scores of insights and discoveries. In its precise and practical discussion of construction of optical apparatus, contemporary understandings of phenomena it is truly fascinating to modern physicists, astronomers, mathematicians. Foreword by Albert Einstein. Preface by I. B. Cohen of Harvard University. 7 pages of portraits, facsimile pages, letters, etc. cxvi + 414pp. 5⅜ x 8.
S205 Paperbound **$2.00**

OPTICS AND OPTICAL INSTRUMENTS: AN INTRODUCTION WITH SPECIAL REFERENCE TO PRACTICAL APPLICATIONS, B. K. Johnson. An invaluable guide to basic practical applications of optical principles, which shows how to set up inexpensive working models of each of the four main types of optical instruments—telescopes, microscopes, photographic lenses, optical projecting systems. Explains in detail the most important experiments for determining their accuracy, resolving power, angular field of view, amounts of aberration, all other necessary facts about the instruments. Formerly "Practical Optics." Index. 234 diagrams. Appendix. 224pp. 5⅜ x 8. S642 Paperbound **$1.65**

PRINCIPLES OF PHYSICAL OPTICS, Ernst Mach. This classical examination of the propagation of light, color, polarization, etc. offers an historical and philosophical treatment that has never been surpassed for breadth and easy readability. Contents: Rectilinear propagation of light. Reflection, refraction. Early knowledge of vision. Dioptrics. Composition of light. Theory of color and dispersion. Periodicity. Theory of interference. Polarization. Mathematical representation of properties of light. Propagation of waves, etc. 279 illustrations, 10 portraits. Appendix. Indexes. 324pp. 5⅜ x 8. S178 Paperbound **$1.75**

FUNDAMENTALS OF ELECTRICITY AND MAGNETISM, L. B. Loeb. For students of physics, chemistry, or engineering who want an introduction to electricity and magnetism on a higher level and in more detail than general elementary physics texts provide. Only elementary differential and integral calculus is assumed. Physical laws developed logically, from magnetism to electric currents, Ohm's law, electrolysis, and on to static electricity, induction, etc. Covers an unusual amount of material; one third of book on modern material: solution of wave equation, photoelectric and thermionic effects, etc. Complete statement of the various electrical systems of units and interrelations. 2 Indexes. 75 pages of problems with answers stated. Over 300 figures and diagrams. xix +669pp. 5⅜ x 8. S745 Paperbound **$2.75**

THE ELECTROMAGNETIC FIELD, Max Mason & Warren Weaver. Used constantly by graduate engineers. Vector methods exclusively: detailed treatment of electrostatics, expansion methods, with tables converting any quantity into absolute electromagnetic, absolute electrostatic, practical units. Discrete charges, ponderable bodies, Maxwell field equations, etc. Introduction. Indexes. 416pp. 5⅜ x 8. S185 Paperbound **$2.00**

ELECTRICAL THEORY ON THE GIORGI SYSTEM, P. Cornelius. A new clarification of the fundamental concepts of electricity and magnetism, advocating the convenient m.k.s. system of units that is steadily gaining followers in the sciences. Illustrating the use and effectiveness of his terminology with numerous applications to concrete technical problems, the author here expounds the famous Giorgi system of electrical physics. His lucid presentation and well-reasoned, cogent argument for the universal adoption of this system form one of the finest pieces of scientific exposition in recent years. 28 figures. Index. Conversion tables for translating earlier data into modern units. Translated from 3rd Dutch edition by L. J. Jolley. x + 187pp. 5½ x 8¾. S909 Clothbound **$6.00**

Hydrodynamics

HYDRODYNAMICS, H. Dryden, F. Murnaghan, Harry Bateman. Published by the National Research Council in 1932 this enormous volume offers a complete coverage of classical hydrodynamics. Encyclopedic in quality. Partial contents: physics of fluids, motion, turbulent flow, compressible fluids, motion in 1, 2, 3 dimensions; viscous fluids rotating, laminar motion, resistance of motion through viscous fluid, eddy viscosity, hydraulic flow in channels of various shapes, discharge of gases, flow past obstacles, etc. Bibliography of over 2,900 items. Indexes. 23 figures. 634pp. 5⅜ x 8. S303 Paperbound **$2.75**

A TREATISE ON HYDRODYNAMICS, A. B. Basset. Favorite text on hydrodynamics for 2 generations of physicists, hydrodynamical engineers, oceanographers, ship designers, etc. Clear enough for the beginning student, and thorough source for graduate students and engineers on the work of d'Alembert, Euler, Laplace, Lagrange, Poisson, Green, Clebsch, Stokes, Cauchy, Helmholtz, J. J. Thomson, Love, Hicks, Greenhill, Besant, Lamb, etc. Great amount of documentation on entire theory of classical hydrodynamics. Vol I: theory of motion of frictionless liquids, vortex, and cyclic irrotational motion, etc. 132 exercises. Bibliography. 3 Appendixes. xii + 264pp. Vol II: motion in viscous liquids, harmonic analysis, theory of tides, etc. 112 exercises. Bibliography. 4 Appendixes. xv + 328pp. Two volume set. 5⅜ x 8.
S724 Vol I Paperbound **$1.75**
S725 Vol II Paperbound **$1.75**
The set **$3.50**

HYDRODYNAMICS, Horace Lamb. Internationally famous complete coverage of standard reference work on dynamics of liquids & gases. Fundamental theorems, equations, methods, solutions, background, for classical hydrodynamics. Chapters include Equations of Motion, Integration of Equations in Special Gases, Irrotational Motion, Motion of Liquid in 2 Dimensions, Motion of Solids through Liquid-Dynamical Theory, Vortex Motion, Tidal Waves, Surface Waves, Waves of Expansion, Viscosity, Rotating Masses of liquids. Excellently planned, arranged; clear, lucid presentation. 6th enlarged, revised edition. Index. Over 900 footnotes, mostly bibliographical. 119 figures. xv + 738pp. 6⅛ x 9¼. S256 Paperbound **$2.95**

See also: **FUNDAMENTAL FORMULAS OF PHYSICS, D. H. Menzel; THEORY OF FLIGHT, R. von Mises; FUNDAMENTALS OF HYDRO- AND AEROMECHANICS, L. Prandtl and O. G. Tietjens; APPLIED HYDRO- AND AEROMECHANICS, L. Prandtl and O. G. Tietjens; HYDRAULICS AND ITS APPLICATIONS, A. H. Gibson; FLUID MECHANICS FOR HYDRAULIC ENGINEERS, H. Rouse.**

Acoustics, optics, electromagnetics

ON THE SENSATIONS OF TONE, Hermann Helmholtz. This is an unmatched coordination of such fields as acoustical physics, physiology, experiment, history of music. It covers the entire gamut of musical tone. Partial contents: relation of musical science to acoustics, physical vs. physiological acoustics, composition of vibration, resonance, analysis of tones by sympathetic resonance, beats, chords, tonality, consonant chords, discords, progression of parts, etc. 33 appendixes discuss various aspects of sound, physics, acoustics, music, etc. Translated by A. J. Ellis. New introduction by Prof. Henry Margenau of Yale. 68 figures. 43 musical passages analyzed. Over 100 tables. Index. xix + 576pp. 6⅛ x 9¼.
S114 Paperbound **$2.95**

THE THEORY OF SOUND, Lord Rayleigh. Most vibrating systems likely to be encountered in practice can be tackled successfully by the methods set forth by the great Nobel laureate, Lord Rayleigh. Complete coverage of experimental, mathematical aspects of sound theory. Partial contents: Harmonic motions, vibrating systems in general, lateral vibrations of bars, curved plates or shells, applications of Laplace's functions to acoustical problems, fluid friction, plane vortex-sheet, vibrations of solid bodies, etc. This is the first inexpensive edition of this great reference and study work. Bibliography. Historical introduction by R. B. Lindsay. Total of 1040pp. 97 figures. 5⅜ x 8.
S292, S293, Two volume set, paperbound, **$4.00**

THE DYNAMICAL THEORY OF SOUND, H. Lamb. Comprehensive mathematical treatment of the physical aspects of sound, covering the theory of vibrations, the general theory of sound, and the equations of motion of strings, bars, membranes, pipes, and resonators. Includes chapters on plane, spherical, and simple harmonic waves, and the Helmholtz Theory of Audition. Complete and self-contained development for student and specialist; all fundamental differential equations solved completely. Specific mathematical details for such important phenomena as harmonics, normal modes, forced vibrations of strings, theory of reed pipes, etc. Index. Bibliography. 86 diagrams. viii + 307pp. 5⅜ x 8. S655 Paperbound **$1.50**

WAVE PROPAGATION IN PERIODIC STRUCTURES, L. Brillouin. A general method and application to different problems: pure physics, such as scattering of X-rays of crystals, thermal vibration in crystal lattices, electronic motion in metals; and also problems of electrical engineering. Partial contents: elastic waves in 1-dimensional lattices of point masses. Propagation of waves along 1-dimensional lattices. Energy flow. 2 dimensional, 3 dimensional lattices. Mathieu's equation. Matrices and propagation of waves along an electric line. Continuous electric lines. 131 illustrations. Bibliography. Index. xii + 253pp. 5⅜ x 8.
S34 Paperbound **$1.85**

TREATISE ON ELECTRICITY AND MAGNETISM, James Clerk Maxwell. For more than 80 years a seemingly inexhaustible source of leads for physicists, mathematicians, engineers. Total of 1082pp. on such topics as Measurement of Quantities, Electrostatics, Elementary Mathematical Theory of Electricity, Electrical Work and Energy in a System of Conductors, General Theorems, Theory of Electrical Images, Electrolysis, Conduction, Polarization, Dielectrics, Resistance, etc. "The greatest mathematical physicist since Newton," Sir James Jeans. 3rd edition. 107 figures, 21 plates. 1082pp. 5⅜ x 8. S636-7, 2 volume set, paperbound **$4.00**

See also: **FUNDAMENTAL FORMULAS OF PHYSICS, D. H. Menzel; MATHEMATICAL ANALYSIS OF ELECTRICAL & OPTICAL WAVE MOTION, H. Bateman.**

Mechanics, dynamics, thermodynamics, elasticity

MECHANICS VIA THE CALCULUS, P. W. Norris, W. S. Legge. Covers almost everything, from linear motion to vector analysis: equations determining motion, linear methods, compounding of simple harmonic motions, Newton's laws of motion, Hooke's law, the simple pendulum, motion of a particle in 1 plane, centers of gravity, virtual work, friction, kinetic energy of rotating bodies, equilibrium of strings, hydrostatics, sheering stresses, elasticity, etc. 550 problems. 3rd revised edition. xii + 367pp. 6 x 9. S207 Clothbound **$3.95**

MECHANICS, J. P. Den Hartog. Already a classic among introductory texts, the M.I.T. professor's lively and discursive presentation is equally valuable as a beginner's text, an engineering student's refresher, or a practicing engineer's reference. Emphasis in this highly readable text is on illuminating fundamental principles and showing how they are embodied in a great number of real engineering and design problems: trusses, loaded cables, beams, jacks, hoists, etc. Provides advanced material on relative motion and gyroscopes not usual in introductory texts. "Very thoroughly recommended to all those anxious to improve their real understanding of the principles of mechanics." MECHANICAL WORLD. Index. List of equations. 334 problems, all with answers. Over 550 diagrams and drawings. ix + 462pp. 5⅜ x 8. S754 Paperbound **$2.00**

THEORETICAL MECHANICS: AN INTRODUCTION TO MATHEMATICAL PHYSICS, J. S. Ames, F. D. Murnaghan. A mathematically rigorous development of theoretical mechanics for the advanced student, with constant practical applications. Used in hundreds of advanced courses. An unusually thorough coverage of gyroscopic and baryscopic material, detailed analyses of the Corilis acceleration, applications of Lagrange's equations, motion of the double pendulum, Hamilton-Jacobi partial differential equations, group velocity and dispersion, etc. Special relativity is also included. 159 problems. 44 figures. ix + 462pp. 5⅜ x 8. S461 Paperbound **$2.00**

THEORETICAL MECHANICS: STATICS AND THE DYNAMICS OF A PARTICLE, W. D. MacMillan. Used for over 3 decades as a self-contained and extremely comprehensive advanced undergraduate text in mathematical physics, physics, astronomy, and deeper foundations of engineering. Early sections require only a knowledge of geometry; later, a working knowledge of calculus. Hundreds of basic problems, including projectiles to the moon, escape velocity, harmonic motion, ballistics, falling bodies, transmission of power, stress and strain, elasticity, astronomical problems. 340 practice problems plus many fully worked out examples make it possible to test and extend principles developed in the text. 200 figures. xvii + 430pp. 5⅜ x 8. S467 Paperbound **$2.00**

THEORETICAL MECHANICS: THE THEORY OF THE POTENTIAL, W. D. MacMillan. A comprehensive, well balanced presentation of potential theory, serving both as an introduction and a reference work with regard to specific problems, for physicists and mathematicians. No prior knowledge of integral relations is assumed, and all mathematical material is developed as it becomes necessary. Includes: Attraction of Finite Bodies; Newtonian Potential Function; Vector Fields, Green and Gauss Theorems; Attractions of Surfaces and Lines; Surface Distribution of Matter; Two-Layer Surfaces; Spherical Harmonics; Ellipsoidal Harmonics; etc. "The great number of particular cases . . . should make the book valuable to geophysicists and others actively engaged in practical applications of the potential theory," Review of Scientific Instruments. Index. Bibliography. xiii + 469pp. 5⅜ x 8. S486 Paperbound **$2.25**

THEORETICAL MECHANICS: DYNAMICS OF RIGID BODIES, W. D. MacMillan. Theory of dynamics of a rigid body is developed, using both the geometrical and analytical methods of instruction. Begins with exposition of algebra of vectors, it goes through momentum principles, motion in space, use of differential equations and infinite series to solve more sophisticated dynamics problems. Partial contents: moments of inertia, systems of free particles, motion parallel to a fixed plane, rolling motion, method of periodic solutions, much more. 82 figs. 199 problems. Bibliography. Indexes. xii + 476pp. 5⅜ x 8. S641 Paperbound **$2.00**